ORGANIC REACTION MECHANISMS · 1966

ORGANIC REACTION MECHANISMS · 1966

An annual survey covering the literature
dated December 1965 *through November* 1966

B. CAPON University of Leicester

M. J. PERKINS King's College, University of London

C. W. REES University of Leicester

INTERSCIENCE PUBLISHERS a division of

John Wiley & Sons   London · New York · Sydney

Made and printed in Great Britain by
Spottiswoode, Ballantyne & Co. Ltd., London and Colchester

Preface to the 1965 Volume

This book is a survey of the work on organic reaction mechanisms published in 1965. For convenience, the literature dated from December 1964 to November 1965, inclusive, was actually covered. The principal aim has been to scan all the chemical literature and to summarize the progress of work on organic reaction mechanism generally and fairly uniformly, and not just on selected topics. Therefore, certain of the sections are somewhat fragmentary and all are concise. Of the 2000 or so papers which have been reported, those which seemed at the time to be the more significant are normally described and discussed, and the remainder are listed.

Our other major aim, second only to comprehensive coverage, has been early publication since we felt that the immediate value of such a survey as this, that of "current awareness", would diminish rapidly with time. In this we have been fortunate to have the expert cooperation of the London office of John Wiley and Sons.

If this book proves to be generally useful, we will continue these annual surveys, and then hope that the series will have some lasting value; some form of cumulative reporting or indexing may even be desirable.

It is not easy to deal rigidly and comprehensively with so ubiquitous and fundamental a subject as reaction mechanism. Any subdivision is a necessary encumbrance and our system, exemplified by the chapter headings, has been supplemented by cross-references and by the form of the subject index. We should welcome suggestions for improvements in future volumes.

February 1966

B.C.
M.J.P.
C.W.R.

Contents

CHAPTER 1

Classical and Non-classical Carbonium Ions

Bicyclic Systems

This year there have been published three reviews[1-3] and a "collection of reprints with commentary"[4] dealing with non-classical ions. All three reviewers and the commentator support the view that *exo*-norbornyl compounds react via a non-classical ion. Brown, on the other hand, has restated his arguments for believing that they do not.[5]

As a result of the discussion by Goering and Schewene[6] and Brown and Tritle[7] of the 2-norbornyl system reported last year,[8] it is now clear that just as the *exo:endo* rate ratio measures the difference only in free energy of activation for ionization of the *exo*- and *endo*-isomers, the *exo:endo* product ratio measures the difference only in free energy of the transition states for capture of the 2-norbornyl ion(s) in the *exo*- and the *endo*-direction and that these two differences are closely related. In the strictest sense, then, it is only valid to draw conclusions about the structures of the transition states from these kinds of result. One may then extrapolate to the structure of the intermediate ion(s), but this involves an assumption that this structure is closely related to that of the transition states. This is undoubtedly frequently valid but it should be remembered that it is an assumption and need not always be valid.

In our opinion the question that should now be asked about solvolysis reactions of 2-norbornyl systems is not "does the *exo*-compound react via a non-classical ion?" but "are the high *exo:endo* rate and product ratios the result of delocalization of the 1,6-bonding electrons in the transition state for ionisation of the *exo*-isomer and for capture of the intermediate ion?"

Sargent in his review[1] accepts Brown's view that the high *exo:endo* rate ratios observed in the solvolyses of tertiary 2-norbornyl derivatives[9] are not

[1] G. D. Sargent, *Quart. Rev. (London)*, **20**, 301 (1966).
[2] G. E. Gream, *Rev. Pure. Appl. Chem.*, **16**, 25 (1966).
[3] C. A. Bunton in "Studies on Chemical Structure and Reactivity", J. H. Ridd, ed., Methuen, London, 1966, p. 73.
[4] P. D. Bartlett, "Non-classical Ions: Reprints and Commentary," W. A. Benjamin, New York, N.Y. 1966.
[5] H. C. Brown, *Chem. Brit.*, **2**, 199 (1966).
[6] H. L. Goering and C. B. Schewene, *J. Am. Chem. Soc.*, **87**, 3516 (1965).
[7] H. C. Brown and G. L. Tritle, *J. Am. Chem. Soc.*, **88**, 1320 (1966).
[8] See *Organic Reaction Mechanisms*, **1965**, 13.
[9] See *Organic Reaction Mechanisms*, **1965**, 8.

the result of participation in the reactions of the *exo*-isomers, but he rejects Brown's explanation that they result because the rates for the *endo*-isomers are low owing to steric hindrance to ionisation. Instead he prefers the explanation that they are caused by the release of steric strain in the transition states for the reactions of the *exo*-isomers arising from the movement away of the 2-methyl or 2-phenyl substituent from the 6-hydrogen atom, and he calculates the strain relieved ($\sim$3 kcal mole^{-1}) to be in good quantitative agreement with the observed *exo*:*endo* rate ratios. On this view, then, the difference in activation energy for the solvolyses of secondary *exo*- and *endo*-derivatives, caused by participation in the reaction of the *exo*-isomer, is, by chance, almost identical with the difference for tertiary derivatives, which results from a quite different factor, namely, release of steric strain.

As pointed out by Rei and Brown,[10] however, equilibration studies (Table 1) indicate that steric strain in *exo*- and *endo*-isomers must be approximately the same as, or at most only slightly greater than, in the 1-norbornyl isomer which they considered to be strain-free as far as the substituents are concerned. It is, therefore, difficult to see how relief of steric strain as envisaged by Sargent could be the cause of the rate differences between tertiary *exo*- and *endo*-isomers.

Rei and Brown[10] also studied the kinetics of the acid-catalysed conversion of 2-methyl-*exo*-norbornan-2-ol into 2-methyl-*endo*-norbornan-2-ol and 1-methyl-*exo*-norborbornan-2-ol and report that the former is formed twice as rapidly as the latter.

Brown and Takeuchi[11] report that the rates of ethanolysis of 2-aryl-*exo*-norbornyl chlorides can be correlated by the σ^{+} constants to yield a ρ-value (-4.3) similar to that observed with 1-arylcyclopentyl (-4.5) and 2-aryl-2-propyl chlorides (-4.9). It was thought that if there were participation of the 1,6-bonding electrons in the reactions of the *exo*-norbornyl chlorides the proportion of this should increase on going from the *p*-methoxyphenyl (extrapolated $k = 2.5 \times 10^{2}$ sec^{-1}) to the *p*-nitrophenyl compound ($k = 7.08 \times 10^{-5}$ sec^{-1}) and that this would lead to a curved Hammett plot. Apparently this does not occur and it seems reasonable to suppose that there is no participation.

Brown and Muzzio[12] have attempted to correlate the solvolysis rates of bicyclic arenesulphonates with rates of borohydride reduction of the corresponding ketones. Although a fast borohydride reduction tended to accompany a slow arenesulphonate solvolysis the plot of log (partial rate factor) for ketone reduction against log $k_{\text{rel.}}$ for toluene-*p*-sulphonate solvolysis was not a straight line even when compounds believed to undergo solvolysis with

[10] M-H. Rei and H. C. Brown, *J. Am. Chem. Soc.*, **88**, 5335 (1966).
[11] H. C. Brown and K. Takeuchi, *J. Am. Chem. Soc.*, **88**, 5336 (1966).
[12] H. C. Brown and J. Muzzio, *J. Am. Chem. Soc.*, **88**, 2811 (1966).

Table 1. Percentages of *exo-* and *endo*-2-norbornyl and 1-norbornyl derivatives present at equilibrium.

			Conditions	Ref.
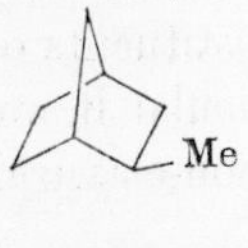 25	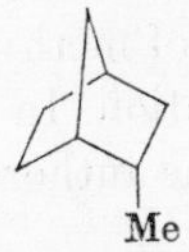 5	 70	H_2SO_4 at 20—50°	13
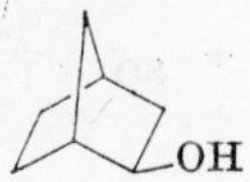 80	 20		Acetone at 100—137°	14
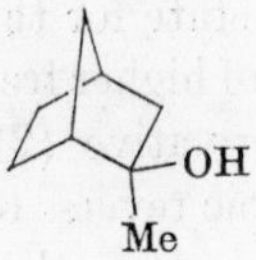 22	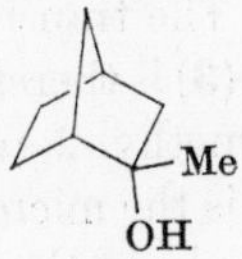 17	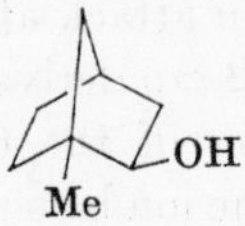 61	60% Aqueous dioxan at 25°	10
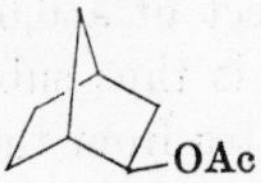 84	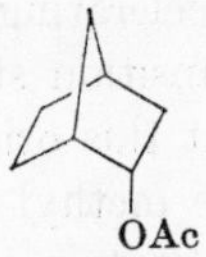 16		AcOH at 48.9°	6

participation were excluded. In particular, the rate constants for *endo*-derivatives were very poorly correlated. Thus the solvolysis of *endo*-norbornyl toluene-*p*-sulphonate is slower than that of cyclopentyl toluene-*p*-sulphonate and the reduction of 2-norbonanone from the *endo*-direction is also slower than the reduction of cyclopentanone. This breakdown in the quantitative correlation was attributed to unusual slowness of both attack from, and departure in, the *endo*-direction.

13 N. A. Belikova, A. F. Platé, and Kh. E. Sterin, *J. Gen. Chem. U.S.S.R.*, **34**, 125 (1964).
14 C. F. Wilcox, M. Sexton, and M. F. Wilcox, *J. Org. Chem.*, **28**, 1079 (1963); E. L. Eliel, S. H. Schroeter, T. J. Brett, F. J. Biros, and J. C. Richer, *J. Am. Chem. Soc.*, **88**, 3327 (1966).

Schleyer and his co-workers' assignment[15] of the slower solvolysis of 6,6-dimethyl-2-*exo*-norbornyl toluene-*p*-sulphonate than of *exo*-norbornyl toluene-*p*-sulphonate to an unfavourable steric interaction between the methyl groups and $C_{(1)}$ and $C_{(2)}$ in a non-classical transition state[15] has been further substantiated by Berson, McRowe, and Bergman.[16] These workers set out to test whether this slower rate was the result of an initial or transition-state energy difference by investigating the effect of methyl substituents on the site of capture by solvent of the norbornyl cation. In particular it was found that attack at $C_{(2)}$ of cation (**1**) (written by the authors as non-classical)

(**1**)   (**2**)   (**3**)

occurred 8—10 times faster than attack at $C_{(1)}$. The transition state for the formation of the 6-*endo*-methyl-2-*exo*-derivatives (**3**) is therefore of higher free energy than that for formation of the 6-*exo*-methyl-2-*exo*-derivative (**2**). Inasmuch, then, as capture of the ion by solvent is the microscopic reverse of ionization of the toluene-*p*-sulphonate, this result shows that a 6-*endo*-methyl group has a destabilizing effect on the transition state for the latter as well as for the former; Schleyer's assignment of the decelerating effect of a 6,6-dimethyl substituent to a steric effect in the transition state is thus substantiated. It was suggested by Berson *et al.* that this originates from the interaction between the hydrogen at $C_{(2)}$ and the methyl group at $C_{(6)}$. A *syn*-methyl group at $C_{(7)}$ was shown to favour substitution at $C_{(2)}$, but with a methyl group at $C_{(5)}$ and an *anti*-methyl group at $C_{(7)}$ there were approximately equal amounts of substitution at $C_{(1)}$ and $C_{(2)}$.

A 3-*endo*-phenyl substituent slightly accelerates the acetolysis of *endo*-norbornyl toluene-*p*-sulphonate but a 3-*exo*-phenyl substituent causes a 260-fold rate decrease; this was attributed to steric hindrance to solvation. It was also found that a 3-*exo*-substituent causes a large (130-fold) decrease in the rate of acetolysis of *exo*-norbornyl toluene-*p*-sulphonate, possibly arising from the same cause[17] (see also, ref. 26, p. 8 below).

Following the observations by Takeuchi, Oshika, and Koga reported last year[18] that *exo*- and *endo*-5,6-trimethylene-*exo*-2-norbornyl toluene-*p*-

[15] See *Organic Reaction Mechanisms*, **1965**, 17.
[16] J. A. Berson, A. W. McRowe and R. G. Bergman, *J. Am. Chem. Soc.*, **88**, 1067 (1966).
[17] D. C. Kleinfelter, E. S. Trent, J. E. Mallory, and T. E. Dye, *J. Am. Chem. Soc.*, **88**, 5350 (1966).
[18] See *Organic Reaction Mechanisms*, **1965**, 15.

sulphonate gave significantly different proportions of acetates on acetolysis, Cash and Wilder[19a] have now reported that decomposition of the corresponding chlorosulphites (4) and (7) yields strikingly different proportions of the chlorides (6) and (9). Typically, in cyclohexane at 28° (4) yields 34% of (5) and 47% of (9), while (7) yields 2.6% of (6) and 97.4% of (9). *If* these reactions proceed via carbonium ions then they must involve trapping of the classical ions (5) and (8) before their interconversion or conversion into a non-classical ion.

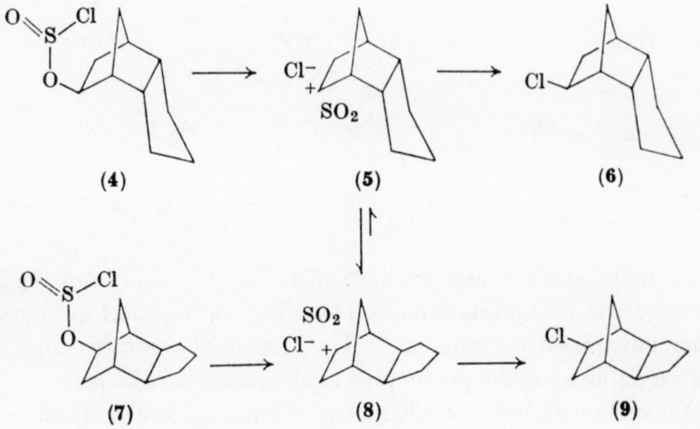

(4)   (5)   (6)

(7)   (8)   (9)

The reaction of *exo-* and *endo-*norbornanol with thionyl chloride and decomposition of the resulting chlorosulphites has also been investigated. 2,3,3-Trideuterio-*exo*-norbornan-2-ol (10) yielded the deuterated norbornyl chlorides shown, indicating that there had been some Wagner–Meerwein and 2,6-hydride shift, but that the former had not occurred to the extent required by intervention of a non-classical ion as the sole intermediate.[19b]

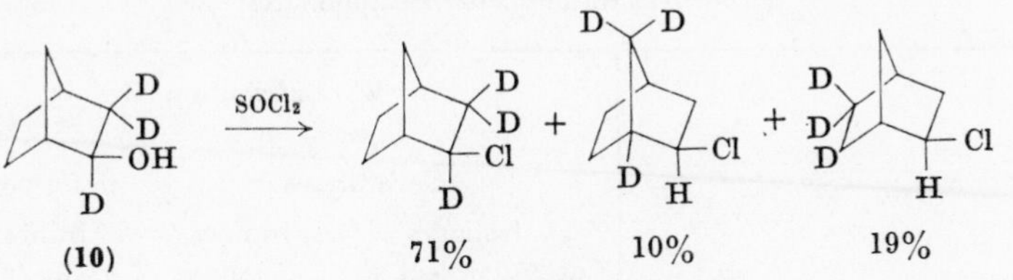

(10)   71%   10%   19%

Total yield 34%

In a very interesting investigation Sauers, Parent, and Damle[20] have studied the acetolysis of *exo-* and *endo-*tricyclo[3.2.1.0^{3,6}]oct-2-yl toluene-*p*-

[19a] D. J. Cash and P. Wilder, *Chem. Comm.*, **1966**, 662.
[19b] J. K. Stille and F. M. Sonnenberg, *J. Am. Chem. Soc.*, **88**, 4915 (1966).
[20] R. R. Sauers, R. A. Parent, and S. B. Damle, *J. Am. Chem. Soc.*, **88**, 2257 (1966).

sulphonate (**11a** and **11b**) which both yield unrearranged *exo*-acetate. That of the *exo*-isomer proceeds about 200 times faster than that of the *endo*-isomer and about 500 times faster than was calculated by use of Schleyer's correlation. If the *exo*-isomer reacts by way of non-classical ion (**12**), this must then react with exclusive attack at $C_{(2)}$.

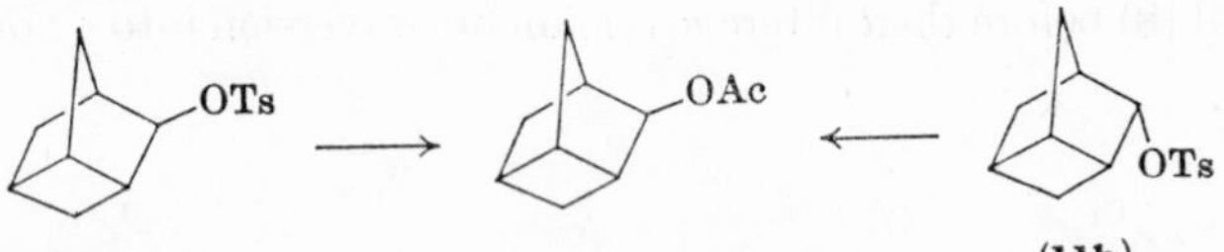

(**11a**)   (**11b**)

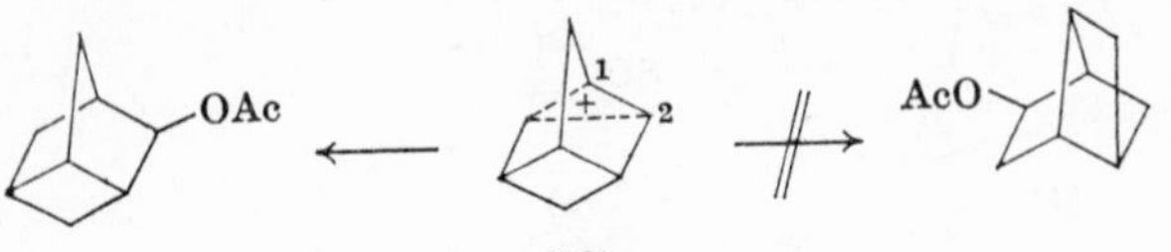

(**12**)

Tritium distribution in the products of the acetolyses of *exo*- and *endo*-2-tritio-2-norbornyl *p*-bromobenzenesulphonates and of the formolysis of the *exo*-isomer have been determined.[21] The extent of rearrangement was expressed (see Table 2) as the percentage of the products with:

(i) all the carbon atoms equivalent, arising from 3,2- and 6,2(or 6,1)-hydride shifts and Wagner–Meerwein shifts;

(ii) $C_{(1)}$, $C_{(2)}$, and $C_{(6)}$ equivalent, arising from a 6,2(or 6,1)-hydride shift and Wagner–Meerwein shifts; and

(iii) $C_{(1)}$ and $C_{(2)}$ equivalent, arising from a Wagner–Meerwein shift only. Of particular interest is the very much greater proportion of 3,2-hydride shift

Table 2. Rearrangement in the products of acetolysis and formolysis of
norbornyl *p*-bromobenzenesulphonates.

	% Contribution		
	in acetolyses		in formolysis
	from *exo*	from *endo*	from *exo*
	at 25° at 45°	reflux	at 25°
S_N2	0 0	5	0
Complete equivalence	10 7	5	35.2
$C_{(1)}$, $C_{(2)}$, and $C_{(6)}$ equivalent	45 38	47	21.6
$C_{(1)}$ and $C_{(2)}$ equivalent	45 55	43	43.2

21 C. C. Lee and L. K. M. Lam, *J. Am. Chem. Soc.*, **88**, 2831, 5355 (1966).

found with the formolysis than with the acetolysis of the *exo*-isomer, consistent with the carbonium ion's having a longer lifetime in the former reaction.

Following Berson and Grubb's work reported last year,[22] Benjamin and Collins have now described several more examples of stereospecific $6 \rightarrow 2$ and $6 \rightarrow 1$ hydride shifts in norbornyl systems. Thus treatment of diol (13) yielded ketone (15) which analysis by NMR showed to have less than 3% deuterium at the bridgehead.[23] It was therefore concluded that migration of the *exo*-6-deuterium of ion (14) occurred with a stereospecificity of at least 94% and the reaction was formulated as shown in Scheme 1.

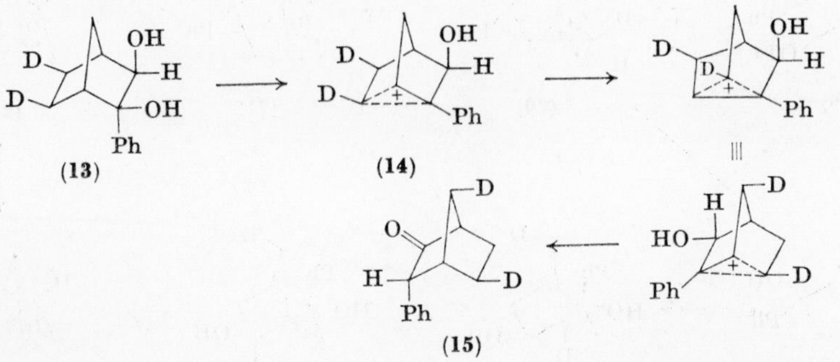

Scheme 1

Further examples were found in the hydrolysis of toluene-*p*-sulphonate (16) which in aqueous acetone containing sodium carbonate yields (17) (60%) formed by a Wagner–Meerwein shift, (18) (25%) formed by stereospecific elimination of the 6-*exo*-deuterium, and (19) (15%) formed by stereospecific *exo*-6,1 deuteride migration $(20) \rightarrow (21) \rightarrow (22)$.[24] In addition, a trace of (24) was formed and this consisted of 9 parts of (24b), formed by two stereospecific hydride shifts $(20) \rightarrow (22)$ and $(22) \rightarrow (25)$, and 1 part of (24a), formed by *endo*-6,2-hydride shift $(20) \rightarrow (23)$. The formation of (24a and b) in this way was confirmed by showing that toluene-*p*-sulphonate (26) yields (27a and b) in an approximately 1:9 ratio.[24]

Other examples of exclusive *exo*-2,3-shifts in norbonyl systems have also been reported. Finch and Vaughan[25] found that sulphonation of (+)-[8-^{14}C]-camphor (28) yields racemic camphor π-sulphonic acid (32) with half the label at $C_{(10)}$ and half at $C_{(9)}$. Resolution of the product yielded (+)-camphor-π-sulphonic acid with all its label at $C_{(8)}$. These results were explained by the

[22] See *Organic Reaction Mechanisms*, **1965**, 22.

[23] B. M. Benjamin and C. J. Collins, *J. Am. Chem. Soc.*, **88**, 1556 (1966).

[24] B. M. Benjamin, B. W. Ponder, and C. J. Collins, *J. Am. Chem. Soc.*, **88**, 1558 (1966); B. M. Benjamin and C. J. Collins, *Tetrahedron Letters*, **1966**, 5477.

[25] A. M. T. Finch and W. R. Vaughan, *J. Am. Chem. Soc.*, **87**, 5520 (1965).

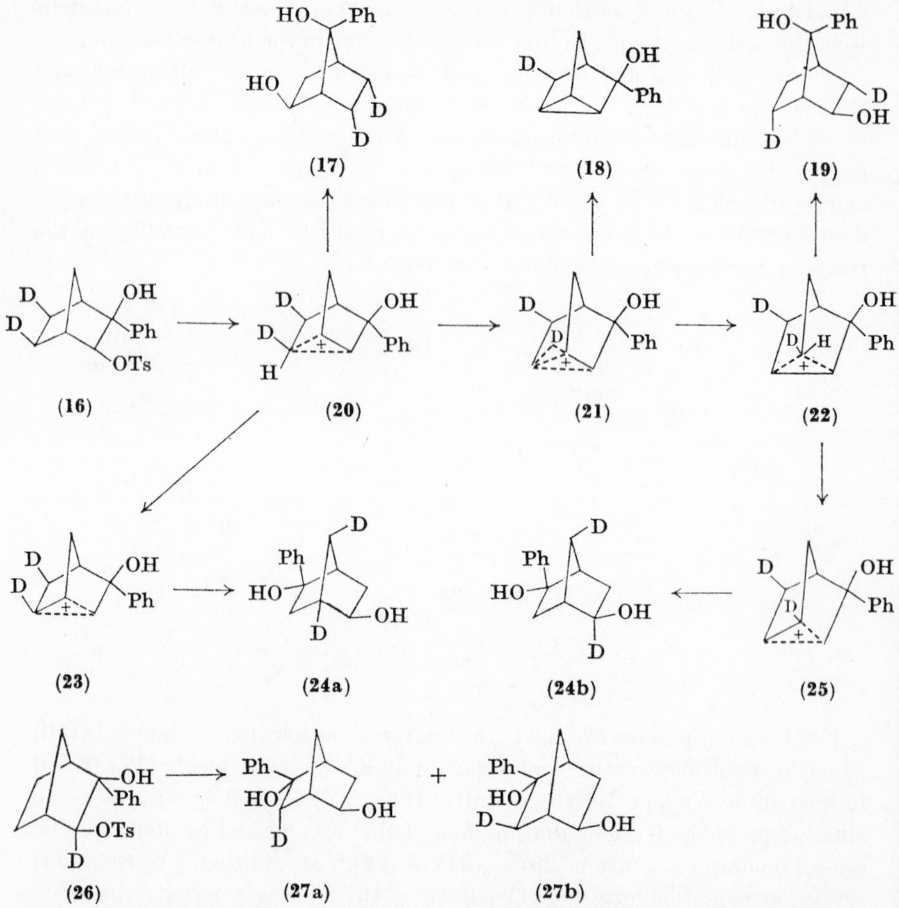

(17)   (18)   (19)

(16)   (20)   (21)   (22)

(23)   (24a)   (24b)   (25)

(26)   (27a)   +   (27b)

series of reactions given in Scheme 2 involving exclusive *exo*-2,3-methyl shifts which were considered to be compelling evidence for the intervention of non-classical ions. In our opinion, however, the only definite conclusion that can be drawn is that the free energies of the transition states for *exo*-migration (**29, 30,** and **31**) are considerably lower than those of the transition states for *endo*-migration and that this may possibly be due to delocalization of the 1,6-bonding electrons, but there could be other explanations.[22]

An unsuccessful attempt has been made to observe an *endo*-2,3-hydride shift in the 2-*p*-methoxyphenyl-3-*exo*-hydroxy-2-norbornyl cation (**34**).[26] This cation was generated by dissolving the corresponding alcohol (**33**) in sulphuric acid and was considered to have a classical structure which, it was thought, would be favourable for an *endo*-hydride shift. However, the only

[26] D. C. Kleinfelter and T. E. Dye, *J. Am. Chem. Soc.*, **88**, 3174 (1966).

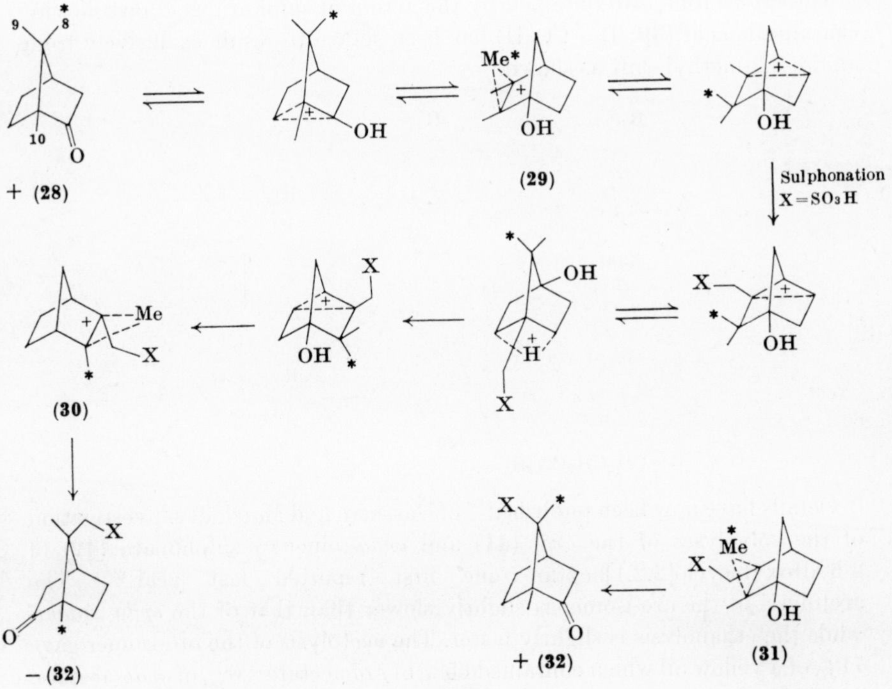

Scheme 2

non-sulphonated product isolated was 3-*endo-p*-methoxyphenyl-2-norbornanone (**38**), formed presumably via ions (**35**) to (**37**). The driving force for this rearrangement was considered to be the instability of ion (**34**), due to steric hindrance to solvation by the *exo*-hydroxyl group (see also ref. 17, p. 4 above).

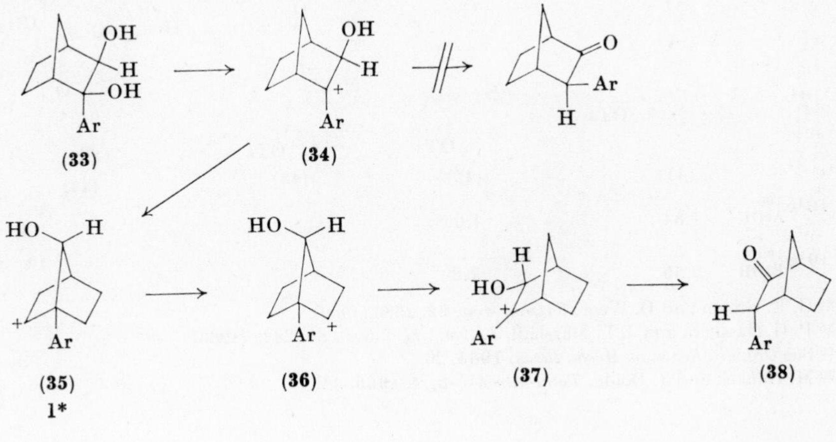

The *exo*-lactone **(40)** obtained by the action of sulphuric acid on tricyclo-ekasantalic acid **(39**; $R = CO_2H$) has been shown to result exclusively from an *exo*-3,2-methyl shift as shown.[27]

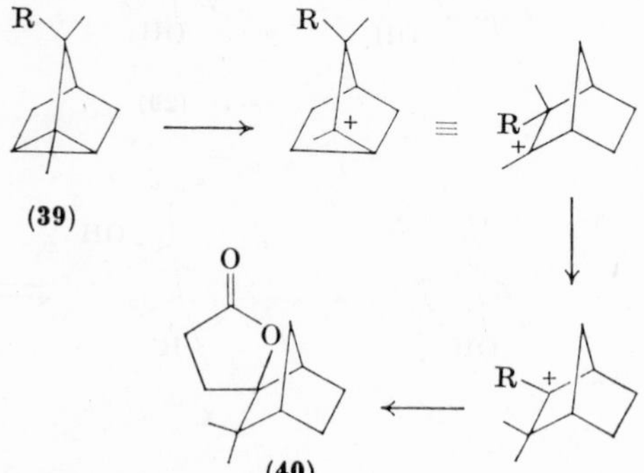

(39)

(40)

$R = CH_2CH_2CO_2H$

Details have now been published[28] of Gassman and Marshall's investigation of the solvolyses of the *exo-* **(41)** and *endo*-toluene-*p*-sulphonate **(42)** of 2-hydroxybicyclo[2.2.1]heptan-7-one first reported last year.[29] The acetolysis of the *exo*-isomer is slightly slower than that of the *endo*-isomer, while the ethanolysis is slightly faster. The acetolysis of the *exo*-isomer gave 71% of a yellow oil which contained 65% of *exo*-acetate, 20% of *endo*-acetate, and 15% of six other unidentified products. The *endo*-isomer (88.9% pure) yielded 59% of a yellow oil which contained 76% of *exo*-acetate, 3% of *endo*-acetate, and 21% of unidentified components. Possible explanations, symbolized by **(43)** and **(44)**, for the relatively high rates for the *endo*-isomer were excluded and it was concluded that the *exo:endo* rate ratios found here are those to be expected from norbornyl systems in the absence of participation by the 1,6-bonding electrons. Hanack and Dolde[30] have reported that the

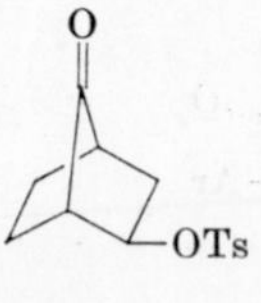

	(41)	**(42)**	**(43)**	**(44)**
$10^4 k_{AcOH}^{100}$	1.84	4.66		
$10^4 k_{EtOH}^{100}$	2.56	1.2		

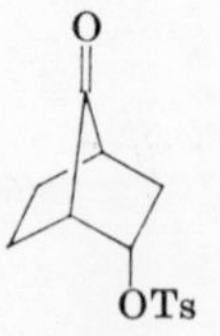

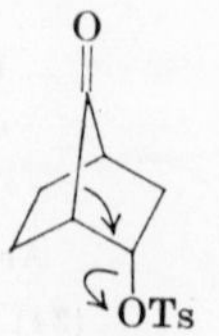

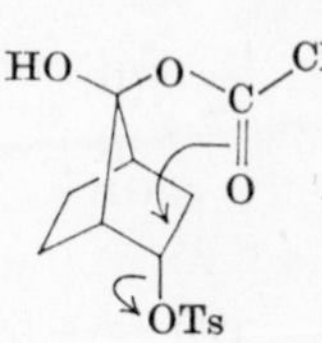

[27] G. E. Gream and D. Wege, *Tetrahedron*, **22**, 2583 (1966).
[28] P. G. Gassman and J. L. Marshall, *J. Am. Chem. Soc.*, **88**, 2822 (1966).
[29] See *Organic Reaction Mechanisms*, **1965**, 26.
[30] M. Hanack and J. Dolde, *Tetrahedron Letters*, **1966**, 321.

solvolysis of a 73:27% mixture of the *endo*- and *exo*-toluene-*p*-sulphonates yields some cyclohex-3-ene-1-carboxylic acid.[30]

Another very interesting investigation of the solvolysis of a pair of *exo*- and *endo*-norbornyl derivatives with which there is no participation of the 1,6-bonding electrons in the reactions of the *exo*-isomer has been reported by Traylor and Perrin.[31] These workers measured the rates of acid-catalysed exchange of the *exo*- and *endo*-methoxyl groups of camphor dimethyl ketal (**47**) and 2-norbornanone dimethyl ketal (**45**) in deuteriomethanol and the relative rates of capture of the intermediate ion (**46**) from the *exo*- and *endo*-directions by methanol and by borohydride. With the norbornanone ketal the *exo*-

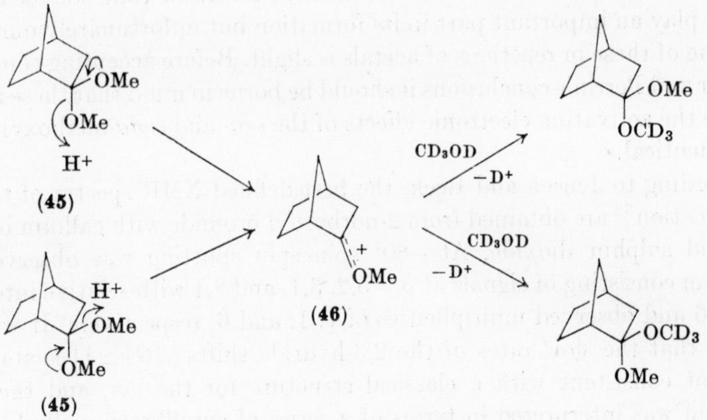

OMe
OMe
H⁺
(**45**)

H⁺
OMe
OMe
(**45**)

CD₃OD
−D⁺

+
OMe
(**46**)

CD₃OD
−D⁺

OMe
OCD₃

OCD₃
OMe

methoxyl group was exchanged 16 times more rapidly than the *endo*-group, and ion (**46**) was captured 20 and 24 times more rapidly from the *exo*-direction by methanol and borohydride, respectively. If then this reaction is a good model for how *exo*- and *endo*-norbornyl toluene-*p*-sulphonates would react in the absence of participation by the 1,6-bonding electrons these results indicate that only part of the 1600-fold rate enhancement found with the *exo*-isomer can be the result of steric hindrance to ionization and suggest that most of it must result from participation. An even more striking effect was found with the camphor acetal (**47**) with which the *exo*-methoxyl group was exchanged 10 times more *slowly* than the *endo*-group and capture of the ion by methanol and borohydride was 10 and 8 times, respectively, more rapid from the *endo*-direction. Traylor and Perrin concluded then that the higher rates of solvolyses of *exo*-norbornyl toluene-*p*-sulphonate and of isobornyl chloride than those of their *endo*-isomers are in the main the result of participation, but they suggested that part of the driving force could arise from relief of steric strain on lengthening of the 1,6-bond in the transition state.

31 T. G. Traylor and C. L. Perrin, *J. Am. Chem. Soc.*, **88**, 4934 (1966).

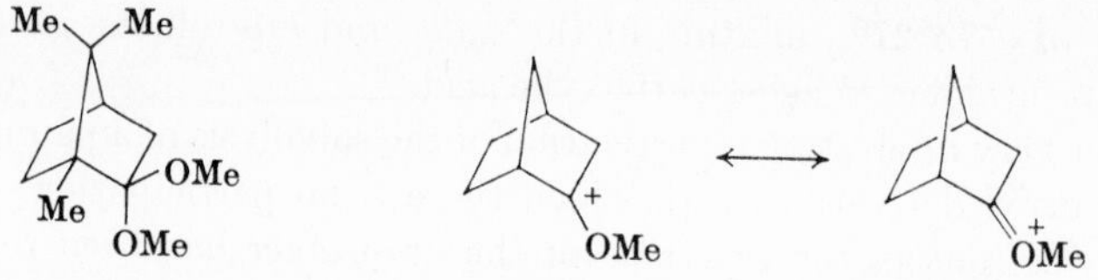

(47)   (48)   (49)

The validity of these conclusions depends on the assumption that ion (46) is a good model for a classical norbornyl cation. The most important contributing structure to ion (46) is, however, not the carbonium ion structure (48) but the oxonium ion structure (49) and the carbon–oxygen bond must have considerable double-bond character. This could mean that stereoelectronic factors play an important part in its formation but unfortunately our understanding of these in reactions of acetals is slight. Before accepting completely Traylor and Perrin's conclusions it should be borne in mind that these authors assume the activating electronic effects of the *exo-* and *endo-*methoxyl groups to be identical.

According to Jensen and Beck, the best defined NMR spectra of the norbornyl cation[32] are obtained from 2-norbornyl bromide with gallium bromide in liquid sulphur dioxide. At −80° spin–spin splitting was observed, the spectrum consisting of signals at $\delta = 5.2$, 3.1, and 2.1 with relative intensities of 4:1:6 and observed multiplicities of 7, 1, and 6, respectively. It was considered that the slow rates of the 2,3-hydride shifts ($\Delta G^{\ddagger} \simeq 11$ kcal mole^{-1}) were not consistent with a classical structure for the ion, and the NMR spectrum was interpreted in terms of a series of equilibrating alkyl-bridged and protonated cyclopropane structures, as shown in Scheme 3.[33]

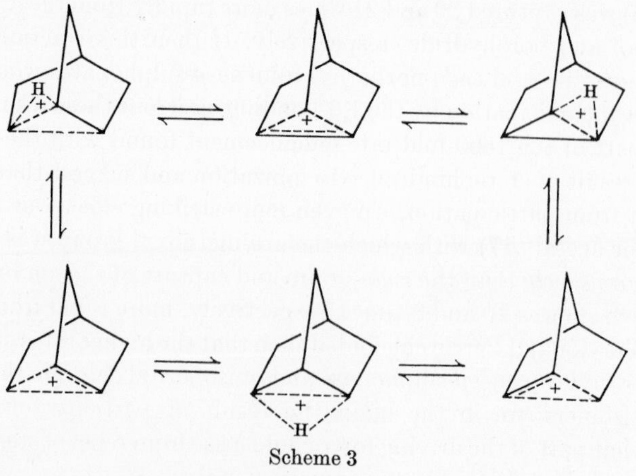

Scheme 3

[32] See *Organic Reaction Mechanisms*, 1965, 23—25.
[33] F. R. Jensen and B. H. Beck, *Tetrahedron Letters*, 1966, 4287.

It has been calculated from their mass spectra that the rate of fragmentation of the ion $C_7H_{11}Br^+$ from *exo*-norbornyl bromide to yield $C_7H_{11}^+$ is 10 times greater than that of the analogous ion from *endo*-norbornyl bromide.[34]

Decomposition of norbornan-2-one tosylhydrazone by hot alkoxide solutions leads to nortricyclene. In the aprotic medium, diglyme, the yield is greater than 99% and when the 6-*exo*- or 6-*endo*-deuterionorbornan-2-one derivative was used the tricyclene had the same deuterium content as the starting norbornanone. It was suggested that this reaction involved a carbene insertion with an intramolecular transfer of hydrogen or deuterium. In a protic medium, ethylene glycol, the yield of nortricyclene was still very high (92—93%), but now deuterium was lost when 6-*exo*- or 6-*endo*-deuterionorbornan-2-one was starting material. Strikingly, however, the loss of 6-*endo*-deuterium, 52%, was larger than the loss of 6-*exo*-deuterium, 19%. It was concluded, therefore, that in the protic medium the reaction could not involve solely protonation of the carbene to a 2-norbornyl cation since this would be expected to be either a non-classical ion or a rapidly equilibrating pair of classical ions which would make the 6-*endo*- and 6-*exo*-positions equivalent. Instead, protonation of the intermediate diazoalkane (**50**) from the *exo*-direction to give an *endo*-diazonium ion (**51**) which undergoes a 1,3-elimination was suggested as an important pathway.[35]

        (**50**)   (**51**)

Other investigations of norbornyl systems include studies of the solvolyses of 2-norbornyl,[36] 1,3,3-trimethyl-2-norbornyl (fenchyl),[37] and 1,5,5-trimethyl-2-norbornyl (isofenchyl)[37] toluene-*p*-sulphonates and of the lead tetra-acetate oxidation of norborn-5-ene-2-carboxylic acid in the presence of lithium chloride;[38] see also p. 143.

The formation of different products, or of the same products in different proportions, from apparently identical carbonium ions that are derived by ring expansion of different starting materials has been designated a "memory effect."[39] This year another investigation of the acetolyses of *syn*-

34 D. C. DeJongh and S. R. Shrader, *J. Am. Chem. Soc.*, **88**, 3881 (1966).
35 A. Nickon and N. H. Werstiuk, *J. Am. Chem. Soc.*, **88**, 4543 (1966).
36 W. Hückel and O. Vogt, *Ann. Chem.*, **695**, 16 (1966).
37 W. Hückel and H.-J. Kern, *Annalen*, **687**, 40 (1965).
38 R. M. Moriarty, H. Gopal, and H. G. Walsh, *Tetrahedron Letters*, **1966**, 4369.
39 J. A. Berson and M. S. Poonian, *J. Am. Chem. Soc.*, **88**, 170 (1966).

(52) and *anti*-norborn-2-en-7-ylmethyl arenesulphonate (57) originally studied by Berson and Gajewski[40] has been reported.[41] The products of ring expansion may be divided into the L series, (61)—(63), previously shown by LeBel to result from carbonium ion reactions of *exo*-2-bicyclo[2.2.2]octen-5-yl derivatives, and the G series, (55)—(56), previously obtained by Goering

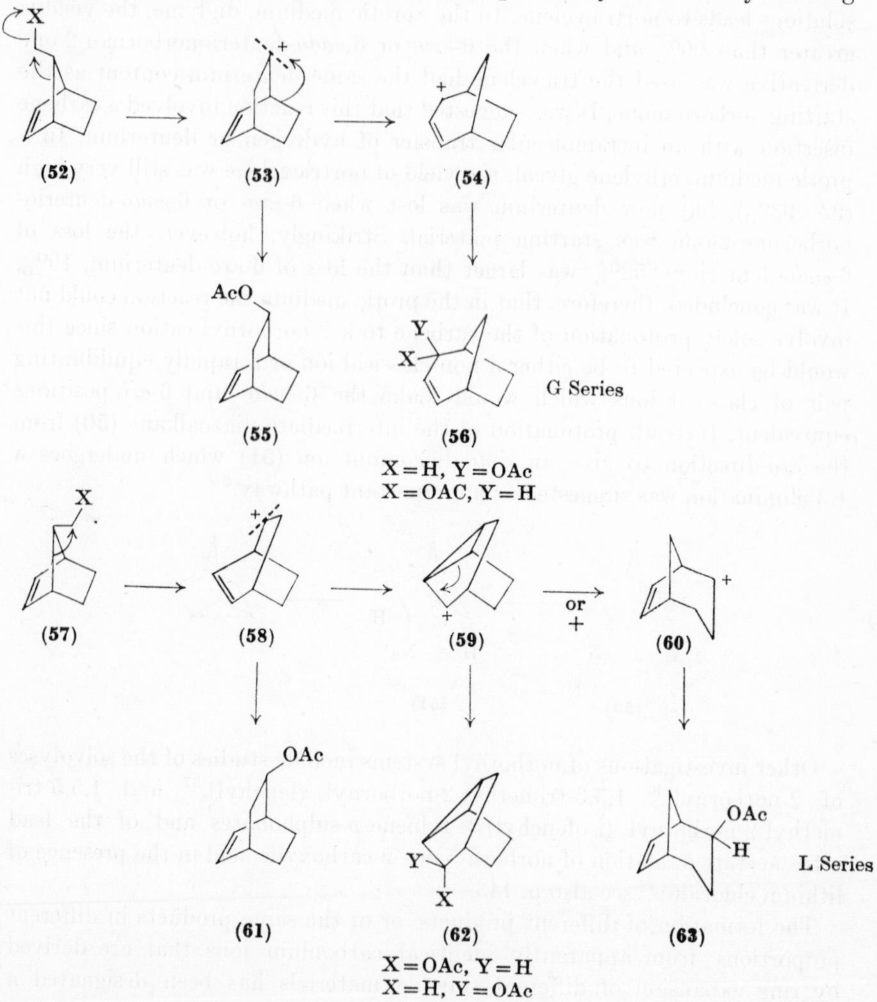

(52)   (53)   (54)

AcO

(55)   (56)   G Series

X = H, Y = OAc
X = OAC, Y = H

(57)   (58)   (59)   or   (60)

OAc

(61)   (62)   (63)   L Series

X = OAc, Y = H
X = H, Y = OAc

from *endo*-2-bicyclo[2.2.2]octen-5-yl derivatives. The *syn-p*-bromobenzene-sulphonate yields a mixture of L and G acetates in the ratio 1:20—40 while the *anti*-isomer yields only L acetates. It appears then either that the bond

[40] J. A. Berson and J. J. Gajewski, *J. Am. Chem. Soc.*, **86**, 5020 (1964).
[41] R. K. Bly and R. S. Bly, *J. Org. Chem.*, **31**, 1577 (1966).

migrations, (52) → (53) → (54), and (57) → (58) → (59) + (60), are largely concerted or that the conformationally isomeric carbonium ions (53) and (58) (the vacant *p*-orbitals of which lie along the broken lines) are formed as the first intermediates in the ring expansions and are trapped before they can interconvert. Delocalization of the 1,7-bond of ion (53) leads to products of the G-series and delocalization of the 1,6-bond or of the 5,6-π-electrons of ion (58) leads to the L series. That the L:G ratio in the products derived from *anti-p*-bromobenzenesulphonate is greater than the G:L ratio in those derived from *syn-p*-bromobenzenesulphonate indicates that π-trapping in carbonium ion (58) is more efficient than σ-trapping in ion (53).

Another example of a "memory effect" was reported by Berson and Poonian.[39] Solvolysis of 7-norbornylmethyl *p*-bromobenzenesulphonate (64) and deamination of the corresponding amine yield mixtures of 2-*exo*- and 2-*endo*-bicyclo[3.2.1]octyl and 2-bicyclo[2.2.2]octyl derivatives as well as unrearranged products. The *exo*-bicyclo[3.2.1]octyl derivatives (67) are formed by a double carbonium ion rearrangement and the second of these, (65) → (66), was shown by specific deuterium labelling to proceed with preferential migration of the *anti*-bridge (65, type *x*) rather than of the *syn*-bridge (65, type *y*). The ratio of *anti* to *syn*-migration was larger in the deamination (5.7—6.6) than in the solvolysis of the *p*-bromobenzenesulphonate (1.4—1.6).

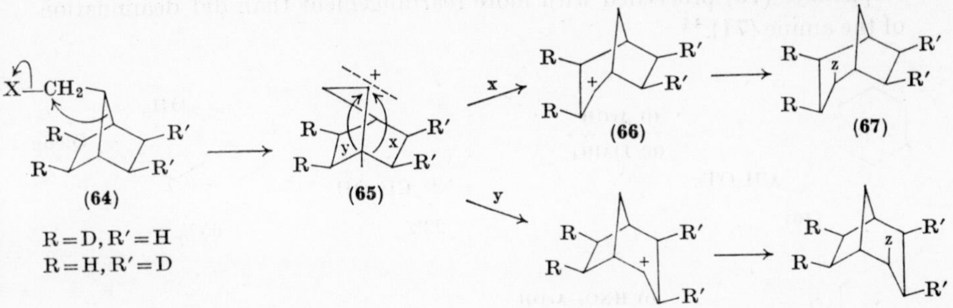

R = D, R′ = H
R = H, R′ = D

The ring expansion of 2-norbornylmethyl derivatives has also been investigated.[42]

Wiberg and Ashe's investigation of the acetolysis of *exo*- and *endo*-6-bicyclo[3.1.0]hexanylmethyl toluene-*p*-sulphonates[43] has been supplemented by an investigation of the deamination of the corresponding amines (68) and (69).[44]

[42] W. Kraus and P. Schmutte, *Chem. Ber.*, **99**, 2259 (1966).
[43] See *Organic Reaction Mechanisms*, **1965**, 28.
[44] F. T. Bond and L. Scerbo, *Tetrahedron Letters*, **1965**, 4255.

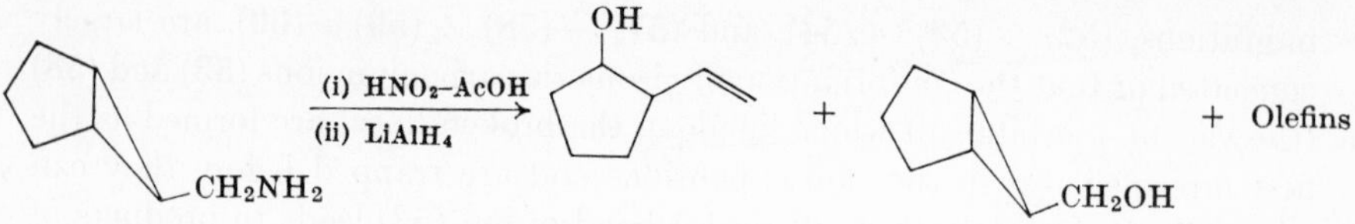

(68)   16%   69%

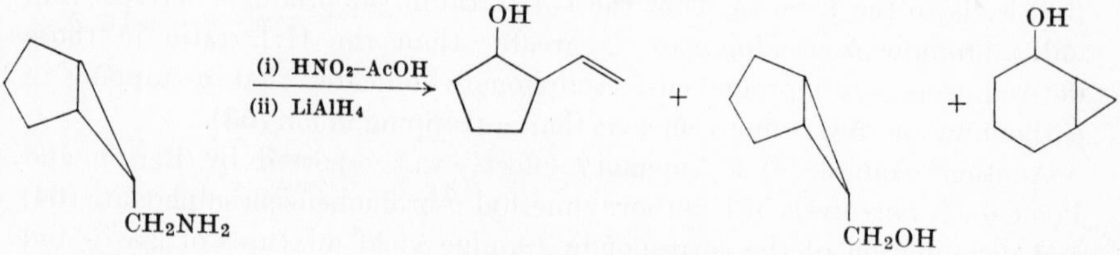

(69)   12%   70%   11%

+ Olefins

Similar products were obtained but in different proportions. In particular, the deamination reactions yielded a much higher proportion of the unrearranged alcohols. It was suggested that the initially formed cyclopropylmethyl cation is trapped before it can rearrange. The *exo*-bicyclo[4.1.0]heptylmethyl system was also investigated. Again solvolysis of the toluene-*p*-sulphonate **(70)** proceeded with more rearrangement than did deamination of the amine **(71)**.[44]

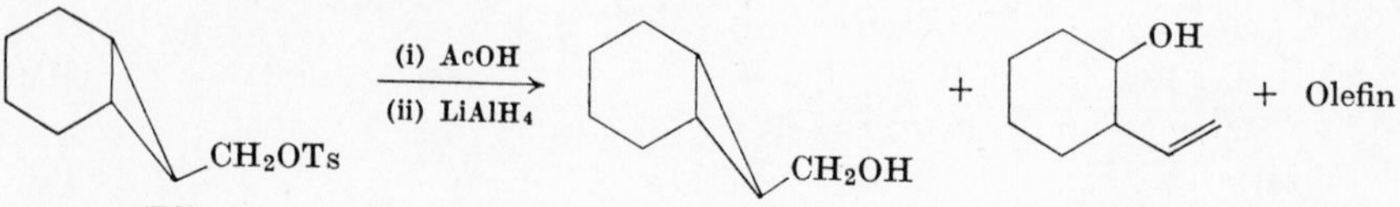

(70)   22%   65%

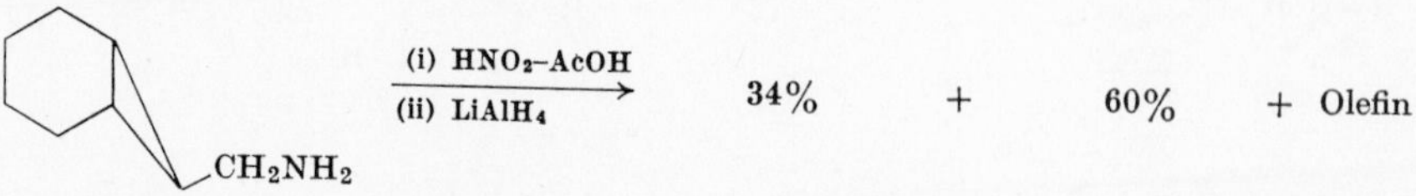

(71)   34%   +   60%   + Olefin

The kinetics and products of the acetolysis of the bridged cyclobutylmethyl toluene-*p*-sulphonates **(72)**—**(75)** have been investigated and compared with those for cyclobutylmethyl toluene-*p*-sulphonate **(76)** itself.[45] Unrearranged acetate from optically active *endo*-5-bicyclo[2.1.1]hexyl[α-^{2}H]methyl toluene-*p*-sulphonate was formed with complete inversion of configuration, so this

[45] K. B. Wiberg and B. A. Hess, *J. Am. Chem. Soc.*, **88**, 4433 (1966).

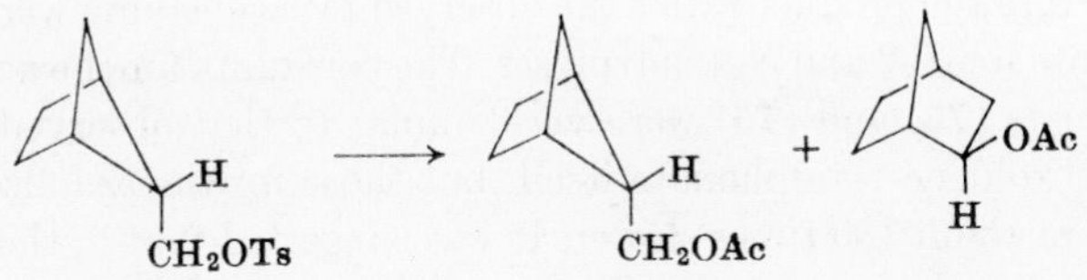

(72)   71%   29%

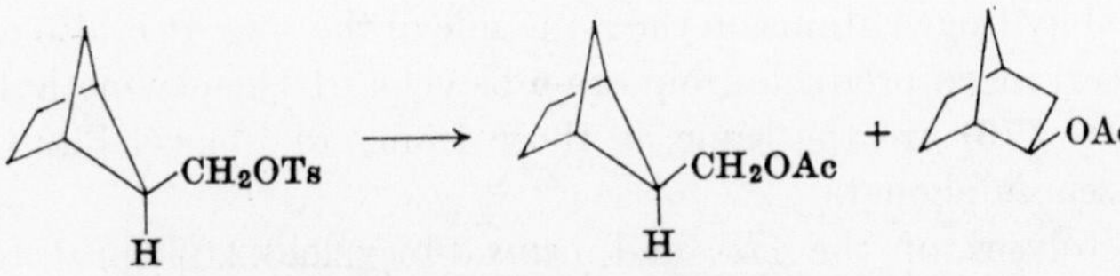

(73)   4%   96%

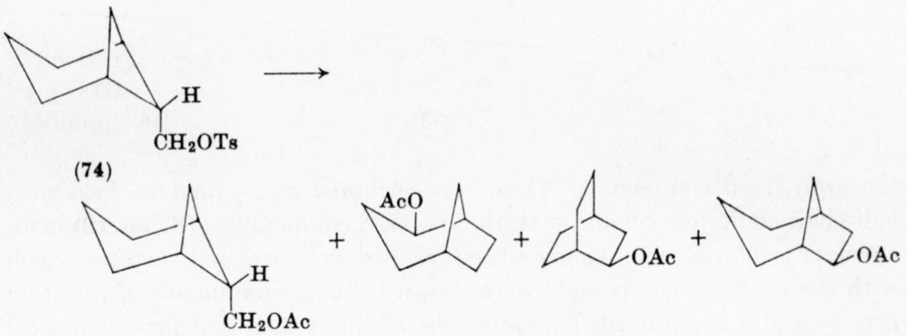

(74)

16%   22%   25%   37%

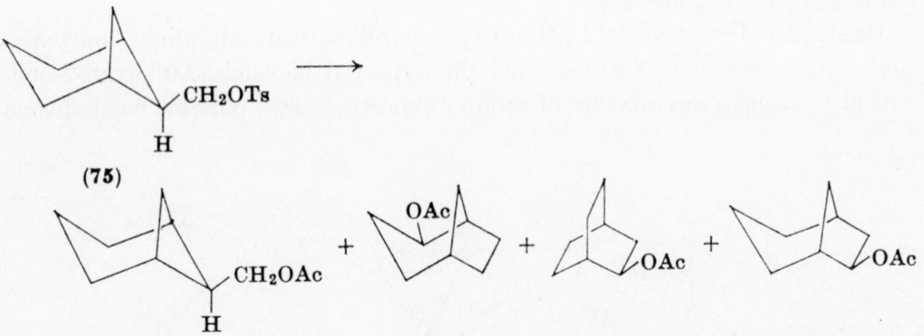

(75)

∼0.4%   40%   45%   15%

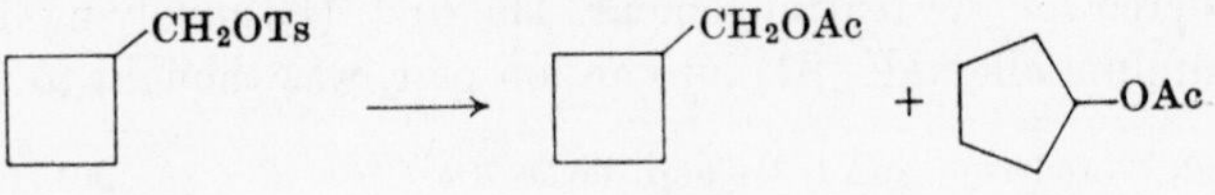

(76)   1%   99%

and the other unrearranged acetates were considered to be formed by S_N2 processes. From the product ratios the observed rate constants were dissected into constants for S_N2 and S_N1 solvolyses. The constants for the acetolyses of the *exo*-isomers (**73**) and (**75**) were very similar to that observed for cyclo-butylmethyl toluene-*p*-sulphonate itself, but those for the *endo*-isomers (**72**) and (**74**) were about 100 times slower. It was suggested that in the transition states for the *endo*-isomers there was an unfavourable non-bonding 1,3-interaction between one of the methyl-hydrogen atoms and the axial or pseudoaxial hydrogen atoms on the same side of the ring. It is also of interest that the rearranged products from *exo*-6-bicyclo[3.1.1]heptylmethyl toluene-*p*-sulphonate (**75**) are the same as those from *exo*-6-bicyclo[3.2.1]octyl *p*-bromobenzenesulphonate.

The acetolyses of the *cis*- and *trans*-3-bicyclo[3.2.0]heptyl toluene-*p*-sulphonates (**77**), (**78**), and (**79**) have been studied. It was thought that with

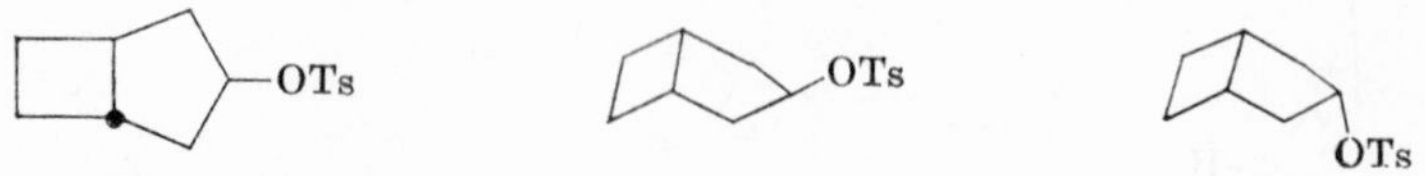

(77)   (78)   (79)

the *trans*-fused compound (**77**) the cyclopentane ring would be held in a half-chair conformation and with the *cis*-fused compounds (**78** and **79**) in an envelope conformation. The reactions yielded unrearranged acetates which with the *cis*-fused compounds were shown to be predominantly those from inversion of configuration. The rates were all lower than that for cyclopentyl toluene-*p*-sulphonate itself, that for the *trans*-fused compound (**77**) (the slowest) being 55 times less.[46]

Oxidation of *exo*-bicyclo[2.2.0]hexan-2-ol (**80**) with aluminium *tert*-butoxide and "quinone ether" did not yield the expected bicyclo[2.2.0]hexan-2-one, but instead gave the mixture of products shown.[47] Two possible mechanisms

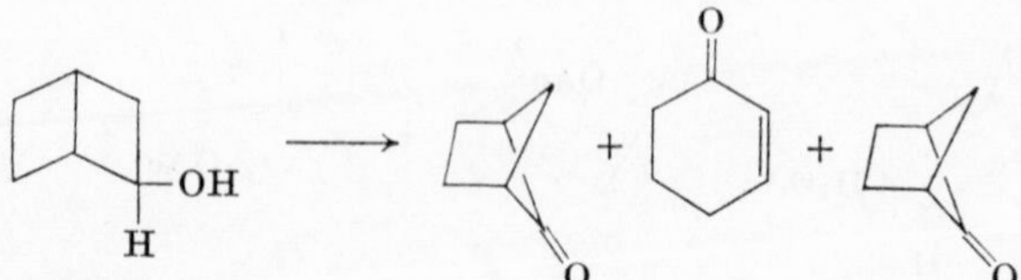

(80)

were considered for the rearrangement. The first, (1), involving dissociation of the aluminium alkoxide (**81**) into an ion pair, was thought to be unlikely

[46] J. Meinwald, P. Anderson, and J. J. Tufariello, *J. Am. Chem. Soc.*, **88**, 1301 (1966).
[47] R. N. McDonald and C. E. Reineke, *Tetrahedron Letters*, **1966**, 2739.

since no bicyclo[2.1.1]hexan-5-one was obtained with aluminium *tert*-butoxide alone. The second, (2), was therefore favoured, and to explain the absence of a norbornyl type of rearrangement[48] it was suggested that the hydride transfer occurred simultaneously with the migration of the 1,4-bridge.

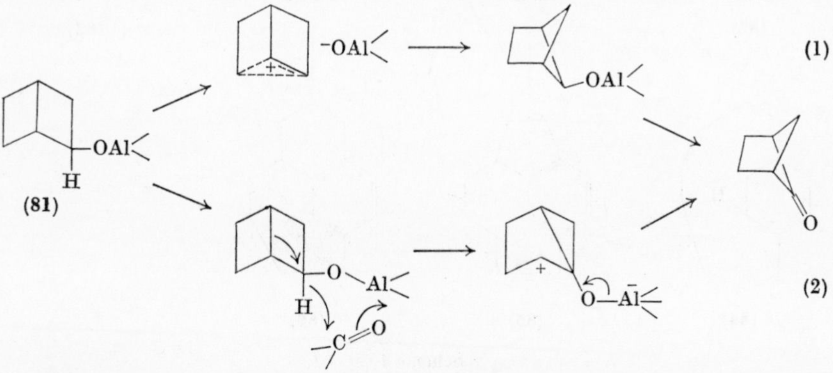

(1)

(2)

(81)

Other reactions of bicyclic and polycyclic systems which have received attention include the solvolytic rearrangement of substituted bicyclo[4.3.1]-decyl methanesulphonates to bicyclo[5.3.0]decanes,[49] of pinyl toluene-*p*-sulphonates,[50] of 1,1'-bishomocubyl methanesulphonate, and of homocubyl-methyl toluene-*p*-sulphonate,[51] and the reaction of bicyclo[2.2.2]octane-2-carboxylic acid with bromine to yield 2-(axial)bromobicyclo[3.2.1]octane-1-carboxylic acid.[52]

Phenonium Ions

There has been relatively little work this year on phenonium ions or on equilibrating phenethyl cations.[53a]

Cram, Montgomery, and Knox have investigated the acetolysis of [8]para-cyclophan-3-yl toluene-*p*-sulphonate (82).[53b] The rate is compared with that of other paracyclophane toluene-*p*-sulphonates in Table 3. The products were [8]paracyclophan-4-ene (83) (60%) and two other hydrocarbons (39% and 1%), the major one being either (85) or (86). These are shown in Scheme 3 as

[48] See *Organic Reaction Mechanisms*, **1965**, 30.

[49] J. A. Marshall and J. J. Partridge, *Tetrahedron Letters*, **1966**, 2545.

[50] W. Hückel and D. Holzwarth, *Ann. Chem.*, **697**, 69 (1966); H. Schmidt, M. Mühlstädt, and P. Son, *Chem. Ber.*, **99**, 2736 (1966).

[51] W. G. Dauben and D. L. Whalen, *J. Am. Chem. Soc.*, **88**, 4739 (1966).

[52] A. W. Chow, D. R. Jakas, and J. R. E. Hoover, *Tetrahedron Letters*, **1966**, 5427.

[53a] See, however, M. Brookhart, F. A. L. Anet, and S. Winstein, *J. Am. Chem. Soc.*, **88**, 5657 (1966); M. Brookhart, F. A. L. Anet, D. J. Cram, and S. Winstein, *ibid.*, p. 5659; G. A. Olah, C. U. Pittman, E. Namanworth, and M. B. Comisarow, *ibid.*, p. 5571.

[53b] D. J. Cram, C. S. Montgomery, and G. R. Knox, *J. Am. Chem. Soc.*, **88**, 515 (1966).

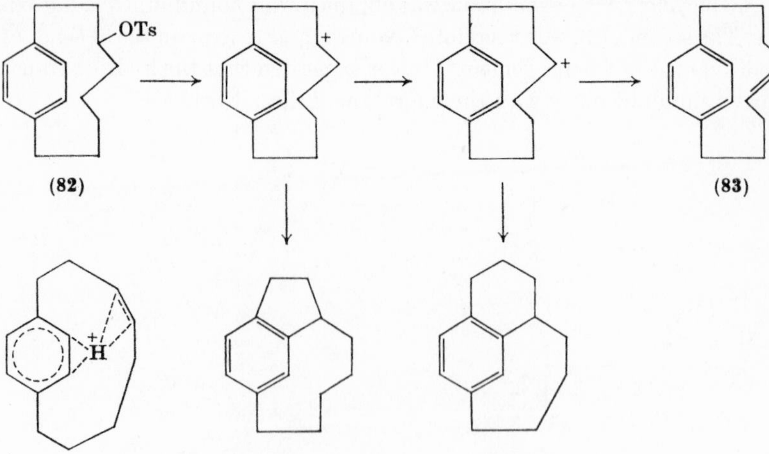

(82)   (83)

(84)   (85)   (86)

Scheme 4

being formed through a series of classical ions, although in the original paper
it was suggested that the intermediate was a composite bridged ion (84) "in
which a proton is imbedded in the two π-clouds, that of the incipient olefin
and that of the benzene ring".

Table 3. Relative rates of acetolysis of
cyclic toluene-p-sulphonates at 50°.

Toluene-p-sulphonate	Relative rate
Cyclohexyl	1
Cyclodecyl	539
[10]Paracyclophan-5-yl	15
[9]Paracyclophan-3-yl	60
[9]Paracyclophan-5-yl	170
[9]Paracyclophan-4-yl	1800
[8]Paracyclophan-3-yl	52

[2.2]Paracyclophan-1-ylmethyl   toluene-p-sulphonate   (87)   undergoes
acetolysis with concurrent rearrangement to the [2.3]paracyclophanyl
acetate (88) and toluene-p-sulphonate (89).[54] The total rate of ionization is
only 28 times greater than that of β-methylphenethyl toluene-p-sulphonate

[54] E. Hedaya and L. M. Kyle, *J. Am. Chem. Soc.*, **88**, 3667 (1966).

and 3.8 times greater than that of 1-tetralylmethyl toluene-*p*-sulphonate, so that little of the 15—20 kcal difference in strain energy of the [2.2]- and [2.3]-paracyclophane systems is released in the transition state. This may arise, however, from difficulty in attaining the correct geometry for phenyl participation.

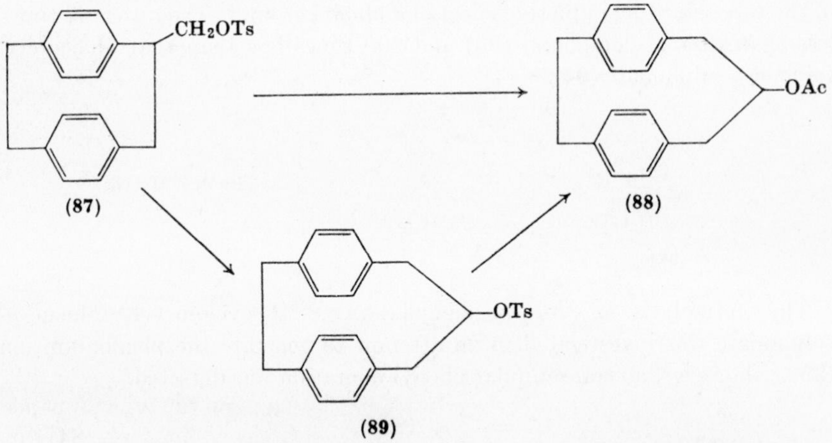

The reaction therefore proceeds as shown for compounds (87), (88), and (89).

Acetolysis and formolysis of 2-(α-naphthyl)[1-^{14}C]ethyl toluene-*p*-sulphonate yields acetate and formate in which there have been, respectively, 46% and 50% migration of the label from $C_{(1)}$ to $C_{(2)}$. Toluene-*p*-sulphonate recovered from the acetolysis, but not from the formolysis, after 50% reaction also shows appreciable (38%) migration. The rates were slightly higher than those for the phenethyl compound, suggesting weak anchimeric assistance.[55a]

The hydrolysis of (*R*)-1-indanylmethyl toluene-*p*-sulphonate (**90**) in aqueous dioxan yields (*R*)-tetrahydro-α-naphthol (**91**) with at least 80% stereospecificity.[55b] The reaction therefore proceeds as shown.

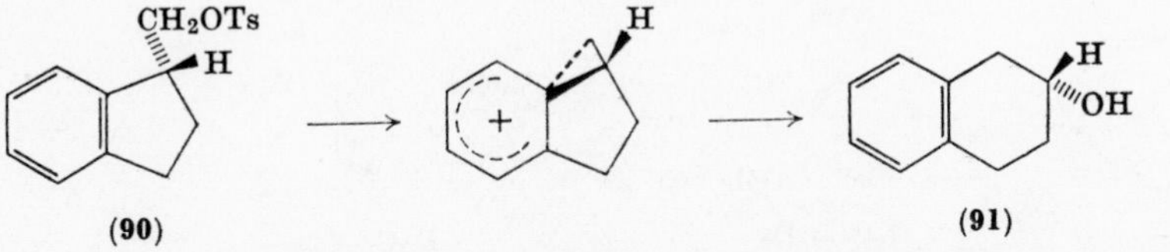

The *exo*:*endo* rate ratios (4000—7000) for the solvolyses of benzonorbornen-2-yl, 2-methylbenzonorbornen-2-yl, and 2-phenylbenzonorbornen-2-yl derivatives are very similar. It was suggested that this indicates that participation

[55a] C. C. Lee and A. G. Forman, *Can. J. Chem.*, **43**, 3387 (1965).
[55b] D. Battail-Robert and D. Gagnaire, *Bull. Soc. Chim. France*, **1966**, 208,

by the phenyl ring is not important in the rate-determining steps of these reactions since this should decrease with increasing carbonium ion stability at $C_{(2)}$.[7]

The acetolysis of compound (92), in which phenyl participation through overlap of the π-cloud with the developing carbonium ion centre is prevented by the geometry of the molecule, has been investigated to provide a measure of the rate-retarding inductive effect of a phenyl group.[56] The rate is 47 times less than that of compound (93) and 800 times less than that of neophyl toluene-*p*-sulphonate (94).

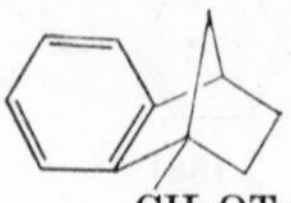

CH$_2$OTs   CH$_2$OTs   PhMe$_2$CH$_2$OTs

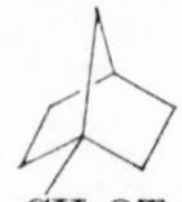

(92)   (93)   (94)

The formolysis of *trans*-5-phenyl[1,2,2,8,8-^{2}H$_5$]cyclo-octyl toluene-*p*-sulphonate was investigated in an attempt to generate the phenonium ion (95);[57] however, no transannular phenyl migration was detected.

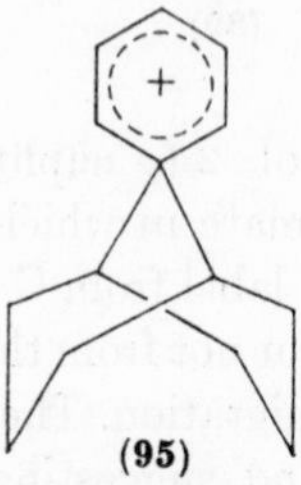

(95)

The amount of aryl migration occurring in the acetolysis and formolysis of 2,4- (96) and 3,5-dimethoxy[1,1-^{2}H$_2$]phenethyl (97) *p*-bromobenzene-sulphonate have been determined.[58] Both the acetate and formate from (96)

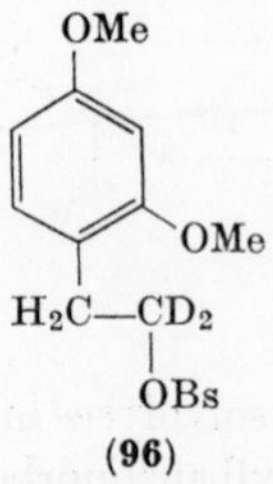

OMe

OMe

H$_2$C—CD$_2$

OBs

(96)

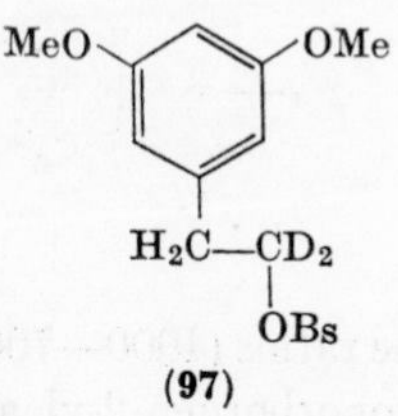

MeO   OMe

H$_2$C—CD$_2$

OBs

(97)

[56] J. W. Wilt, C. A. Schneider, J. P. Berliner, and H. F. Dabek, *Tetrahedron Letters*, 1966, 4073.
[57] A. C. Cope and R. B. Kinnel, *J. Am. Chem. Soc.*, 88, 752 (1966).
[58] C. C. Lee and L. Noszkó, *Can. J. Chem.*, 44, 2481, 2491 (1966).

have half the deuterium label at $C_{(1)}$ and half at $C_{(2)}$, indicating the intervention of a symmetrical species. Ion-pair return also occurs in the acetolysis since unchanged starting compound isolated after 70% reaction has deuterium at $C_{(2)}$; it was calculated that the ratio of the total rate constant, k_α, to the rate constant for acetolysis, k_t, was 2.3. Ion-pair return was not observed in the formolysis of (96). With the 3,5-dimethoxy-compound, as might be expected, the amount of aryl participation was much smaller (14% and 26% of deuterium, respectively, on $C_{(2)}$ of acetate and formate). For the acetolysis $k_\alpha/k_t = 1.3$. A small α-secondary isotope effect was also observed in the solvolyses of (96) and (97).

The ratios of the rates of migration of the aryl groups to the rates of proton expulsion from the ions formed from labelled 1-p-tolyl-2,2-diphenylethanol (98) and 1,2-diphenyl-2-p-tolylethanol (*erythro-* or *threo*) (99) have been calculated by Raaen, Lietzke, and Collins[59] from the previous results of Collins and Bonner[60] to be $k_\phi/k_H \geqslant 63.5$, $k_\phi'/k_H \geqslant 200$, and $k_r/k_H' \geqslant 1200$ (see Chart 1).

Chart 1

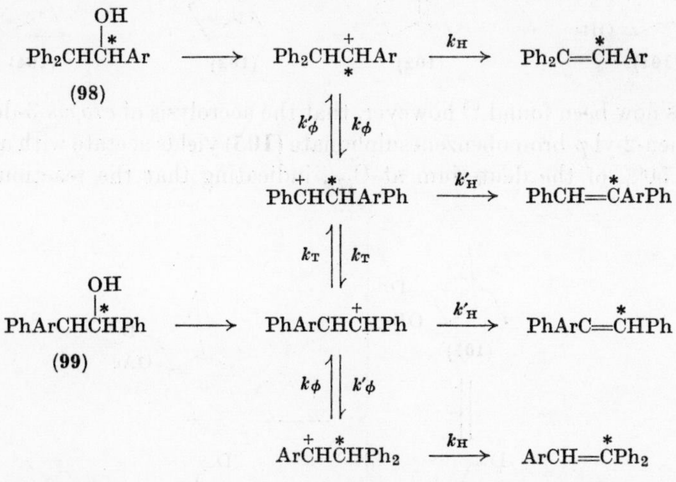

Ar = p-tolyl

The solvolytic rearrangement of 1-phenylcycloheptylmethyl toluene-p-sulphonate (100) has been reinvestigated.[61] It is confirmed that the rate of this type of reaction varies with ring size in the order $7 > 6 > 4 > 5$ (see also p. 287).

59 V. F. Raaen, M. H. Lietzke, and C. J. Collins, *J. Am. Chem. Soc.*, 88, 369 (1966).
60 C. J. Collins and W. A. Bonner, *J. Am. Chem. Soc.*, 77, 6725 (1955).
61 J. W. Wilt, J. F. Zawadzki, and D. G. Schultenover, *J. Org. Chem.*, 31, 876 (1966).

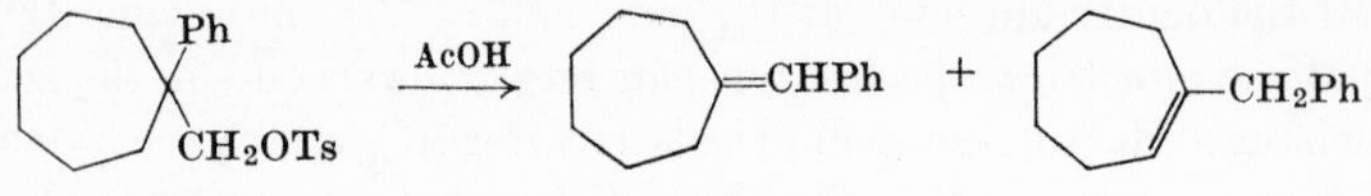

(100)

Participation by Double and Triple Bonds

Reviews of the formation of cyclopropane and cyclobutane rings through participation by double bonds[62] and on transannular participation[63] have been published.

It was originally reported[64] that the acetolysis of *exo*-norbornen-2-yl *p*-bromobenzenesulphonate (101) labelled with ^{14}C at $C_{(2)}$ and $C_{(3)}$ yielded acetate in which the label was scrambled, but not as much as required by the intervention of the symmetrical ion (102). It was therefore proposed that an unsymmetrical ion, as (103), was formed first and that some of this was trapped by solvent before it isomerized to its enantiomorph (104) or to the symmetrical ion (102).

(101)   (102)   (103)   (104)

It has now been found,[65] however, that the acetolysis of *exo,cis*-3-deuterionorbornen-2-yl *p*-bromobenzenesulphonate (105) yields acetate with approximately 50% of the deuterium at $C_{(7)}$, indicating that the reaction passes

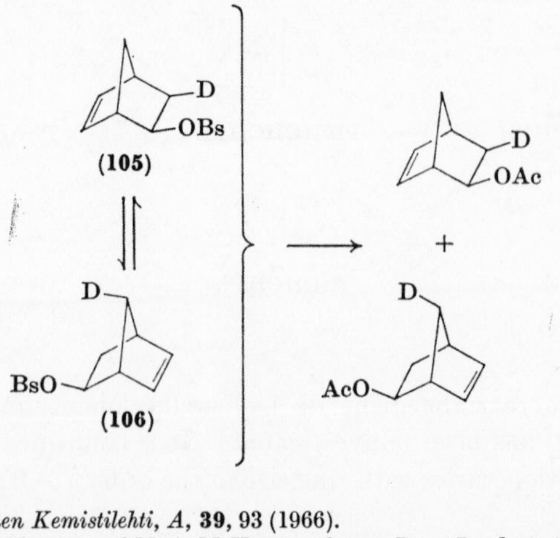

(105)

(106)

[62] M. Hanack, *Suomen Kemistilehti, A*, **39**, 93 (1966).

[63] A. C. Cope, M. M. Martin, and M. A. McKervey, *Quart. Rev. (London)*, **20**, 119 (1966).

[64] J. D. Roberts, C. C. Lee, and W. H. Saunders, *J. Am. Chem. Soc.*, **77**, 3034 (1955).

[65] S. J. Cristol, T. C. Morrill, and R. A. Sanchez, *J. Am. Chem. Soc.*, **88**, 3087 (1966); S. J. Cristol, T. C. Morrill, and R. A. Sanchez, *J. Org. Chem.*, **31**, 2719 (1966).

through a symmetrical intermediate. Extensive ion-pair return resulting in the formation of the 7-deuteriated *p*-bromobenzenesulphonate (**106**) also occurs and this is about 12 times faster than the acetolysis. Most of the acetate in the product was therefore formed from *p*-bromobenzenesulphonate in which the label was already scrambled and so it is impossible to decide definitely the symmetry of the ions from which it was formed. Nevertheless, the report[64] that the gross acetate product is unsymmetrical appears definitely to be incorrect. Two other points of interest to note from this work are (i) that the rate of ionization of *exo*-norbornen-2-yl *p*-bromobenzenesulphonate must be at least 13 times greater than its rate of acetolysis and (ii) that ion-pair return apparently does not yield any nortricyclyl *p*-bromobenzenesulphonate.

The methanolysis of *anti*-7-norbornenyl toluene-*p*-sulphonate in the presence of 4M sodium methoxide yields 51.5% of the *endo*-tricyclic ether (**107**), but in an acetate buffer there is only 0.3% of this compound in the kinetically controlled product which consists mainly of the *anti*-7-norbornyl

TsO	4M-NaOMe in MeOH at 25°		MeO
		OMe	
		51.5%	48.5%
		(**107**)	(**108**)

ether (**108**).[66] It was considered that (**107**) was not formed by an S_N2' mechanism (the effect of the concentration of MeO⁻ on the rate was not reported) but by capture of the norbornen-7-yl cation by MeO⁻, partitioning between attack at the 7- and the 2-position being highly sensitive to nucleophilicity. The highly stereospecific reaction at $C_{(2)}$ from the *endo*-direction argues strongly for a non-classical structure for the norbornen-7-yl cation.[67] Norbornadien-7-yl chloride reacts similarly with sodium methoxide in methanol–dioxan (5:1), to yield an appreciable quantity of the analogous *endo*-tricyclic ether.[68] In this reaction sodium methoxide was shown to have only a small effect on the rate.

The acid-catalysed hydrolysis of the tricyclic ether (**107**) in 80% aqueous acetone was also investigated. It proceeded 7×10^6 times faster than that of the *anti*-norbornenyl ether (**108**), owing to a much higher initial-state free-energy (see Figure 1).[66]

66 A. Diaz, M. Brookhart, and S. Winstein, *J. Am. Chem. Soc.*, **88**, 3133 (1966).
67 M. Brookhart, A. Diaz, and S. Winstein, *J. Am. Chem. Soc.*, **88**, 3135 (1966).
68 H. Tanida, T. Tsuji, and T. Irie, *J. Am. Chem. Soc.*, **88**, 864 (1966).

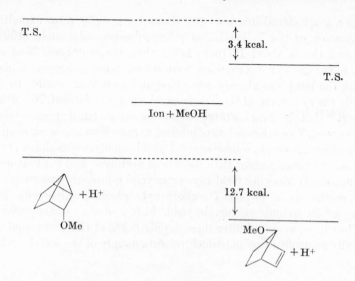

Fɪɢ. 1. Free-energy diagram for the acid-catalysed hydrolyses of *anti*-norbornenyl methyl ether and *endo*-2-methoxytricyclo[4.1.0.0^{3,7}]heptane.

The norbornen-7-yl cation has been generated by adding a solution of norbornen-7-ol in CH_2Cl_2–CCl_4 at $-50°$ to cold SO_2–SbF_5–FSO_3H[67] or a solution in SO_2 to FSO_3H at $-78°$,[69] and its NMR spectrum was measured (see **109** for τ'-values). As with the norbornadien-7-yl cation (**110**),[70] the signal of the proton at $C_{(7)}$ occurs at a relatively high field, indicating that much of the charge must be delocalized. It is of interest that solutions of the norbornadienyl cation in FSO_3H are stable for hours at room temperature and also that under these conditions the unsymmetrical structure is apparently retained[69] (cf. ref. 95, p. 34). The NMR spectra of the 7-methyl- and 7-hydroxy-norbornen-7-yl cations were also determined.[69]

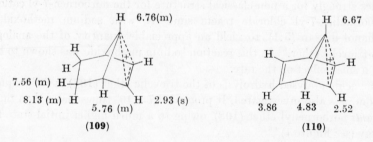

[69] H. G. Richey and R. K. Lustgarten, *J. Am. Chem. Soc.*, **88**, 3136 (1966).
[70] P. R. Story, L. C. Snyder, D. C. Douglass, E. W. Anderson, and R. L. Kornegay, *J. Am. Chem. Soc.*, **85**, 3630 (1963).

The reaction of norbornadien-7-yl chloride with sodium cyanide has also been investigated.[71]

The effect on the rate of acetolysis of introducing a second 7-methoxyl or 7-methyl substituent into 6-methoxy- or 6-methyl-*anti*-9-benzonorbornenyl *p*-bromobenzenesulphonate is the same as for the introduction of the first methoxyl or methyl group (Table 4).[72] The results strongly suggest a symmetrical transition state, as (111).

Table 4. Acetolysis of *anti*-benzonorbornen-9-yl
p-bromobenzenesulphonates at 77.6°.

Substituents	6,7-(MeO)$_2$	6-MeO	6,7-Me$_2$	6-Me	H
Relative rates	3000	54	36	5.7	1

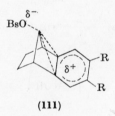

(111)

Two more investigations of the solvolyses of cyclo-oct-4-enylmethyl *p*-bromobenzenesulphonate (112) have been reported.[73—75] The products were again found to contain appreciable quantities of *exo*-bicyclo[3.3.1]nonan-2-yl derivatives, e.g. (114), as well as the *endo*-isomer, e.g. (113); and bicyclo[4.2.1]nonan-2-yl derivatives[74] were also reported to be present. The formation of (114) suggests that the non-classical ion (116) cannot be the sole product-forming intermediate. Indeed it seems likely that it is not an important intermediate at all, since, if it were, it should be formed in the solvolyses of *endo*-bicyclo[3.3.1]nonan-2-yl *p*-bromobenzenesulphonate (115), which should then yield the same products. Quite different product ratios were, however, obtained from the solvolyses of this compound. The higher proportion of *endo*-acetate formed in the acetolysis of (112) was therefore attributed to preferential solvation from the *endo*-direction (as 117), which is reduced in the solvolysis of (115) owing to shielding by the departing anion, as shown in (118).

[71] G. W. Klumpp and F. Bickelhaupt, *Tetrahedron Letters*, **1966**, 865.

[72] H. Tanida and H. Ishitobi, *J. Am. Chem. Soc.*, **88**, 3663 (1966); H. Tanida, H. Miyazaki, and H. Ishitobi, *Can. J. Chem.*, **44**, 98 (1966).

[73] H. Felkin, G. Le Ny, C. Lyon, W. D. K. Macrosson, J. Martin, and W. Parker, *Tetrahedron Letters*, **1966**, 157.

[74] W. Kraus, W. Rothenwöhrer, W. Kaiser, and M. Hanack, *Tetrahedron Letters*, **1966**, 1705.

[75] See *Organic Reaction Mechanisms*, **1965**, 41.

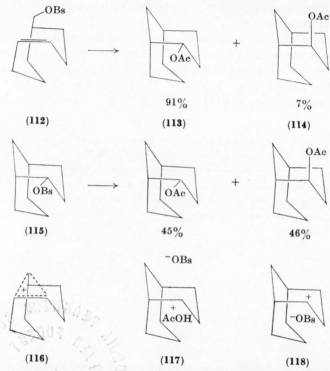

Since the acetolysis of (112) proceeds 70 times faster than that of the analogous saturated compound, there is clearly participation by the double bond, but this leads to a classical rather than to a non-classical ion.

The ^{14}C distribution in the *exo*-norbornyl acetate formed from the acetolysis of 2-(cyclopent-3-enyl)[2-^{14}C]ethyl *p*-nitrobenzenesulphonate (119) has been determined (Table 5).[76] If the *exo*-norbornyl acetate were formed without

Table 5. [14]C Distribution in *exo*-norbornyl acetate from the acetolyses of 2-(cyclopent-3-enyl)[2-^{14}C]ethyl *p*-nitrobenzenesulphonate (119) and *exo*-[2,3-[14]C$_2$]norbornyl *p*-bromobenzenesulphonate (A).

	[14]C (%) at positions			
	$C_{(2)}$–$C_{(3)}$	$C_{(1)}$–$C_{(4)}$	$C_{(7)}$	$C_{(5)}$–$C_{(6)}$
(119) at 60°	37	1	25	36
(A) at 45°	40	23	22	15

[76] C. C. Lee and L. K. M. Lam, *J. Am. Chem. Soc.*, **88**, 2834 (1966); *Tetrahedron Letters*, **1966**, 138.

further rearrangement, after ring closure all the label would be at $C_{(5)}$. A 2,6-hydride shift in the initially formed ion (**120**) (shown here as classical) would result in $C_{(3)}$ and $C_{(5)}$ becoming equivalent and this was found to have occurred (see Table 5). This result contrasts with that observed in the acetolysis of *exo*-norbornyl *p*-bromobenzenesulphonate where only partial equivalence

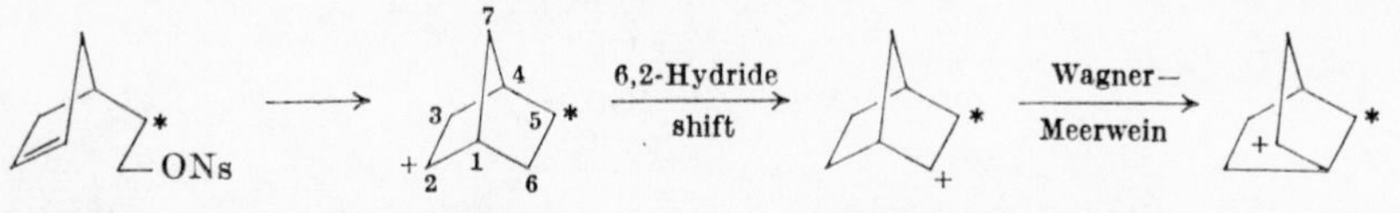

(119) ——→ (120)　6,2-Hydride shift ——→ (121)　Wagner–Meerwein ——→

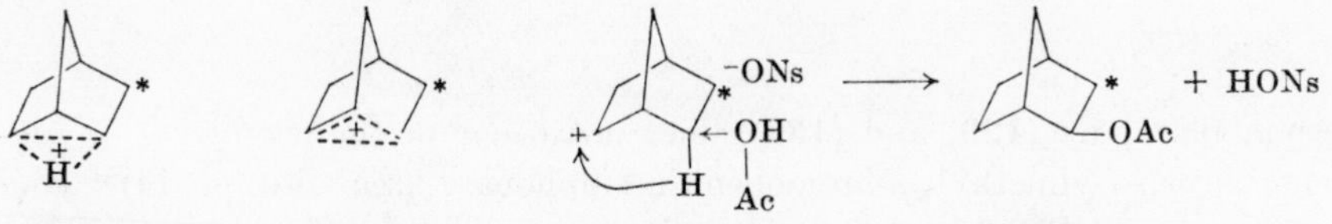

(123)　　(122)　　(124)　——→　(125)　+ HONs

between $C_{(3)}$ and $C_{(5)}$ was found.[77] Subsequent Wagner–Meerwein rearrangement of ion (**121**) would lead to $C_{(7)}$ becoming equivalent to $C_{(5)}$ and $C_{(3)}$, but this was found to have occurred only partially. This result is unexpected since Wagner–Meerwein shifts in norbornyl systems are generally considered to occur more rapidly than 2,6-hydride shifts and indeed on non-classical-ion theory $C_{(7)}$ and $C_{(3)}$ would be equivalent (see ion **122**). Two explanations were offered for these interesting results. The first, which was favoured, was that the 6,2-hydride shift involved a concerted rearrangement, (**124**) → (**125**), the driving force for which was the resulting reduction of charge separation. Alternatively it was suggested that the products were formed directly from the edge-protonated cyclopropane (**123**).

Changing the group R of the cyclohexenylethyl *p*-bromobenzenesulphonate (**126**) from hydrogen to methyl results in a 25-fold increase in the rate of acetolysis.[78] It was suggested that this was because conformer (**127**) with the CH_2OBs group axial, and in a suitable position to undergo nucleophilic attack by the double bond, was more highly populated for the compound in which R = Me. The reverse was observed with cycloheptenylmethyl *p*-bromobenzene-sulphonates, (**128**), the compound with R = Me undergoing acetolysis at least 50 times more slowly than that for which R = H. This was attributed to an unfavourable eclipsing interaction in the transition state between the group R and the departing *p*-bromobenzenesulphonate anion.

Rate and product studies indicate that participation of the double bond, as

[77] C. C. Lee and L. K. M. Lam, *J. Am. Chem. Soc.*, **88**, 2831 (1966); J. D. Roberts, C. C. Lee, and W. H. Saunders, *ibid.*, **76**, 4501 (1954).
[78] C. Chuit, F. Colard, and H. Felkin, *Chem. Commun.*, **1966**, 118.

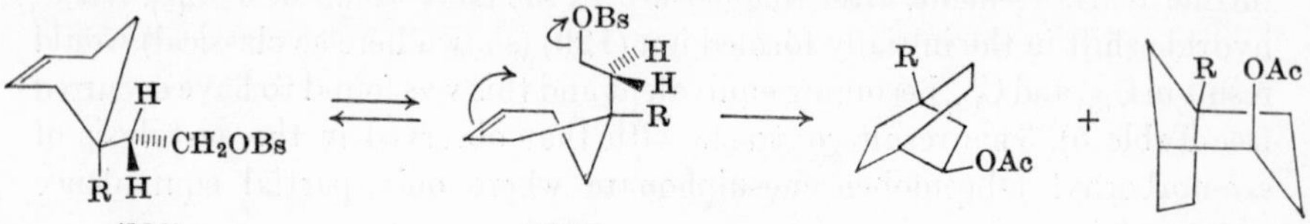

(126)   (127)

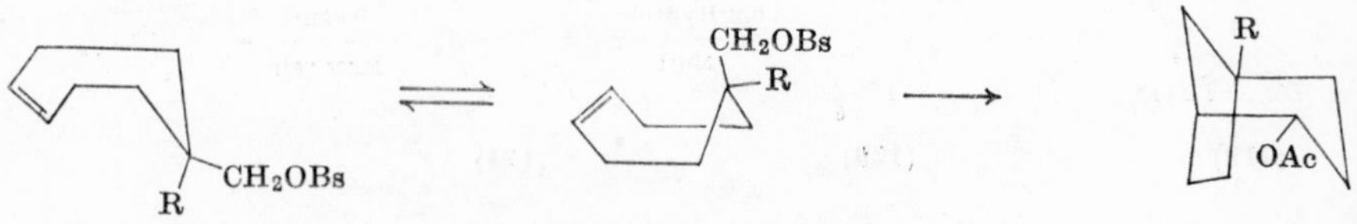

(128)

symbolized by (129) and (130), does not occur in the acetolyses of *syn*-norbornen-7-ylmethyl *p*-bromobenzenesulphonate (see also p. 14)[41] and *cis-exo*-bicyclo[3.2.0]hept-6-en-3-yl toluene-*p*-sulphonate.[46]

(129)   (130)

The rates and products of solvolysis of a series of homoallylic halides and arenesulphonates of general structure $R_2CH=CH-CH_2-CH_2-X$ have been determined.[79]

Other investigations of participation by double bonds include studies of ion-pair return in the perchloric acid isomerization of isochloesteryl acetate (see p. 47),[80] homoallylic rearrangements of 19-substituted[81a] and 5(10)-unsaturated[81b] steroids, the conversion of presenegenin into senegenin,[82] the solvolysis of 6-methylcholesteryl iodide,[83a] and 2-(3-indenyl)ethyl *p*-bromobenzenesulphonate,[83b] and cyclizations of epoxyolefins[84] and certain terpenes.[85a]

[79] M. Hanack, S. Kang, J. Häffner, and K. Gorler, *Ann. Chem.*, **690** (1966).

[80] A. Ehret and S. Winstein, *J. Am. Chem. Soc.*, **88**, 2048 (1966).

[81a] J. Tadanier, *J. Org. Chem.*, **31**, 2124, 3204 (1966); K. Syhora, J. A. Edwards, and A. D. Cross, *ibid.*, p. 3411.

[81b] S. G. Levine and N. H. Eudy, *Tetrahedron Letters*, **1966**, 2265.

[82] S. W. Pelletier, S. Nakamura, and Y. Shimizu, *Chem. Commun.*, **1966**, 727.

[83a] G. Just and E. Lee-Ruff, *Can. J. Chem.*, **44**, 2587 (1966).

[83b] W. D. Closson, S. A. Roman, G. T. Kwiatkowski, and D. A. Corwin, *Tetrahedron Letters*, **1966**, 2271.

[84] D. J. Goldsmith, B. C. Clark, and R. C. Joines, *Tetrahedron Letters*, **1966**, 1149.

[85a] S. Geyer, W. Zieger, and R. Mayer, *Z. Chem.*, **6**, 138 (1966).

Participation by the double bonds of allene derivatives has also been demonstrated. Thus solvolysis of penta-3,4-dienyl and hexa-3,4-dienyl derivatives yields some methyl and ethyl cyclopropyl ketone. The rates of acetolysis of the naphthalene-2-sulphonates are, respectively, 3.5 and 9.5 times faster than that of *n*-pentyl naphthalene-2-sulphonate, indicating moderate anchimeric assistance.[85b]

Neighbouring-group participation by a triple bond occurs in the trifluoro-acetolysis of hept-6-yn-2-yl toluene-*p*-sulphonate (130a) which yields 3-methylcyclohexenyl trifluoroacetate (130c), formed, presumably, via the vinyl cation (130b). The rate of reaction was similar to that for 1-methylhexyl toluene-*p*-sulphonate and this was considered to indicate substantial anchimeric assistance since it was estimated that the triple bond would have a 17.5-fold rate-retarding inductive effect.[85c] (Other intramolecular reactions of triple bonds are discussed on pp. 98 and 127.)

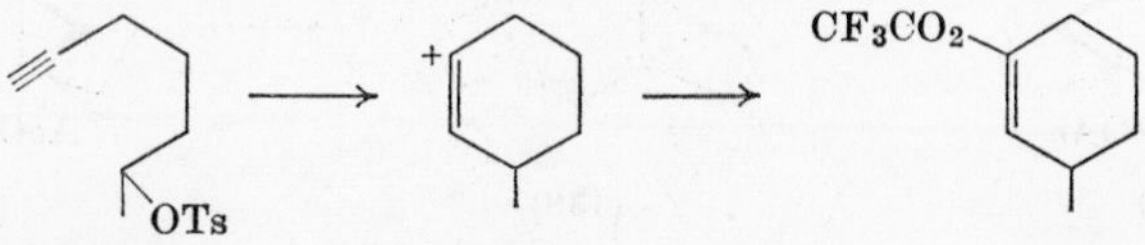

(130a)   (130b)   (130c)

Cyclopropyl Carbonium Ions

Support for a symmetrical transition state (131) in the solvolysis of cyclo-propylmethyl derivatives has been provided by Schleyer and Van Dine[86] who found that the effects of introducing methyl groups on the rates of solvolysis of cyclopropylmethyl 3,5-dinitrobenzoates in aqueous acetone at 100° are as shown in (134), (135), and (136). The introduction of a 2- or 3-methyl

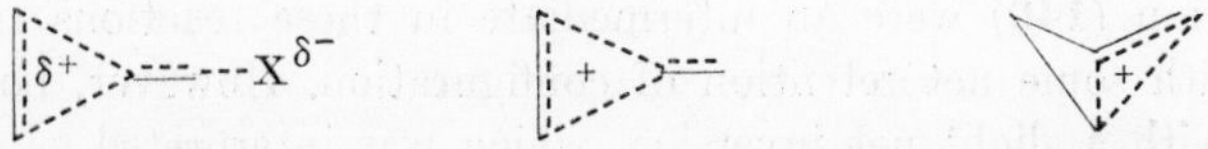

(131)   (132)   (133)

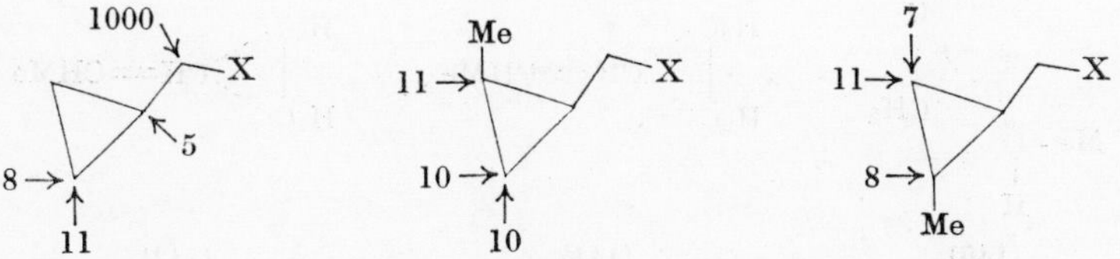

(134)   (135)   (136)

[85b] M. Hanack and J. Häffner, *Chem. Ber.*, **99**, 1077 (1966).
[85c] P. E. Peterson and R. J. Kamat, *J. Am. Chem. Soc.*, **88**, 3152 (1966); J. A. Landgrebe, and R. H. Rynbrandt, *J. Org. Chem.*, **31**, 2585 (1966).
[86] P. von R. Schleyer and G. W. Van Dine, *J. Am. Chem. Soc.*, **88**, 2321 (1966).

substituent has almost the same effect (10—11-fold for *trans*; 7—10-fold for *cis*) whether or not there is already one such substituent. On the assumption that the ions have similar structures to the transition states leading to them, these results support the symmetrical homoallylic structure (**132**) rather than the bicyclobutonium structure (**133**) for the cyclopropylmethyl cation, in accord with the NMR results reported last year.[87]

The solvolyses of 1-methylcyclopropylmethyl toluene-*p*-sulphonate in methanol, ethanol, and acetic acid proceed 4—5 times faster than those of cyclopropylmethyl toluene-*p*-sulphonate and yield exclusively 1-methyl-cyclobutyl derivatives.[88]

Winstein and his co-workers[89] also preferred a bis-symmetrical homoallylic structure for the ion (**138**) derived from the highly reactive acetates (**137**) and (**139**).

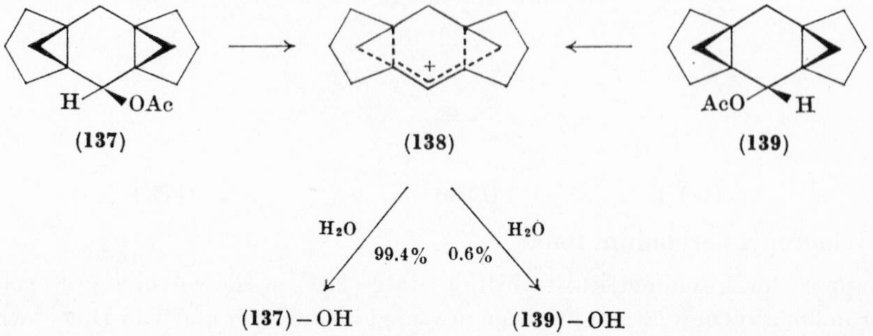

(**137**)　　　　　　　　　　(**138**)　　　　　　　　　　(**139**)

(**137**)−OH　　　　　　(**139**)−OH

Vogel and Roberts[90] have studied the deamination of (+)-1-cyclopropyl-ethylamine and the solvolysis in 80% aqueous ethanol of (+)-*N*-methyl-4-(1′-cyclopropylethoxy)pyridinium iodide. It was thought that if the bicyclo-butonium ion (**140**) were an intermediate in these reactions they would proceed with some net retention of configuration. However, both yielded products with a slight net inversion, which was interpreted as supporting

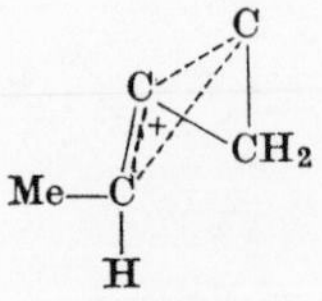

(**140**) 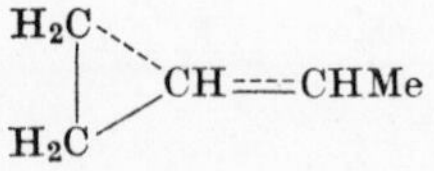　　　　　　　　　(**141**) 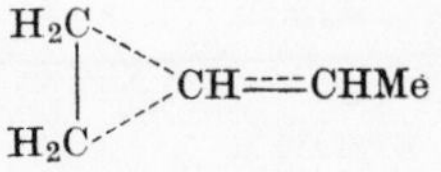　　　　　　　　　(**142**)

[87] See *Organic Reaction Mechanisms*, **1965**, 43.
[88] D. D. Roberts, *J. Org. Chem.*, **31**, 2000 (1966).
[89] L. Birladeanu, T. Hanafusa, and S. Winstein, *J. Am. Chem. Soc.*, **88**, 2315 (1966); L. Birladeanu, T. Hanafusa, B. Johnson, and S. Winstein, *ibid.*, p. 2316.
[90] M. Vogel and J. D. Roberts, *J. Am. Chem. Soc.*, **88**, 2262 (1966).

structure (**141**) or (**142**) for the intermediate ion. A similar conclusion has been reached by Richey and Richey[91] who found that the rate of the acid-catalysed racemization of optically active 1-cyclopropylethanol was equal to the rate of ^{18}O-exchange.

The hydrolyses of cyclopropylmethyl and cyclobutyl chlorides have values of $\Delta S^{\ddagger}$ (+8.0 and +11.5 cal deg^{-1} mole^{-1}) and $\Delta C_p^{\ddagger}$ (−81 and −107 cal deg^{-1} mole^{-1}) similar to those normally shown for $S_N 1$ reactions.[92]

In contrast to the observation by Hart *et al.*[93] that replacing the isopropyl groups of tri-isopropylmethyl derivatives successively by cyclopropyl groups causes almost identical rate enhancements, the introduction of a second cyclopropyl ring into the nortricyclyl system (**143**) to yield quadricyclic derivatives (**144**) has a very much smaller effect than the introduction of the first cyclopropyl ring.[94] The reactions of the quadricyclic *p*-bromobenzene-

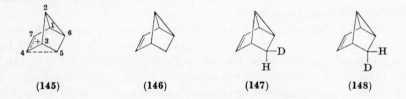

| Rel. rate | 1 | 6.3×10^8 | 1.0×10^{10} | |
| | | (**143**) | (**144**) | |

sulphonate (**144**; $X = p\text{-BrC}_6\text{H}_4 \cdot \text{SO}_2 \cdot \text{O}$) has now been investigated[95] using the borohydride trapping technique of Brown and Bell (see p. 40). In 80% aqueous diglyme, 15% of a hydrocarbon product was isolated and this consisted of tricyclene (**146**) 10%, quadricyclene 89%, and norbornadiene ~1%. To test whether the tricyclene arose from the norbornadien-7-yl cation the reaction was carried out with sodium borodeuteride. Under these conditions the norbornadien-7-yl cation from norbornadien-7-yl chloride yields

(**145**)	(**146**)	(**147**)	(**148**)

[91] H. G. Richey and J. M. Richey, *J. Am. Chem. Soc.*, **88**, 4971 (1966).

[92] C. Y. Wu and R. E. Robertson, *J. Am. Chem. Soc.*, **88**, 2666 (1966); C. Y. Wu and R. E. Robertson, *Chem. Ind.* (*London*), **1966**, 195.

[93] H. Hart and J. M. Sandri, *J. Am. Chem. Soc.*, **81**, 320 (1959); H. Hart and P. A. Law, *ibid.*, **86**, 1957 (1964).

[94] H. G. Richey and N. C. Buckley, *J. Am. Chem. Soc.*, **85**, 3057 (1963).

[95] P. R. Story and S. R. Fahrenholtz, *J. Am. Chem. Soc.*, **88**, 374 (1966).

2

tricyclene which is exclusively *endo*-deuteriated (see **148**). The quadricyclic
p-bromobenzenesulphonate, however, yielded tricyclene which was 10%
exo-deuteriated (**147**). It was suggested that the *endo*-deuteriated tricyclene
arose from the norbornadienyl cation since the ratio of this to norbornadiene
is that usually found on reduction of this cation, and the *exo*-deuterated
tricyclene arose from reduction of the quadricyclyl cation (**145**) at $C_{(5)}$.

The acetolysis of 7-deuterioquadricyclic toluene-*p*-sulphonate (**149**) was
also investigated. This yielded an approximately 50:50 mixture of unrearranged quadricyclic acetate (**152**) and norbornadienyl acetate (**151**) which,
very interestingly, was formed in a highly (perhaps completely) stereospecific
way in which the norbornadien-7-yl cation (**150**) retains its configuration[95]
(see also ref. 69, p. 26).

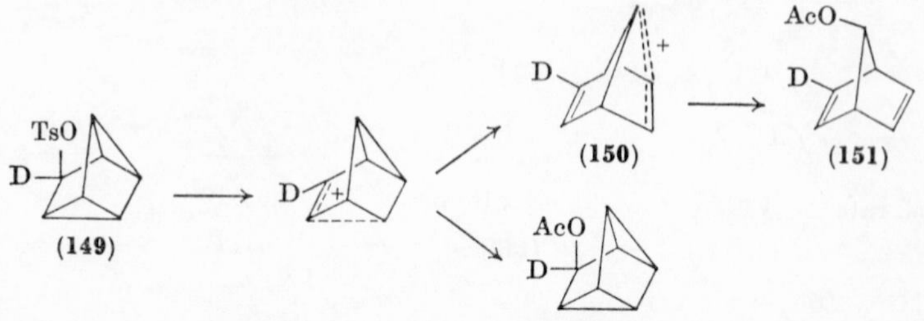

Attempts to generate the trishomocyclopropenyl cation by the electrolytic
decarboxylation of *cis*- and *trans*-bicyclo[3.1.0]hexane-3-carboxylic acids
were unsuccessful since the products obtained were not those expected from
this ion.[96]

The NMR spectra of all four thujyl toluene-*p*-sulphonates in concentrated
sulphuric acid are identical and correspond to that of the 1-isopropyl-2,3-
dimethylcyclopentadienyl cation.[97]

Formolysis of 2-cyclopropylethyl *p*-bromobenzenesulphonate (**153**) yields
the products shown.[98] 1-Cyclopropyl formate was probably also formed but
was shown to rearrange under the reaction conditions to the formates (**154**)
and (**155**). Deuterium-labelling experiments, which indicated considerable
scrambling, were interpreted in terms of interconverting classical ions. The
solvolyses of 2,2-dicyclopropylethyl, 2-cyclopropylpropyl, and β-cyclopropyl-
phenethyl toluene-*p*-sulphonates have also been investigated.[99]

[96] P. G. Gassman and F. V. Zalar, *J. Am. Chem. Soc.*, **88**, 2252 (1966).
[97] S. Forsén and T. Norin, *Tetrahedron Letters*, **1966**, 4183.
[98] R. R. Sauers and R. W. Ubersax, *J. Org. Chem.*, **31**, 495 (1966).
[99] M. Hanack and H. M. Ensslin, *Tetrahedron Letters*, **1965**, 4445; see also *Ann. Chem.*, **697**,
    100 (1966).

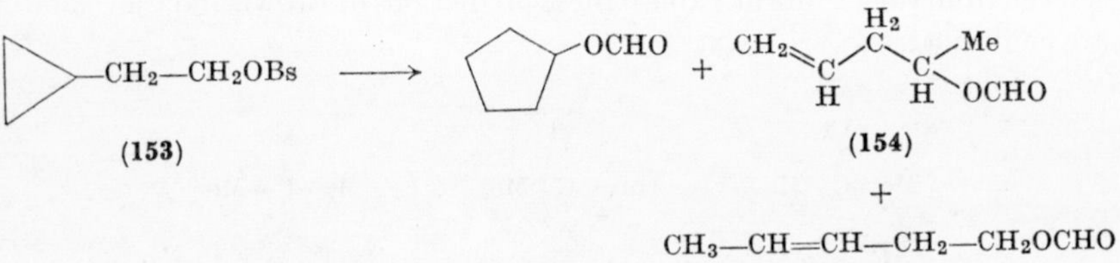

(153)

(154)

+

$$CH_3-CH=CH-CH_2-CH_2OCHO$$

(155)

Participation by the cyclopropyl ring of compound (156) apparently does not occur in its acetolysis, which at 206° proceeds 2.7 times more slowly than that of 7-norbornyl *p*-bromobenzenesulphonate.[100]

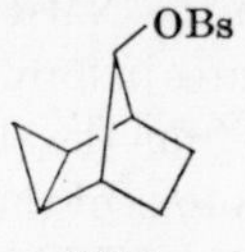

(156)

A 4-cyclopropyl substituent has a larger rate-enhancing effect in the solvolysis of 7-cumenyl chloride in aqueous dioxan[101] and aqueous acetone[102] than a 4-isopropyl substituent (Table 6). This result presumably involves a

Table 6. Rate constants for the solvolysis of substituted 7-cumenyl chlorides in 90% aqueous acetone at 25°.

Subst.:	H	4-Pr^l	3-Me	4-cycloPr	3-Me,4-cycloPr	3,5-Me$_2$	3,5-Me$_2$-4-cycloPr
$10^5 k$ (sec^{-1}):	12.4	221	24.8	1947	2133	47.3	460

conjugative interaction between the cyclopropyl ring and the developing carbonium-ion centre in the transition state, and hence the rate should be sensitive to steric inhibition of conjugation. From the results reported last year[103] it would be expected that conjugation would be a maximum in the bisected conformation (157). If this is so, a single 3-methyl substituent should not have a large effect since the conformation (158) should be available. With 3,5-dimethyl-substitution (159), however, there should be a large effect.

[100] J. Haywood-Farmer, R. E. Pincock, and J. I. Wells, *Tetrahedron*, **22**, 2007 (1966).
[101] H. C. Brown and J. D. Cleveland, *J. Am. Chem. Soc.*, **88**, 2051 (1966).
[102] L. B. Jones and V. K. Jones, *Tetrahedron Letters*, **1966**, 1493.
[103] See *Organic Reaction Mechanisms*, **1965**, 43, ref. 125.

As seen from the results in Table 6 these predictions of Brown and Cleveland[101] are confirmed.

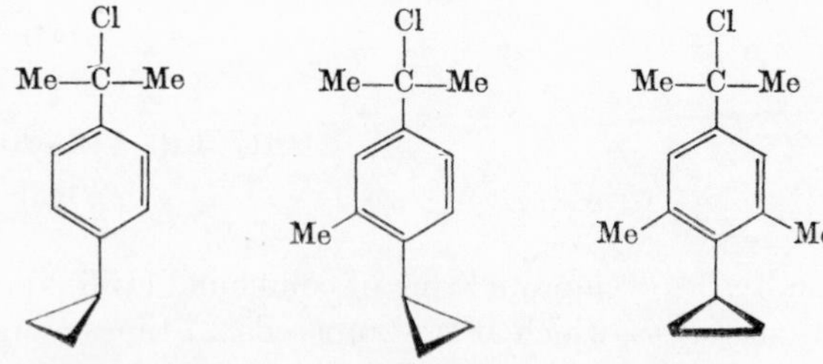

(157)   (158)   (159)

A similar effect is observed in the NMR spectrum of the tri(cyclopropyl-phenyl)methyl cation.[104] The figures in formulae (160)—(162) are the changes in chemical shift (c.p.s.) on going from the alcohol to the ion and it is seen that this is much larger with the β-protons of the cyclopropyl group in (160) than with those of the isopropyl group in (162) or the cyclopropyl group flanked by two methyl groups in (161).

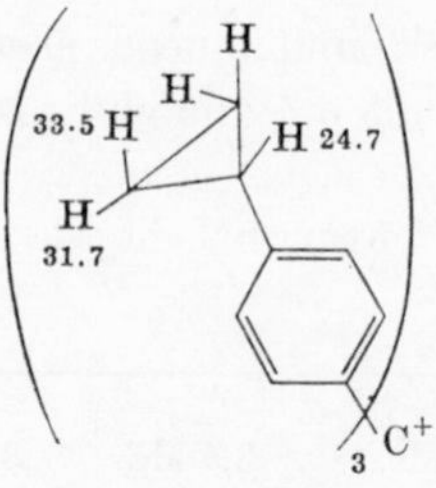

(160) 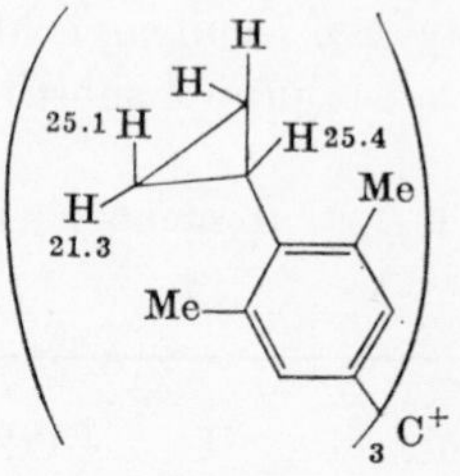   (161)

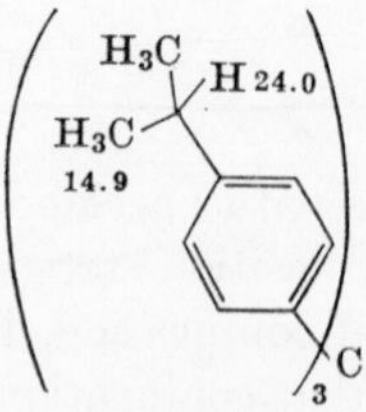

(162)

The NMR spectra of a large number of arylcyclopropylmethyl cations have been reported[105] and certain differences from those reported last year[106] noted.

104 T. Sharpe and J. C. Martin, *J. Am. Chem. Soc.*, **88**, 1815 (1966).
105 T. J. Sekuur and P. Kranenburg, *Tetrahedron Letters*, **1966**, 4769.
106 See *Organic Reaction Mechanisms*, **1965**, 43.

It is of interest that in these ions the *ortho*-protons of the aryl rings are not equivalent to one another.

Other spectroscopic investigations of the conformations of molecules with cyclopropyl rings adjacent to unsaturated centres are given in ref. 107.

Acetolysis of β-tropylphenethyl toluene-*p*-sulphonate (**163**) yields, *inter alia*, *cis*- and *trans*-1,3-diphenylpropene whose formation was thought to involve first a phenyl migration and then a cyclopropyl–homoallyl type rearrangement of the norcaradiene structure (**164**).[108]

(**163**)

(**164**)

PhCH=CHCH₂Ph ← (from diene intermediate)

Other reactions in which cyclopropyl carbonium ions are thought to be intermediates are described in ref. 109.

Cationic Opening of Cyclopropane and Cyclobutane Rings

An extensive investigation of the effect of methyl substituents on the rate of the solvolytic ring-opening of cyclopropyl toluene-*p*-sulphonates has been reported.[110,111] The fact that the acetolysis of 1-methylcyclopropyl toluene-*p*-sulphonate proceeds only 150 times faster than that of cyclopropyl toluene-*p*-sulphonate at 150° suggests that the ring-opening is concerted with ionisation and that the reactions do not involve the free cyclopropyl cation. The effect of 2,3-dimethyl substituents on the rate depends on whether they are *cis* or *trans* to the leaving toluene-*p*-sulphonyloxy-group (see Table 7). This difference was interpreted in terms of Woodward and Hoffmann's prediction[112] that the preferred modes of ring opening are the disrotatory ones (**165**) and

107 J. L. Pierre and P. Arnaud, *Bull. Soc. Chim. France*, **1966**, 1690; W. Lüttke, A. de Meijere, H. Wolff, H. Ludwig, and H. W. Schrötter, *Angew. Chem. Intern. Ed. Engl.*, **5**, 123 (1966); O. Bastiansen and A. de Meijere, *ibid.*, p. 124; W. Lüttke and A. de Meijere, *ibid.*, p. 512; G. R. De Mare, and J. S. Martin, *J. Am. Chem. Soc.*, **88**, 5033 (1966).
108 W. A. Bonner, E. K. Raunio, and D. M. Bowen, *J. Org. Chem.*, **31**, 912 (1966).
109 P. J. Kropp, *J. Am. Chem. Soc.*, **88**, 4926 (1966); W. Kirmse, M. Kapps, and R. B. Hager, *Chem. Ber.*, **99**, 2855 (1966); L. L. Darko and J. G. Cannon, *Tetrahedron Letters*, **1966**, 423.
110 P. von R. Schleyer, G. W. Van Dine, U. Schöllkopf, and J. Paust, *J. Am. Chem. Soc.*, **88**, 2868 (1966).
111 C. H. DePuy, L. G. Schnack, and J. W. Hausser, *J. Am. Chem. Soc.*, **88**, 3343 (1966).
112 See *Organic Reaction Mechanisms*, **1965**, 44.

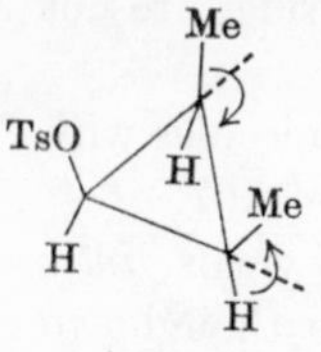

(165) 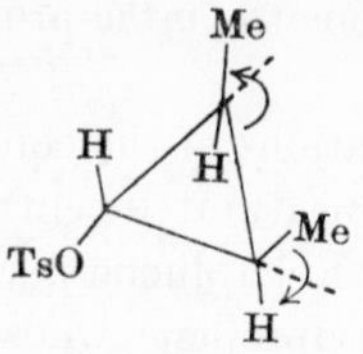   (166)

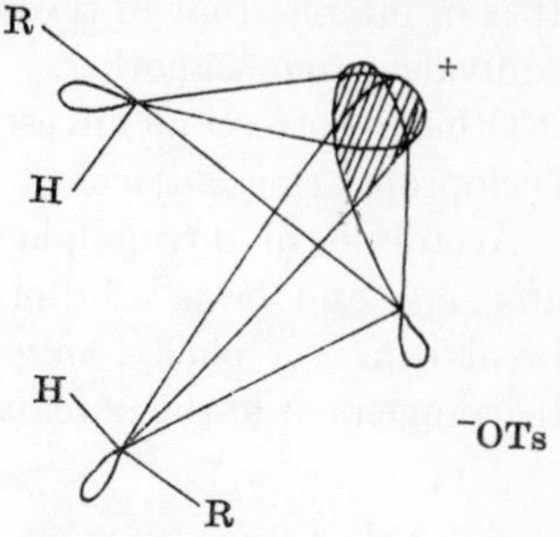

(167)

(166) in which the electrons of the $C_{(2)}$–$C_{(3)}$ bond can overlap with the back lobe of the developing p-orbital on $C_{(1)}$, as shown (167). With the 2,3-*cis*-dimethyl compound the large electronic effect of the methyl groups in stabilizing the transition state in which charge is delocalized to $C_{(2)}$ and $C_{(3)}$ is largely counterbalanced by the unfavourable steric factor which results from the methyl groups moving towards one another. With the 2,3-*trans*-isomer, however, the methyl groups move away from one another and hence there is a favourable steric factor which reinforces the rate-enhancing electronic effect.

Table 7. Effect of methyl substituents on the rate of acetolysis of cyclopropyl toluene-p-sulphonate.

Substituents	Rel. rate at 100°	Rel. rate at 150°
Unsubstituted	1.0[a]	1.0[b]
2-*cis*,3-*cis*-Dimethyl	—	4.0
2-*trans*,3-*trans*-Dimethyl	41,000	18,000
2-*cis*-3-*trans*-Dimethyl	490	260
2,2-Dimethyl	470	330
2,2,3-*cis*-Trimethyl	—	80
2,2,3-*trans*-Trimethyl	48,000	—
2,2,3,3-Tetramethyl	8,050	5,500

[a] $k = 3.89 \times 10^{-8}$ sec^{-1}.
[b] 7.76×10^{-6} sec^{-1}, calculated from the data of J. D. Roberts and V. C. Chambers *J. Am. Chem. Soc.*, **73**, 5034 (1951).

Probably for a similar reason *endo*-7-norcaryl toluene-p-sulphonate (168) undergoes acetolysis about 10,000 times faster than that of its *exo*-isomer (169) at 100°. With the *endo*-isomer ring-opening of the cyclopropyl ring according to Woodward and Hoffmann's predictions would lead to the favourable *cis*-allylic ion, but with the *exo*-isomer it would lead to the *trans*-allylic ion.

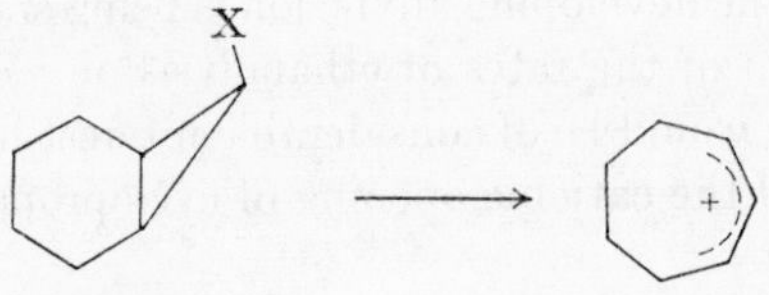

(168)

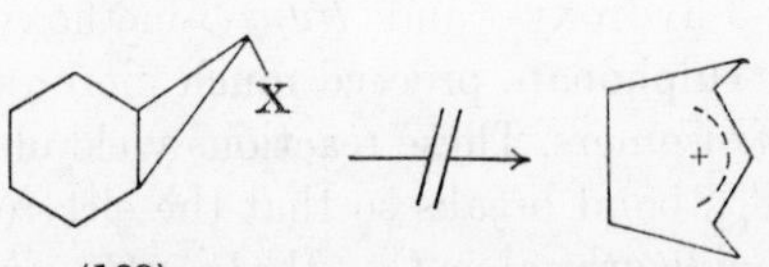

(169)

Details have been published[111] of DePuy, Schnack, and Hausser's investigation of the acetolysis of 1- and 2-arylcyclopropyl toluenesulphonates which was reported in preliminary form last year.[112] The *trans*-2-phenyl compound reacts about 30 times faster than its *cis*-isomer, and its rate is sensitive to substituents in the aryl ring ($\rho = 1.65$), consistently with delocalization of charge to the 2-position in the transition state.

A 2-ethoxy-substituent also strongly enhances the rate of the solvolytic ring opening of cyclopropyl derivatives.[113] Thus 1,1-dichloro-2-ethoxycyclopropane **(170)** in refluxing ethanol solution in the presence of pyridine yields the acetal **(171)**; under these conditions alkyl-substituted *gem*-dichlorocyclopropanes are quite stable. Both *cis*- and *trans*-1,1-dichloro-2-ethoxy-3-methyl-

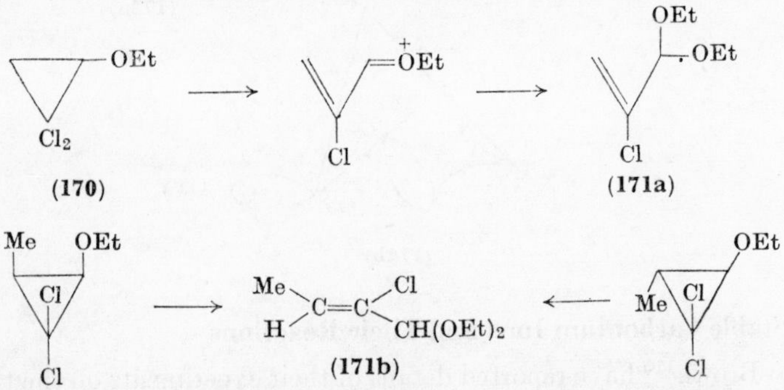

(170)   **(171a)**

(171b)

cyclopropane yield the *trans*-acetal **(172)**, consistently with the departing chlorine's being the one *trans* to the methyl group. This is readily understandable with the *cis*-isomer, since it follows from the Woodward–Hoffmann rules that to give the *cis*-acetal the methyl and ethoxyl groups would have to rotate inwards towards one another. With the *trans*-isomer the exclusive formation

113 L. Skattebøl, *J. Org. Chem.*, **31**, 1554 (1966).

of the isomer in which the chloride *trans* to the methyl group and *cis* to the ethoxyl group departs suggests that an additional stereoelectronic factor may be important when the developing allylic ion is being stabilized by an ethoxyl group. A comparison of the rates of ethanolysis of *cis*- and *trans*-2-ethoxycyclopropyl chloride would be of considerable interest here.

Other examples of the cationic opening of cyclopropane rings are given in ref. 114*a*.

Similar effects are also found with cyclobutane ring opening. Thus the solvolyses of *trans*-3-hydroxy- and *trans*-3-methoxy-2,2,3,3-tetramethylcyclobutyl toluene-*p*-sulphonate proceed much more rapidly (10^2—10^3-fold) than those of their *cis*-isomers. These reactions yield olefins derived from ion (**172a**). If the $C_{(2)}$–$C_{(3)}$ bond breaks so that the electrons in it overlap with the rear of the developing orbital on $C_{(1)}$, the $C_{(1)}$–$C_{(2)}$ and $C_{(3)}$–$C_{(4)}$ bonds will rotate as shown in (**172b**). A *cis*-3-substituent (Y) thus moves towards the 2-methyl group but a *trans*-3-substituent (X) moves away, and so the *trans*-isomer reacts faster than the *cis*. It would appear, though, that little positive charge can be delocalized to $C_{(3)}$ in the transition state since the *trans*-3-methyl compound is solvolysed only about five times faster than the compound unsubstituted at $C_{(3)}$, while the *trans*-3-hydroxy-compound reacts slightly slower.[114b]

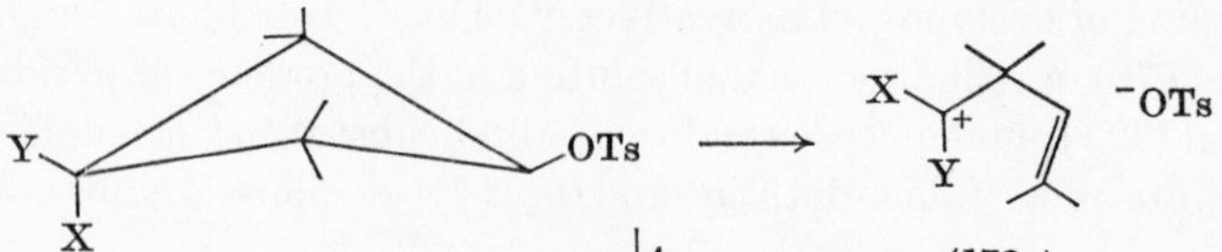

(172a)

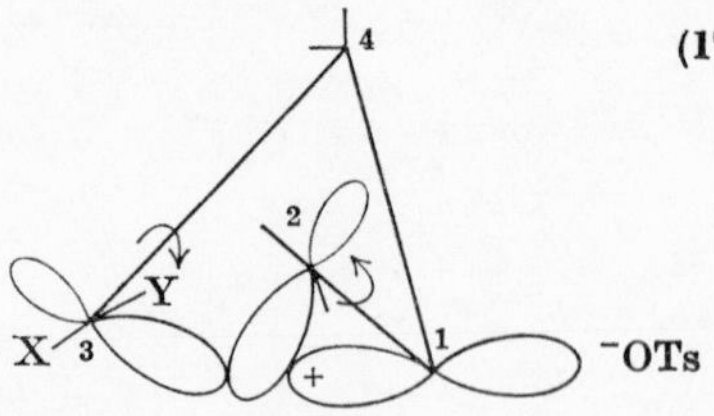

(172b)

Other Stable Carbonium Ions and Their Reactions

Bell and Brown[115] have reported details of their experiments on the trapping of carbonium ions by borohydride. Sodium borohydride (1.80M) reacts only very slowly with benzhydryl chloride (0.25M) in anhydrous diglyme at 45°,

[114a] C. W. Jefford and R. Medary, *Tetrahedron Letters*, **1966**, 2069; E. T. Marquis and P. D. Gardner, *ibid.*, p. 2793; S. W. Tobey and R. West, *J. Am. Chem. Soc.*, **88**, 2478 (1966).

[114b] C. F. Wilcox and R. J. Engen, *Tetrahedron Letters*, **1966**, 2759; L. J. Dolby and C. Wilkins, *ibid.*, p. 2751.

[115] H. M. Bell and H. C. Brown, *J. Am. Chem. Soc.*, **88**, 1473 (1966).

but 60 times faster in 80% aqueous diglyme with a first-order rate constant 2.1×10^{-4} sec^{-1} to yield 72—75% of diphenylmethane. In the absence of borohydride, benzhydryl chloride underwent solvolysis with $k = 1.34 \times 10^{-4}$ sec^{-1}. The yield of diphenylmethane increased with increasing borohydride concentration but was, within the rather narrow variation possible, independent of water content. Benzhydryl bromide under the above conditions gave a higher yield of diphenylmethane (87%) than did benzhydryl chloride (72—75%). The yield of hydrocarbon obtained parallels the stability of the carbonium ion derived from the starting halide. Thus triphenylmethyl chloride, *p*-methoxybenzhydryl chloride, benzhydryl chloride, and *p*-chlorobenzhydryl chloride yield respectively 97, 97, 73, and 62% of hydrocarbon under the same reaction conditions. If it is assumed that the small difference in the rate constants in the presence and absence of borohydride is due to a salt effect, then it seems likely that in these reactions the borohydride is trapping carbonium ions. The facts that the yield is independent of water concentration and is different for benzhydryl bromide and chloride suggests, however, that these are not free, and here trapping of an ion pair seems more likely.

Further evidence has been reported[116] which is claimed to support the view that metal-atom participation is unimportant in reactions of ferrocenylmethyl derivatives.[117] It was thought that if participation were important such compounds should not show enhanced reactivity in S_N2 reactions since intramolecular nucleophilic attack by the metal atom would preclude intermolecular attack by an external nucleophile. However, if an α-ferrocenyl group acts like an α-methoxyl group it should enhance the rate of S_N2 reactions in the same way as an α-methoxyl group is claimed to,[118] by stabilizing the positive carbon in the transition state. The ratio of the first-order constants for solvolysis in 9:1 ether–ethanol was found to be:

$$k_{\text{Ferr.CH}_2\text{Cl}}/k_{\text{MeOCH}_2\text{Cl}} = 7.6$$

and of the second-order rate constants for reaction with sodium ethoxide in the same solvent

$$k_{\text{Ferr.CH}_2\text{Cl}}/k_{\text{MeOCH}_2\text{Cl}} = 8.6$$

It was therefore concluded that the metal-atom participation is not important in the reaction of the ferrocenyl compound and that the ferrocenyl group acts in a similar way to a methoxyl group in stabilizing the transition state. This argument assumes, however, that the second-order reactions with ethoxide are concerted S_N2 processes and not attack of ethoxide on a reversibly formed ion pair, which in our opinion is not unlikely (cf. ref. 119).

116 T. T. Tidwell and T. G. Traylor, *J. Am. Chem. Soc.*, **88**, 3442 (1966).
117 See *Organic Reaction Mechanisms*, **1965**, 47.
118 P. Ballinger, P. B. D. de la Mare, G. Kohnstam, and B. M. Prestt, *J. Chem. Soc.*, **1955**, 3641.
119 See p. 44 and *Organic Reaction Mechanisms*, **1965**, 53.

2*

The NMR spectra of a series of ferrocenylmethyl cations have been interpreted as indicating that they are stabilized by metal participation.[120]

The substituent effects of a ferrocenyl group have been determined.[121]

Solvolysis of optically active α-phenyl-α-biphenyl-α-1-naphthylmethyl benzoate (173) in 95% aqueous acetone yields the corresponding alcohol with 50% net retention of configuration.[122] It was suggested that the reaction involves an optically active carbonium ion (174) which reacts more rapidly with water on the side from which benzoate has departed than it is converted into its enantiomer (175) (i.e., $k_3 > k_2$).

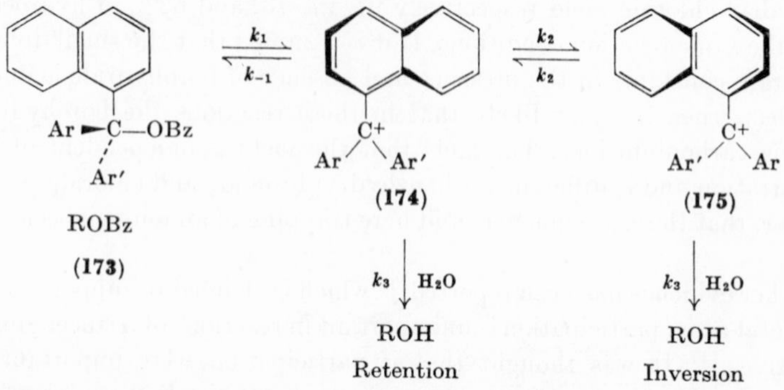

The rates of reaction of a series of triphenylmethyl cations with water have been measured.[123] A plot of log k against log K, where k and K are rate and equilibrium constants for the reaction, is not a single straight line, although more limited correlations exist. An NMR method for determining carbonium-ion stabilities has been reported.[124a]

Hydride-transfer reactions of the triphenylmethyl cation with tertiary amines,[124b] and internal hydride shifts of carbonium ions,[124c] have been investigated.

[120] M. Cais, J. J. Dannenberg, A. Eisenstadt, M. I. Levenberg, and J. H. Richards, *Tetrahedron Letters*, 1966, 1695; see also M. Cais, *Record Chem. Progr.*, 27, 177 (1966).

[121] A. N. Nesmeyanov, E. G. Perevalova, S. P. Gubin, K. I. Grandberg, and A. G. Kozlovsky, *Tetrahedron Letters*, 1966, 2381; E. G. Perevalova, K. I. Grandberg, N. A. Zharikova, S. P. Gubin, and A. N. Nesmeyanov, *Izv. Akad. Nauk. SSSR, Ser. Khim.*, 1966, 832; *Chem. Abs.*, 65, 5344 (1966).

[122] B. L. Murr and C. Santiago, *J. Am. Chem. Soc.*, 88, 1826 (1966).

[123] R. A. Diffenbach, K. Sano, and R. W. Taft, *J. Am. Chem. Soc.*, 88, 4747 (1966); G. S. Idlis and O. F. Ginzburg, *Reaktsionnaya Sposobnost. Organ. Soedin. Tartusk. Gos. Univ.*, 2, 106 (1965); *Chem. Abs.*, 63, 17862 (1965).

[124a] A. E. Young, V. R. Sandel, and H. H. Freedman, *J. Am. Chem. Soc.*, 88, 4532 (1966).

[124b] R. Damico, and C. D. Broaddus, *J. Org. Chem.*, 31, 1607 (1966).

[124c] D. M. Brouwer, C. Maclean, and E. L. Mackor, *Discussions Faraday Soc.*, No. 39, 121 (1965); see also R. J. Gillespie, *ibid.*, p. 135.

A review entitled "Spectroscopic Observation of Alkylcarbonium Ions in Strong Acid Solutions" has been published.[125]

The NMR spectra of the following carbonium ions have been reported: alkynyl carbonium ions,[126] benzyl cations,[127] phenyl and diphenylfluorocarbonium ions,[128] chlorodiphenyl carbonium ion,[129] cyclobutenyl cations,[130] alkoxymethyl cations,[131] trifluoromethyl carbonium ions,[132] dioxodicarbonium ions,[133] cyclo- and polycyclo-alkyloxocarbonium ions,[134] and methylbenzenium ions.[135]

Proton–carbon-13 spin coupling in the NMR spectra of carbonium ions has been discussed.[136]

The rearrangements of pentadienyl cations in FSO_3H–SbF_5 solution have been followed by NMR spectroscopy.[137]

The NMR spectra of protonated alcohols, the precursors of carbonium ions, in strong acids have been determined.[138]

X-Ray crystal-structure determinations have been reported for *syn*-triphenylcyclopropenium perchlorate[139] and acetylium hexafluoroantimonate.[140]

The ultraviolet and visible spectra of carbonium ions have been discussed.[141]

Other stable cations which have been investigated include 1,3-dioxenium ions,[142] benzyl cations in polystyrene,[143] mesomeric phosphonium dications,[144] di- and tri-carbonium ions,[145] and the 1,2-dithiolium cation.[146]

125 G. A. Olah and C. U. Pittman, *Adv. Phys. Org. Chem.*, **4**, 305 (1966).
126 C. U. Pittman, and G. A. Olah, *J. Am. Chem. Soc.*, **87**, 5632 (1965).
127 C. A. Cupas, M. B. Comisarow, and G. A. Olah, *J. Am. Chem. Soc.*, **88**, 361 (1966).
128 G. A. Olah, C. A. Cupas, and M. B. Comisarow, *J. Am. Chem. Soc.*, **88**, 362 (1966).
129 H. Volz and W. D. Mayer, *Tetrahedron Letters*, **1966**, 5249.
130 E. H. Gold and T. J. Katz, *J. Org. Chem.*, **31**, 372 (1966).
131 B. G. Ramsey and R. W. Taft, *J. Am. Chem. Soc.*, **88**, 3058 (1966).
132 G. A. Olah and C. U. Pittman, *J. Am. Chem. Soc.*, **88**, 3310 (1966).
133 G. A. Olah and M. B. Comisarow, *J. Am. Chem. Soc.*, **88**, 3313 (1966).
134 G. A. Olah and M. B. Comisarow, *J. Am. Chem. Soc.*, **88**, 4442 (1966).
135 D. M. Brouwer, E. L. Mackov, and C. Maclean, *Rec. Trav. Chim.*, **84**, 1564 (1965).
136 J. Karabatsos, C. E. Orzech, and N. Hsi, *J. Am. Chem. Soc.*, **88**, 1817 (1966); G. A. Olah and M. B. Comisarow, *ibid.*, p. 1818.
137 G. A. Olah, C. U. Pittman, and T. S. Sorensen, *J. Am. Chem. Soc.*, **88**, 2331 (1966).
138 G. A. Olah and E. Namanworth, *J. Am. Chem. Soc.*, **88**, 5327 (1966).
139 M. Sundaralingam and L. H. Jensen, *J. Am. Chem. Soc.*, **88**, 198 (1966).
140 F. P. Boer, *J. Am. Chem. Soc.*, **88**, 1572 (1966).
141 G. A. Olah, C. U. Pittman, R. Waack, and M. Doran, *J. Am. Chem. Soc.*, **88**, 1488 (1966); V. Bertoli and P. H. Plesch, *Chem. Commun.*, **1966**, 625; A. Gandini and P. H. Plesch, *J. Chem. Soc.*, B, **1966**, 7; P. E. Blatz and D. L. Pippert, *Tetrahedron Letters*, **1966**, 1117.
142 G. Schneider, *Tetrahedron Letters*, **1966**, 5921.
143 S. Bywater and D. J. Worsfold, *Can. J. Chem.*, **44**, 1671 (1966).
144 G. H. Birum and C. N. Matthews, *J. Am. Chem. Soc.*, **88**, 4198 (1966).
145 H. Volz and M. J. Volz de Lecea, *Tetrahedron Letters*, **1966**, 4683, 4675.
146 E. Klingsberg, *J. Org. Chem.*, **31**, 3489 (1966); *J. Heterocyclic Chem.*, **3**, 243 (1966); H. Prinzbach, E. Futterer, and A. Lüttringhaus, *Angew. Chem. Internat. Edn. Engl.*, **5**, 513 (1966).

CHAPTER 2

Nucleophilic Aliphatic Substitution

Borderline Mechanisms and Ion-pair Phenomena

Sneen and Larson have provided evidence additional to that reported last year[1] that second-order nucleophilic displacement reactions may involve an attack of the nucleophile on a reversibly formed ion pair rather than a concerted S_N2 process.[2] They studied the reaction of 1-methylheptyl methanesulphonate in 25% and 30% aqueous dioxan containing sodium azide, where the product is a mixture of 1-methylheptyl alcohol and 1-methylheptyl azide. The ion-pair and the concerted S_N2 mechanism can be written as equations (1) and (2), respectively:

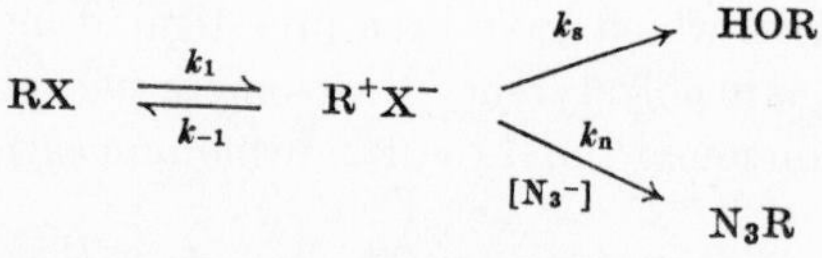

$$\text{RX} \underset{k_{-1}}{\overset{k_1}{\rightleftharpoons}} \text{R}^+\text{X}^- \underset{[\text{N}_3^-]}{\overset{k_s}{\underset{k_n}{\diagup}}} \begin{matrix} \text{HOR} \\ \text{N}_3\text{R} \end{matrix} \tag{1}$$

$$\text{RX} \overset{k'_s}{\underset{[\text{N}_3^-]}{\overset{k'_n}{\diagup}}} \begin{matrix} \text{HOR} \\ \text{N}_3\text{R} \end{matrix} \tag{2}$$

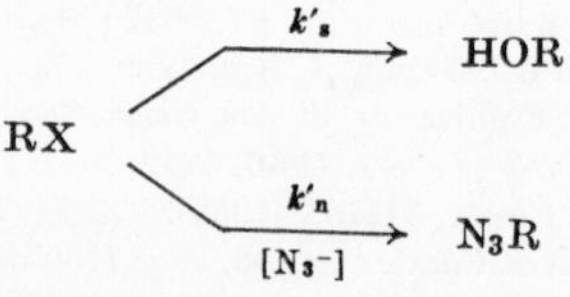

It was shown that the variation of pseudo-first-order rate constant with sodium azide concentration and the ratio of alcohol:azide in the product fitted the relationship deduced from equation (1) on the assumption that $k_{-1}/k_s = 2$—3, but deviated markedly from that deduced for equation (2). This elegant demonstration of the ion-pair mechanism will undoubtedly stimulate much more activity in the field.

Sneen, Carter, and Kay[3] have shown that there is a linear free-energy relationship between the reactivity of compounds reacting via carbonium ions and the selectivity for attack on the ion. Thus the plot of $\log k_t$ against $\log (k_n/k_s)$ [see equation (3)] for the solvolysis of a series of alkyl chlorides in 80% aqueous dioxan at 0° in the presence of sodium azide is a straight line of

[1] See *Organic Reaction Mechanisms*, **1965**, 53.
[2] R. A. Sneen and J. W. Larson, *J. Am. Chem. Soc.*, **88**, 2593 (1966).
[3] R. A. Sneen, J. V. Carter, and P. S. Kay, *J. Am. Chem. Soc.*, **88**, 2594 (1966).

slope 2.83 and intercept -2.60. For instance the relatively unreactive *tert*-butyl chloride shows a selectivity of only 1.45, but the 10^7-fold more reactive

$$\text{RCl} \xrightarrow{k_t} \text{R}^+ \quad \begin{array}{c} \xrightarrow{k_s[\text{H}_2\text{O}]} \text{ROH} \\ \xrightarrow{k_a[\text{N}_3^-]} \text{RN}_3 \end{array} \tag{3}$$

triphenylmethyl chloride has a selectivity of 1.12×10^4. The results for 1-methylheptyl and 1-methylallyl derivatives deviate from this relationship with selectivities 1250 and 3100 times larger than predicted. It is possible that this results from azide capturing an undissociated ion pair instead of free ions, as with the compounds obeying the relationship, and indeed it was suggested that non-adherence to the relationship could be used as evidence for azide attack at the ion-pair stage.

Competition for a series of benzhydryl ions by chloride ion and water has also been investigated.[4] This was done by comparing the rate of hydrolysis of the benzhydryl chlorides in aqueous acetone with the rates of chloride exchange of the ^{36}Cl-labelled compounds with added HCl or NaCl. Again it was found that the selectivity of the ion increased with the reactivity of the corresponding chloride. With some of the chlorides, p-Ph$\cdot$C$_6$H$_4\cdot$CHPhCl and p-MeO$\cdot$C$_6$H$_4\cdot$C$_6$H$_4\cdot$CHCl$\cdot$C$_6$H$_4\cdot$OMe-p, the selectivity was high for their reactivity as judged by the results for the other compounds. This, it was suggested, resulted because the substituents in these compounds are polarizable with respect to the electron-demanding centre but not greatly accelerating for S_N1 reactions. There is presumably also the possibility that capture of ion pairs as well as of free ions occurs with these compounds.

The borderline region between the S_N1 and S_N2 mechanisms has also been investigated by Ceccon, Papa, and Fava.[5] They studied the exchange reaction between substituted benzhydryl thiocyanate and labelled sodium thiocyanate in acetonitrile. In general, these reactions followed a rate law:

$$\text{Rate} = k_1[\text{RSCN}] + k_2[\text{RSCN}][\text{NaSCN}]$$

but the relative values of k_1 and k_2 depended on the substituents in the benzhydryl group. Thus with 4,4'-dimethylbenzhydryl thiocyanate the k_2 term was unimportant and with 4-nitrobenzhydryl thiocyanate the k_1 term was unimportant. It was therefore concluded that these compounds reacted

[4] T. H. Bailey, J. R. Fox, E. Jackson, G. Kohnstam, and A. Queen, *Chem. Commun.*, **1966**, 122; K. Tanabe and T. Sano, *J. Res. Inst. Catalysis Hokkaido Univ.*, **13**, 102 (1966); *Chem. Abs.*, **64**, 14053 (1966); K. Tanabe and T. Sano, *J. Res. Inst. Catalysis Hokkaido Univ.*, **13**, 110 (1966); *Chem. Abs.*, **64**, 12479 (1966).
[5] A. Ceccon, I. Papa, and A. Fava, *J. Am. Chem. Soc.*, **88**, 4643 (1966).

respectively by S_N1 and S_N2 mechanisms. The benzhydryl and 4-chloro-benzhydryl thiocyanate, with which both the k_1 and the k_2 terms are important, were thought, however, to react by concurrent S_N1 and S_N2 mechanisms. The possibility was considered that the second-order components of these reactions were not true S_N2 reactions but were attacks on reversibly formed ion pairs as envisaged by Sneen *et al.* This was ruled out for the compounds with electron-withdrawing substituents since here it was found that the rate of exchange was greater than the rate of ionization as estimated from a study of the thiocyanate isothiocyanate isomerization, whereas the reverse must hold with this mechanism if the kinetics are to be second-order as observed. However, for some of the compounds with electron-releasing substituents it was considered that the relatively unimportant second-order reaction could be following an ion-pair mechanism.

Concurrent S_N1 and S_N2 processes are also thought to occur in the solvolysis of α-methylbenzyl chloride in ethanol–water mixtures.[6] The products, ethyl α-methylbenzyl ether and α-methylbenzyl alcohol, are both formed with net inversion of configuration; and this remains constant (~30% for the ether and ~23% for the alcohol) when the concentration of water is greater than 50% v/v but increases markedly at high ethanol concentrations, tending to 100% and 50% inversion for alcohol and ether formation in pure ethanol. It was suggested that the reaction proceeded by an S_N1 mechanism in solvents of water content greater than 50%, but that in the more strongly ethanolic media there was a concurrent S_N2 reaction which was the sole mechanism for alcohol formation in nearly 100% ethanol; it was thought, however, that ether was still formed by both mechanisms in this medium.

Although triphenylmethyl halides have a strong tendency to undergo nucleophilic substitution by the S_N1 mechanism it is possible by a suitable choice of substrate and conditions to impose an S_N2 mechanism.[7] Thus the chloride exchange reactions of 4,4′,4″-trinitrotriphenyl methyl chloride and 4,4′-dinitrotriphenylmethyl chloride in acetone with tetraethylammonium [³⁶Cl]chloride, at constant ionic strength maintained by the addition of tetraethylammonium perchlorate, follow a rate law,

$$\text{Rate} = k_1[\text{RCl}] + k_2[\text{RCl}][\text{Et}_4\text{NCl}].$$

The trinitro-compound reacts with azide by a second-order process which is about 500 times faster than chloride exchange. The rates of chloride exchange decrease with increasing electrolyte concentration owing to a decrease in the value of k_2. It was considered that if the k_2 term resulted from capture of a reversibly formed ion pair the reaction would show a positive salt effect. The

[6] K. Okamoto, N. Uchida, S. Saitô, and H. Shingu, *Bull. Chem. Soc. Japan*, **39**, 307 (1966).
[7] U. Miotti and A. Fava, *J. Am. Chem. Soc.*, **88**, 4274 (1966).

second-order terms were therefore considered to result from concerted S_N2 processes.

The reaction of optically active α-methylbenzyl chloride with mixture of phenol and other organic compounds (e.g., benzene, anisole, acetonitrile) in the presence of aniline or triethylamine yields α-methylbenzyl phenyl ether formed with net retention (20—50%) of configuration. In mixtures of acetonitrile and phenol the proportion of retention of configuration decreased with increasing amine concentration, and when this was high net inversion was observed. In benzene–phenol mixtures the steric course was almost independent of amine concentration. C-Alkylated phenol was also obtained, but this was always formed with inversion of configuration. It was suggested that this and the ether of inverted configuration were formed by reaction of the phenoxide anion with an ion pair, whereas the ether of retained configuration was formed from an ion pair and a phenol molecule via a four-centered transition state as (1).[8a]

(1)   (2)

Similar transition states [e.g., (2)] were suggested for the solvolysis of α-methylbenzyl chloride in phenol–water mixtures, which yielded α-methylbenzyl alcohol and methylbenzyl phenyl ether, both with net (6—19%) retention of configuration.[8b]

A very interesting collapse of a carbonium ion–perchlorate ion pair has been shown to occur in the perchloric acid($\sim 10^{-4}$M)-catalysed rearrangement of isocholesteryl acetate($\sim 10^{-2}$M) to cholesteryl acetate in acetic acid, which is first order in perchloric acid but zero order in isocholesteryl acetate. This unusual kinetic behaviour arises because most of the perchloric acid is converted into covalent perchlorate, mainly cholesteryl perchlorate. The reaction may then be formulated as in Scheme 1, and this was shown to conform to the observed kinetics. Loss of perchloric acid from the solution during the reaction was also demonstrated by indicator studies.[9]

Ion-pair return in the ethanolysis of benzhydryl benzoate has been investigated by studying ^{18}O-equilibration of the $C^{18}O$-labelled compound.[10] The fraction of ion pairs returning was estimated to be 0.47 at 100°. This was very

[8a] K. Okamoto, H. Yanada, I. Nitta, and H. Shingu, *Bull. Chem. Soc. Japan*, **39**, 299 (1966).
[8b] K. Okamoto, M. Hayashi, and H. Shingu, *Bull. Chem. Soc., Japan*, **39**, 408 (1966).
[9] A. Ehret and S. Winstein, *J. Am. Chem. Soc.*, **88**, 2048 (1966).
[10] A. F. Diaz and S. Winstein, *J. Am. Chem. Soc.*, **88**, 1318 (1966).

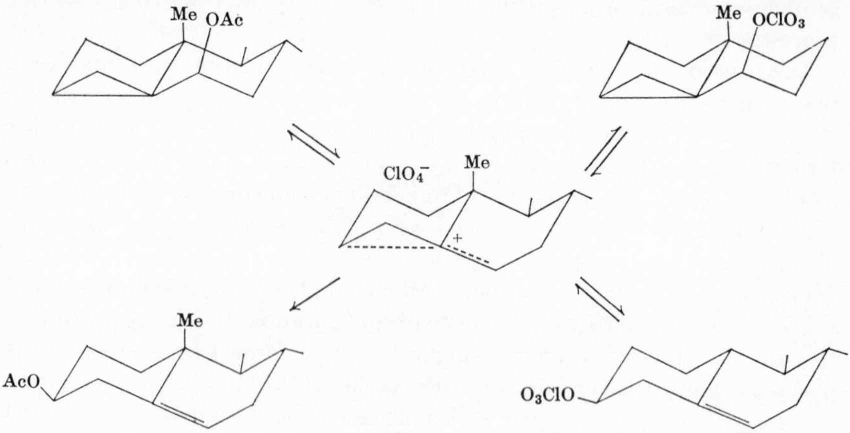

Scheme 1

similar to the ratios (0.53) of benzhydryl ether to benzhydryl benzoate obtained from the reaction of diazodiphenylmethane and benzoic acid under the same conditions. The mechanism for this reaction, equation (4), involving a benz-

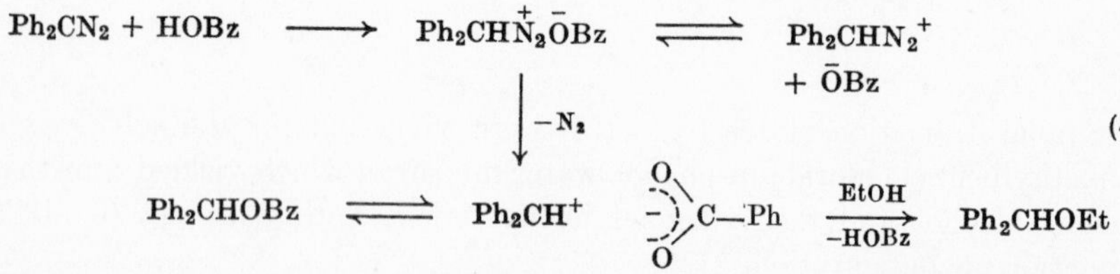

$$\text{Ph}_2\text{CN}_2 + \text{HOBz} \longrightarrow \text{Ph}_2\text{CH}\overset{+}{\text{N}_2}\overset{-}{\text{OBz}} \rightleftharpoons \text{Ph}_2\text{CHN}_2{}^+ + \overset{-}{\text{OBz}}$$

$$\downarrow -\text{N}_2 \qquad\qquad\qquad\qquad\qquad\qquad\qquad (4)$$

$$\text{Ph}_2\text{CHOBz} \rightleftharpoons \text{Ph}_2\text{CH}^+ \quad \overset{O}{\underset{O}{\overset{\|}{{-}}}}\text{C}{-}\text{Ph} \quad \overset{\text{EtOH}}{\underset{-\text{HOBz}}{\longrightarrow}} \text{Ph}_2\text{CHOEt}$$

hydryl benzoate ion pair is thus supported. It was suggested that the slightly smaller value of the fraction of ion-pair return as measured by the ^{18}O-equilibration experiments might be the result of a slight non-equivalence in the oxygen atoms of the benzoate in the ion pair.

Competition by alcohols for the ion pairs from the reaction of diazodiphenyl-methane and benzoic acid in acetonitrile has also been investigated.[11a]

The isomerization of cyclopropylmethyl thiocyanate has been investi-gated.[11b]

The rate of racemization of optically active *p*-chlorobenzhydryl *S*-methyl thiocarbonate (**3**) in benzonitrile is about four times faster than its rate of decomposition to *p*-chlorobenzhydryl methyl sulphide.[12] This suggests that the reaction does not involve the synchronous fission of the carbon–oxygen

[11a] D. Bethell and R. D. Howard, *Chem. Commun.*, **1966**, 94.
[11b] L. A. Spurlock and P. E. Newallis, *Tetrahedron Letters*, **1966**, 303.
[12] J. L. Kice and M. A. Dankleff, *Tetrahedron Letters*, **1966**, 1783.

and carbon–sulphur bonds,[13] but rather a stepwise fission with the initial step reversible, as shown in equation (5a).

$$\underset{Ar}{\overset{Ar'}{>}}CHOCSR \;\rlap{\raise2pt{\rightharpoonup}}{\lower2pt{\leftharpoondown}}\; \underset{Ar}{\overset{Ar'}{>}}CH^+ \; {}^-O_2CSR \xrightarrow{-CO_2} \underset{Ar}{\overset{Ar'}{>}}CH^+ \; {}^-SR \longrightarrow \underset{Ar}{\overset{Ar'}{>}}CHSR$$

(3)   (5a)

On treatment of alkyl chlorocarbonates with silver toluene-p-sulphonate in acetonitrile the alkyl toluene-p-sulphonate is formed via the mixed sulphonic-carbonic anhydride (4) which may be isolated at low temperatures.[14] Labelling experiments showed that the rearrangement of (4) proceeded with alkyl–oxygen fission, and when isobutyl chlorocarbonate was used products derived from the *sec*-butyl and *tert*-butyl cations were obtained and so the annexed mechanism was proposed:

$$ArSO_3Ag + Cl\!-\!\underset{\underset{O}{\|}}{C}\!-\!OR \longrightarrow ArSO_3\!-\!\underset{\underset{O}{\|}}{C}\!-\!OR + AgCl$$

(4)

$$ArSO_3\!-\!\underset{\underset{O}{\|}}{C}\!-\!OR \longrightarrow ArSO_3^- + O{=}\overset{+}{C}\!-\!OR$$

$$O{=}\overset{+}{C}\!-\!OR \longrightarrow R^+ + CO_2$$

$$R^+ + ArSO_3^- \longrightarrow RO_3SAr$$

The chloride ion-catalysed decomposition of alkyl chloroformate in acetonitrile,[15] and the rearrangement of chlorosulphates of glycosides,[16] have also been investigated.

Ion pairing has been investigated by ESR[17] and infrared spectroscopy,[18] conductometrically,[19] and by ultrasonic relaxation.[20]

13 See *Organic Reaction Mechanisms,* **1965**, 54.
14 A. Yamamoto and M. Kobayashi, *Bull. Chem. Soc. Japan,* **39**, 1283, 1288 (1966).
15 D. N. Kevill, G. H. Johnson, and W. A. Neubert, *Tetrahedron Letters,* **1966**, 3727.
16 A. G. Cottrell, E. Buncel, J. K. N. Jones, *Chem. Ind., (London),* **1966**, 552.
17 T. E. Hogen-Esch and J. Smid, *J. Am. Chem. Soc.,* **88**, 307, 318 (1966); W. H. Bruning, G. Henrici-Olivé, and S. Olivé, *Z. Physik. Chem. (Frankfurt),* **47**, 114 (1965); N. M. Atherton, and E. E. Goggins, *Trans. Faraday Soc.,* **62**, 1702 (1966); N. M. Atherton, *ibid.,* p. 1707; R. Chang and C. S. Johnson, *J. Am. Chem. Soc.,* **88**, 2338 (1966); N. Hirota, and R. Kreilick, *ibid.,* p. 614.
18 W. F. Edgell, A. T. Watts, J. Lyford, and W. M. Risen, *J. Am. Chem. Soc.,* **88**, 1815 (1966).
19 P. Chang, R. V. Slates, and M. Szwarc, *J. Phys. Chem.,* **70**, 3180 (1960); C. Carvajal, K. J. Tölle, J. Smid, and M. Szwarc, *J. Am. Chem. Soc.,* **87**, 5548 (1965).
20 M. J. Blandamer, M. J. Foster, N. J. Hidden, and M. C. R. Symons, *Chem. Commun.,* **1966**, 62.

Solvent Effects

An important review on the structural properties of alcohol–water mixtures has appeared.[21]

The interesting observation has been made that the solvation enthalpy ($\Delta \bar{H}_s$) of sodium tetraphenylborate in *tert*-butyl alcohol–water mixtures is very sensitive to composition at low alcohol composition and low temperatures.[22] Thus at 4° it changes from -7.43 kcal mole^{-1} in pure water to $+17.41$ kcal mole^{-1} at 0.06 mole fraction of *tert*-butyl alcohol. This enhanced effect at low temperature presumably results because the "structuredness" of water is very sensitive to temperature change. The plots of $\Delta \bar{H}_s$ at 4° and 25° against mole fraction of water ($\chi_{\mathrm{H_2O}}$) both show maxima at $\chi_{\mathrm{H_2O}} = 0.94$—0.95 and the plot of ΔC_p shows a sharp inflexion at the same value. It was therefore suggested that solvent–temperature studies of heats of activation should be a useful specialized tool for the study of reactions. Indeed the values of $\Delta C_p{}^{\ddagger}$ [i.e. $(\partial \Delta H^{\ddagger}/\partial T)_p$] for the solvolysis of *tert*-butyl chloride in water and 27:73, 37:63, and 50:50 v/v ethanol–water mixtures are -83, -116, -49, and -34 cal mole^{-1} deg^{-1}, respectively, and thus pass through a minimum with changing solvent composition in a similar way to $\Delta H^{\ddagger}$.[23]

Hyne, Golinkin, and Laidlaw[24] have measured the variation of $\Delta V^{\ddagger}$ and of $(\partial \Delta V^{\ddagger}/\partial p)_T$ with solvent composition for the solvolysis of benzyl chloride in ethanol–water mixtures. The plots of both these quantities against mole fraction of ethanol (χ_{EtOH}) show minima at $\chi_{\mathrm{EtOH}} = 0.3$, significantly different from the value ($\chi_{\mathrm{EtOH}} \simeq 0.1$) where the plots of $\Delta H^{\ddagger}$ and $\Delta S^{\ddagger}$ show minima. At this stage it is not possible to say if the minimum in the $\Delta V^{\ddagger}$–χ_{EtOH} plot is an initial- or transition-state effect or a combination of the two. It was, however, noted that the plot of the molal volume of barium chloride in ethanol–water mixtures shows a maximum at $\chi_{\mathrm{EtOH}} = 0.3$. Therefore, on the "crude assumption" that the transition state for solvolysis of benzyl chloride resembles that for barium chloride, it was tentatively suggested that the minimum in the $\Delta V^{\ddagger}$ plot may be due to changes in transition-state solvation.

The plots of the shifts in certain absorption bands of nitroanilines and dye molecules against $\chi_{\mathrm{H_2O}}$ in water–*tert*-butyl alcohol mixtures show extrema at $\chi_{\mathrm{H_2O}} \simeq 0.96$.[25]

There has been a detailed discussion of ground- and initial-state solvation

[21] F. Franks and D. J. G. Ives, *Quart. Rev.* (*London*), **20**, 1 (1966).
[22] E. M. Arnett and D. R. McKelvey, *J. Am. Chem. Soc.*, **88**, 5031 (1966).
[23] J. G. Martin and R. E. Robertson, *J. Am. Chem. Soc.*, **88**, 5353 (1966).
[24] J. B. Hyne, H. S. Golinkin, and W. G. Laidlaw, *J. Am. Chem. Soc.*, **88**, 2104 (1966); H. S. Golinkin, W. G. Laidlaw, and J. B. Hyne, *Can. J. Chem.*, **44**, 2193 (1966).
[25] E. M. Arnett and D. Hufford, *J. Am. Chem. Soc.*, **88**, 3140 (1966); E. M. Arnett, D. Hufford, and D. R. McKelvey, *ibid.*, p. 3142.

in the solvolysis of *tert*-butyl chloride, mainly in terms of the enthalpy of activation.[26a]

The controversy as to the correct interpretation of the solvent isotope effect for the hydrolyses of alkyl halides in water continues.[26b]

A detailed argument has been presented that the change in free energy of activation with change in solvent is more closely related to changes in solvation of the transition state than is the change in enthalpy of activation.[27]

The rates of S_N2 reactions of alkyl chlorides relative to those of the corresponding alkyl iodides are much greater in methanol than in dimethylformamide. Thus methyl chloride reacts 150 times slower than methyl iodide with azide ion in methanol but 3100 times slower in dimethylformamide. It was suggested that the transition states for the reactions of the chlorides were stabilized more by hydrogen-bond donation by the methanol than was that for the reactions of the iodides. The large differences in nucleophilicities and leaving-group mobilities found with S_N2 and $S_N\text{Ar}$ reactions have also been discussed;[28] see also p. 163.

It has also been found that the relative rates of reaction of methyl iodide with phenoxide and carboxylate ions change markedly when the solvent is changed from methanol to dimethylformamide.[29] Thus the order in methanol

$$4\text{-}NO_2C_6H_4S^- > C_6H_5O^- > 4\text{-}NO_2C_6H_4O^- \approx C_6H_5CO_2^- \approx$$
$$CH_3CO_2^- > ClCH_2CO_2^- > 2,4\text{-}(NO_2)_2C_6H_3O^-$$

changes to

$$C_6H_5O^- > 4\text{-}NO_2C_6H_4S^- > CH_3CO_2^- > ClCH_2 \cdot CO_2^- \approx C_6H_5CO_2^- > Cl_2CHCO_2^- \approx$$
$$4\text{-}NO_2C_6H_4O^- > 2,4\text{-}(NO_2)_2C_6H_3O^-$$

in dimethylformamide. Again, hydrogen-bonding interaction with the solvent was thought to be important. This will be much stronger in methanol than in dimethylformamide, but will be the weaker the more the negative charge is dispersed within the ion.

Further examples have been reported of increase in rates of nucleophilic displacement by negative ions due to the addition of dimethyl sulphoxide (DMSO). Thus the rates of reaction of benzyl chlorides with hydroxide ion in

[26a] E. S. Rudakov and V. P. Tret'yakov, *Reaktsionnaya Sposobnost Organ. Soedin., Tartusk. Gos. Univ.*, **2**, 142 (1965); *Chem. Abs.*, **65**, 7008 (1966).

[26b] E. R. Thornton, *Ann. Rev. Phys. Chem.*, **17**, 349 (1966); C. G. Swain and D. F. Evans, *J. Am. Chem. Soc.*, **88**, 383 (1966); R. E. Robertson, S. E. Sugamori, R. Tse, and C.-Y. Wu, *Can. J. Chem.*, **44**, 487 (1966).

[27] R. F. Hudson, *J. Chem. Soc.*, B, **1966**, 761; R. F. Hudson and G. W. Loveday, *ibid.*, p. 766; R. F. Hudson, G. W. Loveday, S. Fliszár, and G. Salvadori, *ibid.*, p. 769; R. F. Hudson and I. Stelzer, *ibid.*, p. 775.

[28] B. O. Coniglio, D. E. Giles, W. R. McDonald, and A. J. Parker, *J. Chem. Soc.*, B, **1966**, 152; B. W. Clare, D. Cook, E. C. F. Ko, Y. C. Mac, and A. J. Parker, *J. Am. Chem. Soc.*, **88**, 1911 (1966); A. J. Parker, *J. Chem. Soc.* A, **1966**, 220.

[29] D. Cook, I. P. Evans, E. C. F. Ko, and A. J. Parker, *J. Chem. Soc.*, B, **1966**, 404.

DMSO–water mixtures[30] and with methoxide ion in DMSO–methanol mixtures[31] increases with increasing DMSO content. The rates of the solvolyses of benzyl chlorides in water–DMSO mixtures decrease, however, with decreasing water content but less so than in water–acetone and water–dioxan mixtures.[32] The plots of ΔH against solvent composition for benzyl and 4-methylbenzyl chloride, but not for 3-chloro- and 4-nitro-compounds, show shallow minima at mole fractions of DMSO 0.1–0.15.

By studying the reactions in the presence of an excess of solid phase the difference in chemical potential between the transition states for the decomposition of trimethylsulphonium bromide in dimethylformamide and in ethanol has been evaluated as $\mu^{E} - \mu^{D} = +2.12$ kcal mole^{-1}.[33]

A striking counter-ion effect has been noted in the reaction of *n*-butyl bromide and tetra-*n*-butylammonium phenoxide in dioxan which proceeds 3×10^{4} times faster than that of potassium phenoxide.[34] The rate of reaction with the tetra-*n*-butylammonium salt varies only slightly over the solvent range dioxan, tetrahydrofuran, acetonitrile, and dimethylformamide, but that of potassium phenoxide increases by a factor of $\sim 10^{5}$ on going from dioxan to dimethylformamide. It was suggested that the degree of association into ion pairs was similar for both the potassium and tetrabutylammonium salts but that the tetrabutylammonium phenoxide ion pair has a low cation–anion interaction energy and high reactivity which is uninfluenced by solvent.

A review on dipolar-aprotic solvents has been published,[35] and other relevant work in this field includes measurements of the relative enthalpies of transfer of alkali-metal ions from water to DMSO[36] and from water to propylene carbonate,[37] investigations of ion association of lithium and tetrabutylammonium salts in acetone,[38] and studies of the reactions of alkyl bromides with tetraethylammonium azide[39] and neopentyl toluene-*p*-sulphonate with amines[40] in a range of dipolar aprotic solvents and of the solvolysis of *tert*-butyl bromide in 1-methyl-2-pyrrolidone.[41]

The rate constants for hydrolysis of primary alkyl halides in aqueous perchloric acid decrease with increasing perchloric acid content owing to a

[30] E. Tommila and I. P. Pitkänen, *Acta Chem. Scand.*, **20**, 937 (1966).
[31] E. Tommila and M. Savolainen, *Acta Chem. Scand.*, **20**, 946 (1966).
[32] E. Tommila, *Acta Chem. Scand.*, **20**, 923 (1966).
[33] I. P. Evans and A. J. Parker, *Tetrahedron Letters*, **1966**, 163; see also, Y. Pocker and A. J. Parker, *J. Org. Chem.*, **31**, 1526 (1966).
[34] J. Ugelstad, T. Ellingsen, and A. Berge, *Acta Chem. Scand.*, **20**, 1593 (1966).
[35] F. Madaule-Aubry, *Bull. Soc. Chim. France*, **1966**, 1456.
[36] E. M. Arnett and D. R. McKelvey, *J. Am. Chem. Soc.*, **88**, 2598 (1966).
[37] Y.-C. Wu and H. L. Friedman, *J. Phys. Chem.*, **70**, 501 (1966).
[38] L. G. Savedoff, *J. Am. Chem. Soc.*, **88**, 664 (1966).
[39] J. J. Delpuech, *Bull. Soc. Chim. France*, **1966**, 1624, 1631.
[40] J. Seyden-Penne and B. Danrée, *Bull. Soc. Chim. France*, **1966**, 3086.
[41] P. O. I. Virtanen, *Suomen Kemistilehti, A*, **39**, 113 (1966).

decrease in the activity of water, but that for *tert*-butyl chloride increases owing to electrophilic catalysis.[42]

Other reactions for which solvent effects have been reported include the Menschutkin reactions of ω-bromoacetophenone with α-picoline[43] and of benzyl bromide with pyridine,[44] and solvolyses of ethylene oxide[45] and of *tert*-butyl chloride.[46]

Neighbouring-group Participation[47]

Further examples of participation by a carbonyl group through enolization[48] have been reported.[49] The acetolysis of *anti*-7-hydroxynorbornan-2-one toluene-*p*-sulphonate (5) proceeds about 10^7 times faster than that of 7-norbornyl toluene-*p*-sulphonate, to yield *anti*-7-acetoxynorbornan-2-one (7), and the reaction of *anti*-7-chloronorbornanone (8) with potassium methoxide proceeds more than 10^5 times faster than that of its *syn*-isomer, the product being the *anti*-methoxy-ketone (10). It was suggested that these reactions proceed via the enol (6) and the enolate ion (9). This view is supported by the reaction of (5) in AcOD yielding first-order rate constants which decrease with

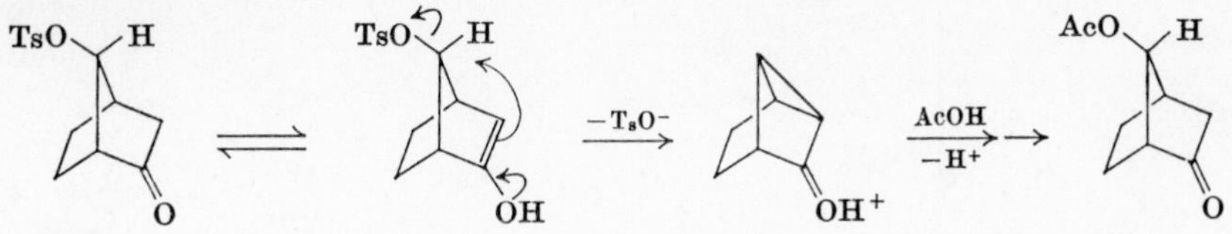

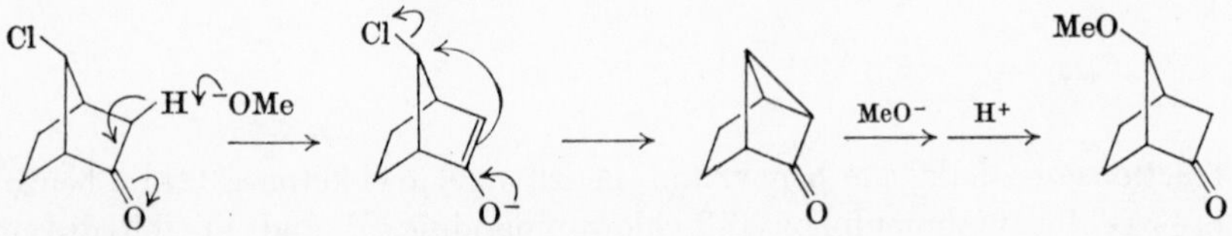

42 J. Koskikallio and S. Klemetti, *Suomen Kemistilehti*, *A*, **39**, 113 (1966).
43 H. Heydtmann, A. P. Schmidt, and H. Hartmann, *Ber. Bunsenges. Physik. Chem.*, **70**, 444 (1966).
44 N. K. Vorob'ev and G. F. Titova, *Izv. Vysshikh. Uchebn. Zavedenii, Khim. i Khim. Tekhnol*, **9**, 218 (1966); *Chem. Abs.*, **65**, 12074 (1966).
45 P. O. I. Virtanen, *Suomen Kemistilehti*, *B*, **38**, 135 (1965); *ibid.*, **39**, 115 (1966).
46 I. Koppel, *Reaktsionnaya Sposobnost. Organ. Soedin. Tartusk. Gos. Univ.*, **2**, 148, 169 (1965); *Chem. Abs.*, **64**, 14050 (1966).
47 A review on transannular reactions has been published by A. C. Cope, M. M. Martin, and M. A. McKervey, *Quart. Rev.* (*London*), **20**, 119 (1966).
48 For an earlier example see H. L. Goering, A. C. Olson, and H. H. Espy, *J. Amer. Chem. Soc.*, **78**, 5371 (1956).
49 P. G. Gassman and J. L. Marshall, *J. Am. Chem. Soc.*, **88**, 2599, (1966); J. T. Lumb and G. H. Whitham, *Chem. Commun.*, **1966**, 400.

time, and by the isolation from the reaction mixture of starting material which is partially deuterated. In this reaction, then, the total rate is at least partly controlled by the rate of enolization which is slower for deuterated than for undeuterated (5).

Neighbouring-group participation by a ketone group via the adduct with methoxide has also been reported.[50] Thus treatment of both 16α- and 16β-bromo-3β-hydroxyandrostan-17-one [(12) and (11)] with sodium methoxide yields the dimethyl ketal of 3β,16α-dihydroxyandrostan-17-one. Clearly the 16α-bromo-compound (12) must have reacted via the 16β-bromo-compound (11), and not directly since then it would have yielded the 16β-hydroxy-compound which was not formed. Similar participation is observed in the

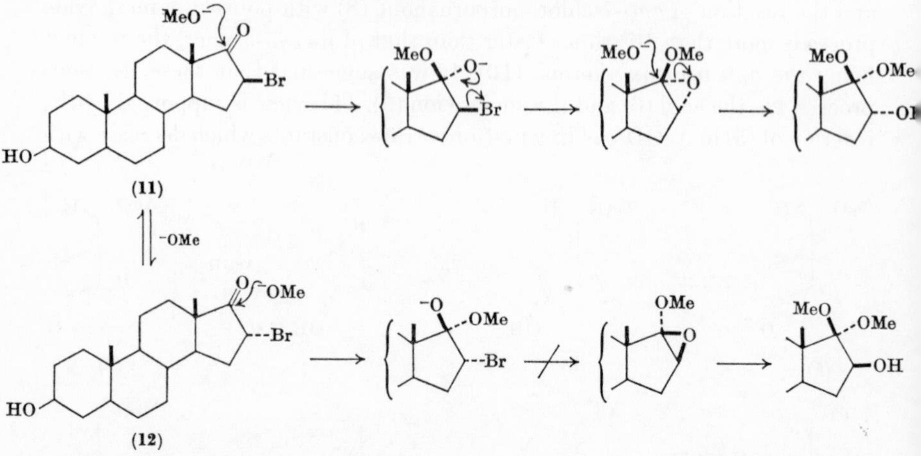

reactions of α-halogeno-benzyl and -benzhydryl aryl ketones[51a] of 3-benzoyl-α(+)-1-(10-camphorsulphonyl)-3-chloro-piperidine,[51b] and of β-hydroxypivalophenone toluene-p-sulphonate (13)[52] with sodium methoxide in methanol.

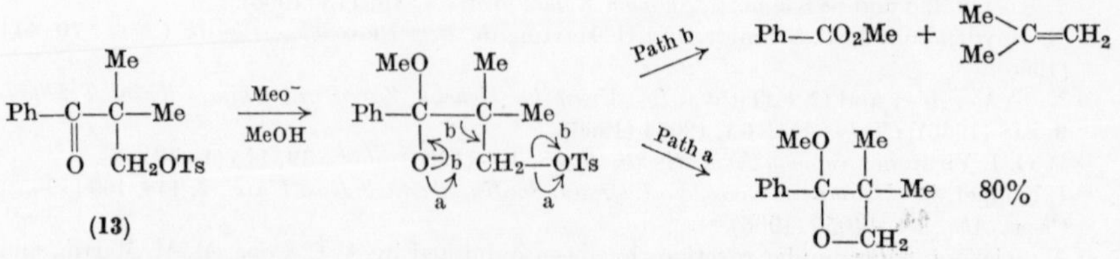

[50] A. Hassner and P. Catsoulacos, *J. Org. Chem.*, **31**, 3149 (1966).
[51a] T. I. Temnikova and V. S. Karavan, *J. Org. Chem. USSR.*, **1**, 606, 2115 (1965).
[51b] H. Patel and G. Hite, *J. Org. Chem.*, **30**, 4337 (1965).
[52] F. Nerdel and U. Kretzschmar, *Ann. Chem.*, **688**, 61 (1965).

With the latter compound participation (path a) yields a four- and not a three-membered ring as with the other compounds, and formation of this is accompanied by some fragmentation (path b).

In the absence of ring-size effects participation by the amide group usually proceeds with *O*-attack when it is un-ionized and *N*-attack when it is ionized.[53] This year, however, examples of participation by an un-ionized amide group with *N*-attack[54] and of participation by an ionized amide group with *O*-attack[55] have been reported. Thus acetolysis of 2-benzyl-6-*endo*-toluene-*p*-sulphonyloxy-2-azabicyclo[2.2.2]octan-3-one (**14**) yields *endo*-acetate (**16**) and 7-*endo*-acetoxy-2-benzyl-2-azabicyclo[3.2.1]octan-3-one (**17**), both formed presumably through the acylaziridinium ion (**15**).[54]

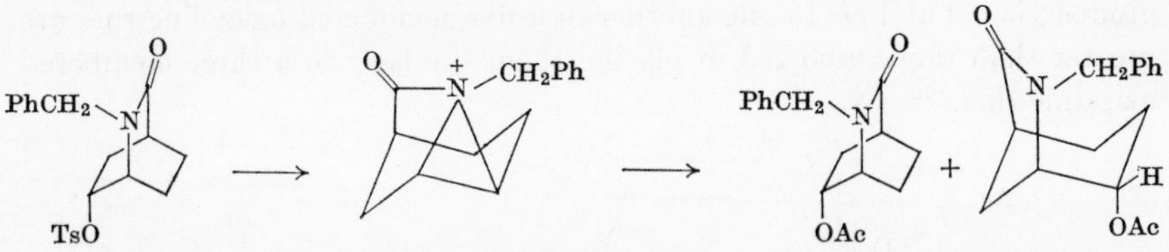

The rate of cyclization of 4-bromobutyranilide (**18**) in 1:9 acetonitrile–water is independent of pH in the range 2—10, and the reaction proceeds with exclusive O-5 participation to yield the lactone imide (**20**). Above pH 10 the rate is proportional to the HO⁻ concentration and both the lactone imide (**20**)

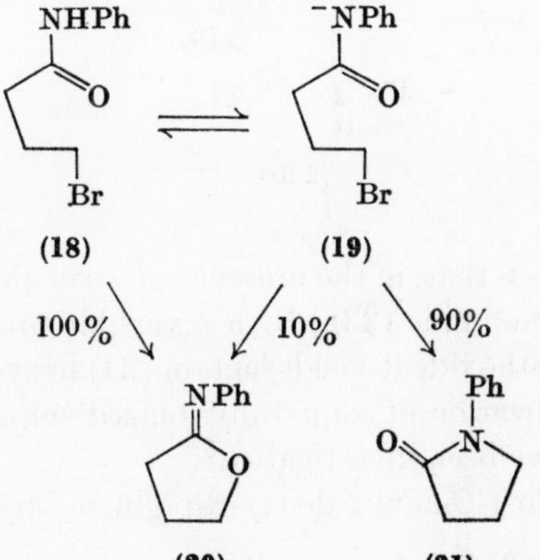

53 Cf. B. Capon, *Quart. Rev. (London)*, **18**, 71 (1966).
54 J. W. Huffman and T. Kamiya, *Tetrahedron Letters*, **1966**, 1857.

and pyrrolidone (**21**) are formed. At pH 13.7 the contribution of cyclization of the un-ionized anilide to the total rate is less than 0.5%, but the product still contains 10% of lactone imide. It was therefore concluded that this results from cyclization of the ionized anilide (**19**) which thus proceeds with both O^--5 and N^--5 participation. This is the first example to be reported of O^--5 participation by an amide group competing significantly with N^--5 participation.[55]

Another interesting and related observation is that on treatment with sodium ethoxide in ethanol *threo*-N-(2-chloro-1,2-diphenylethyl)-*p*-nitro-benzamide (**22a**) yields an aziridine and not an oxazoline, whereas its *erythro*-isomer (**22b**) yields an oxazoline and not an aziridine. Apparently, with (**22a**) the unfavourable steric factors which have to be overcome to place two phenyl groups vicinal and *cis* to one another in a five-membered oxazoline ring are greater than those involved in placing them similarly in a three-membered aziridine ring.[56a]

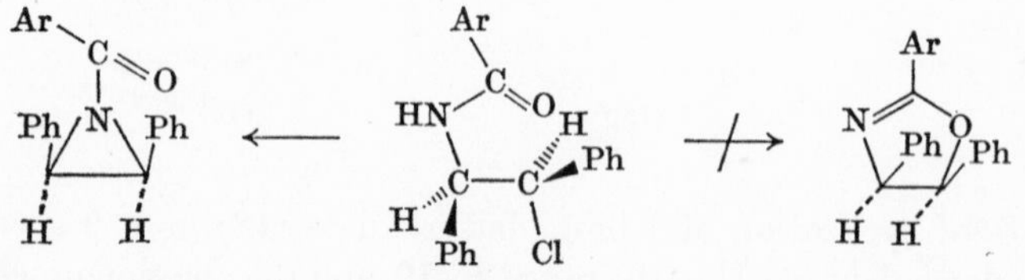

(22a)

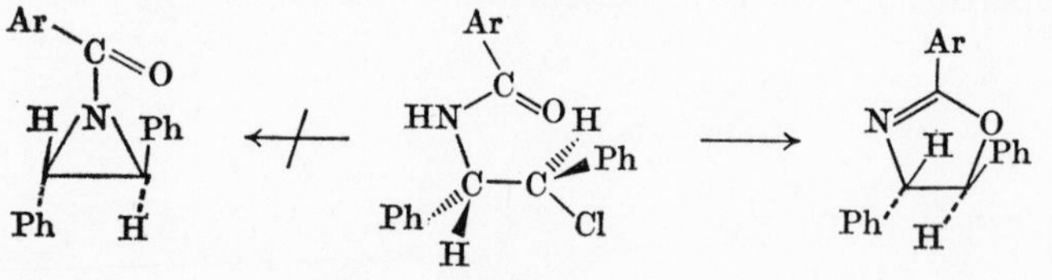

(22b)

It has also been shown that, in the presence of weak amine bases, the amide (**23a**) yields the lactone imide (**23b**) by a reversible process, whereas in the presence of sodium methoxide it yields lactam (**24**) irreversibly.[56b]

The kinetics of cyclization of some fully ionized sulphonamides (**25**) with N^--3 participation have been investigated.[57]

Several 2-acetamido-1-*O*-acyl-2-deoxy-β-D-gluco- and -galacto-pyranose

[55] B. A. Cunningham and G. L. Schmir, *J. Org. Chem.*, **31**, 3751 (1966).

[56a] H. W. Heine, D. C. King, and L. A. Portland, *J. Org. Chem.*, **31**, 2662 (1966).

[56b] H. E. Zaugg, R. J. Michaels, A. D. Schaefer, A. M. Wenthe, and W. H. Washburn, *Tetrahedron*, **22**, 1257 (1966).

[57] W. J. Gensler and B. A. Brooks, *J. Org. Chem.*, **31**, 568 (1966).

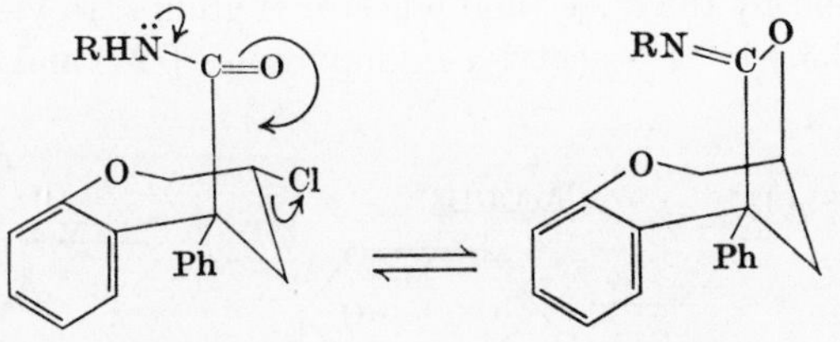

(23a) (23b)

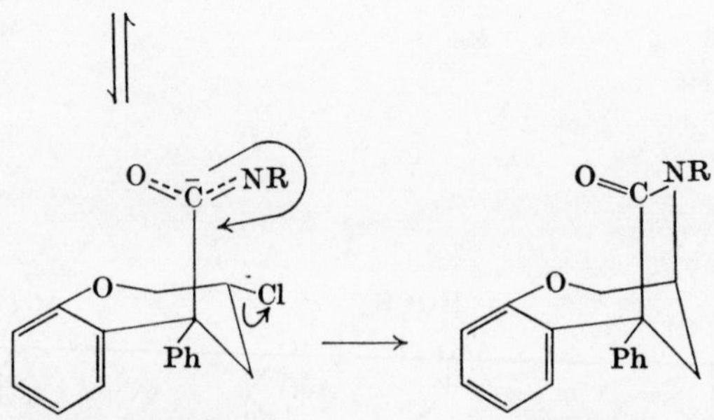

R = Cyclopropyl (24)

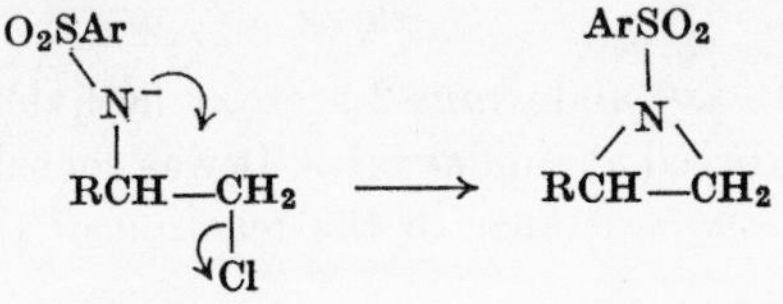

(25)

derivatives undergo ready methanolyses and hydrolyses involving participation of the amide group [see, for example, equation (5b)].[58]

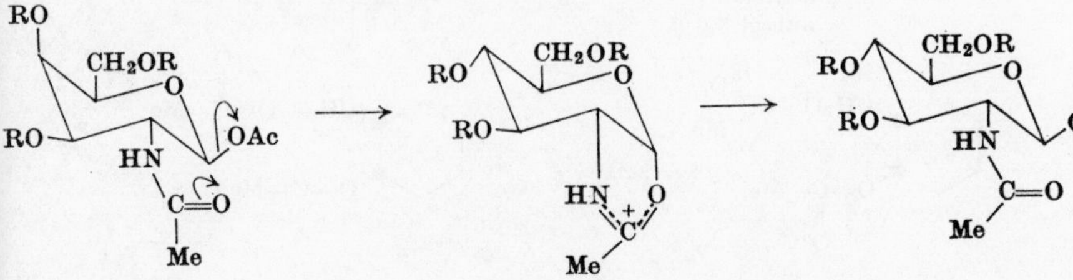

(5b)

On treatment of the oxonium hexachloroantimonate (26) with aqueous sodium acetate a very interesting series of reactions occurs, involving succes-

[58] T. D. Inch and H. G. Fletcher, *J. Org. Chem.*, **31**, 1810 (1966).

sive participation by the 3-, 4-, and 6-acetoxyl groups, to yield a mixture of 1,2,3,6- and 1,2,3,4-tetra-O-acetyl-α-D-idopyranose [(**27**) and (**28**)].[59]

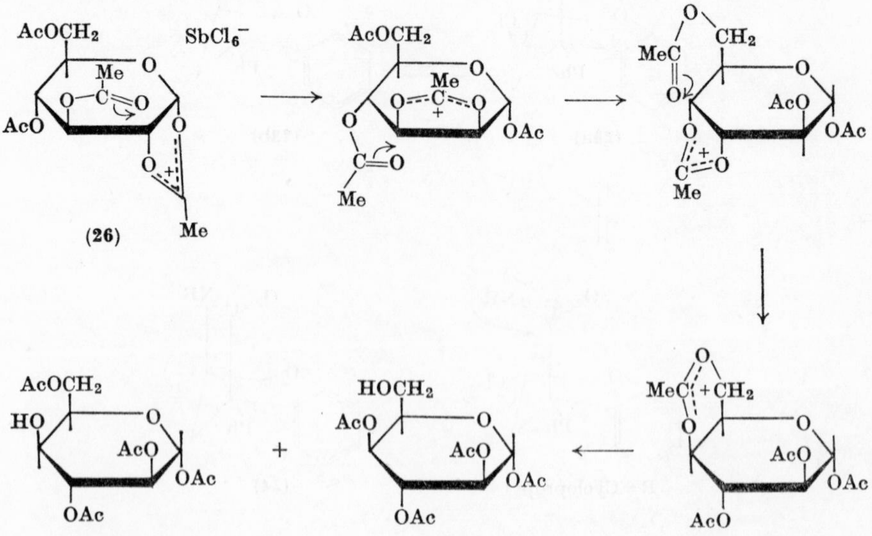

(26)

(27)   +   (28)

The acetolyses of *cis*- and *trans*-2-acetoxymethylcyclohexyl *p*-bromo-benzenesulphonate proceed at similar rates. It was considered[60] that this was evidence for anchimeric assistance in the reaction of the *trans*-isomer (**29**)

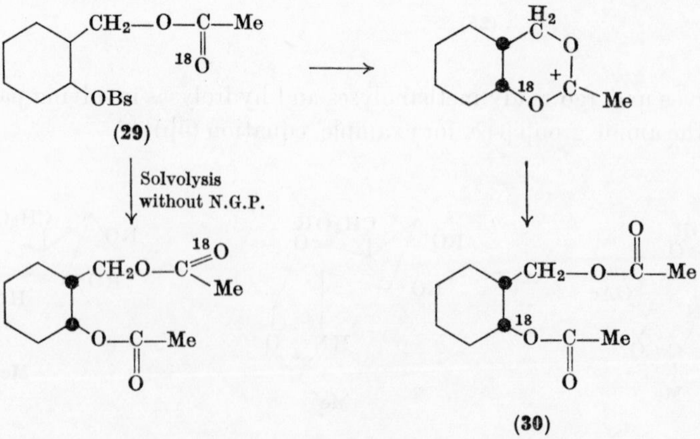

(29)

Solvolysis
without N.G.P.

(30)

Scheme 2

[59] H. Paulsen, W.-P. Trautwein, F. Garrido-Espinosa, and K. Heyns, *Tetrahedron Letters*, **1966**, 4131, 4137.
[60] L. J. Dolby and M. J. Schwarz, *J. Org. Chem.*, **30**, 3581 (1965).

since it was thought that in the absence of this the *cis*-isomer would react much more rapidly. The *trans*-isomer yielded mainly *cis*-2-acetoxymethylcyclohexyl acetate (**30**), and this was shown to be formed with AcO-6 participation since *trans*-2-[$C^{18}O$]acetoxymethylcyclohexyl *p*-bromobenzenesulphonate yielded (after acetolysis and saponification of the resulting *cis*-diacetate) *cis*-2-hydroxymethylcyclohexanol which contained about 80% of the ^{18}O. The reaction therefore proceeds as shown in Scheme 2.

The reaction of 2,3-dibromopropyl benzoate with thiourea to yield compound (**31**) involves participation by the benzoate group, as shown, since, when benzoate from 2,3-dibromopropanol containing ^{18}O was used, all the label was found to be in the carbonyl group of (**31**).[61]

Diaxial opening of five-membered acyloxonium (dioxolium) ions fused to six-membered rings has been shown to be preferred to diequatorial opening [cf. equations (6) and (7)].[62] With compound (**32**), however, where diaxial opening is inhibited by the *cis*-axial 19-methyl group, twice as much diequatorial as diaxial opening occurs. However, ring opening of the analogous epoxide with HBr still yields diaxial bromohydrin, so it appears that the tendency for diaxial opening of an acyloxonium ion is not as large as with epoxides. Since, presumably, the diaxial isomers are of higher free energy than the diequatorial, these results must mean also that the anchimeric assistance for participation by a *trans*-axial acetoxy-group is greater than for participation by a *trans*-diequatorial one.

Other investigations of acetoxonium ions include those of the perchlorates of 3α,5α-steroidal acetoxonium ions,[63] the tetrafluoroborates of dioxenium cations,[64] and on the NMR spectra of 1,3-dioxolium ions.[65]

The pH–rate profile for the conversion of bromo-ketone (**33**) into 3,3-dimethylisochroman-1,4-dione (**35**) is sigmoid, the rate being proportional to the concentration of ionized form (**34**).[66] It was estimated that the rate

[61] E. D. Sverdlov, V. P. Zvolinskii, B. E. Zaitsev, and V. M. Fedoseev, *Dokl. Akad. Nauk SSSR.*, **166**, 1143 (1966); *Chem. Abs.*, **64**, 17415 (1965).
[62] J. F. King and A. D. Allbutt, *Chem. Commun.*, **1966**, 14.
[63] M. J. Coppen, M. P. Hartshorn, and D. N. Kirk, *J. Chem. Soc., C*, **1966**, 576.
[64] G. Schneider, *Tetrahedron Letters*, **1966**, 5921.
[65] H. Hart and D. A. Tomalia, *Tetrahedron Letters*, **1966**, 3383, 3389.
[66] E. T. Harper and M. L. Bender, *J. Am. Chem. Soc.*, **87**, 5625 (1965).

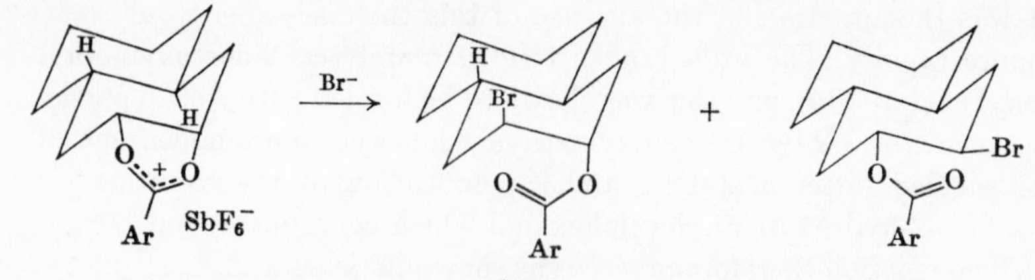

(6)

95%   5%

(7)

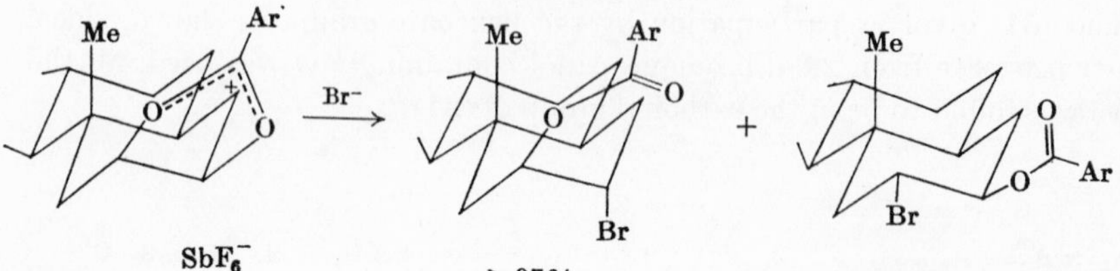

> 97%   < 3%

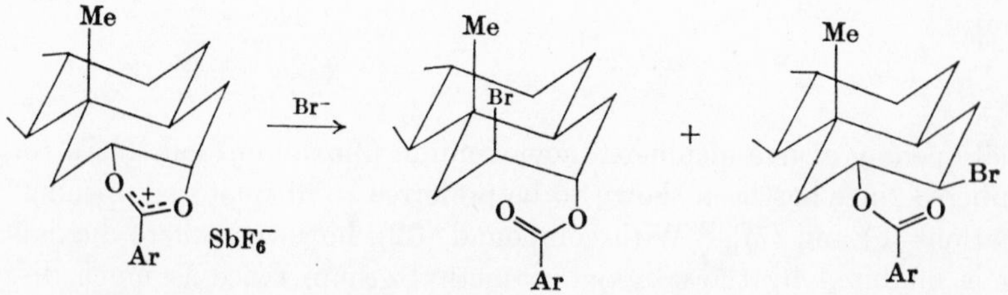

(32)

~33%   ~66%

Ar = ————⟨   ⟩———— OMe

constant for this reaction was equal to that for the hypothetical intermolecular reaction of α-bromoisobutyrophenone with 10^3M-carboxylate ion.

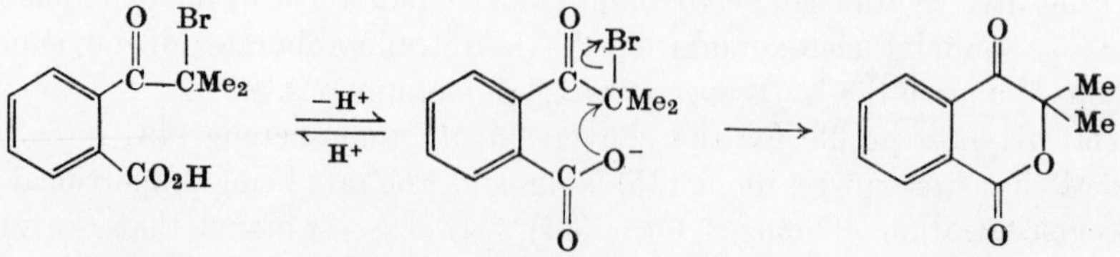

(33)   (34)   (35)

The anion of 3-bromopropionic acid is hydrolysed about 14 times faster than the acid itself in water and about 2500 times faster in 80% aqueous dimethyl sulphoxide; the anchimeric assistance associated with carboxylate ion participation thus increases with increasing dimethyl sulphoxide content of the solvent. A similar but smaller effect was found with bromoacetic acid. The hydrolyses of DL- and *meso*-dibromosuccinic acid were also investigated.[67]

The interesting example of neighbouring-carboxyl participation (**37**) → (**38**), occurs when the bromo-anhydride (**36**) is treated with *NN*-dimethyl-aniline.[68]

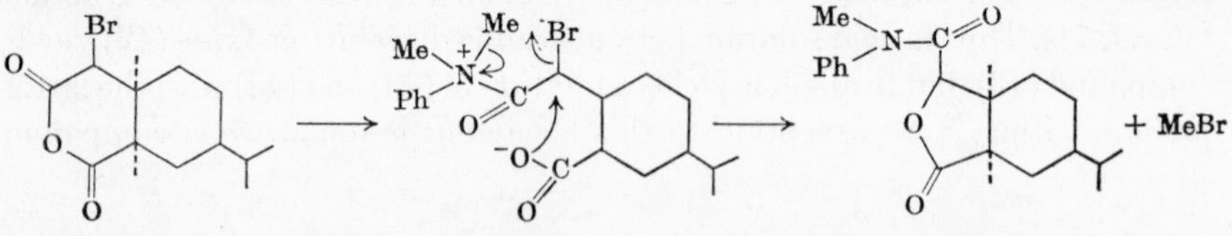

(**36**)   (**37**)   (**38**)

The failure to observe neighbouring-group participation in the reactions of benzyl bromides with *o*-carboxyl and methoxycarbonyl groups has been discussed.[69]

An interesting example of intramolecular nucleophilic catalysis of the opening of an oxetane ring has been reported by Buchanan and Oakes[70] who showed that the 3,5-oxide ring of 3,5-anhydro-1,2-*O*-isopropylidene-α-D-glucofuranose (**39**) is opened more rapidly than that of the corresponding xylose derivative through the reversible formation of the 5,6-epoxide (**40**). The latter also yields a small amount of 3,6-oxide (**41**) which is stable.

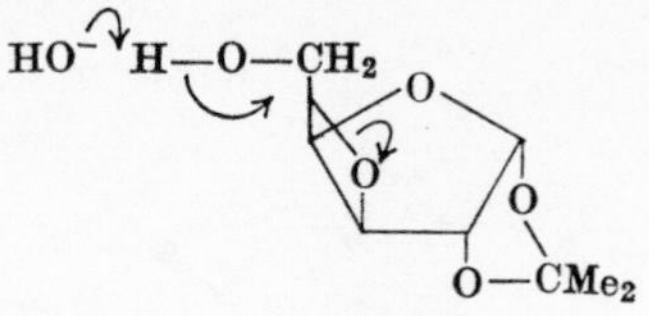

(**39**)

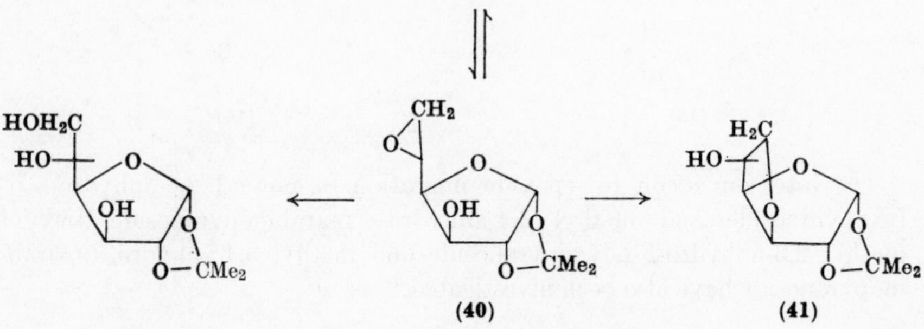

(**40**)   (**41**)

[67] C. A. Kingsbury, *J. Am. Chem. Soc.*, **87**, 5409 (1965); see also J. Leska, *Coll. Czech. Chem. Commun.*, **31**, 3903 (1966).
[68] A. Corbella, G. Jommi, C. Scolastico, and J. Krepinsky, *Gazz. Chim. Ital.*, **96**, 760 (1966).
[69] L. Chauffee, L. J. Andrews, and R. M. Keefer, *J. Org. Chem.*, **31**, 3758 (1966).

3,5-Anhydro-1,2-*O*-isopropylidene-α-L-idofuranose behaves similarly to its glucose analogue.[70]

Other examples of oxide migrations investigated include intramolecular displacements by hydroxyl groups on unsymmetrical (secondary–tertiary) epoxides. Generally, as would be expected, the tendency for attack on the tertiary carbon is greater in the acid- than in the base-catalysed reaction (cf. ref. 71). Thus in acid solution heterobetuline diacetate epoxide (**42**) yields compound (**43**), but in alkali it yields a mixture of (**43**) and (**44**) with the latter predominating.[72] An exception to this behaviour is found when compound

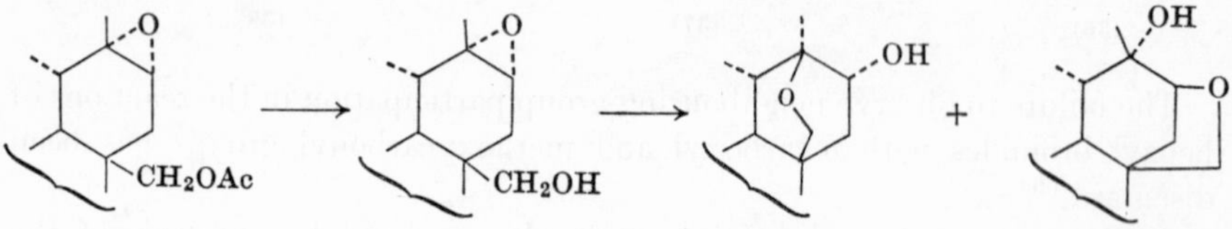

(**42**)   (**43**)   (**44**)

(**45**), obtained from the osmium tetroxide-catalysed oxidation of caryo-phyllene oxide, is treated with methanolic potassium hydroxide;[73] here intramolecular attack on the secondary carbon of the epoxide is disfavoured sterically and the product is compound (**46**), formed by attack on the tertiary carbon.

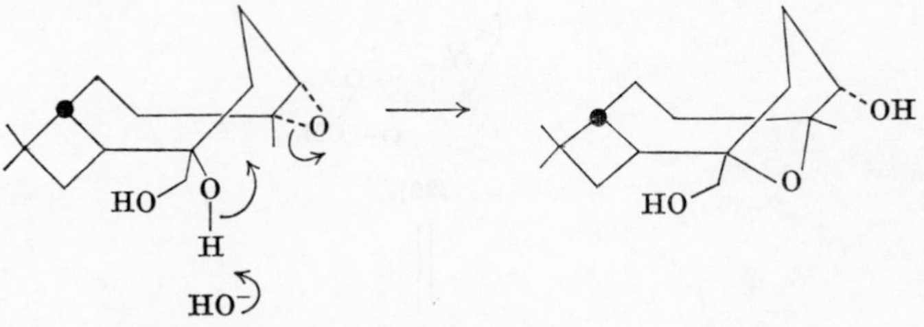

(**45**)   (**46**)

The interconversion by epoxide migration of methyl 2,3-anhydro-α-D-lyxopyranoside and methyl 3,4-anhydro-α-D-arabinopyranoside and of methyl 2,3-anhydro-β-L-lyxopyranoside and methyl 3,4-anhydro-β-L-arabinopyranoside have also been investigated.[74]

[70] J. G. Buchanan and E. M. Oakes, *Carbohydrate Res.*, **1**, 242 (1965).
[71] M. Mousseron-Canet, C. Levallois and H. Huerre, *Bull. Soc. Chim. France*, **1966**, 658.
[72] E. Řihová and A. Vystrčil, *Coll. Czech. Chem. Commun.*, **31**, 3163 (1966).
[73] E. W. Warnhoff and V. Srinivasan, *Can. J. Chem.*, **44**, 2259 (1966).
[74] J. G. Buchanan and R. Fletcher, *J. Chem. Soc.*, *C*, **1966**, 1926.

The rates of the apparent nucleophilic displacement of chloride from epichlorohydrin by hydroxide and phenoxide ions have values the same as those calculated from linear free-energy relationships for the rates of opening of the epoxide rings by these nucleophiles. The mechanism of equation (8) was therefore proposed.[75]

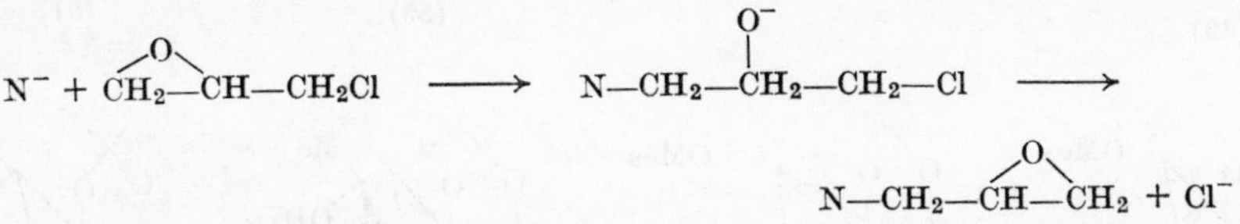

$$N^- + \overset{O}{\underset{\diagup\diagdown}{CH_2-CH}}-CH_2Cl \longrightarrow N-CH_2-\overset{O^-}{\underset{|}{CH_2}}-CH_2-Cl \longrightarrow$$

$$N-CH_2-\overset{O}{\underset{\diagup\diagdown}{CH}}-CH_2 + Cl^- \quad (8)$$

The interesting suggestion has been made that the reaction of the tertiary 2-chloro-1,1-dimethylethyl hydroperoxide **(47)** with sodium hydroxide in aqueous methanol to yield acetone and formaldehyde proceeds with participation of the peroxide group via the four-membered cyclic peroxide.[76]

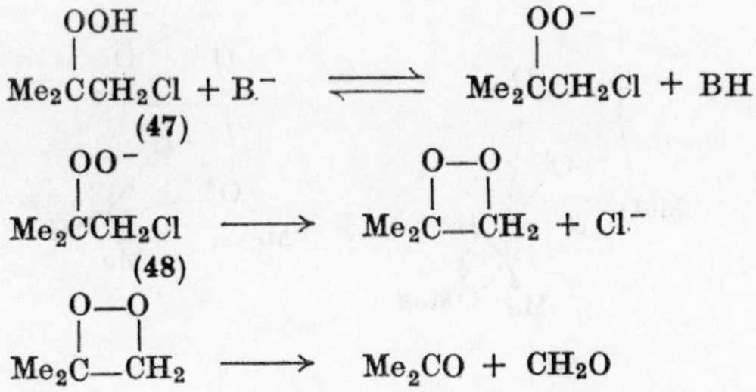

$$\underset{\textbf{(47)}}{\overset{OOH}{\underset{|}{Me_2CCH_2Cl}}} + B^- \rightleftharpoons \overset{OO^-}{\underset{|}{Me_2CCH_2Cl}} + BH$$

$$\underset{\textbf{(48)}}{\overset{OO^-}{\underset{|}{Me_2CCH_2Cl}}} \longrightarrow \overset{O-O}{\underset{|\quad\;\;|}{Me_2C-CH_2}} + Cl^-$$

$$\overset{O-O}{\underset{|\quad\;\;|}{Me_2C-CH_2}} \longrightarrow Me_2CO + CH_2O$$

Consistent with the ionized form of the hydroperoxide **(48)** being the reactive species, the reaction is zero order in base at high base concentrations, where all the hydroperoxide would be expected to be ionized. Unfortunately, the anchimeric assistance estimated to accompany this participation was not reported.

Interesting examples of neighbouring-group participation by the ring-oxygen of pyranose sugar derivatives have been reported.[77,78] Thus, compound **(49)**, on treatment with sodium acetate in dimethylformamide, yields the ring-contracted compounds **(50)** and **(51)** in the ratio of 7:1.[77] When heated to 170° in dioxan–water (9:1) in the presence of sodium hydrogen carbonate it yielded **(50a)**, **(51a)**, and **(52)** in the ratio of 1:2:6. It was considered

[75] J. Konecny, *Helv. Chim. Acta*, **49**, 1743 (1966); J. Myszkowski, A. Z. Zielinski, and K. Zielinski, *Chem. Stosowana, Ser. A.*, **10**, 57 (1966).

[76] W. H. Richardson, J. W. Peters, and W. K. Konopka, *Tetrahedron Letters*, **1966**, 5531.

[77] C. L. Stevens, R. P. Glinski, K. G. Taylor, P. Blumbergs, and F. Sirokman, *J. Am. Chem. Soc.*, **88**, 2073 (1966).

[78] S. Hanessian, *Chem. Commun.*, **1966**, 796.

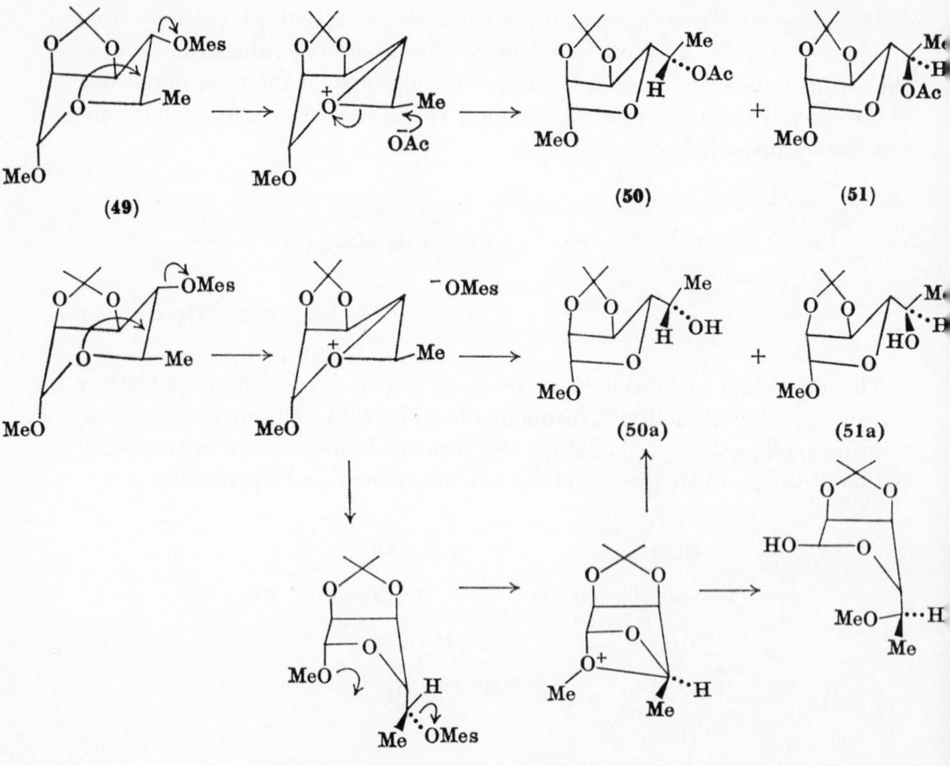

(49)   (50)   (51)

(50a)   (51a)

(53)   (52)

that (52) was formed by rearrangement to (53) by ion-pair return and subsequent methoxyl participation.[77] Support for this was obtained by the observation that the *p*-bromobenzenesulphonate analogous to (53) yielded (50a) 9%, (51a) 2%, and (52) 89%, under the same reaction conditions.[77]

Whereas the reaction of *cis*-7-chloro-8-methylthiodibenzobicyclo[2.2.2]-octadiene (54) with silver acetate in acetic acid proceeded stereospecifically, to yield the *syn-exo*-[3.2.1] acetate (55), that of its *trans*-isomer (56) yielded a 2:1 mixture of the *syn*- and *anti*-[3.2.1] acetates.[79] This result indicates weak participation by the sulfide group, as shown; and, as expected, with the corresponding *trans*-phenylthio-compound the *syn:anti* ratio in the products was reduced to 1:1.

The sulpholen–sulphur dichloride adducts (57) and (59) are hydrolysed considerably faster in aqueous acetone than is 3-chlorosulpholan, suggesting that neighbouring-group participation by a sulfide linkage is occurring.[80]

[79] S. J. Cristol, R. Caple, R. M. Sequeira, and L. O. Smith, *J. Am. Chem. Soc.*, **87**, 5679 (1965).
[80] S. N. Lewis and W. D. Emmons, *J. Org. Chem.*, **31**, 3572 (1966).

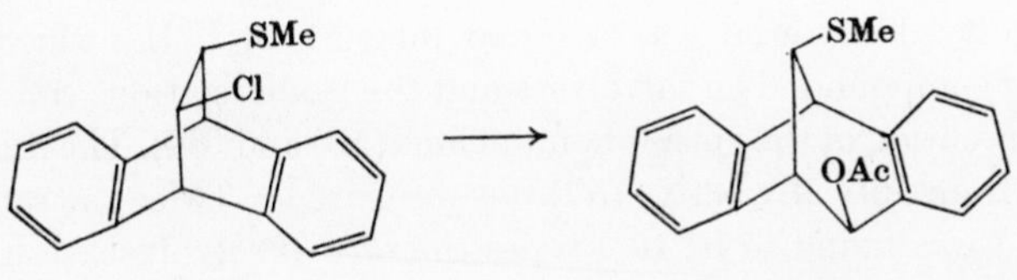

(1)

(2)

(54) → (55)

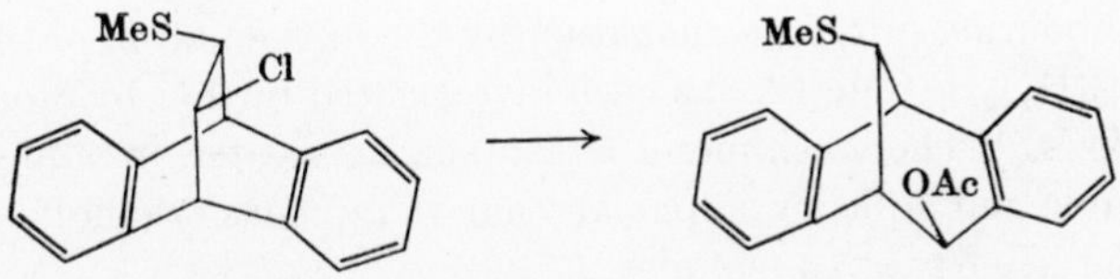

(56)

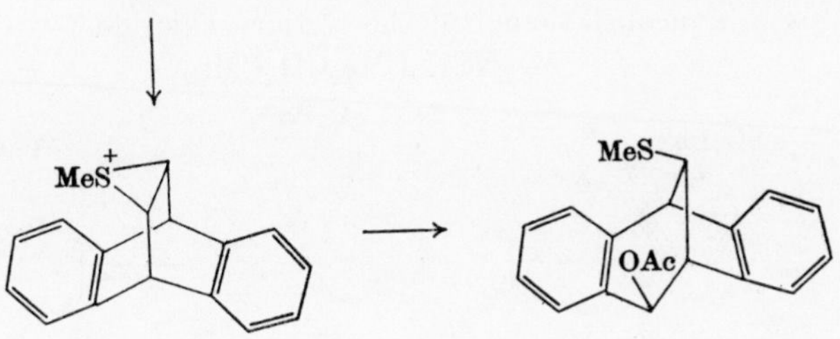

(57) D or L

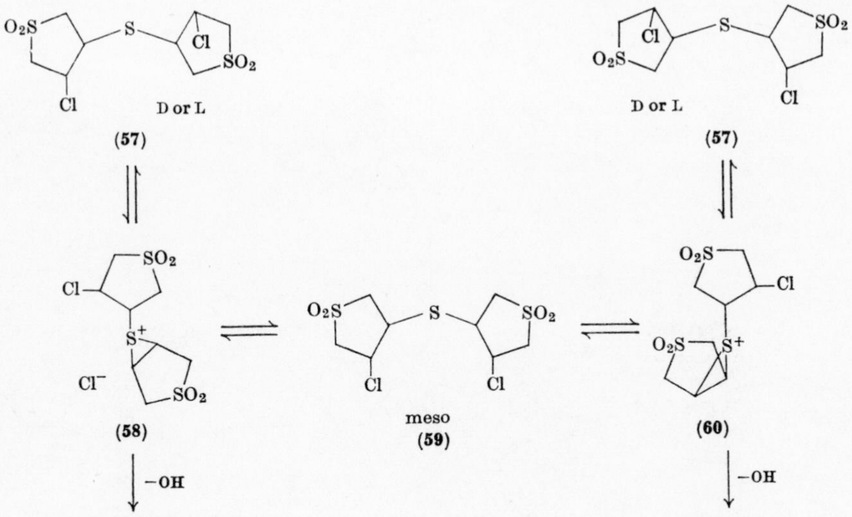

(57) D or L

(58)

meso
(59)

(60)

Cl⁻

−OH

−OH

Products

Products

This is also indicated by the observation that after 25% hydrolysis the unhydrolysed material was a 50:50 mixture of both, whichever was the starting compound. The solvolyses and the isomerizations can be interpreted by intervention of the episulphonium ions (58) and (60). The rate of formation of that from optically active (57) was measured as twice the rate of racemization and was found to be 16.6 times the rate of solvolysis. Ion pair return is therefore very efficient despite the medium (40% aqueous acetone) being so highly solvating.

Neighbouring-group participation by the oxygen atom of the sulphoxides, $PhSO \cdot [CH_2]_{n-3} \cdot CMe_2Cl$, has been investigated further by Montanori and his co-workers.[81] The anchimeric assistance is greater in aqueous dimethylformamide and aqueous sulpholan than in aqueous ethanol and decreases in the order $n = 6 > 5 > 4$ (see also, p. 128).

Some anchimeric assistance is also provided by the amino-group in the solvolysis in aqueous ethanol of the tertiary chloride, $Me_2NCH_2CMe_2CH_2CMe_2Cl$,

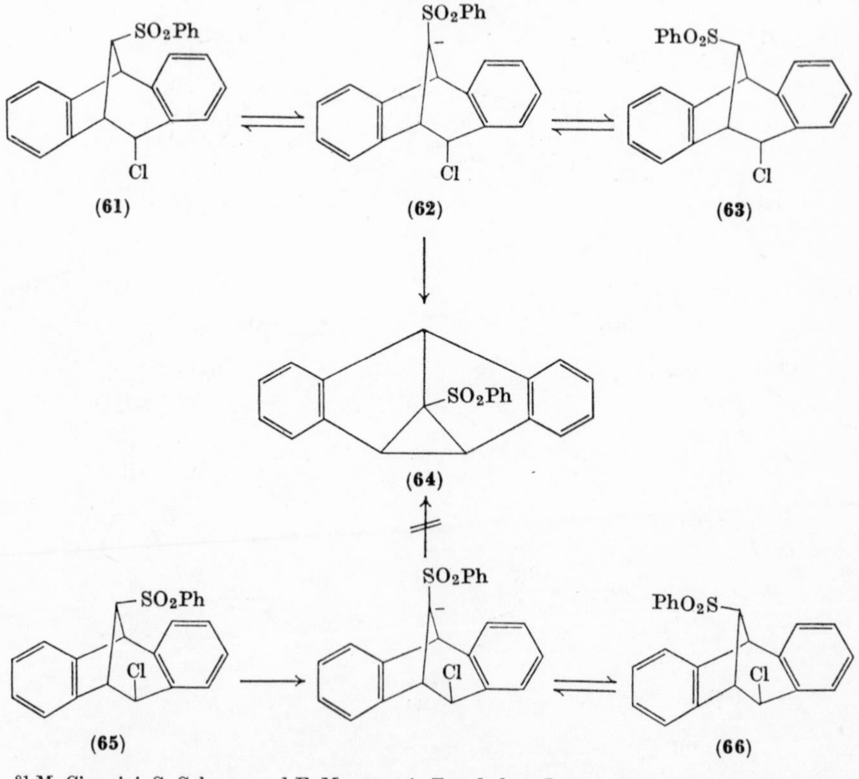

(61)   (62)   (63)

(64)

(65)   (66)

[81] M. Cinquini, S. Colonna and F. Montanari, *Tetrahedron Letters*, **1966**, 3181; H. Hogeveen, G. Maccagnani, and F. Montanari, *J. Chem. Soc., C*, **1966**, 1585.

which proceeds 7.2 times faster than that of $Me_2CHCH_2CMe_2CH_2CMe_2Cl$, to yield 79% of a pyrrolidinium salt and 12% of olefin.[82]

The chlorosulphones (**61**) and (**63**) are rapidly interconverted by sodium ethoxide in ethanol to yield a mixture which contains a slight excess of the *anti*-isomer (**63**). This reaction presumably proceeds via the carbanion (**62**) and this reacts, more slowly, with intramolecular displacement to yield the cyclopropane derivative (**64**). The *syn-exo*-chloride (**65**) is also converted to the *anti*-isomer (**66**) by sodium methoxide, but the reverse reaction does not occur, the equilibrium mixture consisting, understandably, of the *anti*-isomer exclusively. Formation of (**64**) occurred only on treatment with potassium *tert*-butoxide in dimethyl sulphoxide, presumably after a base-promoted isomerization to the *endo*-chloro-compounds.[83]

The yield of cyclopropane formed through carbanion participation when compounds $PhCH_2CHRCH_2SOCH_3$ are treated with "dimsylsodium" in dimethyl sulphoxide increases with the size of R from 0% when R = H to 97% when R = Bu^t [see equation (9)].[84]

$$PhCH_2CHRCH_2SOMe \longrightarrow Ph\bar{C}HCHRCH_2SOMe \longrightarrow PhCH{\overset{\displaystyle CHR}{\underset{\displaystyle CH_2}{|}}}$$

(9)

Acetolysis of 1-adamantyl toluene-*p*-sulphonate (**67**) yields 93—94% of the ring-expanded acetate (**69**) and 6—7% of the unrearranged acetate (**68**).[85]

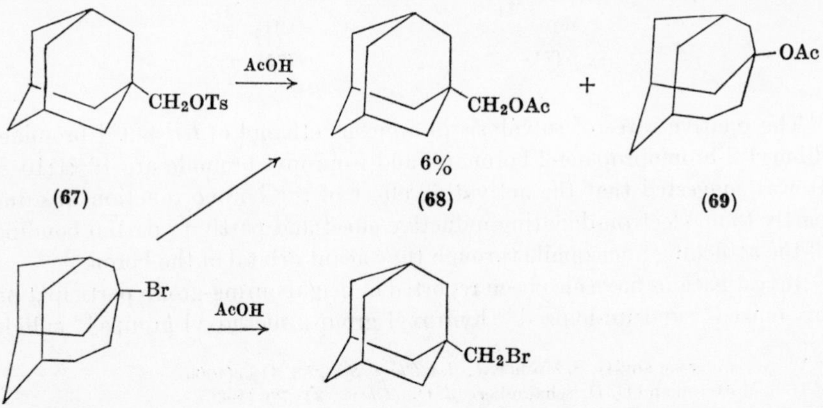

$$\begin{array}{cccc} (67) & & (68) & (69) \end{array}$$

6%

(70)

[82] A. M. Braun, C. E. Ebner, C. A. Grob, and F. A. Jenny, *Tetrahedron Letters*, 1965, 4733.
[83] S. J. Cristol and B. B. Jarvis, *J. Am. Chem. Soc.*, 88, 3095 (1966); see also, S. J. Cristol, J. K. Harrington, and M. S. Singer, *ibid.*, p. 1529.
[84] R. Baker and M. J. Spillett, *Chem. Commun.*, 1966, 757.
[85] J. E. Nordlander, S. P. Jindal, P. von R. Schleyer, R. C. Fort, J. J. Harper, and R. D. Nicholas, *J. Am. Chem. Soc.*, 88, 4475 (1966).

Acetolysis of 3-homoadamantyl bromide (70) yields the same products in the same proportions plus some adamantylmethyl bromide which is stable under the reaction conditions. The rate of acetolysis of (67) is slightly greater than that of neopentyl toluene-p-sulphonate which involves a similar rearrangement. It was therefore concluded that the migrating methyl group of the neopentyl compound cannot be providing anchimeric assistance, for it was thought that, if it were, this would be much reduced with the 1-adamantyl methyl compound in which the corresponding migration of a methylene group results in conversion of the strain-free adamantyl structure into the less stable homoadamantyl one. It was therefore concluded that these migrations must occur after the rate-determining steps; e.g. as in equation (10).

$$\text{Me}_3\text{C—CH}_2\text{OTs} \rightarrow \text{Me}_3\text{C—CH}_2{}^+ \ {}^-\text{OTs} \rightarrow \text{Me}_2\overset{+}{\text{C}}\text{—CH}_2\text{Me} \ {}^-\text{OTs} \rightarrow \text{Products} \qquad (10)$$

On the other hand, it has been shown that the "de-oxidation" of (S)-1-deuterioneopentyl alcohol (71) with bromoform and potassium hydroxide proceeds stereospecifically, to yield (S)-3-deuterio-2-methylbut-1-ene (72) with inversion of configuration. It was thought, therefore, that the reaction did not involve a free neopentyl cation but that migration of the methyl group was concerted with carbon–oxygen bond breaking.[86]

(71)   (72)

The relative rates of solvolysis in aqueous ethanol of *tert*-butyl bromide, dibutyl 2-bromopropane-2-boronate, and isopropyl bromide are $10^2:1:10^{-2}$. It was suggested that the activating effect of the borono function was due partly to an electron-donating inductive effect and partly to partial bonding of the attacking nucleophile through the vacant orbital of the boron.[87]

Investigations have also been reported of neighbouring-group participation by ionized[88] and un-ionized[89] hydroxyl groups, methoxyl groups,[90] sulfide

[86] W. A. Sanderson and H. S. Mosher, *J. Am. Chem. Soc.*, **88**, 4185 (1966).

[87] D. S. Matteson and G. D. Schaumberg, *J. Org. Chem.*, **31**, 726 (1966).

[88] R. E. Pincock and T. E. Kiovsky, *J. Am. Chem. Soc.*, **88**, 4455 (1966); J. Myszkowski, A. Z. Zielinski, and E. Laskowska, *Przemysl Chem.*, **44**, 565 (1965); *Chem. Abs.* **64**, 6427 (1966); N. I. Shuikin, M. Bartok, and B. Kozma, *Izv. Akad. Nauk SSSR, Ser. Khim.*, **1966**, 878; *Chem. Abs.*, **65**, 10458 (1966).

[89] B. L. Phillips and P. A. Argabright, *J. Heterocyclic Chem.*, **3**, 84 (1966); N. Baggett, J. M. Duxbury, A. B. Foster, and J. M. Webber, *J. Chem. Soc.*, *C*, **1966**, 208; A. T. Rowland, *Steroids*, **7**, 527 (1966).

[90] A. Kirrmann and L. Wartski-Froim, *Rev. Roumaine Chim.*, **10**, 1277 (1965).

groups,[91] amino-groups,[92] a thioureido-group,[93] and a diphenylphosphine group.[94a]

Important applications of neighbouring-group participation in synthesis have also been reported.[94b]

Isotope Effects[95]

The equilibrium constant for the reaction

$$(CH_3)_3CCl + (CD)_3C^+ \overset{K}{\rightleftharpoons} (CH_3)_3C^+ + (CD_3)_3CCl$$

has been calculated, from the vibrational frequencies of the chlorides and ions, to be 2.358 at 25° and 2.511 at 5.686°. This is the ratio of the constants for the equilibria:

$$(CH_3)_3CCl \overset{K_H}{\rightleftharpoons} (CH_3)_3C^+ + Cl^-$$

$$(CD_3)_3CCl \overset{K_D}{\rightleftharpoons} (CD_3)_3C^+ + Cl^-$$

and $K = K_H/K_D$. The close similarity of the numerical results to those for the kinetic isotope effect for the solvolyses of these chlorides in 50:50 ethanol water, $k_H/k_D = 2.387$ at 25° and 2.542 at 5.686°, suggests that the transition states are structurally similar to the carbonium ions.[96]

Secondary deuterium isotope effects attributed to the larger steric requirements of hydrogen than of deuterium have been reported.[97a] Thus 2,6-di-[²H₃]methylpyridine reacts 9% faster than the undeuteriated compound with methyl iodide (see also, ref. 31, p. 115).

Kinetic deuterium and carbon-13 isotope effects for the exchange reaction with iodide ion and the hydrolysis of methyl iodide have also been reported.[97b]

[91] S. Lamdan, C. M. Vaga, and C. H. Gaozza, *J. Med. Chem.*, **9**, 79 (1966); W. Davis and W. C. J. Ross, *ibid.*, **8**, 757 (1965).
[92] J. Rabinowitz, S. Jaccard, C. Moghissi, and M. Verdan, *Chimia*, **20**, 20 (1966); E. Cherbuliez, S. Colak-Antic, and J. Rabinowitz, *Arch. Sci. (Geneva)*, **18**, 282 (1965); *Chem. Abs.*, **64**, 1913 (1966); H. M. Raven and H. Palla, *Arzneimittel Forsch.*, **16**, 40 (1966); N. J. Leonard, *Record Chem. Prog.*, **26**, 211 (1965); O. E. Edwards, G. Fodor, and L. Marion, *Can. J. Chem.*, **44**, 13 (1966); V. R. Gaertner, *Tetrahedron Letters*, **1966**, 4691; L. S. Yaguzhinskii and A. D. Chinaeva, *Zh. Obshch. Khim.*, **36**, 671 (1966); *Chem. Abs.*, **65**, 8700 (1966); H. Patel and G. Hite, *J. Org. Chem.*, **30**, 4336, 4337 (1965).
[93] E. Cherbuliez, H. Jindra, and J. Rabinowitz, *Helv. Chim. Acta*, **49**, 1951 (1966).
[94a] R. W. Turner and A. H. Soloway, *J. Org. Chem.*, **30**, 4031 (1965).
[94b] B. R. Baker and T. L. Hullar, *J. Org. Chem.*, **30**, 4038, 4045, 4049, 4053, (1965); E. J. Reist, L. V. Fischer, and D. E. Gueffroy, *ibid.*, **31**, 226 (1966).
[95] See P. Lazlo and Z. Welvart, *Bull. Soc. Chim. France*, **1966**, 2412.
[96] J. C. Evans and G. Y.-S. Lo, *J. Am. Chem. Soc.*, **88**, 2118 (1966).
[97a] H. C. Brown and G. J. McDonald, *J. Am. Chem. Soc.*, **88**, 2514 (1966); H. C. Brown, M. E. Azzaro, J. G. Koeling, and G. J. McDonald, *ibid.*, p. 2520; see also, C. Heitner and K. T. Leffek, *Can. J. Chem.*, **44**, 2567 (1966).
[97b] A. V. Willi, *Can. J. Chem.*, **44**, 1889 (1966).

Deaminations and Related Reactions

Whiting, in his Tilden Lecture,[98] has summarized much of his hitherto unpublished work in which the products of decomposition of aliphatic diazonium ions generated in various ways are compared with one another,[99] with the products from the solvolyses of the corresponding nitrobenzenesulphonates, and with those from additions to the corresponding olefins. The occurrence of hydride shifts in all these reactions, when carbonium ions are intermediates, was emphasized and examples were reported of reactions of these ions before establishment of equilibrium in solvation and in conformation of the polymethylene chain.

Hydride shifts occurring in the deamination of [2,6-$^2H_2$]cyclohexylamine have been investigated.[100]

As well as yielding olefins and substitution products, deamination of *n*-butylamine, isobutylamine, and *sec*-butylamine in aprotic solvents (e.g., $CHCl_3$) yields some methylcyclopropane, possibly formed by way of a protonated cyclopropane as shown in Scheme 3. It was also shown that hydride shifts occur much less on deamination of *n*-butylamine in aprotic solvents than in aqueous acetic acid.[101]

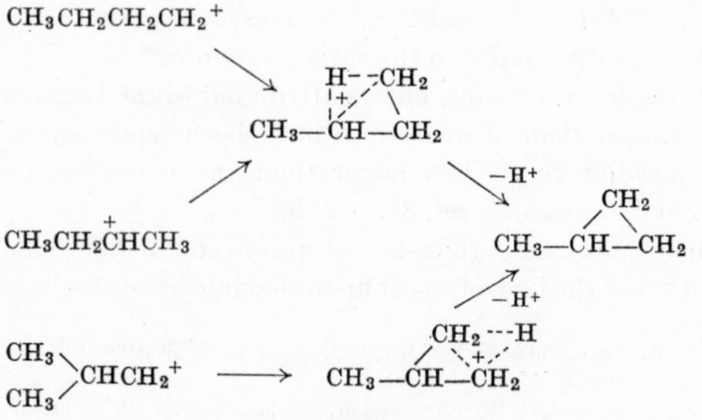
CH3CH2CH2CH2+
H--CH2
CH3—CH—CH2
−H+
CH2
CH3—CH—CH2
CH3CH2CHCH3
−H+
CH2---H
CH3
CHCH2+
CH3
CH3—CH—CH2

Scheme 3

Deamination of the substituted phenethylamine (**73**) yields products in which there has been approximately 40% of migration of the phenyl group. It was hoped that the intermediate (**74**) would be trapped as the dispiro compound (**75**), but products derived from this, i.e., (**76**) and (**77**), were not obtained.[102]

[98] M. C. Whiting, *Chem. Brit.*, **2**, 482 (1966).
[99] See *Organic Reaction Mechanisms*, **1966**, 66.
[100] Y. G. Bundel, V. A. Savin, M. N. Ryabtsev, and O. A. Reutov, *Dokl. Akad. Nauk SSSR*. **165**, 1303 (1965); *Chem. Abs.*, **64**, 9527 (1966); Y. G. Bundel, V. A. Savin, A. A. Lubovich, and O. A. Reutov, *Dokl. Akad. Nauk SSSR*, **165**, 1078 (1965); *Chem. Abs.*, **64**, 11048 (1966).
[101] J. H. Bayless, F. D. Mendicino, and L. Friedman, *J. Am. Chem. Soc.*, **87**, 5790 (1965).
[102] M. C. Caserio, R. D. Levin, and J. D. Roberts, *J. Am. Chem. Soc.*, **87**, 5651 (1965).

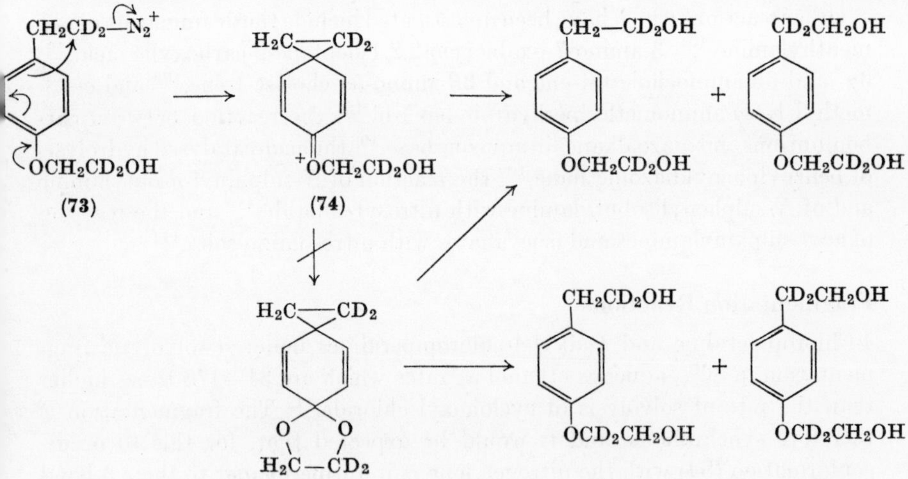

(73) → (74) → (76), (77)

(75) → (76), (77)

Treatment of 3-pyrrolines with nitrohydroxylamine gives dienes in high yield. *trans*-2,5-Dimethyl-3-pyrroline (**78**) yielded *cis,trans*-hexa-2,4-diene (**79**), and the *cis*-pyrroline (**80**) yielded *trans,trans*-hexa-2,4-diene (**81**).[103] The reactions therefore proceed with bond rotations as shown in (**83**), termed a sigmasymmetric process, rather than as in (**82**), an axisymmetric process. The sigmasymmetric process was shown to be the one expected from orbital-overlap considerations (see also, p. 156).

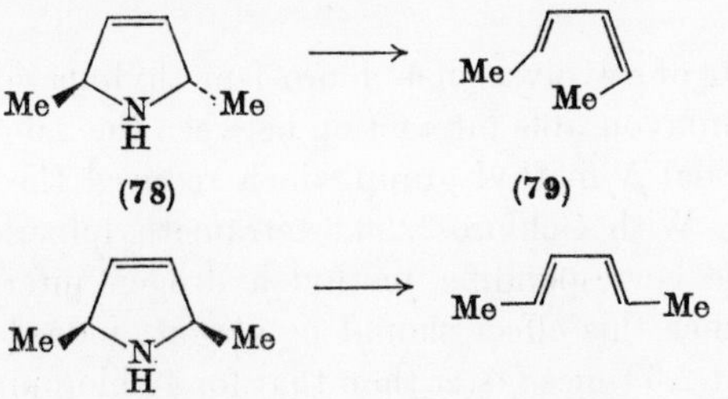

(78) → (79)

(80) → (81)

Axisymmetric (82)   Sigmasymmetric (83)

[103] D. M. Lemal and S. D. McGregor, *J. Am. Chem. Soc.*, **88**, 1335 (1966); see also, W. L. Mock, *ibid.*, p. 2857; S. D. McGregor and D. M. Lemal, *ibid.*, p. 2858.

Other reactions which have been investigated include the deamination of iso-menthylamine,[104] 3-amino-7-oxabicyclo[2.2.1]heptane-2-carboxylic acid,[105] 3α- and 3β-aminocholest-4-ene and 3β-amino-5α-cholest-1-ene,[106] and cis-8-methyl-1-exo-aminomethylperhydroinden-1-ol,[107] the reaction between carbonium ions and diazoalkanes in aqueous base,[108] the acid-catalysed hydrolysis of benzoylphenyldiazomethane,[109] the reaction of N-sulphinyl-n-butylamine and of N-sulphenylisobutylamine with nitrosyl chloride,[110] and the reaction of acyl-sulphinylamines and isocyanates with nitrosonium salts.[111]

Fragmentation Reactions

4-Chloropiperidine and 1-alkyl-4-chloropiperidines undergo solvolytic fragmentation in 80% aqueous ethanol at rates which are 34—178 times higher than the rate of solvolysis of cyclohexyl chloride.[112] The fragmentation is therefore synchronous, and it would be expected that, for this to occur, conformation (84) with the nitrogen lone pair antiperiplanar to the 2,3-bond and the N-alkyl group or hydrogen axial would be necessary. Consistent with this, introduction of 2,2,6,6-tetramethyl substituents caused a 15-fold

(84)

decrease in the rate of solvolysis of 4-chloro-1-methylpiperidine owing, it was suggested, to an unfavourable interaction between the 2,6-equatorial methyl groups and the axial N-methyl group which reduced the concentration of this conformation. With 4-chloro-2,2,6,6-tetramethylpiperidine it would be expected that the corresponding methyl–hydrogen interaction would be negligible, and hence this effect should be absent; indeed the rate for this compound is about 2.5 times faster than that for 4-chloropiperidine.

[104] W. Hückel and N. C. Franklin, *Chem. Ber.*, **99**, 353 (1966).
[105] N. S. Zefirov, R. A. Ivanova, R. S. Filatova, and Y. Z. Yur'ev, *J. Gen. Chem. U.S.S.R.*, **35**, 1794 (1966).
[106] C. W. Shoppee, J. K. Hummer, R. E. Lack, P. Ram, and S. K. Roy, *Tetrahedron*, **1966**, Suppl. No. 7, 315.
[107] G. Di Maio and P. A. Tardella, *Tetrahedron*, **22**, 2069 (1966).
[108] R. A. Moss, *J. Org. Chem.*, **31**, 1082 (1966).
[109] J. B. F. N. Engeberts, N. F. Bosch, and B. Zwanenburg, *Rec. Trav. Chim.*, **85**, 1068 (1966).
[110] M. Kobayashi and K. Honda, *Bull. Chem. Soc. Japan*, **39**, 1778 (1966).
[111] G. A. Olah, N. Friedman, J. M. Bollinger, and J. Lukas, *J. Am. Chem. Soc.*, **88**, 5328 (1966).
[112] R. D'Arcy, C. A. Grob, T. Kaffenberger, and V. Krasnobajew, *Helv. Chim. Acta*, **49**, 185 (1966); R. Fankhauser, C. A. Grob and V. Krasnobajew, *ibid.*, p. 690.

The solvolyses of the *p*-nitrobenzoate esters (**85**) and (**86**) in aqueous dioxan proceed at similar rates, and both occur with fragmentation.[113] This was thought to occur after initial ionization, rather than synchronously with it, since only compound (**85**) has the correct stereochemistry for the synchronous reaction.

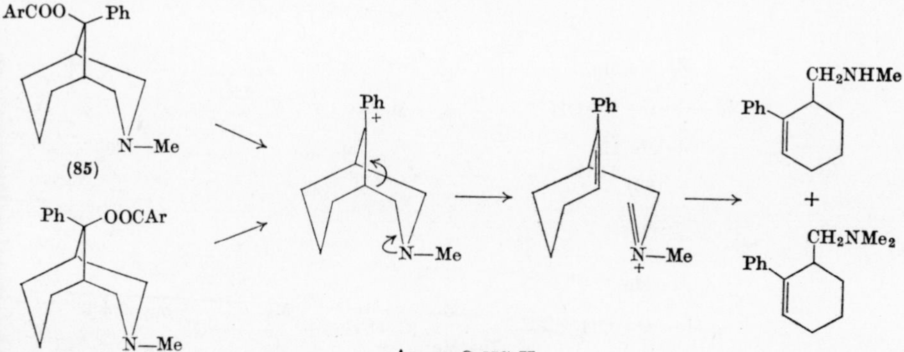

Ar = *p*-$O_2NC_6H_4$

Fragmentation of carbonium ion (**88**) did not occur when it was formed irreversibly in the solvolysis of chloride (**87**) but, instead, olefin (**89**) was

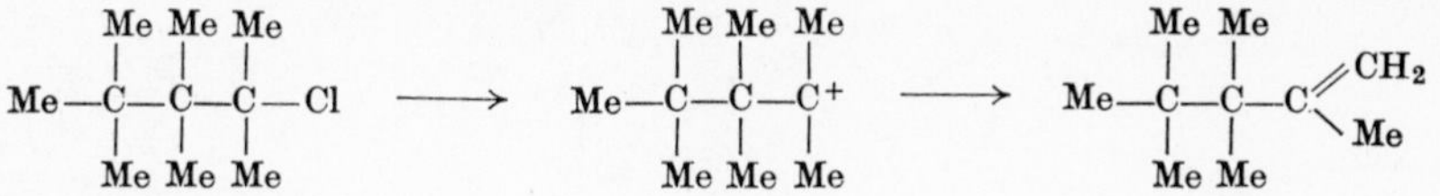

formed.[114] However, when the ion was generated reversibly from olefin (**93**) or alcohol (**92**) by the action of sulphuric acid in aqueous dioxan a slow fragmentation was observed. The dehydration of alcohol (**90**) and the conversion of the resulting olefin (**91**) into olefin (**93**) by a methyl migration were also investigated. The second-order rate constants (l. mole^{-1} sec^{-1}) for these processes (temperature unspecified) are given in Scheme 4. The migration of a *tert*-butyl group was also shown to occur in ion (**95**). When olefin [(**94**)≡(**93**)] was dissolved in D_2SO_4–dioxan there was first a slow exchange of protons *c* [see (**94**)], corresponding to carbonium ion formation ($k = 5 \times 10^{-5}$ l. mole^{-1} sec^{-1}). This was followed by exchange of protons *b*, indicating that migration

113 H. O. House, and W. M. Bryant, *J. Org. Chem.*, **31**, 3482 (1966).
114 V. J. Shiner and G. F. Meier, *J. Org. Chem.*, **31**, 137 (1966).

3*

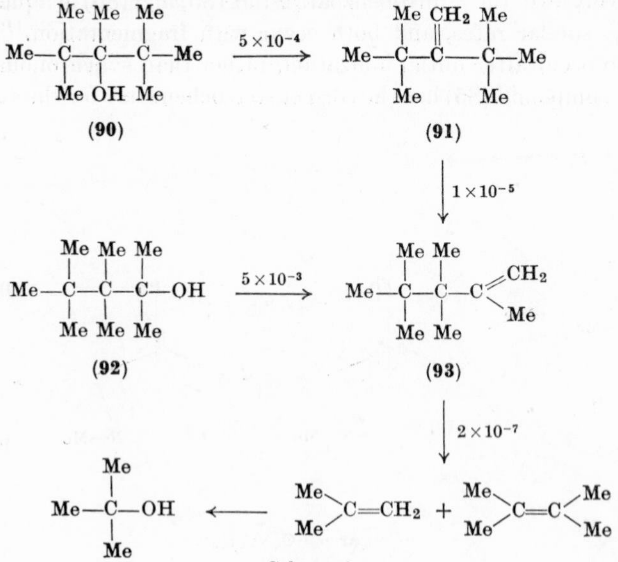

$$
\underset{(90)}{\overset{\displaystyle \underset{\displaystyle \text{Me}}{\overset{\displaystyle \text{Me Me Me}}{\text{Me}-\text{C}-\text{C}-\text{C}-\text{Me}}}}{\underset{\text{OH}}{}}} \quad \xrightarrow{\;5\times10^{-4}\;} \quad \underset{(91)}{\overset{\displaystyle \text{Me CH}_2\ \text{Me}}{\text{Me}-\text{C}-\text{C}-\text{C}-\text{Me}}}
$$

Me Me Me
Me—C—C—C—Me 5×10^{-4} Me CH₂ Me
    | | | ⟶   Me—C—C——C—Me
    Me OH Me | |
                                      Me   Me
      (90)   **(91)**

$\downarrow\, 1\times10^{-5}$

Me Me Me
Me—C—C—C—OH 5×10^{-3} Me Me
    | | | ⟶   Me—C—C—C⟨CH₂
    Me Me Me | | Me
                                      Me Me
      (92)   **(93)**

$\downarrow\, 2\times10^{-7}$

    Me   Me⟍   Me⟍   ⟋Me
    | C=CH₂ +   C=C
Me—C—OH   ⟵   Me⟋   Me⟋   ⟍Me
    |
    Me

Scheme 4

                    Me Me
                Me—C—C—C⟨CH₂   **(94)**
                    | | Me
                    Me Me
                 (a) (b)   (c)

‖

  Me   Me⟍   ⟋Me   Me Me Me   Me Me Me
  | C=C | | | | | |
Me—C⁺ +   Me⟋   ⟍Me   ⟵   Me—C—C—C⁺   ⇌   ⁺C—C—C—Me
  | | | | | | |
  Me   Me Me Me   Me Me Me
  (96)   **(95)**   **(97)**

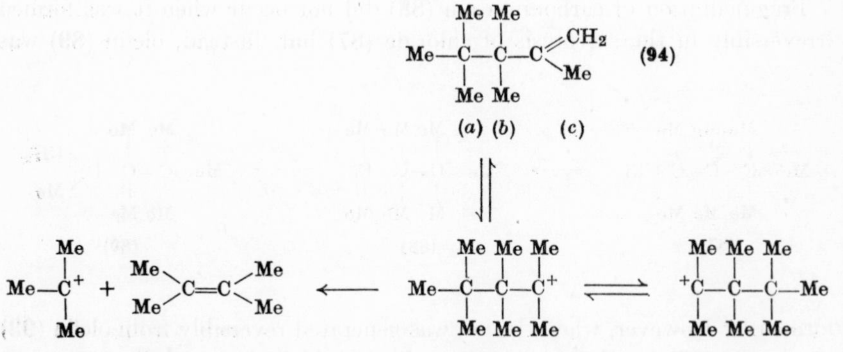

of the *tert*-butyl group had occurred ($k = 7 \times 10^{-7}$ l. mole^{-1} sec^{-1}). No exchange of protons *a* was observed, however, indicating that migration of a methyl group in carbonium ion **(95)** does not occur. It was thus estimated that for every 200 cations **(95)** formed, three undergo *tert*-butyl migration (**95** → **97**) and one fragments (**95** → **96**).[114]

Two interesting fragmentations are observed when the unsaturated methanesulphonate **(98)** is treated with diborane.[115] The product is an 85:15 mixture of hydrocarbons **(100)** and **(102)**, thought to be formed by

115 J. A. Marshall and G. L. Bundy, *J. Am. Chem. Soc.*, **88**, 4291 (1966).

fragmentation of the initially produced boranes (**99**) and (**101**). (For a similar example see ref. 46, p. 120.)

(**98**) (**99**) (**100**) (**101**) (**102**)

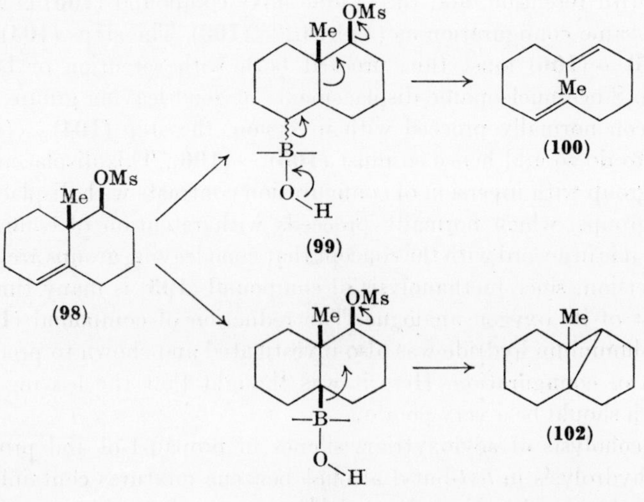

The fragmentation of 1,2-diaryl-4-dimethylamino-3-methylbut-2-yl chloride,[116] 3-aminothietan dioxides,[117] and 1,2-cyclohexylidene-5-*O*-mesyl-D-glucofuranuronic acid hydrazide[118] have also been described.

Displacement Reactions at Elements other than Carbon

Displacement reactions at silicon[119] and phosphorus[120] have been reviewed.

The steric course of nucleophilic displacements of compounds with silicon–sulphur bonds has been investigated by Sommer and McLink[121] who carried

$$2\,(+)\text{-}R_3Si^*H \;\longrightarrow\; 2\,(-)\text{-}R_3Si^*Cl \;\xrightarrow[Et_3N]{H_2S}\; (+)\text{-}R_3\overset{*}{Si}\text{—}S\text{—}Si^*R_3$$

(**103**) (**104**) (**105**)

$$(105) \xrightarrow{MeOH,\ Et_2NH} (+)\text{-}R_3Si^*S^-\,Et_2NH_2^+ \;+\; (+)\text{-}R_3Si^*OMe$$

(**107**) (**106**)

[116] A. F. Casy, J. L. Myers, and P. Pocha, *Tetrahedron*, **22**, 1001 (1966).
[117] L. A. Paquette and M. Rosen, *Tetrahedron Letters*, **1966**, 311.
[118] H. Paulsen and D. Stoye, *Chem. Ber.*, **99**, 908 (1966).
[119] G. Schott, *Z. Chem.*, **6**, 361 (1966).
[120] R. F. Hudson, "Structure and Mechanism in Organophosphorus Chemistry", Academic Press, New York, N.Y., 1965.
[121] L. H. Sommer and J. McLick, *J. Am. Chem. Soc.*, **88**, 5359 (1966).

out the sequence of reactions (**103**) → (**107**) (R_3Si = methyl-α-naphthyl-phenylsilyl).[121] Chlorination of the hydride, (**103**) → (**104**), is known to proceed with retention, and the (+)-methoxy-compound (**106**) is known to have the same configuration as (+)-hydride (**103**). The steps (**104**) → (**105**) and (**105**) → (**106**) must thus proceed both with retention or both with inversion. Since nucleophilic displacements of good leaving groups (e.g., Cl) from silicon normally proceed with inversion, the step (**104**) → (**105**) was thought to do so and hence so must (**105**) → (**106**). This displacement of a sulphur group with inversion of configuration contrasts with displacement of oxygen groups, which normally proceeds with retention of configuration; however, it is in accord with the concept that good leaving groups are displaced with inversion, since methanolysis of compound (**105**) is many times faster than that of its oxygen analogue. The reduction of compound (**107**) with lithium aluminium hydride was also investigated and shown to proceed with retention of configuration. Here it was thought that the leaving group is S^{2-}, which should be a very poor one.

The alcoholysis of acyloxytriarylsilanes in propan-1-ol and propan-2-ol, and the hydrolysis in *tert*-butyl alcohol–benzene mixtures containing water [equation (11)] has been investigated:[122]

$$Ar_3SiOCOR + ROH \rightarrow Ar_3SiOR + RCO_2H \tag{11}$$

The reactions are catalysed by acetate ions, and the rates are enhanced by electron-withdrawing substituents in the aryl ring, decreased by electron-releasing substituents in the aryl ring, and enhanced by electron-withdrawing substituents in acyl group. Clearly both bond-forming and bond-breaking have developed in the transition state.

General-base catalysis by acetate and phenoxide ions has been demonstrated for the methanolysis of phenoxytriphenylsilane; the approximate value of β is 0.7.[123]

Nucleophilic displacement reactions of organosilicon hydrides[124] and the condensation of silanediols[125] have also been investigated.

An electron-impact study of the ionization and dissociation of trimethylsilane has been reported.[126]

122 G. Schott, H. Kelling, and R. Schild, *Chem. Ber.*, **99**, 291 (1966); G. Schott and K. Deibel, *ibid.*, p. 301.
123 R. L. Schowen and K. S. Latham, *J. Am. Chem. Soc.*, **88**, 3795 (1966).
124 V. O. Reikhsfel'd and V. A. Prokhovova, *Zh. Obshch. Khim.*, **35**, 182, 1826, 1830 (1965); J. Hetflejš, F. Mareš, and V. Chvalovský, *Coll. Czech. Chem. Commun.*, **31**, 586 (1966); V. O. Reisfel'd, *Intern. Symp. Organosilicon Chem.*, *Sci. Commun. Suppl.*, *Prague*, 1965, 34; *Chem. Abs.*, 10448 (1966); V. V. Korol'ko and V. O. Reikhsfel'd, *Reaksionnaya Sposobnost Organ. Soedin. Tartusk. Gos. Univ.*, **2**, 98 (1965); *Chem. Abs.*, **64**, 1917 (1966).
125 Z. Lasocki and Z. Michalska, *Bull. Acad. Polon. Sci.*, *Ser. Sci. Chim.*, **13**, 261, 597 (1965); J. Chojnowski and S. Chrzczonowicz, *ibid.*, **14**, 17 (1966).
126 G. G. Hess, F. W. Lampe, and L. H. Sommer, *J. Am. Chem. Soc.*, **87**, 5327 (1965).

An interesting intramolecular nucleophilic displacement from sulphur occurs when *cis*-3-thiocyanatoacrylamide is dissolved in buffers of pH 0—5.5. It was thought that in the pH range 5.5—3.5 the ionized form undergoes cyclization, but that at pH's less than 3.0 the neutral molecule does this (see Scheme 5).[127] The latter conclusion is of considerable interest since, if correct, this reaction provides an example of participation by an un-ionized amide group proceeding with exclusive *N*-attack (on sulphur) when *O*-attack would lead to a ring of equal size (see also, p. 55).

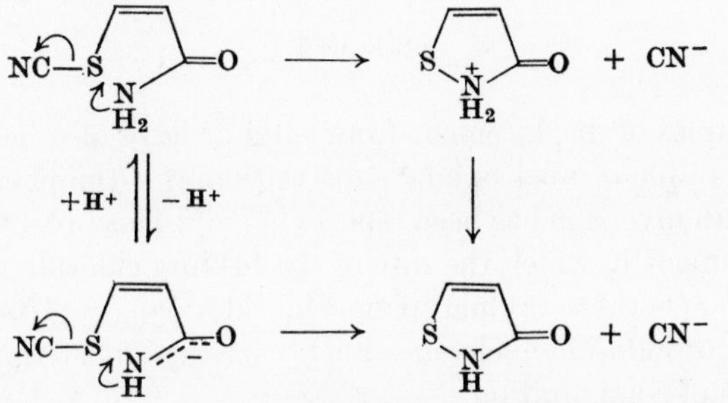

Scheme 5

Alkyl sulphides have a striking catalytic effect on the sulphuric acid-catalysed hydrolysis of the sulphinyl sulphones (**108**), tetrahydrothiophen being particularly effective. A mechanism involving nucleophilic–electrophilic catalysis, consistent with the low energy of activation (6.5 kcal mole^{-1}) and strongly negative entropy of activation (−40 e.u.), was proposed.[128]

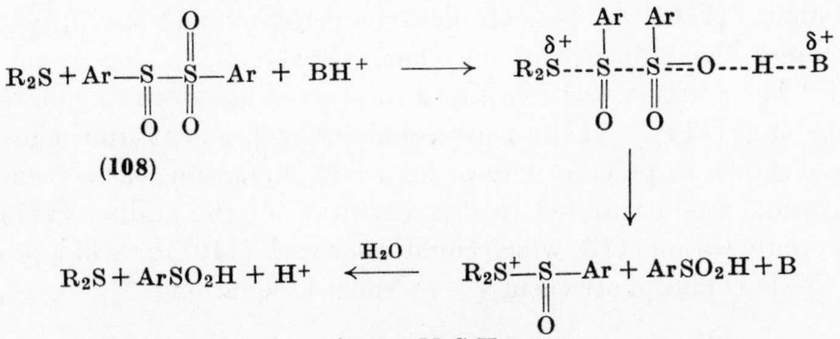

$$Ar = p\text{-MeC}_6\text{H}_4$$

Predominant inversion of configuration (98%) in a nucleophilic displacement from sulphur has been observed by performing the cycle of reactions given in Scheme 6.[129]

[127] W. D. Crow and I. Gosney, *Austral. J. Chem.*, **19**, 1693 (1966).
[128] J. L. Kice and G. Guaraldi, *Tetrahedron Letters*, **1966**, 501.
[129] C. R. Johnson and D. McCants, *J. Am. Chem. Soc.*, **87**, 5404 (1965).

$$\text{(+)} \quad \underset{C_6H_4Me\text{-}p}{\overset{\ddot{S}}{O}}\!\!\diagdown\!\!CH_2C_6H_5 \quad \xrightarrow{\quad Et_3O^+ \ BF_4^- \quad} \quad \text{(+)} \quad \underset{C_6H_4Me\text{-}p}{\overset{\overset{\ddot{}}{S}^+}{EtO}}\!\!\diagdown\!\!CH_2C_6H_5 \quad \overline{\ }BF_4$$

$$\Bigg\uparrow -OH \qquad\qquad\qquad\qquad\qquad\qquad\qquad\qquad \Bigg\downarrow -OH$$

$$\text{(}-\text{)} \ C_6H_5CH_2 \cdots \underset{C_6H_4Me\text{-}p}{\overset{\overset{+}{S}}{\diagup}}\!\!\diagdown\!\!OEt \quad \overset{BF_4^-}{\underset{\ }{\xleftarrow{\quad Et_3O^+ \ BF_4^- \quad}}} \quad \text{(}-\text{)} \ C_6H_5CH_2 \underset{p\text{-}MeC_6H_4}{\overset{\ddot{S}}{\diagup}}\!\!=\!\!O$$

Scheme 6

Other examples of displacement from sulphur have also been reported.[130] Another example of nucleophilic substitution at a thiophosphonyl centre proceeding with inversion has been reported.[131, 132] This involved the classical type of experiment in which the rate of the lithium chloride-promoted racemization of (−)-O-ethyl ethylphosphonochloridothionate (109) was found to be twice that of chloride exchange. Each exchange must therefore proceed with inversion of configuration.

$$LiCl^* + \underset{Et}{\overset{EtO}{\diagdown}}\!\!\underset{\underset{S}{\|}}{P}\!\!-\!\!Cl \quad \longrightarrow \quad \underset{Et}{\overset{EtO}{\diagdown}}\!\!\underset{\underset{S}{\|}}{P}\!\!-\!\!Cl^* + LiCl$$

$$\text{(}-\text{)}\,(109) \qquad\qquad\qquad\qquad\qquad \text{(}+\text{)}\,(109)$$

The steric course of the condensation of (−)-O-ethyl hydrogen ethylthiophosphonate (110) to (+)-O,O-diethyl diethylmonothiopyrophosphonate (112) under the influence of dicyclohexylcarbodiimide has been investigated.[133] The reaction was considered to proceed as shown in equation (12), with the step (111) → (112) a nucleophilic displacement from phosphorus. This was shown to proceed with at least 50% inversion; the accompanying racemization was attributed to decomposition of the adduct (111) into a phosphonium cation (113) which could react with (110) to yield a product in which the P–O phosphorus centre is racemized [equation (13)].

[130] T. Nakabayashi, S. Kawamura, T. Kitao, and J. Tsurigi, *J. Org. Chem.*, **31**, 861 (1966), S. Kawamura, T. Nakabayashi, T. Kitao, and J. Tsurigi, *ibid.*, p. 1985; J. Cifka and V. Vins, *J. Labelled Compds.*, **1**, 189 (1965); M. Kobayashi and M. Terao, *Bull. Chem. Soc. Japan*; **39**, 1343 (1966); R. T. van Aller, R. B. Scott, and E. L. Brocklebank, *J. Org. Chem.*, **31**, 2357 (1966); R. E. Davis, J. B. Louis, and A. Cohen, *J. Am. Chem. Soc.*, **88**, 1 (1966); E. S. Wagner and R. E. Davis, *ibid.*, p. 5940.

[131] J. Michalski, M. Mikolajczyk, A. Halpern, and K. Prószyńska, *Tetrahedron Letters*, **1966**, 1919; J. Michalski, and M. Mikolajczyk, *Tetrahedron*, **22**, 3055 (1966).

[132] See *Organic Reaction Mechanisms*, **1965**, 70—71.

[133] M. Mikolajczyk, *Chem. Ber.*, **99**, 2083 (1966).

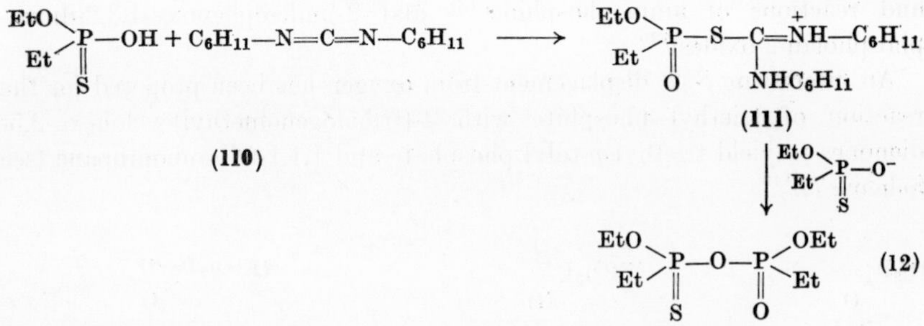

$$EtO, \!\!\diagdown P\!\!-\!\!OH + C_6H_{11}\!\!-\!\!N\!\!=\!\!C\!\!=\!\!N\!\!-\!\!C_6H_{11} \longrightarrow$$

(110)

(111)

(12)

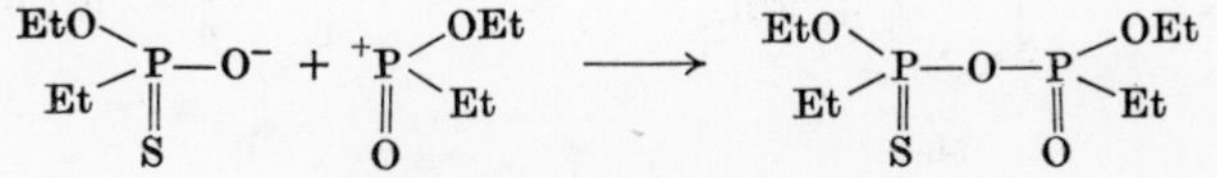

(112)

(13)

(113)

The rates of the HO^--promoted decomposition of a series of benzyl-*o*-tolyl-phosphonium salts were only slightly slower than those of the analogous *p*-tolyl compounds.[134] This absence of steric effects was attributed to counter-balancing of the unfavourable increase in non-bonding interactions in the initial addition step (14) by the favourable decrease in the carbanion-expulsion step (16):

$$R_4P^+ + HO^- \underset{}{\overset{Fast}{\rightleftharpoons}} R_4POH \tag{14}$$

$$R_4POH + HO^- \underset{}{\overset{Fast}{\rightleftharpoons}} R_4PO^- + H_2O \tag{15}$$

$$R_4PO^- \longrightarrow R_3PO^- + R^- \tag{16}$$

$$R^- + H_2O \longrightarrow RH + HO^- \tag{17}$$

The reactions of tetraphenylstibonium salts with bases have also been investigated.[135]

Other nucleophilic displacement reactions involving phosphorus, which have been investigated, include the alkaline ring opening of 1-methyl-1,2,5-triphenylphospholium iodide and 1-methyl-1,2,3,4,5-pentaphenylphospho-lium iodide,[136] the alkaline hydrolysis of tetrahedral phosphorus derivatives,[137]

[134] R. U. Pagilagan and W. E. McEwen, *Chem. Commun.*, **1966**, 652.
[135] G. H. Briles and W. E. McEwen, *Tetrahedron Letters*, **1966**, 5191, 5299.
[136] K. Bergesen, *Acta Chem. Scand.*, **20**, 899 (1966).
[137] S. M. Markov, A. M. Polekhin, N. A. Loshadkin, G. A. Kostenko, Z. V. Morozova, and M. M. Yakubovich, *Zh. Obsch. Khim.*, **36**, 1098 (1966); *Chem. Abs.*, **65**, 13467 (1966); N. A. Loshadkin, S. M. Markov, A. M. Polekhin, A. A. Neimysheva, F. L. Maklyaev, and I. L. Knunyants, *Zh. Obshch. Khim.*, **36**, 1105 (1966); *Chem. Abs.*, **65**, 13467 (1966); I. L. Knunyants, N. A. Loshadkin, A. A. Neimysheva, S. M. Markov, and A. M. Polekhin, *Reaktsionnaya Sposobnost Organ. Soedin. Tartusk. Gos. Univ.*, **2**, 236 (1965); *Chem. Abs.*, **65**, 13468 (1966).

and reactions of aminophosphines[138] and 2-p-nitrophenoxy-1,3,2-dioxa-phospholan 2-oxides.[139]

An interesting S_N2' displacement from oxygen has been proposed for the reaction of triethyl phosphite with 4-(trihalogenomethyl)cyclohexa-2,5-dienones to yield triethyl p-tolyl phosphate and 1,1,1-tribromopropane (see Scheme 7).[140]

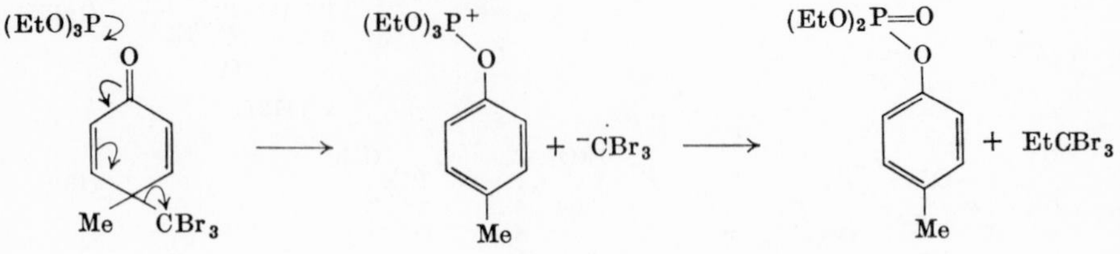

Scheme 7

The reactions of optically active methylphenylpropylphosphine with peroxides (nucleophilic substitution on oxygen) and with bromine (nucleophilic substitution on bromine) yield products which have inverted, retained, or racemized configurations depending on the solvent.[141]

The reaction of triphenylphosphine with sulphoxides[142a] to yield triphenylphosphine oxide and the corresponding sulphide, and the reaction of diphenyl sulphoxide with bromine,[142b] have also been investigated.

Further examples of reactions of triphenylphosphine with α-halogeno-carbonyl compounds which proceed with an initial attack of the phosphine on halogen have been reported.[143] Thus the reaction of α-aryl-$\alpha\alpha$-dichloro-N-methylacetanilide with triphenyl phosphine to yield the dichlorovinylamine, which has a ρ-value of $+2.6$, was formulated as shown in equation (18).[144] The reaction of triphenylphosphine with 2-bromocyclohexanone is also thought to involve initial attack on bromine.[145]

It is considered that the volumes of activation for the reactions of NH_2Cl, $MeNHCl$, and Me_2NCl with HO^- (-2.6, -0.6, and -1.1 cm^3 mole^{-1}, respectively) support an S_N2 displacement from nitrogen rather than an α-elimination mechanism. The rates of reaction of these three compounds are

138 R. F. Hudson and R. J. G. Searle, *Chimia (Aarau)*, **20**, 117 (1966).
139 T. R. Fukuto and R. L. Metcalf, *J. Med. Chem.*, **8**, 759 (1965).
140 B. Miller, *J. Am. Chem. Soc.*, **88**, 1841 (1966).
141 D. B. Denney and N. G. Adin, *Tetrahedron Letters*, **1966**, 2569.
142a H. H. Szmant and O. Cox, *J. Org. Chem.*, **31**, 1595 (1966).
142b W. Tagaki, K. Kikukawa, N. Kunieda, and S. Oae, *Bull. Chem. Soc. Japan*, **39**, 614 (1966).
143 See *Organic Reaction Mechanisms*, **1965**, 77—78.
144 A. J. Speziale and L. J. Taylor, *J. Org. Chem.*, **31**, 2450 (1966).
145 P. A. Chopard and R. F. Hudson, *J. Chem. Soc., B*, **1966**, 1089.

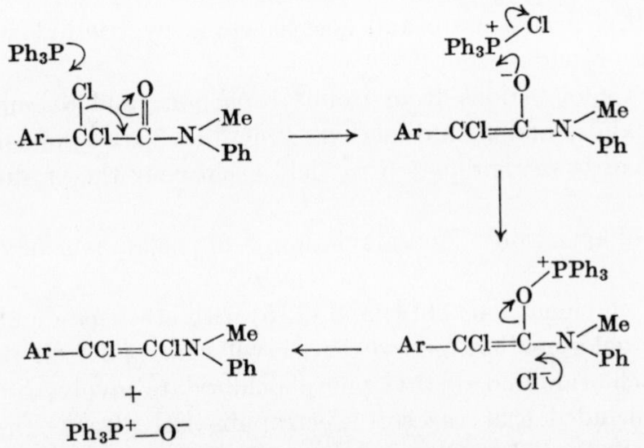

$$(18)$$

very similar, so α-methyl-substitution apparently has little effect on the rate of nucleophilic substitution on nitrogen.[146]

It has been proposed that the alkoxide-promoted decomposition of N-alkyl-N-nitrosoureas proceeds with attack on the nitroso-nitrogen atom. However, N-alkyl-N-nitrosourethanes and N-alkyl-N-nitrosoamides undergo competitive attack on the nitroso-nitrogen and carbonyl-carbon.[147] The decomposition of N-nitroamides and N-nitrocarbamates has been investigated.[148]

Ambident Nucleophiles[149]

There has been relatively little work on ambident nucleophiles reported this year and that has been mostly concerned with alkylation and acylation of enolate ions.[150] Further reports[151] of extensive O-alkylation in dipolar aprotic solvents have appeared,[152] but the ratio of O- to C-alkylation depends markedly on the leaving group, the structure of the alkyl group, and the metal ion. It was concluded from studies with the ethyl acetoacetate anion that, rather surprisingly, both halogen and alkyl-group effects indicate that "increased S_N2 reactivity is correlated with an increased 'O'/'C'-product ratio."

O-Alkylation has also been observed in the alkylation of the enolate ions of monoketones with triethyloxonium fluoroborate. The proportion of this is greater with dimethyl sulphoxide than with 1,2-dimethoxyethane as solvent.

146 W. J. leNoble, *Tetrahedron Letters*, **1966**, 727.
147 W. M. Jones, D. L. Muck, and T. K. Tandy, *J. Am. Chem. Soc.*, **88**, 68 (1966); W. M. Jones and D. L. Muck, *ibid.*, p. 3798.
148 E. H. White and L. A. Dolak, *J. Am. Chem. Soc.*, **88**, 3790 (1966); E. H. White, M. C. Chen, and L. A. Dolak, *J. Org. Chem.*, **31**, 3038 (1966).
149 For a review see M. Mikolajczyk, *Wiadomosci Chem.*, **19**, 545 (1965); *Chem. Abs.*, **63**, 16154 (1965).
150 R. E. Davis, *Tetrahedron Letters*, **1966**, 5021.
151 See *Organic Reaction Mechanisms*, **1965**, 74.
152 W. J. le Noble and J. E. Puerta, *Tetrahedron Letters*, **1966**, 1087.

O-Alkylation of ethyl acetoacetate and acetylacetone by triethyloxonium fluoroborate has also been reported.[153,154]

Acylation of the enolate ions from isobutyrophenone and di-isopropyl ketone with acyl halides and with dimethylketene, in a variety of solvents and with a variety of bases, is reported to yield exclusively the products of *O*-acylation.[155]

Other examples of acylation[156] and alkylation[157] of enolate ions have also been reported.

The reactions of ambident ions (**114**) and (**115**) with ethyl iodide involve *Se*-alkylation, with chloromethyl methyl ether involve *Se*- and *S*-alkylation, and with benzoyl chloride and diethyl phosphochloridate involve *S*-acylation.[158] It was concluded that the soft electrophile EtI attacks the soft nucleophilic centre Se, but that the acylating agents are hard electrophiles and attack the harder nucleophilic centre S.

(**114**)   (**115**)

Other reactions of ambident ions that have been investigated include intramolecular *C*-alkylation of a nitronate anion,[159] acylation of pyrryl-magnesium bromide,[160] and reaction of 3β-cholestanyl toluene-*p*-sulphonate with sodium cyanide.[161]

Other Reactions

1-Methylheptyl halides react with silver nitrite and silver nitrate with inversion of configuration in a wide range of solvents. α-Methylbenzyl chloride, on the other hand, reacts with inversion of configuration in acetonitrile or light petroleum, but with retention of configuration in ethyl ether or benzene. It was considered that these reactions proceed by a concerted process with varying amounts of push-and-pull. Thus the reactions of 1-methylheptyl halides in light petroleum and in benzene were thought to take place on the

[153] G. J. Heiszwolf and H. Kloosterziel, *Chem. Comm.*, **1966**, 51.
[154] T. A. Mastryukova, A. E. Shipov, V. V. Abalyaeva, E. E. Kugacheva, and M. I. Kabachnik, *Dokl. Akad. Nauk SSSR*, **164**, 340 (1965).
[155] K. Yoshida and Y. Yamashita, *Tetrahedron Letters*, **1966**, 693.
[156] W. M. Muir, P. D. Ritchie, and D. H. Lyman, *J. Org. Chem.*, **31**, 3790 (1966).
[157] S. J. Rhoads and R. W. Hasbrouck, *Tetrahedron*, **22**, 3557 (1966); K. G. Hampton, T. M. Harris, and C. R. Hauser, *J. Org. Chem.*, **31**, 1035 (1966).
[158] J. Michalski and Z. Tulimowski, *Bull. Acad. Polon. Sci., Ser. Sci. Chim.*, **14**, 217 (1966).
[159] S. J. Etheredge, *Tetrahedron Letters*, **1965**, 4527.
[160] G. P. Bean, *J. Heterocyclic Chem.*, **2**, 473 (1965).
[161] J. F. Biellmann, *Bull. Soc. Chim. France*, **1965**, 2338.

surface of the silver salt. It was suggested that the initial interaction was between the halogen and a silver ion, but that this did not lead to reaction unless a nitrite or nitrate ion was suitably situated at the rear to provide nucleophilic assistance. If this were not so, desorption–adsorption would then take place until such a suitable site on the surface was found, and nucleophilic displacement with inversion occurred. A similar process was thought to occur with α-methylbenzyl chloride, except that here when the solvent was ether or benzene the developing carbonium ion would be solvated from the rear; this solvated ion would then react with nitrate or nitrite, to yield a product formed with overall retention of configuration. The silver salts are soluble in acetonitrile, and the nitrite and nitrate ion are not constrained to the salt lattice; they can therefore, without difficulty, carry out a nucleophilic attack on carbon concerted with electrophilic attack on halogen by the silver ion to yield a product of inverted configuration.[162]

The mercuric chloride-catalysed solvolysis of α-methyl-4-alkylbenzyl chlorides in aqueous acetone and ethanol has been investigated.[163]

The reactions of benzyl bromide and ethyl iodide with diethylamine in cyclohexane follow rate laws of the form:

$$\text{Rate} = k_2[\text{RX}][\text{Et}_2\text{NH}] + k_3[\text{RX}][\text{Et}_2\text{NH}]^2$$

although the value of k_2 for ethyl iodide is very small. The results were discussed in terms both of specific solvation of the transition state and of association of the amine in the initial state as alternatives.[164]

Heppolette and Robertson[165] have measured the effects on the rates and activation parameters for the hydrolysis of alkyl halides and sulphonates in water (Table 1). It is seen that while there is a fairly systematic variation in $\Delta S^{\ddagger}$ there is none in $\Delta H^{\ddagger}$.

The rates of hydrolysis of a series of methyl arenesulphonates, $\text{MeO} \cdot \text{SO}_2 \cdot \text{C}_6\text{H}_4\text{X-}p$, vary over a range of 9—10 from $X = \text{NO}_2$ to $X = \text{MeO}$. This was shown to be largely the result of variations in $\Delta S^{\ddagger}$; $\Delta H^{\ddagger}$ and $\Delta C_p^{\ddagger}$ remained almost constant.[166]

The relative rate of nucleophilic displacement (or elimination) of an alkyl bromide to that of the corresponding toluene-p-sulphonate $k_{\text{Br}}/k_{\text{OTs}}$ depends markedly on the reaction. Thus for the reaction of the methyl compounds with sodium toluene-p-thiolate $k_{\text{Br}}/k_{\text{OTs}} = 0.36$, while for the E-1 elimination of the *tert*-butyl compounds in acetonitrile it is 5000.[167]

[162] N. Kornblum, W. J. Jones, and D. E. Hardies, *J. Am. Chem. Soc.*, **88**, 1704 (1966); N. Kornblum and D. E. Hardies, *ibid.*, p. 1707.
[163] R. Anantaraman and M. R. Nair, *Can. J. Chem.*, **44**, 2415 (1966).
[164] R. F. Hudson and I. Stelzer, *J. Chem. Soc.*, B, **1966**, 775.
[165] R. L. Heppolette and R. E. Robertson, *Can. J. Chem.*, **44**, 677 (1966).
[166] R. E. Robertson, A. Stein, and S. E. Sugamori, *Can. J. Chem.*, **44**, 685 (1966).
[167] H. M. R. Hoffmann, *J. Chem. Soc.*, **1965**, 6753; H. M. R. Hoffmann, *ibid.*, p. 6762.

Table 1. The effect of α-methyl substituents on the rate, and on the enthalpy and entropy of activation, for hydrolyses of alkyl halides and arenesulphonates in water.

Displaced anion	k_{Me}/k_{Et}	k_{Pr^i}/k_{Et}	$\Delta H^{\ddagger}_{Me} - \Delta H^{\ddagger}_{Et}$ (cal mole⁻¹)	$\Delta H^{\ddagger}_{Pr^i} - \Delta H^{\ddagger}_{Et}$ (cal mole⁻¹)	$\Delta S^{\ddagger}_{Me} - \Delta S^{\ddagger}_{Et}$ (e.u.)	$\Delta S^{\ddagger}_{Pr^i} - \Delta S^{\ddagger}_{Et}$ (e.u.)
Benzenesulphonate	1.03	63.2	−600	−250	−1.3	6.4
Toluene-*p*-sulphonate	1.08	57.8	−520	−290	−1.5	7.4
Methanesulphonate	1.18	50.9	−680	120	−1.8	8.3
Chloride	1.15	9.5	−290	−560	−0.2	3.4
Bromide	0.99	9.9	−40	20	−0.7	4.6
Iodide	0.51	17.4	350	−60	−0.3	5.5

Nucleophilicities (k_2^1) of a large number of electrochemically generated metallic and metalloid anions toward alkyl halides have been determined and there was shown to be a linear correlation between log k_2^1 and the potential required to oxidize the anion to a radical at a platinum electrode.[168] There has been further discussion of oxibase parameters[169] and leaving-group tendencies.[170]

Racemization of *tert*-butylethylmethylsulphonium perchlorate (116) in ethanol, acetic acid, water, and acetone occurs about 15 times faster than solvolysis in the same solvents. It was suggested that the racemization involved either cleavage to a *tert*-butyl cation–ethyl methyl sulphide ion–neutral molecule pair which returned to racemic sulphonium salt, or inversion

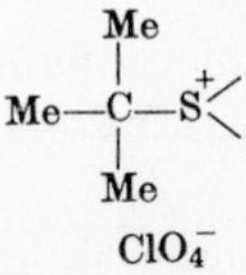

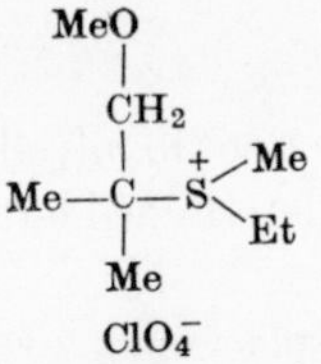

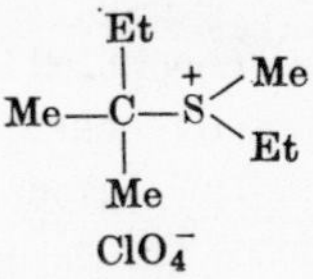

	(116)	(117)	(118)
Relative k solvolysis	1	0·06	6·3
Relative k Racemisation	1	1·7	3·8

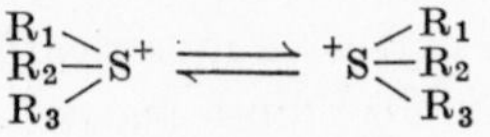

(119)

about the central sulphur atom analogous to inversion of an ammonia molecule. To distinguish between these possibilities the rates of solvolyses and racemization of compound (117) and (118) were also investigated. The fact that replacement of hydrogen of the *tert*-butyl group by an electron-withdrawing or -releasing substituent increases the rate of racemization argues strongly against the ionization mechanism. It is consistent, however, with the sulphonium ion undergoing an inversion as shown in (119), since increase in size of the R groups should result in a rate increase if non-bonded interactions are less in the transition state than in the initial state.[171]

168 R. E. Dessy, R. L. Pohl, and R. B. King, *J. Am. Chem. Soc.*, 88, 5121 (1966).
169 R. E. Davis, H. Nakshbendi, and A. Ohno, *J. Org. Chem.*, 31, 2702 (1966); R. E. Davis, R. Nehring, S. P. Molnar, and L. A. Suba, *Tetrahedron Letters*, 1966, 885.
170 L. M. Litvinenko and A. F. Popov, *Reaksionnaya Sposobnost. Organ. Soedin. Tartusk. Gos. Univ.*, 2, 44 (1965); *Chem. Abs.*, 63, 17861 (1965).
171 D. Darwish and G. Tourigny, *J. Am. Chem. Soc.*, 88, 4303 (1966).

trans-2,3-Dichlorohexafluorobut-2-ene reacts 3.82 times as fast as its *cis*-isomer with potassium ethoxide in ethanol.[172] The products are the *cis*- and *trans*-ethoxides, (**120**) and (**121**), formed in the ratios *cis:trans* = 29.9:70.0 from the *trans*-chloride, and *cis:trans* = 94.5:5.61 from the *cis*-chloride. It was

$$
\begin{array}{ccc}
\underset{Cl}{\overset{CF_3}{\diagdown}}C=C\underset{CF_3}{\overset{Cl}{\diagup}} & \xrightarrow{\ ^{-}OEt\ } & \underset{Cl}{\overset{CF_3}{\diagdown}}C=C\underset{CF_3}{\overset{OEt}{\diagup}} \quad + \quad \underset{Cl}{\overset{CF_3}{\diagdown}}C=C\underset{OEt}{\overset{CF_3}{\diagup}} \\
 & & 29.9\% \qquad\qquad\qquad 70\% \\
 & & (\mathbf{120}) \qquad\qquad\qquad (\mathbf{121})
\end{array}
$$

$$
\underset{Cl}{\overset{CF_3}{\diagdown}}C=C\underset{Cl}{\overset{CF_3}{\diagup}} \quad \xrightarrow{\ ^{-}OEt\ } \quad 5.61\% \quad + \quad 94.5\%
$$

concluded that the reactions involved a planar carbanion intermediate "whose stereochemical fate is determined largely by differences in steric interaction of the various rotamers."

The preferential displacement of the vinylic fluorine rather than of the vinylic chlorine of 1-chloro-2,3,3,4,4,5,5-heptafluorocyclopentene by a number of nucleophilic reagents has been reported.[173]

Tracer studies with ^{18}O-labelled phenol have shown that the condensation of phenol and methanol to anisole promoted by dicyclohexylcarbodi-imide proceeds with methyl–oxygen not phenyl–oxygen fission.[174]

There have been extensive investigations of the alkylation of conformationally rigid 1-alkylpiperidines and related compounds.[175–178] It appears that, contrary to one report,[176] axial and not equatorial alkylation is the predominant reaction.[177,178]

The fact that the signals in the NMR spectra from the protons of the *erythro*- and *threo*-isomers of 2-deuterio-1,2-diphenylethyl compounds can usually be distinguished from one another has been made use of in determining the steric course of their reaction. Thus the reactions of the alcohols (**122**) and (**122a**) with thionyl chloride and concentrated hydrochloric acid have been shown to proceed with, respectively, retention of configuration and race-

[172] J. D. Park and E. W. Cook, *Tetrahedron Letters*, **1965**, 4853.

[173] A. W. Frank, *J. Org. Chem.*, **31**, 1917 (1966); D. J. Burton and R. L. Johnson, *Tetrahedron Letters*, **1966**, 2681; W. J. Feast, D. R. A. Perry, and R. Stephens, *Tetrahedron*, **22**, 433 (1966).

[174] E. Vowinkel, *Chem. Ber.*, **99**, 42 (1966).

[175] C. D. Johnson, R. A. Y. Jones, A. R. Katritzky, C. R. Palmer, K. Schofield, and R. J. Wells, *J. Chem. Soc.*, **1965**, 6797.

[176] J.-L. Imbach, A. R. Katritzky, and R. A. Kolinski, *J. Chem. Soc., B*, **1966**, 556.

[177] H. O. House, B. A. Tefertiller, and C. G. Pitt, *J. Org. Chem.*, **31**, 1073 (1966).

[178] D. R. Brown, B. G. Hutley, J. McKenna, and J. M. McKenna, *Chem. Commun.*, **1966**, 719.

mization. The chlorides would not be distinguished by NMR, so they were converted into the phenyl sulphides which were easily distinguishable.[179]

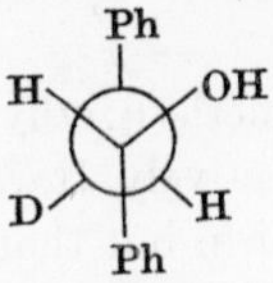

Ph
H — OH
D — H
Ph
(122)

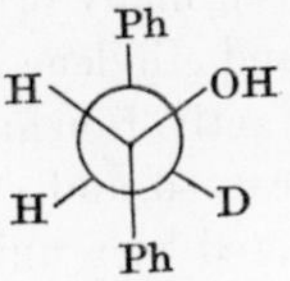

Ph
H — OH
H — D
Ph
(122a)

The stereochemistry of the ring-opening of 1-methyl-*cis*- and *trans*-4-*tert*-butylcycloxene oxide with lithium aluminium hydride has been investigated.[180] The *cis*-isomer **(123)** reacts with exclusive diaxial opening, and the *trans*-isomer **(124)** with about 60% of diaxial opening with attack at the tertiary carbon and 30% of diequatorial opening with attack at the secondary carbon. It was suggested that the latter reaction proceeded with attack on the epoxide in conformation **(124)** via a twist conformation.

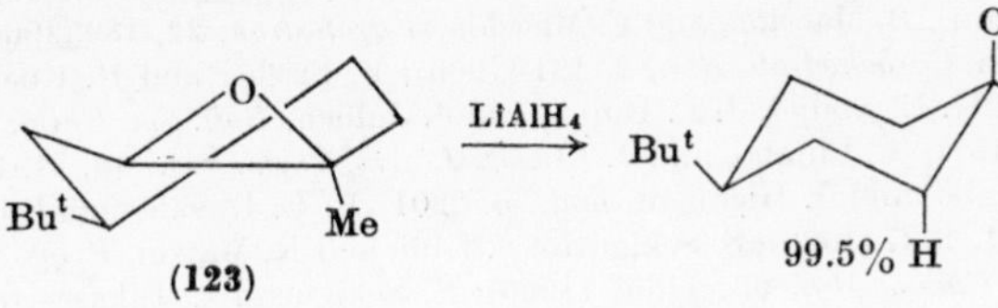

O
Bu^t — Me
(123)

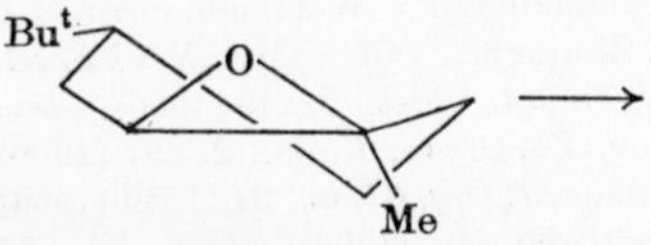

LiAlH₄ →

OH
Bu^t — Me
99.5% H

Bu^t — O
Me
(124)

→

H
Bu^t — Me
OH
60%

+

Me
Bu^t — OH
H
30%

+ products formed via a ketone

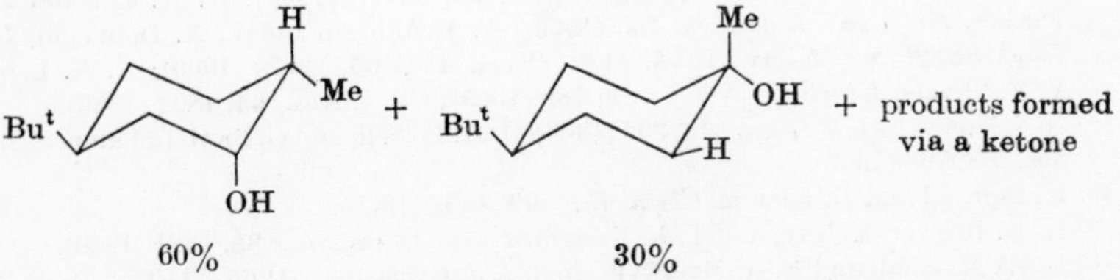

It is considered that the balance of evidence supports an *A*-2 mechanism for the perchloric acid-catalysed ring opening of trimethylene oxide. This

179 C. A. Kingsbury and W. B. Thornton, *J. Am. Chem. Soc.*, **88**, 3159 (1966).
180 N. A. LeBel and G. G. Ecke, *J. Org. Chem.*, **30**, 4316 (1965).

reaction proceeds only about nine times slower than that of ethylene oxide but the ⁻OH-promoted reaction proceeds about 6000 times slower and a spontaneous ring opening in water could not be detected.[181] There have been many other investigations of the opening of epoxide,[182] episulphide,[183] and ethylene imine[184] rings.

The volume of activation for the hydrolysis of methyl-, ethyl-, and isopropyl-mercuric ions are 0, +6, and +9 cm³ mole⁻¹, respectively. It was suggested that the last two reacted by a unimolecular mechanism but that there was some nucleophilic assistance in the reaction of the methyl compound.[185]

Other reactions which have received attention include: reactions of methyl halides with potassium cyanide in aqueous solution;[186] reaction of chloro-acetate ion with thiocyanate ion;[187] alcoholyses of 2,3,4,6-tetra-O-acetyl-α-D-glucopyranosyl bromide,[188a] and 3α-chloro-4-oxa-5α-œstrane;[188b] solvolyses of α-fluorobenzyl halides,[189] benzotrichloride,[190] aryl α-chloroethyl ethers,[191]

[181] P. O. I. Virtanen, *Suomen Kemistilehti, B*, **39**, 58, 64 (1966).
[182] R. E. Parker and B. W. Rockett, *J. Chem. Soc., B*, **1966**, 681; N. S. Isaacs, *Tetrahedron Letters*, **1965**, 4549, 4553; P. O. I. Virtanen, *Suomen Kemistilehti, B*, **38**, 231 (1965); G. Berti, F. Bottari, P. L. Ferrarini, and B. Macchia, *J. Org. Chem.*, **30**, 4091 (1965); G. Berti, F. Bottari, B. Macchia, and F. Macchia, *Tetrahedron*, **22**, 189 (1966); E. J. Reist and S. L. Holton, *Carbohydrate Res.*, **2**, 181 (1966); F. Fischer and H. Koch, *Chem. Ber.*, **99**, 2000 (1966); H. E. Audier, J. F. Dupin, and J. Jullien, *Bull. Soc. Chim. France*, **1966**, 2811; D. J. Pasto, C. C. Cumbo, and J. Fraser, *J. Am. Chem. Soc.*, **88**, 2194 (1966); D. J. Pasto, C. C. Cumbo, and J. Hickman, *ibid.*, p. 2201; E. E. Royals and J. C. Leffingwell, *J. Org. Chem.*, **31**, 1937 (1966); S. Sekiguchi, S. Ishii, and K. Matsui, *KogyoKagakuZasshi*, **68**, 286 (1965); *Chem. Abs.*, **63**, 14667 (1965); S. Sekiguchi, I. Takase, and K. Matsui, *Kogyo Kagaku Zasshi*, **68**, 945 (1965); *Chem. Abs.*, **63**, 16157 (1965); B. L. van Duuren and B. M. Goldschmidt, *J. Med. Chem.*, **9**, 77 (1966); J. Weinman and S. Weinman, *Steroids*, **6**, 699 (1965); A. N. Pudovik, E. M. Faizullin, and G. I. Zhuravlev, *Dokl. Akad. Nauk SSSR*, **165**, 586 (1965); E. N. Zil'berman and G. I. Shilov, *Zh. Organ. Khim.*, **2**, 248 (1966); *Chem. Abs.*, **65**, 2083 (1966); N. N. Lebedev and V. M. Kozlov, *Zh. Organ. Khim.*, **2**, 261 (1966); *Chem. Abs.*, **65**, 2085 (1966); H. Kakiuchi, and T. Tanaka, *J. Org. Chem.*, **31**, 1559 (1966); M. Repas, V. Macho, and E. J. Mistrik, *Chem. Zvesti*, **20**, 501 (1966); *Chem. Abs.*, **65**, 15181 (1966); Y. I. Baranov and N. N. Lebedev, *Tr. Mosk. Khim.-Tekhnol. Inst.*, No. 8, 58 (1965); No. 48, 64 (1965); *Chem. Abs.*, **65**, 15178 (1966); N. N. Lebedev and V. M. Kozlov, *Kinetika i Kataliz*, **7**, 455 (1966); A. A. Akhrem and V. N. Dobrynin, *Izv. Akad. Nauk SSSR, Ser. Khim.*, **1966**, 1122; *Chem. Abs.*, **65**, 12120 (1966); N. N. Lebedev and V. F. Shvets, *Kinetika i Kataliz*, **6**, 782 (1965); *Chem. Abs.*, **64**, 4892 (1966).
[183] N. S. Isaacs, *Can. J. Chem.*, **44**, 395 (1966); J. R. Lowell, and G. K. Helmkamp, *J. Am. Chem. Soc.*, **88**, 768 (1966).
[184] K. Ponsold and D. Klemm, *Chem. Ber.*, **99**, 1502 (1966).
[185] K. R. Brower, B. Gay, and T. L. Konkol, *J. Am. Chem. Soc.*, **88**, 1681 (1966).
[186] B. W. Marshall and E. A. Moelwyn-Hughes, *J. Chem. Soc.*, **1965**, 7119.
[187] T. I. Crowell, J. E. Hicks, and C. C. Lai, *J. Phys. Chem.*, **70**, 2116 (1966).
[188a] L. R. Schroeder, J. W. Green, and D. C. Johnson, *J. Chem. Soc., B*, **1966**, 447.
[188b] J. T. Edward and J.-M. Ferland, *Can. J. Chem.*, **44**, 1299 (1966).
[189] G. Kohnstam, D. Routledge, and D. L. H. Williams, *Chem. Commun.*, **1966**, 113.
[190] K. Tanabe and T. Sano, *J. Res. Inst. Catalysis, Hokkaido Univ.*, **13**, 102 (1965).
[191] M. F. Shostakovskii, A. V. Kalabina, and K. K. Zikherman, *Zh. Organ. Khim.*, **2**, 689 (1966).

polyvinylsulphonic acid esters,[192] dimethyl and diethyl sulphate,[193a] α-chloroalkyl esters,[193b] neoisomenthyl toluene-p-sulphonates,[193c] and *tert*-butyl chloride;[194] formolysis of benzyl fluoride[195] and other alkyl halides;[196] chloride-exchange reactions of alkyl and cycloalkyl chlorides;[197] interaction of methyl iodide and triethylamine in frozen benzene;[198] reaction of 1,2,3,4,7,7-hexachloro-5-phenylnorbornadienes with sodium methyl sulfide;[199] reaction of α-aryl-α-halogenoacetophenones with pyridine and aniline,[200] of dodecyl bromide with pyridine,[201] of methyl iodide with naphthyloxide ions,[202] of butyl bromide with butyl-lithium,[203] of long-chain alkyl halides with hydroxide ion in DMSO–water mixtures,[204] of allyl bromide with Schiff bases,[205] of bis(chloronitroso)-compounds with piperdine,[206] and of tetramethylammonium dialkyl phosphates with alkyl halides;[207] methanolyses of 5-substituted 2-chloromethylselenophenes,[208] 2,5- and 3,4-bis(chloromethyl)-furans,[209] and 2-chloromethyl-5-nitrofuran;[210] nucleophilic displacement of the 3-acetoxy-group of cephalosporic acid;[211] interconversion of $3\beta,6\alpha$- and

[192] S. Yoshikawa, O.-K. Kim, and T. Hori, *Bull. Chem. Soc., Japan*, **39**, 1937 (1966).

[193a] R. E. Robertson and S. E. Sugamori, *Can. J. Chem.*, **44**, 1728 (1966).

[193b] E. K. Euranto and T. Yrjana, *Suomen Kemistilehti, B*, **38**, 214 (1965); E. K. Euranto, *ibid.*, *A*, **39**, 110 (1966); E. K. Euranto and J. N. Cleve, *Reaktsionnaya Sposobnost Organ. Soedin. Tartusk. Gos. Univ.*, 2, 183 (1965); *Chem. Abs.*, **64**, 3308 (1966); N. J. Cleve, *Suomen Kemistilehti, A*, **39**, 111 (1966).

[193c] W. Huckel and S. Gupte, *Chimia (Aaran)*, **20**, 274 (1966).

[194] G. P. Valueva and E. S. Rudakov, *Reaktsionnaya Sposobnost Organ. Soedin. Tartusk. Gos. Univ.*, **2**, 291 (1965); *Chem. Abs.*, **65**, 3687 (1966); J. Landais and C. Prevost, *Bull. Soc. Chim. France*, **1966**, 3331.

[195] J. J. Delpuech, *Bull. Soc. Chim. France*, **1966**, 1598, 1611.

[196] A. Kirrmann, C. Beguin, and J. Delpuech, *Compt. Rend.*, **261**, 4075 (1965).

[197] O. Christ and H. Elias, *Chem. Ber.*, **99**, 1 (1966); H. Elias and S. Krutzik, *ibid.*, p. 1026; H. Elias and H. Strecker, *ibid.*, p. 1019; Y. J. Park and I. Lee, *Daehan Hwahak Hwoejee*, **9**, 23 (1965); *Chem. Abs.*, **64**, 6431 (1966).

[198] R. E. Pincock and T. E. Kiovksy, *J. Am. Chem. Soc.*, **88**, 51 (1966).

[199] A. J. Fry, *J. Org. Chem.*, **31**, 1863 (1966).

[200] D. J. Cooper and L. N. Owen, *J. Chem. Soc.*, *C*, **1966**, 533.

[201] C. Kimura and K. Murai, *Kogyo Kagaku Zasshi*, **68**, 504 (1965); *Chem. Abs.*, **65**, 3716 (1966); K. Murai and C. Kimura, *Kogyo Kagaku Zasshi*, **68**, 2093 (1965); *Chem. Abs.*, **64**, 14053 (1966).

[202] A. Fischer, M. A. Riddolls, and J. Vaughan, *J. Chem. Soc.*, *B*, **1966**, 106.

[203] A. I. Shatenstein, E. A. Kovrizhnykh, and V. M. Basmanova, *Reaktsionnaya Sposobnost Organ. Soedin, Tartusk Gos. Univ.*, **2**, 135 (1965); *Chem. Abs.*, **64**, 6428 (1966).

[204] J. J. Delpuech, *Bull. Soc. Chim. France*, **1966**, 1616.

[205] V. I. Minkin and E. A. Medyantsera, *Zh. Obshch. Khim.*, **35**, 1956 (1965).

[206] G. Collin, W. Pritzkow, H. Hübner, W. Rolle, and M. Wahren, *Tetrahedron Letters*, **1966**, 3493.

[207] N.-T. Thuong, M. Lao-Colin, and P. Chabrier, *Bull. Soc. Chim. France*, **1966**, 932.

[208] Y. K. Yur'ev, M. A. Gal'bershtam, and A. F. Prokof'eva, *Izv. Vysshikh. Uchebn. Zavedenii, Khim i Khim Tekhnol.*, **8**, 421 (1965); *Chem. Abs.*, **63**, 16151 (1965).

[209] M. A. Gal'bershtam, G. T. Khachaturova, K. Y. Novitskii, and Y. K. Yur'ev, *Izv. Vysshikh. Uchebn. Zavedenii, Khim. i Khim Tekhnol.*, **8**, 776 (1965); *Chem. Abs.*, **64**, 12479 (1966).

[210] M. A. Gal'bershtam, G. T. Khachaturova, K. Y. Novitskii, and Y. K. Yur'ev, *Vestn. Mosk. Univ. Ser 11, Khim.*, **20**, 83 (1965); *Chem. Abs.*, **63**, 16151 (1965).

[211] A. B. Taylor, *J. Chem. Soc.*, **1965**, 7020.

3α,6β-diacetoxycholest-4-enes in acetic acid;[212] acetolysis of benzyl and benzhydryl ethers;[213] self-etherification of benzhydrol;[214] quaternization of purines and pyridazines[215] and of pyridines;[216] dequaternization of azetidinium salts;[217] solvolytic rearrangement of 3,3-dichloro-1,2-diphenyl-aziridines;[218] and alkaline hydrolysis of allyl methanesulphonates.[219]

[212] M. P. Hartshorn and D. N. Kirk, *Tetrahedron*, **22**, 1415 (1966).
[213] A. M. Avédikian, J. Chaput, S. Coffi N'Ketsia, J. Dausque, A. Kermogard, J. M. Rondier, and H. Tautou, *Bull. Soc. Chim. France*, **1966**, 95.
[214] E. F. Pratt and D. G. Jones, *J. Org. Chem.*, **30**, 4362 (1965); J. Kolínský, M. Vašta, R. Chromeček, and M. Bohdanecký, *Coll. Czech. Chem. Comm.*, **31**, 2714 (1966); J. Kolínský, and M. Bohdanecký, *ibid.*, p. 2841.
[215] J. A. Montgomery, K. Hewson, S. J. Clayton and H. J. Thomas, *J. Org. Chem.*, **31**, 2202 (1966); M. S. Bale, A. B. Simmonds, and W. F. Trager, *J. Chem. Soc.*, *B*, **1966**, 867.
[216] A. F. Casy, A. H. Beckett, and M. A. Iorio, *Tetrahedron*, **22**, 2751 (1966).
[217] G. Fodor, *J. Am. Chem. Soc.*, **88**, 1040 (1966).
[218] R. E. Brooks, J. O. Edwards, G. Levey, and F. Smyth, *Tetrahedron*, **22**, 1279 (1966).
[219] R. F. Hudson and R. J. Withey, *J. Chem. Soc.*, *B*, **1966**, 237.

CHAPTER 3

Electrophilic Aliphatic Substitution

Electrophilic aliphatic substitution[1] and ylide chemistry[2] have been reviewed.

The configuration-preserving effects of some more functional groups derived from second-row elements on adjacent carbanion centres have been studied[3] by measuring the rates of deuterium exchange (k_e) and racemization (k_α) in tert-butyl [^{2}H]alcohol containing potassium tert-butoxide. Compounds (2)—(4) gave values of k_e/k_α in the range 37—17 which should be compared with values of 73—1200 previously reported for compound (1). All these

$$
\begin{array}{cccc}
\text{O} \quad \text{Me} & \text{Me} \ \text{O} \quad \text{Me} & \text{O} \quad \text{Me} & \text{O} \quad \text{Me} \\
\uparrow \quad | * & | \quad \uparrow \quad | * & \uparrow \quad | & \uparrow \quad \uparrow * \\
\text{Ph—S—C—H} & \text{PhN—S—C—H} & \text{MeO—S—C—H} & \text{Ph—P—C—H} \\
\downarrow \quad | & \downarrow \quad | & \downarrow \quad | & + | \quad | \\
\text{O} \quad \text{C}_6\text{H}_{13}\text{-n} & \text{O} \quad \text{C}_6\text{H}_{13}\text{-n} & \text{O} \quad \text{C}_6\text{H}_{13}\text{-n} & \text{KO}^- \ \text{C}_6\text{H}_{13} \\
(1) & (2) & (3) & (4)
\end{array}
$$

compounds, therefore, undergo exchange with predominant retention of configuration, and it was concluded that "functional groups centred around second-row elements that bear two charge-carrying negative elements induce asymmetry in attached carbanions". On the other hand, compounds (5)—(9)

$$
\begin{array}{ccc}
\text{O} \quad \text{Me} & \text{O} \quad \text{Me} & \text{Ph} \ \text{O} \quad \text{Me} \\
\uparrow \quad | & \uparrow \quad | & | \quad \uparrow \quad | \\
\text{Ph—S—C}^*\text{—H} & \text{Ph—P—C}^*\text{—H} & ^-\text{N—S—C}^*\text{—H} \\
| & | \quad | & \text{K}^+ \downarrow \quad | \\
\text{C}_6\text{H}_{13}\text{-n} & \text{Ph} \ \text{C}_6\text{H}_{13}\text{-n} & \text{O} \quad \text{C}_6\text{H}_{13}\text{-n} \\
(5) & (6) & (7)
\end{array}
$$

$$
\begin{array}{cc}
\text{O} \quad \text{Me} & \text{O} \quad \text{Me} \\
\uparrow \quad | & \uparrow \quad | \\
^-\text{O—S—C}^*\text{—H} & \text{EtO—P—C}^*\text{—H} \\
\text{K}^+ \downarrow \quad | & | \quad | \\
\text{O} \quad \text{C}_6\text{H}_{13}\text{-n} & \text{EtO} \quad \text{C}_6\text{H}_{13}\text{-n} \\
(8) & (9)
\end{array}
$$

give k_e/k_α values in the range 1.1—3.3 and it was concluded that "functional groups centred around second-row elements that bear one or three charge-carrying negative elements do not induce asymmetry in attached carbanions".

[1] F. G. Thorpe in "Studies on Chemical Structure and Reactivity", J. H. Ridd, ed., Methuen, London, 1966, p. 247.

[2] A. W. Johnson, "Ylid Chemistry", Academic Press, New York, N.Y., 1966.

[3] D. J. Cram, R. D. Trepka, and P. St. Janiak, J. Am. Chem. Soc., 88, 2749 (1966).

On the other hand, Rauk, Buncel, Moir, and Woolfe[4] have provided a striking example of a reaction which proceeds via an asymmetric carbanion attached to a sulphoxide group. The NMR spectrum of benzyl methyl sulphoxide, $PhCH_2SOMe$, in D_2O shows that the hydrogen atoms of the methylene group are not equivalent, as can be seen by inspection of the three most stable conformations (**10**), (**11**), and (**12**). On treatment with M-NaOD in D_2O, one

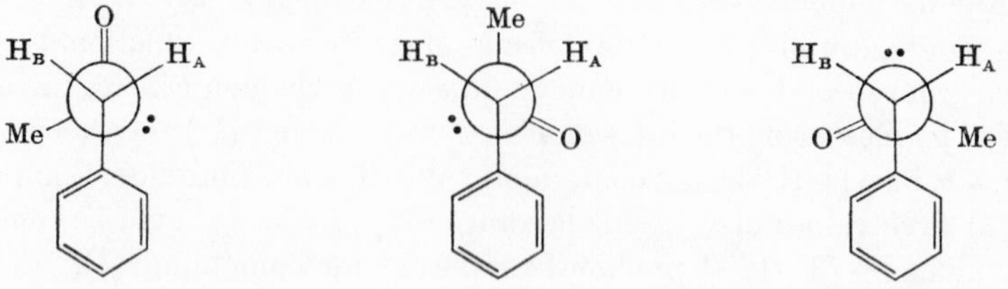

(10)   (11)   (12)

of the protons exchanges 13—14 times faster than the other, and both exchange much faster than the protons of the methyl group. The hydrogen exchange of the methylene group is, therefore, stereoselective and the carbanion is protonated from the side of the departing proton. Yet the carbanionic centre must be nearly flat because of the observed effect of phenyl on the rates. By working with sulphoxide of known absolute configuration it was then shown that the rapidly exchanged proton is H_A. It was suggested that this was abstracted from conformation (**10**) and that the controlling factor is an electrostatic one which results in abstraction of a proton situated on the bisector of the oxygen–sulphur–lone-pair bond angle.[5]

An interesting observation, with obvious analogues in carbanion chemistry, is that the rate of deuteration at the asymmetric nitrogen of the $(-)$-$[Co(NH_3)_4(MeNHCH_2COO)]^{2+}$ ion [see (**13**)] is 4000 times the rate of racemization. The configuration about the nitrogen is thus retained most of the time that the proton is off.[6]

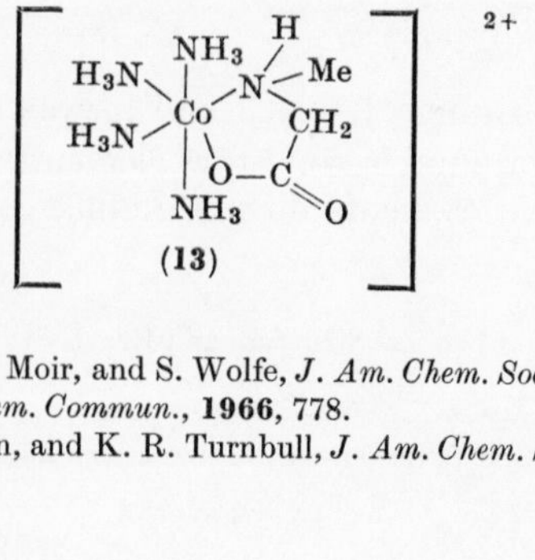

(13)

[4] A. Rauk, E. Buncel, R. Y. Moir, and S. Wolfe, *J. Am. Chem. Soc.*, **87**, 5498 (1965).
[5] S. Wolfe and A. Rauk, *Chem. Commun.*, **1966**, 778.
[6] B. Halpern, A. M. Sargeson, and K. R. Turnbull, *J. Am. Chem. Soc.*, **88**, 4630 (1966).

The base-catalysed 1,5- and 1,3-proton transfers (14) → (15) and (16) → (17) follow intramolecular pathways under suitable conditions. Thus the former

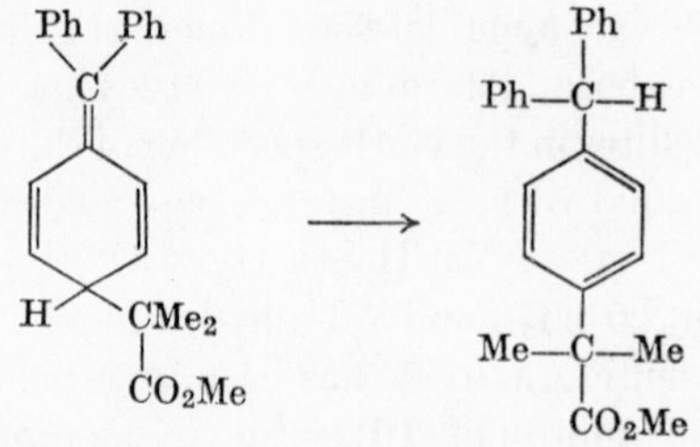

is 99% intramolecular with tripropylamine in 3-ethylpentan-3-[^{2}H$_1$]ol, and the latter is 88% intramolecular with triethylene diamine in dimethyl sulphoxide 1—6M in *tert*-butyl alcohol. It was suggested the proton attached to a base migrates across the face of a π-cloud of electrons containing the negative charge. When piperidine was used instead of triethylenediamine the rearrangement of (16) to (17) dropped from 88% to 58% intramolecular, showing that the piperidinium ion rotates at a rate comparable to that of migration.[7]

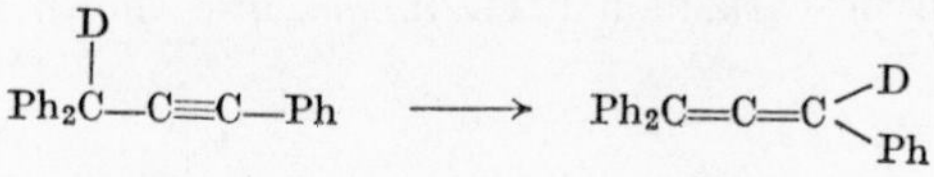

Further measurements of the kinetic isotope effect for proton abstraction from nitroalkanes have been reported.[8] It was concluded that this has a maximum value when the proton transfer is between two acid–base systems of approximately equal pK. In confirmation of earlier work a very large kinetic isotope effect ($k_H/k_D = 20$) was observed for proton abstraction from 2-nitropropane by 2,6-lutidine, suggesting that tunnelling is important.

The tritium and deuterium exchange of diethyl malonate in aqueous solution has been investigated.[9a]

α-Fluoro-substituents have been shown to decrease the acidity of substituted nitromethanes, whereas α-chloro-substituents increase it.[9b]

The relative rates (statistically corrected) of deuterium exchange (25°, other conditions unspecified) of the methyl groups of the compounds Me$_4$P$^+$ I$^-$,

[7] D. J. Cram, F. Willey, H. P. Fischer, H. M. Relles, and D. A. Scott, *J. Am. Chem. Soc.*, **88**, 2759 (1966).
[8] R. P. Bell and D. M. Goodall, *Proc. Roy. Soc. (London)*, A, **294**, 273 (1966).
[9a] K. L. Servis, O. Gjurović-Deletis, S. Borčić, and D. E. Sunko, *Croat. Chem. Acta*, **37**, 191 (1965).
[9b] H. G. Adolph and M. J. Kamlet, *J. Am. Chem. Soc.*, **88**, 4761 (1966).

PhP^+Me_3 Br^-, $Ph_2P^+Me_2$ Br^-, and Ph_3P^+Me Br^- are 1, 23, 481, 9640, showing that the inductive effect of the phenyl group is relayed through the phosphorus.[10]

The rates of proton exchange between dimethyl sulphoxide and Na^+ and Li^+ $^-CH_2SOCH_3$ have been determined by studying the broadening and collapse of the ^{13}C satellites in the NMR spectrum of the dimethyl sulphoxide. The reaction is quite rapid with, for instance, a second-order rate constant of 12 l. mole^{-1} sec^{-1} in 0.1—0.8M-$NaCH_2SOCH_3$ at 37°.[11]

Proton exchange of 2,5- (18) and 2,3-dihydrothiophen 1,1-dioxide (19) in sodium deuteroxide–deuterium oxide has been investigated. Surprisingly the most rapidly exchanged proton of (19) is the vinylic proton at the α-position. This was shown[12] not to involve the product of addition (20) but rather, it was thought, the vinylic carbanion (21). It was also shown that $k_1 > k_2$ and $k_{-1} > k_{-2}$.

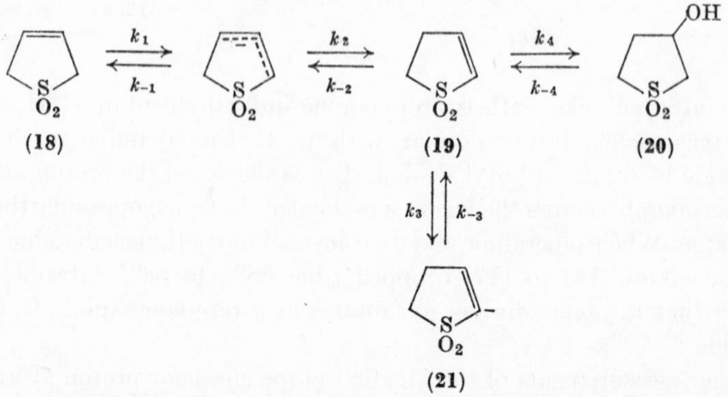

(18)   (19)   (20)

(21)

The high stability of the allylic ylides (23) and (24) is shown by the rates of deuterium exchange of compounds (22) and (25), which are, respectively, 10^{10} and 10^5 times faster than that of the tetramethylammonium cation. All the ring protons of compound (25) were exchanged, showing that the 3,5-ylide (26) was also formed; and its rate of formation was calculated[13] to be about a quarter of that for the 2,4-ylide (24).

Metallation of toluene by 1-methylpropylsodium to yield benzylsodium is the result of kinetic control since the reaction is rapid under conditions where *p*-tolylsodium is only converted slowly into the latter.[14]

10 S. E. Cremer and R. J. Chorvat, *Tetrahedron Letters*, **1966**, 419; see also, E. A. Yakovleva, E. N. Tsvetkov, D. I. Lobanov, M. I. Kabachnik, and A. I. Shatenshtein, *Tetrahedron Letters*, **1966**, 4161.
11 J. I. Brauman and N. J. Nelson, *J. Am. Chem. Soc.*, **88**, 2332 (1966).
12 C. D. Broaddus, *J. Am. Chem. Soc.*, **88**, 3863 (1966); M. Procházka and M. Paleček, *Coll. Czech. Chem. Commun.*, **31**, 3744 (1966).
13 M. Saunders and E. H. Gold, *J. Am. Chem. Soc.*, **88**, 3376 (1966).
14 C. D. Broaddus, *J. Am. Chem. Soc.*, **88**, 4174 (1966).

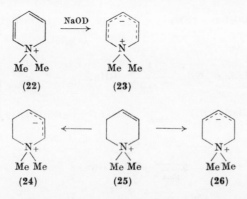

(22)   (23)

(24)   (25)   (26)

In contrast to earlier results it has now been shown that the rates of de-tritiation of substituted phenylacetylenes, $XC_6H_4 \cdot C \equiv C^3H$, are well correlated by the Hammett $\rho\sigma$-relationship.[15] The kinetics of exchange of a series of acetylenes $YC \equiv C^3H$ where Y is a substituted alkyl or arylalkyl group have also been studied.[16]

The application of the "principle of least motion" to the protonation of resonance-stabilized carbanions has been discussed.[17]

The kinetics of the symmetrization of *tert*-butyl α-(bromomercuri)phenyl-acetate by ammonia in chloroform [equation (1)] have been studied by following the change in the NMR signal of the *tert*-butyl group. The rate law is:

$$\text{Rate} = k[\text{RHgX}]^2[\text{NH}_3]^2$$

and mechanisms (2) and (3) were considered, with the latter favoured. The measured rate constant is therefore the product of an equilibrium constant and a rate constant, and previously reported anomalies in substituent effects may result from the fact that effects on the equilibrium constant are greater than those on the rate constant.[18]

The claim[19] that the reaction of di-*sec*-butylmercury with diethylthallium in dimethylformamide follows an $S_{\text{E}}1$ mechanism is incorrect.[20] The reaction which occurs is not an aliphatic electrophilic substitution but oxidation of the mercurial.

The rates of reaction of *cis*- and *trans*-2-chlorovinylmercuric chloride with iodine in benzene and carbon tetrachloride are zero-order in mercurial and first-order in iodine, and the *cis*- and *trans*-compounds react at the same

15 C. Eaborn, G. A. Skinner, and D. R. M. Walton, *J. Chem. Soc., B*, **1966**, 922.
16 C. Eaborn, G. A. Skinner, and D. R. M. Walton, *J. Chem. Soc., B*, **1966**, 989.
17 J. Hine, *J. Org. Chem.*, **31**, 1236 (1966).
18 F. R. Jensen, B. Rickborn, and J. J. Miller, *J. Am. Chem. Soc.*, **88**, 340 (1966); see also, O. A. Reutov, *Dokl. Akad. Nauk SSSR*, **163**, 909 (1965); *Chem. Abs.*, **63**, 13023 (1965).
19 C. R. Hart and Sir Christopher Ingold, *J. Chem. Soc.*, **1964**, 4372.
20 F. R. Jensen and D. Heyman, *J. Am. Chem. Soc.*, **88**, 3438 (1966).

$$\begin{array}{c} \underset{\displaystyle\;\;|}{\text{PhCH}}\text{—CO}_2\text{Bu}^t + 2\text{NH}_3 \longrightarrow (\text{Ph·}\underset{\displaystyle\;\;|}{\text{CH}}\text{—})_2\text{Hg} + \text{HgBr}_2(\text{NH}_3)_2 \\ \text{HgBr} \qquad\qquad\qquad \text{CO}_2\text{Bu}^t \end{array} \tag{1}$$

$$\left.\begin{array}{c} \text{RHgBr} + \text{NH}_3 \;\underset{\text{Fast}}{\overset{K}{\rightleftarrows}}\; \text{R}\bar{\text{H}}\text{g}\!\!\diagdown\!\!\!\!\overset{\displaystyle\overset{+}{\text{NH}_3}}{\underset{\text{Br}}{}} \\[4mm] 2\text{RHgBr}(\text{NH}_3) \;\underset{\text{Slow}}{\overset{k}{\longrightarrow}}\; \text{R}_2\text{Hg} + \text{HgBr}_2(\text{NH}_3)_2 \end{array}\right\} \tag{2}$$

$$\left.\begin{array}{c} \text{RHgBr} + 2\text{NH}_3 \;\underset{\text{Fast}}{\overset{K}{\rightleftarrows}}\; \overset{\displaystyle\overset{+}{\text{NH}_3}}{\underset{\displaystyle\underset{+}{\text{NH}_3}}{\text{R}\text{Hg}^{2-}\text{·Br}}} \\[6mm] \text{RHgBr}(\text{NH}_3)_2 + \text{RHgBr} \;\underset{\text{Slow}}{\overset{k}{\longrightarrow}}\; \text{R}_2\text{Hg} + \text{HgBr}_2(\text{NH}_3)_2 \end{array}\right\} \tag{3}$$

rate. Both compounds yield mixtures of *cis*- and *trans*-1-chloro-2-iodo-ethylene.[21]

The reactions of allylmercuric iodide with aqueous acid,[22a] of benzyl mercuric chloride with iodine[22b] and acids,[22c] of EtHgCH$_2$Ac with MeO$_2$CHgCl,[23] and of organomercury compounds with triarylmethyl bromide[24] have also been investigated, and the importance of nucleophilic assistance in electrophilic substitution of organomercury compounds has been discussed.[25]

The mechanism of formation of Grignard reagents has been discussed.[26]

An elegant demonstration that *endo*-norbornylmagnesium bromide reacts with mercuric bromide and carbon dioxide with retention of configuration has been provided by Jensen and Nakamaye.[27] *exo*- and *endo*-Norbornyl bromide both yield a mixture containing 41% of *exo*- and 59% of *endo*-norbornyl-magnesium bromide, which are readily identified by the signals of the proton

[21] I. P. Beletskaya, V. I. Karpov, and O. A. Reutov, *Izv. Akad. Nauk SSR, Ser. Khim.*, **1966**, 963; *Chem. Abs.*, **65**, 12074 (1966).

[22a] M. M. Kreevoy, P. J. Steinwand, and W. V. Kayser, *J. Am. Chem. Soc.*, **88**, 124 (1966).

[22b] I. P. Beletskaya, T. P. Fetisova, and O. A. Reutov, *Dokl. Akad. Nauk SSSR*, **166**, 681 (1966); *Chem. Abs.*, **64**, 14052 (1966).

[22c] I. P. Beletskaya, L. A. Fedorov, and O. A. Reutov, *Dokl. Akad. Nauk SSSR*, **163**, 1381 (1965).

[23] I. P. Beletskaya, G. A. Artamkina, and O. A. Reutov, *Dokl. Akad. Nauk SSSR*, **166**, 1347 (1966); *Chem. Abs.*, **64**, 17366 (1966).

[24] O. A. Maksimenko, I. P. Beletskaya, and O. A. Reutov, *Izv. Akad. Nauk SSSR, Ser. Khim.*, **1966**, 662; *Chem. Abs.*, **65**, 7016 (1966); I. P. Beletskaya, D. A. Maksimenko, and O. A. Reutov, *Dokl. Akad. Nauk SSSR*, **168**, 333 (1966); *Chem. Abs.*, **65**, 8703 (1966).

[25] O. A. Reutov and I. P. Beletskaya, *Izv. Akad. Nauk SSSR, Ser. Khim.*, **1966**, 955; *Chem. Abs.*, **65**, 15176 (1966).

[26] H. M. Walborsky and A. E. Young, *Baskerville Chem. J. of City College of New York*, **14**, 1 (1965).

[27] F. R. Jensen, and K. L. Nakamaye, *J. Am. Chem. Soc.*, **88**, 3437 (1966); see also, E. A. Hill, *J. Org. Chem.*, **31**, 20 (1966); N. G. Krieghoff and D. O. Cowan, *J. Am. Chem. Soc.*, **88**, 1322 (1966).

at $C_{(2)}$; these occur at $\tau = 10.48$ and 10.12 ppm, respectively. When this mixture is treated with a deficiency of benzophenone (57 moles %) the *exo*-Grignard reagent reacts rapidly, leaving ca. 95% pure *endo*-isomer. This, on treatment with carbon dioxide or mercuric bromide, yields 95% of *endo*-acid and 94% of *endo*-norbornylmercuric bromide, respectively; $S_E i$ mechanisms were considered most likely. The slow conversion of the *endo*-Grignard reagent into the equilibrium mixture could be followed by the change in the NMR spectrum.

Heat of mixing studies of the systems Et_2Mg–$MgBr_2$, Ph_2Mg–$MgBr_2$ Et_2Mg–MgI_2, and Ph_2Mg–MgI_2 (concn. 0.1—0.3M in ether) indicate that the equilibria

$$(R_2Mg) + (MgX_2) \rightleftarrows 2(RMgX)$$

are set up rapidly and lie far to the right.[28] On the other hand, the NMR spectrum of the pentafluorophenyl Grignard reagent (M in ether) shows two signals (triplets) for the *p*-fluorine at 22° which merge and become one triplet at 94°. It was therefore concluded[29] that there are present two species, one which is based on $(C_6F_5)_2Mg \cdot MgBr_2$ and the other on C_6F_5MgBr.

The rate of inversion of the Grignard reagent $EtMeCHCH_2MgBr$ has been determined by following the change in the NMR signal of the CH_2 protons which, in the absence of inversion, are magnetically non-equivalent but become equivalent on inversion. The rate constant is strongly solvent-dependent.[30] Similar experiments have been performed with a series of neo-hexylmetallic compounds, $Me_3CCH_2CH_2M$. In the absence of inversion the two groups of methylene protons form an AA'BB' system, but the signals broaden and collapse to an A_2B_2 system when inversion of the organometallic centre becomes rapid. The relative rates are $RLi > R_2Mg > R_2Zn$, but R_3Al and R_2Hg showed no change in their spectra over the temperature range 30° to 150—160° and it was concluded that they are configurationally stable.[31]

The equilibration of the α- and β-positions of 4,4-diphenylbut-3-enyl-magnesium bromide [equation (4)] occurs considerably more rapidly than with but-4-enylmagnesium bromide itself. There is less than 0.3% of the isomeric

$$\begin{array}{c}Ph \\ Ph\end{array}{>}C{=}CH{-}CH_2{-}CD_2MgBr \rightleftharpoons \begin{array}{c}D_2C \\ H_2C\end{array}{>}CH{-}\overset{\overset{\displaystyle Ph}{|}}{\underset{\underset{\displaystyle Ph}{|}}{C}}{-}MgBr \rightleftharpoons$$

$$\begin{array}{c}Ph \\ Ph\end{array}{>}C{=}CH{-}CD_2{-}CH_2MgBr \quad (4)$$

[28] M. B. Smith and W. E. Becker, *Tetrahedron*, **22**, 3027 (1966).
[29] D. F. Evans and M. S. Khan, *Chem. Commun.*, **1966**, 67.
[30] G. Fraenkel and D. T. Dix, *J. Am. Chem. Soc.*, **88**, 979 (1966).
[31] M. Witanowski and J. D. Roberts, *J. Am. Chem. Soc.*, **88**, 737 (1966).

cyclopropyl(diphenyl)methylmagnesium bromide present at equilibrium.[32] A similar but much slower rearrangement via a cyclobutane derivative also occurs with compounds (27) and (28).[33] Whereas compound (27) does not

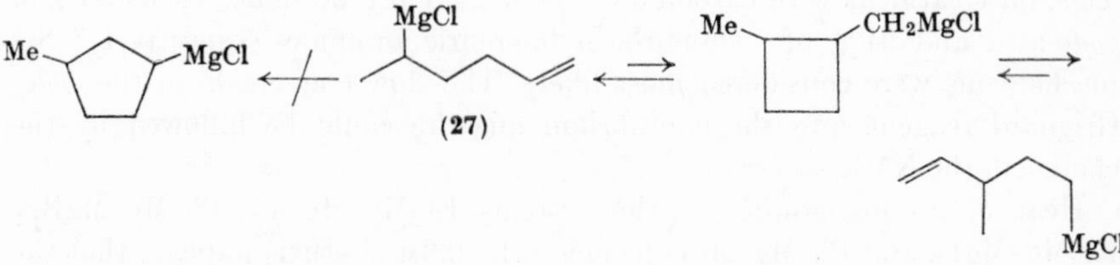

(27)

(28)

undergo ring closure to a cyclopentane, its homologue (30) does, but this in its turn does not form any of the cyclohexane derivative (29).[33]

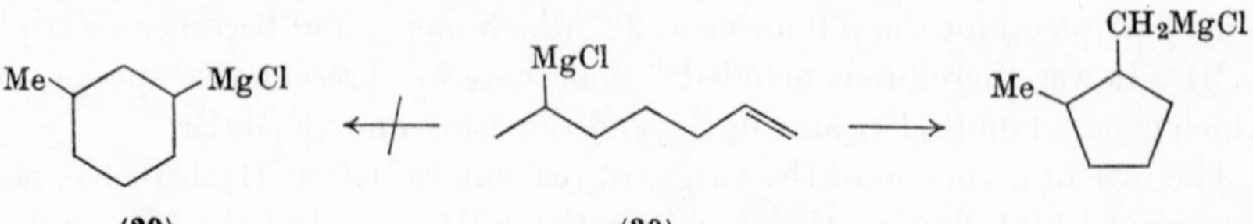

(29)   (30)

Intramolecular additions of organometallic compounds to carbon–carbon triple bonds in the systems (31), (32), and (33) have also been investigated.[34] With system (31), ring closure is observed when the metal is lithium [equation (5)] or when the Grignard reagent is treated with cuprous chloride which was thought to give a radical via an organocopper compound [equation (7)], but not when it was treated with water [equation (6)]. Ring closures were not observed with compound (32), but both the organolithium compound and the Grignard reagent of structure (33) underwent ring closure to yield a five-membered ring [equations (8) and (9)]. It was also demonstrated that 2,2'-bis(phenylethynyl)biphenyl, on being heated or exposed to light, undergoes a cycloaddition reaction.[34] (Other intramolecular reactions of triple bonds are discussed on pp. 31 and 127.)

It has been concluded from the NMR spectra of the α-^{13}C-labelled compounds that the central carbon atoms of triphenylmethyl-, diphenylmethyl-, and benzyl-lithium are substantially sp^2-hybridized in tetrahydrofuran with the electron pair in an orbital having predominant p-character.[35]

The stabilization energies of a series of triphenylmethyl anions have been

32 M. E. H. Howden, A. Maercker, J. Burdon, and J. D. Roberts, *J. Am. Chem. Soc.*, 88, 1732 (1966); A. Maercker and J. D. Roberts, *ibid.*, p. 1742.
33 H. G. Richey and T. C. Rees, *Tetrahedron Letters*, 1966, 4297.
34 S. A. Kandil and R. E. Dessy, *J. Am. Chem. Soc.*, 88, 3027 (1966).
35 R. Waack, M. A. Doran, E. B. Baker, and G. A. Olah, *J. Am. Chem. Soc.*, 88, 1272 (1966).

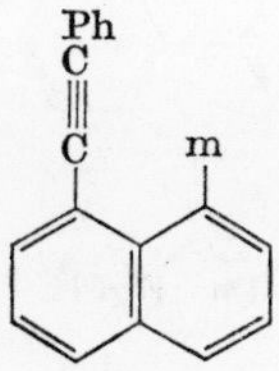

(31)

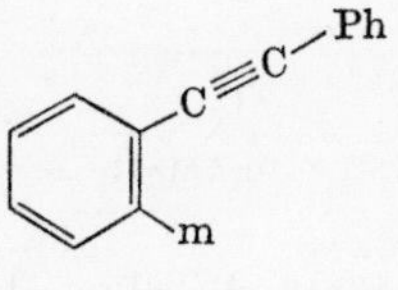

(32)

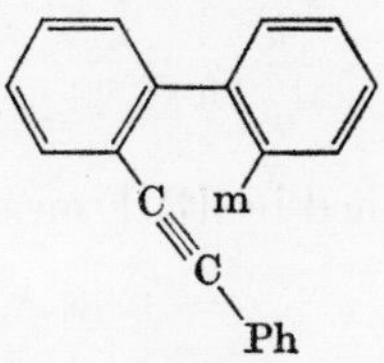

(33)

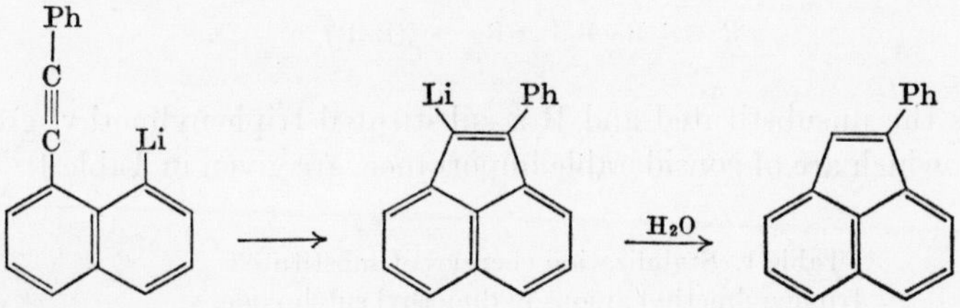

(5)

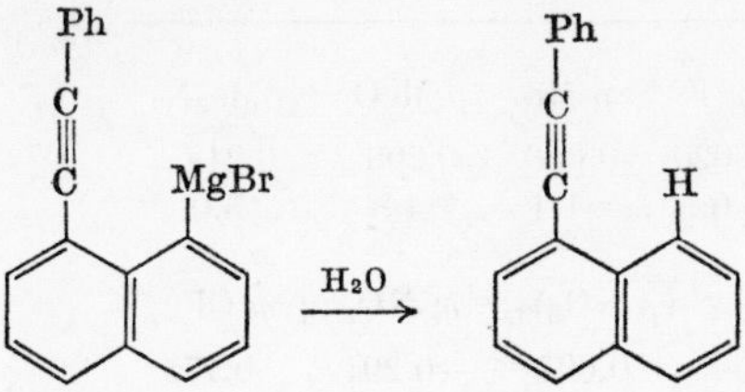

(6)

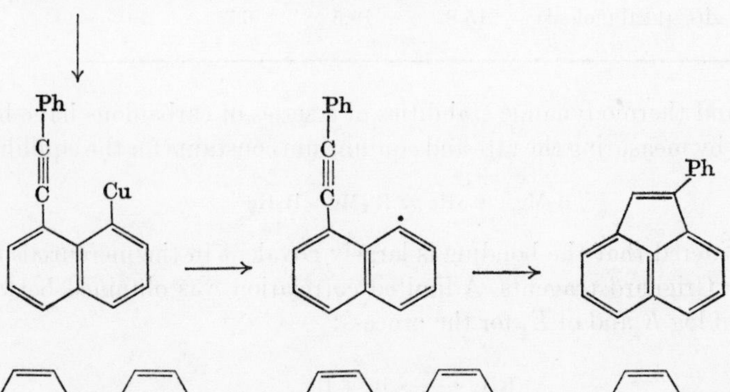

(7)

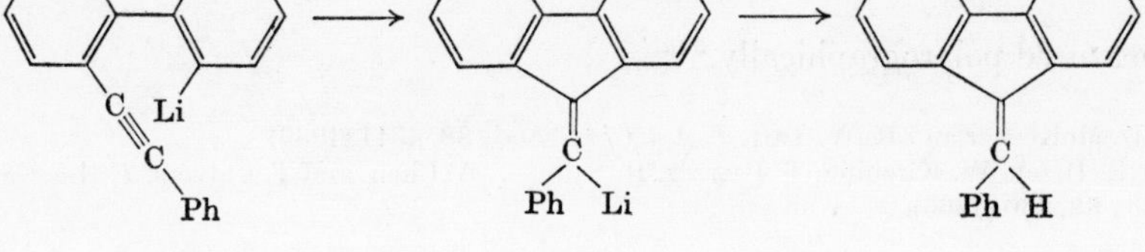

(8)

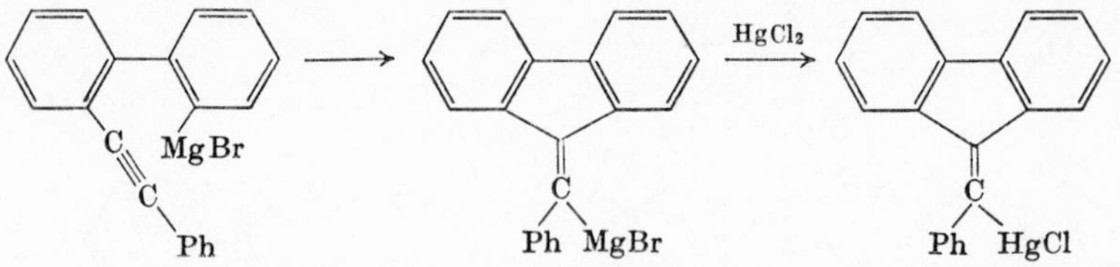

determined by EMF measurements. A cell in which reaction (10) took place:

$$R^-(Na^+) + Ag^+(NO_3^-) \rightleftharpoons \tfrac{1}{2}(R\text{–}R) + Ag + NaNO_3 \qquad (10)$$

was used to determine the value of E° and ΔG° for equation (11):

$$R^- + \tfrac{1}{2}(R_0\text{–}R_0) \rightleftharpoons R_0^- + \tfrac{1}{2}(R\text{–}R) \qquad (11)$$

where R_0 is the unsubstituted and R a substituted triphenylmethyl group. The results, which are of considerable importance, are given in Table 1.[36]

Table 1. Stabilization energies of substituted
triphenylmethyl anions in dimethyl sulphoxide.

Subst.	H	p-F	p-Me	p-MeO	p-Me$_2$N
E° (volt)	0	0.020	0.056	0.209	0.218
ΔG° (kcal mole^{-1})	0	−0.5	−1.4	−4.8	−5.0

Subst.	p-NO$_2$	(p-NO$_2$)$_3$	m-NO$_2$	m-CF$_3$
E° (volt)	−0.685	−0.697	−0.291	−0.175
ΔG° (kcal mole^{-1})	15.8	18.5	6.7	4.0

Kinetic and thermodynamic stabilities of a series of carbanions have been determined by measuring the rate and equilibrium constants for the equilibria:

$$R_2Mg + R'_2Hg \rightleftharpoons R'_2Mg + R_2Hg$$

It was considered that the bonding is largely covalent in the mercurials and ionic in the Grignard reagents. A limited correlation was obtained between the values of log K and of $E_{\frac{1}{2}}$ for the process:

$$RHg \xrightarrow{\ e^-\ } R^- + Hg$$

as measured polarographically.[37a]

[36] L. D. McKeever and R. W. Taft, *J. Am. Chem. Soc.*, **88**, 4544 (1966).
[37a] R. E. Dessy, W. Kitching, T. Psarras, R. Salinger, A. Chen, and T. Chivers, *J. Am. Chem. Soc.*, **88**, 460 (1966).

The acidities of two series of 9-fluorenyltriphenylphosphonium bromides substituted in the fluorenyl and in the phenyl groups can be correlated by the Hammett σ constants with ρ constants of +5.0 and +4.8, respectively.[37b]

Kinetic evidence has been presented that dimeric phenyllithium is a reactive species in the metallation of triphenylmethane and in the addition of phenyllithium to 1,1-diphenylethylene.[38]

The electronic spectra of 1,1-diphenylhexyllithium[39] and of a large number of carbanions[40] have been reported.

Other work on alkyllithiums and Grignard reagents includes investigations of: the reaction of *tert*-butyllithium with fluorene;[41] lithium exchange reactions;[42] the conversion of phenylacetonitrile into a dilithium compound;[43] the steric course of the reaction of butenyl Grignard reagents with electrophilic substrates;[44] the protolysis of but-2-enylmagnesium bromide;[45] reactions of Grignard reagents with benzonitrile[46] and carbonyl compounds[47] (see also, pp. 334—337); polarography of organomagnesium reagents.[48]

An *X*-ray structure determination of the ylide, 2-chloro-2-(triphenyl-phosphoranylidene)acetophenone, has shown that the main contributing resonance structure is the dipolar structure (**34**).[49]

(**34**)

Last year the opening of the cyclopropane ring of bicyclo[2.1.0]pentane with chlorine was recorded;[50] an investigation of the opening of cyclopropane itself with bromine and ferric bromide has now been reported.[51] 1,1-, 1,2, and 1,3-Dibromopropane are all produced, possibly via protonated cyclopropane intermediates (see Scheme 1).

[37b] A. W. Johnson, S. Y. Lee, R. A. Swor, and L. D. Royer, *J. Am. Chem. Soc.*, **88**, 1953 (1966).
[38] R. Waack, P. West, and M. A. Doran, *Chem. Ind. (London)*, **1966**, 1035.
[39] R. Waak, M. A. Doran, and P. E. Stevenson, *J. Am. Chem. Soc.*, **88**, 2109 (1966).
[40] R. Kuhn and D. Rewicki, *Ann. Chem.*, **690**, 50 (1965).
[41] R. A. H. Casling, A. G. Evans, and N. H. Rees, *J. Chem. Soc.*, *B*, **1966**, 519.
[42] K. C. Williams and T. L. Brown, *J. Am. Chem. Soc.*, **88**, 4134 (1966); L. M. Seitz and T. L. Brown, *ibid.*, pp. 2174, 4140; G. E. Hartwell and T. L. Brown, *ibid.*, p. 4625.
[43] E. M. Kaiser and C. R. Hauser, *J. Am. Chem. Soc.*, **88**, 2348 (1966).
[44] H. Felkin, C. Frajerman, and Y. Gault, *Chem. Commun.*, **1966**, 75.
[45] C. Agami, M. Andrac-Taussig, and C. Prévost, *Bull. Soc. Chim. France*, **1966**, 1915.
[46] H. Edelstein and E. I. Becker, *J. Org. Chem.*, **31**, 3375 (1966).
[47] T. Holm, *Acta Chem. Scand.*, **19**, 1819 (1965); **20**, 1139 (1966); *Tetrahedron Letters*, **1966**, 3329.
[48] T. Psarras and R. E. Dessy, *J. Am. Chem. Soc.*, **88**, 5132 (1966).
[49] A. J. Speziale and K. W. Ratts, *J. Am. Chem. Soc.*, **87**, 5603 (1965).
[50] See *Organic Reaction Mechanisms*, **1965**, 88.
[51] N. C. Deno and D. N. Lincoln, *J. Am. Chem. Soc.*, **88**, 5357 (1966); W. Naegele and H. Haubenstock, *Tetrahedron Letters*, **1965**, 4283.

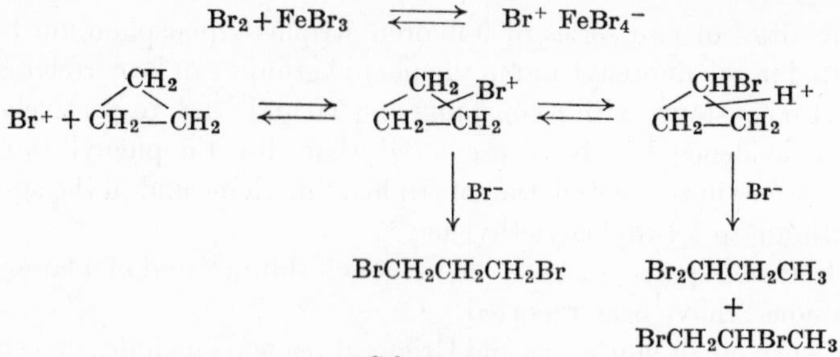

$$Br_2 + FeBr_3 \; \rightleftharpoons \; Br^+ \; FeBr_4^-$$

Scheme 1

The side-chain chlorination of hexamethylbenzene with iodine mono-chloride has been further investigated.[52]

Other reactions that have been investigated include: methanolysis of dimethyl- and diphenyl-zinc;[53] electrolytic reduction of (*S*)-1-bromo-1-methyl-2,2-diphenylcyclopropane (63% retention of configuration);[54] reduction of alkylmercuric hydroxides by borohydride;[55] cleavage of allyl chloride, trimethylammonium halides, alkyl *p*-tolyl sulphides, and cyclopropyltrimethylammonium halides by sodium in liquid ammonia;[56] reaction of trialkylboranes with dimethyloxosulphonium methylide;[57] base-catalysed hydrogen exchange of organic sulfides[58a] and α-butyrolactone;[58b] proton transfer from phenols to the trinitrobenzyl anion;[59] proton removal from 4-nitrodiphenylmethyl chloride;[60] and isonitrozation of (nitroalkyl)benzenes.[61]

[52] R. M. Keefer and L. J. Andrews, *J. Org. Chem.*, **31**, 541 (1966).

[53] G. Allen, J. M. Bruce, D. W. Farren, and F. G. Hutchinson, *J. Chem. Soc., B*, **1966**, 799; J. Malcolm Bruce, B. C. Cutsforth, D. W. Farren, F. G. Hutchinson, F. M. Rabagliati, and D. R. Reed, *J. Chem. Soc., B*, **1966**, 1020.

[54] C. K. Mann, J. L. Webb, and H. M. Walborsky, *Tetrahedron Letters*, **1966**, 2249.

[55] F. G. Bordwell and M. L. Douglass, *J. Am. Chem. Soc.*, **88**, 993 (1966).

[56] E. Grovenstein, S. Chandra, C. E. Collum, and W. E. Davis, *J. Am. Chem. Soc.*, **88**, 1275 (1966).

[57] J. J. Tufariello, and L. T. C. Lee, *J. Am. Chem. Soc.*, **88**, 4757 (1966).

[58a] A. I. Shatenshtein and E. A. Gvozdeva, *Teor. i Eksperim. Khim. Akad. Nauk. Ukr. SSR*, **1**, 353 (1965); *Chem. Abs.*, **63**, 13048 (1965).

[58b] W. Theilacker and K. H. Bremer, *Chem. Ber.*, **99**, 2066 (1966).

[59] J. A. Blake, M. J. B. Evans, and K. E. Russell, *Can. J. Chem.*, **44**, 119 (1966).

[60] D. Bethell and A. F. Cockerill, *J. Chem. Soc., B*, **1966**, 920, 913.

[61] N. Bodor and A. Koevendi, *Rev. Roumaine Chim.*, **11**, 393, 431 (1966); N. Bodor, L. Fey, and A. Kovendi, *ibid.*, pp. 405, 421; *Chem. Abs.*, **65**, 7010—7012 (1966).

CHAPTER 4

Elimination Reactions

Reviews of the transition state of olefin-forming $E2$ eliminations[1] and of quasi-heterolytic gas-phase reactions[2] have been published.

The very interesting suggestion has been made that elimination reactions of cycloalkyltrimethylammonium ions (from medium and large rings) to yield *trans*-cycloalkenes proceed by a *cis*(or *syn*)-mechanism.[3] The rates of formation of *cis*- and *trans*-olefins from a series of cycloalkyldimethylamine N-oxides in *tert*-butyl alcohol were first measured. The rates of both series showed maxima in the medium-ring region, i.e., with the eight-membered ring for the formation of the *cis*-olefins and with the ten-membered ring for the formation of the *trans*-olefins (see Figure 1). This dependence of rate on ring size was taken to be characteristic of *syn*-eliminations. For $E2$ eliminations of cycloalkyltrimethylammonium chlorides by potassium *tert*-butoxide in *tert*-butyl alcohol the dependence of the rates of formation of *cis*- and *trans*-olefins on ring size are quite different from one another (Figure 2). The rates of formation of the *trans*-olefins show a dependence very similar to that shown by the amine oxides, but that of the *cis*-olefins is similar to that shown by S_N2 reactions. On the assumption then that mechanisms with similar "salient steric features" show similar dependence of rate on ring size it was suggested that $E2$ elimination of the cycloalkyltrimethylammonium ions to form *trans*-olefins proceeds by a *syn*-mechanism, and that *cis*-olefins are formed by an *anti*-mechanism.

Further support for this view was obtained from a study of the reactions of the conformationally stabilized[4] NNN-trimethyl-4,4,7,7-tetramethylcyclodecylammonium ion (1).[5] Isotope effects ($k_H/k_D = 2.3$ and 2.8, respectively) were observed in the eliminations that gave both *trans*- and *cis*-olefins (2) from the *trans*-deuterated compound (4) but not from *cis*-deuterated compound (3). It was therefore concluded that the hydrogen atom that was configurationally *trans* to the trimethylammonium group was being eliminated in the formation of both the *trans*- and the *cis*-olefin. This means that the

[1] D. V. Banthorpe in "Studies on Chemical Structure and Reactivity", J. H. Ridd, ed., Methuen, London, 1966, p. 33.

[2] A. Maccoll in "Studies on Chemical Structure and Reactivity", J. H. Ridd, ed., Methuen, London, 1966, p. 53.

[3] J. Sicher, J. Závada, and J. Krupička, *Tetrahedron Letters*, **1966**, 1619; J. Závada, J. Krupička, and J. Sicher, *Coll. Czech. Chem. Commun.*, **31**, 4273 (1966).

[4] J. Sicher, M. Svoboda, J. Závada, R. B. Turner, and P. Goebel, *Tetrahedron*, **22**, 659 (1966).

[5] J. Závada, M. Svoboda, and J. Sicher, *Tetrahedron Letters*, **1966**, 1627.

trans-olefin is being formed by a *syn*-mechanism, and the *cis*-olefin by an *anti*-mechanism. Similar results were obtained in the reaction of the corresponding toluene-*p*-sulphonates with potassium *tert*-butoxide in dimethyl-

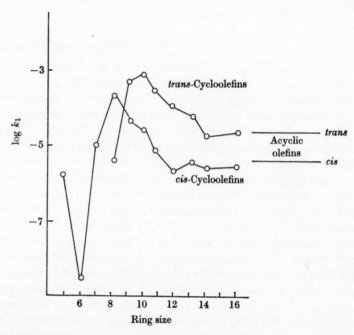

FIG. 1. Effect of ring size on rates of *cis*- and *trans*-cycloalkene formation from cycloalkyldimethylamine *N*-oxides in *tert*-butyl alcohol at 70.6°.

formamide, so the *syn*-mechanism is not restricted to the reactions of compounds with the trimethylammonium leaving group.

It has also been reported that, whereas *trans*-2-methylcyclo-pentyl, -hexyl, and -heptyl toluene-*p*-sulphonates with potassium *tert*-butoxide yield almost exclusively 3-methylcycloalkenes, *trans*-3-methylcyclo-octyl toluene-*p*-sulphonate yields 50% of 1-methylcyclocyclo-octene by elimination of configurationally *cis*-hydrogen and toluene-*p*-sulphonyloxy-groups; the proportions of *cis*- and *trans*-olefins were not determined, however.[6] Also of interest in this investigation were the very small differences reported between

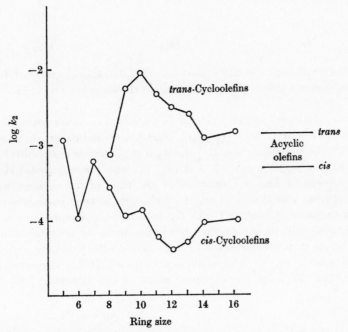

Fig. 2. Effect of ring size on rates of *cis*- and *trans*-cycloalkene formation from cycloalkyl-trimethylammonium chlorides and potassium *tert*-butoxide in *tert*-butyl alcohol at 55°.

the rates of elimination from cyclo-pentyl, -hexyl, -heptyl, and -octyl toluene-*p*-sulphonate (7.81, 2.14, 2.34, and 1.28×10^{-4} l. mole^{-1} sec^{-1}, respectively, at 50°) by potassium *tert*-butoxide in *tert*-butyl alcohol.

Among the most striking examples of a *cis*-elimination reported in recent years are those of *exo*-norbornyl derivatives which react with loss of the *exo*-hydrogen at $C_{(3)}$.[7] The controlling factor here could be either that elimination occurs more readily when the dihedral angle between the eliminated groups is 0° (*cis*-elimination) than when it is 120° (*trans*-elimination) or that the *exo*-hydrogen atom is more readily removed than the *endo*- one. Evidence

6 H. C. Brown and R. L. Klimisch, *J. Am. Chem. Soc.*, **88**, 1430 (1966).
7 H. Kwart, T. Takeshita, and J. L. Nyce, *J. Am. Chem. Soc.*, **86**, 2606 (1964).

4*

that it is the latter factor which is the more important has been obtained by studying the deuterated *endo*-norbornyl chloride (5) which reacted with *tert*-hexoxide in *tert*-hexanol mainly with loss of the *exo*-deuterium by a *trans*-elimination than with loss of *endo*-hydrogen by a *cis*-elimination.

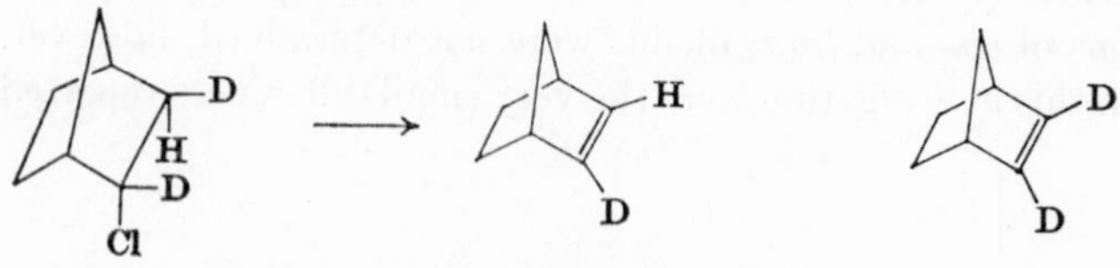

(5)   **86%**   **14%**

From these and earlier results it may be calculated that the rates of dehydro-halogenation of halogenonorbornanes fall in the order *exo-cis* > *trans* > *endo-cis*.[8]

Further examples of the preferred formation of *cis*- over *trans*-alkenes in $E2$ eliminations have been reported. Thus, the second-order reaction of *sec*-butyl toluene-*p*-sulphonate with potassium *tert*-butoxide in *tert*-butyl alcohol yields 62% of 1-, 24% of *cis*-2, and 14% of *trans*-2-butene (note: Hofmann rule followed). A higher proportion of *cis*- than of *trans*-alkene was also obtained from 1-methylbutyl and 1-ethylpropyl toluene-*p*-sulphonate. This behaviour was only observed with the toluene-*p*-sulphonates, not with the halides, and only with potassium *tert*-butoxide in *tert*-butyl alcohol. With *tert*-butoxide in tetrahydrofuran or diglyme, or with potassium ethoxide in ethanol, more *trans*- than *cis*-olefin was obtained. It was suggested by one group[9] that the large steric requirements of the attacking base (Bu^tO^-

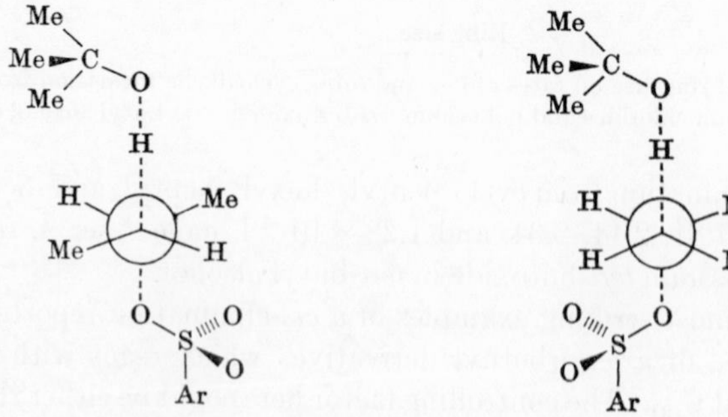

(6)   **(7)**

[8] J. K. Stille and F. M. Sonnenberg, *Tetrahedron Letters*, **1966**, 4587; F. M. Sonnenberg, and J. K. Stille, *J. Org. Chem.*, **31**, 3441 (1966); J. K. Stille, F. M. Sonnenberg, and T. H. Kinstle, *J. Am. Chem. Soc.*, **88**, 4922 (1966).

[9] H. C. Brown and R. L. Klimisch, *J. Am. Chem. Soc.*, **87**, 5517 (1965).

solvated by Bu^{t}OH) and the leaving toluene-*p*-sulphonyloxy-group are accommodated better by transition state (**7**) for the elimination (to give *cis*-alkene) than by transition state (**6**) (to give *trans*-alkene) and by another[10] that in *tert*-butyl alcohol the transition states are ones in which C–H bond breaking is well developed but C–O bond breaking is undeveloped, and that the *cis*-olefin is formed preferentially only because the steric requirements of the toluene-*p*-sulphonyl group are better accommodated in transition state (**7**) than in transition state (**6**).[11]

More examples of *E*2 eliminations of alkyl halides with *tert*-butoxide as base which follow the Hofmann rule have been reported (see Table 1).[12,13] These results, which show that the proportion of terminal olefin increases in the order I < Br < Cl, were considered to be consistent with the steric explanation of the Hofmann rule since it was thought that the steric requirements of the halides would increase in the order I < Br < Cl because the length of the carbon–halogen bond decreases in the order I > Br > Cl. It is interesting that the position of the axial–equatorial equilibrium of the cyclohexyl halides indicates the same order for the steric requirements of the halides.[14] In view of the discussion reported last year,[13] however, these results are presumably also

Table 1. Olefin distributions in the *E*2 reactions of *sec*-butyl and *tert*-pentyl halides with potassium *tert*-butoxide in *tert*-butyl alcohol at 50°.[12]

Halide	Olefin (%)		
	1-	*trans*-2-	*cis*-2-
sec-Butyl chloride	67	18	14
sec-Butyl bromide	54	27.6	18.8
sec-Butyl iodide	34	47.5	21.9
tert-Pentyl chloride	78	22	
tert-Pentyl bromide	73	27	
tert-Pentyl iodide	60	40	

[10] D. H. Froemsdorf, W. Dowd, and K. E. Leimer, *J. Am. Chem. Soc.*, **88**, 2345 (1966).

[11] The results and explanations given here should be contrasted with the report last year that the trimethyl-5-nonylammonium ion yielded more *cis*- than *trans*-olefin with MeO$^-$ in MeOH and EtO$^-$ in EtOH (but not with Bu^{t}O$^-$ in Bu^{t}OH) owing, it was suggested, to an *E*1*cB*-like *cis*-elimination; see *Organic Reaction Mechanisms*, **1965**, 91.

[12] H. C. Brown and R. L. Klimisch, *J. Am. Chem. Soc.*, **88**, 1425 (1966).

[13] See also, *Organic Reaction Mechanisms*, **1965**, 93—95.

[14] A. J. Berlin and F. R. Jensen, *Chem. Ind.* (*London*), **1960**, 998; the ΔG values for chloro-, bromo-, and iodo-cyclohexane are, respectively, 513, 480, and 341 cal mole^{-1}, i.e., the differences between them are very small.

interpretable on the assumption that the Hofmann rule is the result of a transition state with carbanionic character.

An interesting demonstration of the concerted nature of bimolecular elimination reactions has been given by Willi,[15a] who studied the reactions of the 2,2-diphenylethyl arenesulphonates, $Ph_2CHCH_2O \cdot SO_2 \cdot C_6H_4X$, where $X = p\text{-MeO}$, $p\text{-Me}$, H, or $p\text{-NO}_2$, with sodium methoxide in methylcellosolve. These reactions have a ρ value (1.11) similar to that found for the solvolysis of methyl, ethyl, and isopropyl arenesulphonates, indicating a similar degree of $C_\alpha\text{-O}$ bond-breaking in the transition state. The deuterium isotope effects when the β-hydrogen atoms were replaced by deuterium were found to be $k_H/k_D = 5.27$, 5.42, and 6.70 at 49.85° with $X = p\text{-MeO}$, H, and $p\text{-NO}_2$, respectively. It was thought that the increased value found with the p-nitrobenzenesulphonate could not be the result of any direct influence of the nitro-group on the acidity of the β-hydrogen atom, but was rather a result of the concerted breaking of the $C_\alpha\text{-O}$ and $C_\beta\text{-H}$ bonds. It was also concluded that tunnelling is absent in these reactions.[15b]

The elimination reactions in aqueous solution of 2,2-dibromo-, 2,2-dichloro-, and 2-bromo-2-chloro-propane to yield the corresponding propenes have $\Delta C_p{}^\ddagger$ values and β-deuterium isotope effects similar to those shown in unimolecular hydrolyses. It was therefore considered that the mechanism is $E1$.[15c]

Mechanisms involving the reversible formation of carbanions have been excluded for several elimination reactions. Thus the ethoxide-catalysed reaction of phenethyl fluoride, which shows a large ρ-value (+3.1 at 30°), and of 1-methylbutyl fluoride, which follows the Hofmann rule, did not incorporate deuterium (mass spectrometry) after 30—40% reaction with EtO⁻ in EtOD.[16]

It was similarly shown by infrared spectroscopy that $cis\text{-}\beta$-bromo-4-nitrostyrene and $cis\text{-}\beta$-bromo-2,4-dinitrostyrene, which react to give the corresponding acetylenes, did not contain deuterium when recovered after 5—50% reaction with MeO⁻ in MeOD.[17] The much greater rate for the dinitro-compound ($k_2 = 1.06$ l. mole⁻¹ sec⁻¹ at 25°) than of the mononitro-compound ($k_2 = 7.10 \times 10^{-4}$ l. mole⁻¹ sec⁻¹), and the small primary isotope effect ($k_H/k_D = 2.2$ at 25°) observed on deuteration of the latter, suggest, however, that the transition state has considerable carbanionic character.

The possibility that carbanions are intermediates in the elimination reactions of compounds of structures (8) and (9) has also been discussed.[18]

[15a] A. V. Willi, *Helv. Chim. Acta*, **49**, 1725 (1966).
[15b] A. V. Willi, *J. Phys. Chem.*, **70**, 2705 (1966).
[15c] A. Queen and R. E. Robertson, *J. Am. Chem. Soc.*, **88**, 1363 (1966).
[16] W. H. Saunders and M. R. Schreiber, *Chem. Commun.*, **1966**, 145.
[17] G. Marchese, G. Modena, and F. Naso, *Chem. Commun.*, **1966**, 492.
[18] G. Schwenker, *Arch. Pharm.*, **299**, 131 (1966).

(8)

Tr = tropyl

(9)

R = alkyl, aryl, or aralkyl

The sulphur-isotope effect, $100(k_{32}/k_{34} - 1)$, for the reaction of dimethyl-phenethylsulphonium bromide with hydroxide is 0.64 at 59°,[19] not 0.15 as previously reported,[20] indicating that the transition state cannot have the strong carbanionic character that was then proposed. This is consistent with the Hammett ρ-value of +2.6 which may be compared with that of +3.8 found with the corresponding trimethylammonium ion for which the nitrogen isotope effect, $100(k_{14}/k_{15} - 1)$, is about 1.

An extensive investigation of the $E2$ elimination reaction of 1,1,1-trichloro-2,2-di-p-chlorophenylethane (DDT) with thiolate ions has been reported.[21a] These reactions occur very much more slowly than those with oxygen bases, that with benzenethiolate, for instance, occurring 14,000 times more slowly than with ethoxide ion. The reaction with benzenethiolate ion in methanol is so slow that there is significant incursion of an elimination promoted by methoxide ions formed by the equilibrium:

$$PhS^- + MeOH \rightleftarrows PhSH + MeO^-$$

This results in a decrease in the second-order rate constants as the reaction proceeds, owing to the accumulation of the benzenethiol formed in the reaction. The possibility that this behaviour was due to an $E1cB$ mechanism with a reversible step:

$$PhS^- + Ar_2CH \cdot CCl_3 \rightleftarrows PhSH + Ar_2\overset{-}{C} \cdot CCl_3$$

was excluded by labelling experiments with MeO^3H. The Brønsted coefficients for the reaction with a series of substituted benzenethiols and phenols were found to be 0.77 ± 0.05 and 0.88 ± 0.05, respectively, and the β-deuterium isotope effect was $k_H/k_D = 3.4$ with EtO^- and 3.1 with PhS^- as base at 45°.

In contrast with these results cyclohexyl toluene-p-sulphonate and bromide[21b] and *tert*-butyl chloride[21c] undergo an $E2$ elimination more readily with benzenethiolate than with ethoxide as base. These reactions are characterized by a low Brønsted β-value and as the ratio k_{PhS^-}/k_{EtO^-} decreases the

[19] W. H. Saunders, A. F. Cockerill, S. Ašperger, L. Klasinc, and D. Stefanović, *J. Am. Chem. Soc.*, **88**, 848 (1966).

[20] W. H. Saunders and S. Ašperger, *J. Am. Chem. Soc.*, **79**, 1612 (1957).

[21a] B. D. England and D. J. McLennan, *J. Chem. Soc.*, B, **1966**, 696.

[21b] D. J. McLennan, *J. Chem. Soc.*, B, **1966**, 705.

[21c] D. J. McLennan, *J. Chem. Soc.*, B, **1966**, 709.

β-value increases (see Table 2). On the assumption then that the β-value is a measure of the amount of proton transfer, in the transition state, these results support the view[22a] that high reactivity by thiolate ions in $E2$ reactions is associated with a small amount of C–H bond stretching in the transition state. It was considered that all the results could be explained in this way without recourse to a "merged mechanism" of elimination and substitution.

Table 2. Brønsted β coefficients for $E2$ elimination reactions promoted by substituted benzenethiolate ions.

Compound	Temp.	k_{PhS-}/k_{EtO-}	β
Cyclohexyl toluene-p-sulphonate	35°	7.0	0.27
Cyclohexyl bromide	55°	1.6	0.36
Cyclohexyl chloride	55°	0.73	0.39
1,1-Dibromocyclohexane	55°	0.63	0.51
1,1-Dichlorocyclohexane	55°	0.21	0.58
tert-Butyl chloride	45°	—	0.17
tert-Butyldimethylsulphonium ion	25°	—	0.46

Potassium *tert*-butoxide is more effective, however, than potassium *tert*-butyl sulphide in promoting elimination from cyclohexyl toluene-p-sulphonate in dimethyl sulphoxide solution.[22b]

The conversion of β-methylaspartate to mesaconate:

$$^-O_2C-CHMe-CHNH_3^+-CO_2^- \rightarrow \ ^-O_2C-CMe{=}CHCO_2^-$$

by β-methylaspartase is thought to involve a proton abstraction by a thiol group of the enzyme.[23a]

The deuterium isotope effect (k_H/k_D) for the base-catalysed elimination of 9-bromo-9,9'-bifluorenyl into bifluorenylidene has values of 6—8 for a variety of bases at 30°. It was concluded that this is larger than predicted from the difference in zero-point energy for the stretching of the tertiary C–H and C–D bonds and that tunnelling is possibly important.[23b]

Hammett plots for the Cl⁻- and Br⁻-promoted elimination reactions of some substituted 2-benzyl-2-bromoindan-1-ones **(10)** in acetonitrile were curves yielding average ρ-values of $+0.42$ and $+0.16$, respectively.[24] These

[22a] J. F. Bunnett, *Angew. Chem. Internat. Edn.*, **1**, 225 (1962); J. F. Bunnett and E. Baciocchi, *Proc. Chem. Soc.*, **1963**, 238.
[22b] Y. C. Mac and A. J. Parker, *Australian J. Chem.*, **19**, 517 (1966).
[23a] V. R. Williams and W. Y. Libano, *Biochem. Biophys. Acta*, **18**, 144 (1966).
[23b] D. Bethell and A. F. Cockerill, *J. Chem. Soc., B*, **1966**, 917.
[24] D. N. Kevill, E. D. Weiler, and N. H. Cromwell, *J. Am. Chem. Soc.*, **88**, 4489 (1966).

values were interpreted as indicating that carbon–halogen bond-breaking was running ahead of carbon–hydrogen bond-breaking in the transition state, a

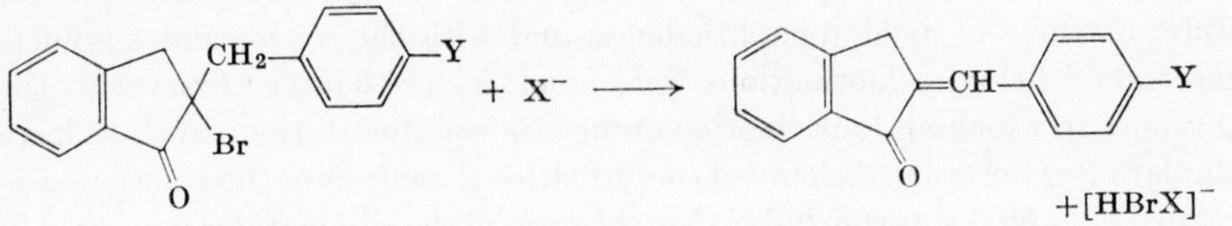

(10)

X = Cl or Br

conclusion that is supported by the relatively small primary isotope effect observed with the Br^--catalysed dehydrobromination of the structurally similar 2-benzyl-2-bromo-3,3-dimethylindan-1-one, $k_H/k_D = 2.5$ at 74°. The similarity of the ρ-values with those found for the reactions of phenethyl chloride and chloromethyl phenyl ketone with iodide ion in acetone, +0.59 and +0.61, respectively, were considered to provide circumstantial support for a merged mechanism in which the transition state for the elimination has "substitution character".

As part of an investigation of the chlorination of naphthalene (see p. 202),

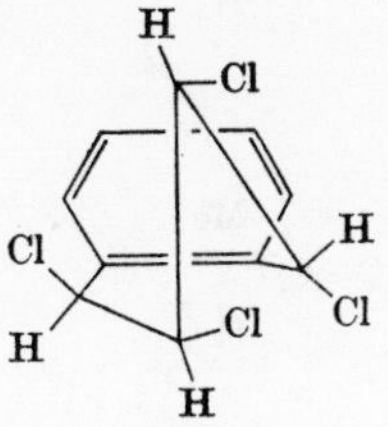

α

(11)

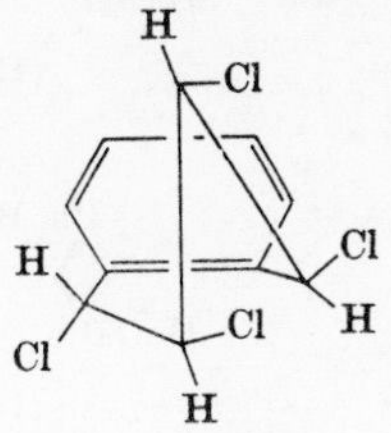

γ

(12)

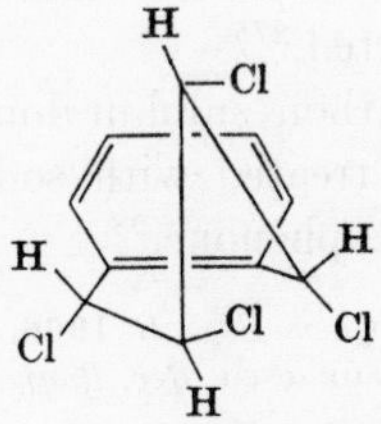

δ

(13)

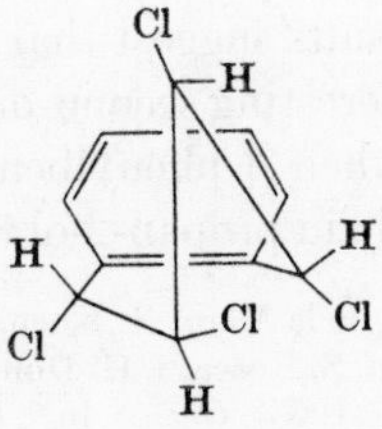

ε

(14)

de la Mare and his co-workers[25] have investigated the kinetics and products of the dehydrochlorination of four naphthalene tetrachlorides (11)—(14) by sodium methoxide in methanol–acetone (80:20 v/v) at 25°. The final products were mixtures of dichloronaphthalenes, and with the α-, δ-, and ϵ-isomers the second dehydrochlorinations were much faster than the first; with the γ-isomer in which all four chlorine atoms are equatorial, the two steps have similar rate constants. A detailed conformational analysis of the reactions was carried out and it was concluded that the rates of the eliminations decreased in the order *trans*(a'-1-H, a-2-Cl) > *trans*-(a-2-H, a'-1-Cl) > *trans*(a-2-H, a-3-Cl) > *cis*(a'-1-H, e-2-Cl) > *cis*-(a-2-H, e'-1-Cl).

The elimination reactions of 1,2-dihalogenocycloalkanes have been discussed.[26]

erythro- and *threo*-1,2-Dibromo-1-phenylpropylphosphonic acid (15) and (16) undergo a stereospecific *trans*-elimination with aqueous sodium hydroxide to yield *trans*- and *cis*-1-bromopropenylbenzene, respectively.[27a] These reactions may also yield the hypothetical metaphosphate ion which has frequently been postulated as an intermediate in the hydrolyses of monoalkyl phosphates.

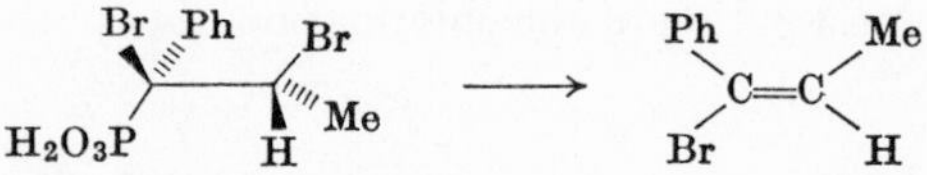

(15)

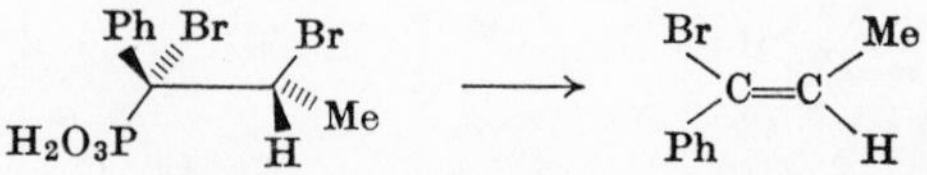

(16)

The elimination of 9-fluorenyl nitrate with acetate ion in anhydrous ethanol, to yield 9-fluorenone, gives primary nitrogen-15 and deuterium isotope effects of 1.0091 and 4.3, respectively. In 85% aqueous ethanol the nitrogen isotope effect is 1.0131 and the deuterium isotope effect is unchanged. These results suggest that the mechanism is concerted.[27b]

An interesting second-order reaction to form a carbon–sulphur double bond occurs when 4-phenylbenzhydryl thiocyanate is treated with sodium isopropoxide in propan-2-ol to yield 4-phenylthiobenzophenone.[28]

[25] P. B. D. de la Mare, R. Koenigsberger, and J. S. Lomas, *J. Chem. Soc.*, B, **1966**, 834.
[26] F. Badea, S. Rosca, I. G. Dinulescu, M. Avram, and C. D. Nenitzescu, *Rev. Roumaine Chim.*, **10**, 1201 (1965); *Chem. Abs.*, **65**, 589 (1966).
[27a] G. L. Kenyon, and F. H. Westheimer, *J. Am. Chem. Soc.*, **88**, 3557, 3561 (1966).
[27b] P. J. Smith and A. N. Bourns, *Can. J. Chem.*, **44**, 2553 (1966).
[28] A. Ceccon, U. Tonellato, and U. Miotti, *Chem. Commun.*, **1966**, 586.

It has been claimed that the rates of the solvolyses of the tertiary ω-amino-alkyl chlorides (**16a**), (**17a**), (**18a**), and (**19a**) (see Table 3) indicate that the components of these reactions which are eliminations proceed with participa-

Table 3. The relative rates of the elimination reactions of some tertiary aminoalkyl chlorides in 80% ethanol in the presence of triethylamine.

	Relative rate of solvolysis	Proportion of elimination	Rate of elimination relative to rate of solvolysis of analogous compound lacking an amino-group
$Me_2NCH_2CMe_2CMe_2Cl$ (**16a**)[a]	125	30%	37.5
$Me_2CHCH_2CMe_2CMe_2Cl$ (**16b**)	1	—	—
$H_2NCMe_2CH_2CMe_2Cl$ (**17a**)[a]	3	70%	2
$MeCMe_2CH_2CMe_2Cl$ (**17b**)	1	—	—
$Me_2NCMe_2CH_2CMe_2Cl$ (**18a**)[a]	27	20%	5.4
$Me_2CHCMe_2CH_2CMe_2Cl$ (**18b**)	1	—	—
$Me_2NCH_2CMe_2CH_2CMe_2Cl$ (**19a**)[b]	7.2	12%	0.9
$Me_2CHCH_2CMe_2CH_2CMe_2Cl$ (**19b**)	1	—	—

[a] Accompanied by fragmentation.
[b] Accompanied by ring closure.

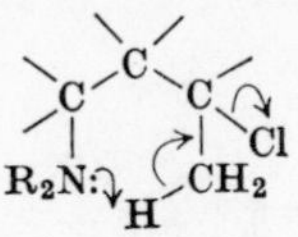

tion of the amino-groups in the rate-determining steps as shown in (**20**) and (**21**).[29a] Only with compound (**16a**), however, is the rate of elimination substantially greater than the rate of the unimolecular solvolysis of the analogous compound without the amino-group (see Table 3). With compounds (**17a**), (**18a**), and (**19a**) this rate enhancement is slight and participation in the rate-determining step can, therefore, only be marginal. It is possible,

(**20**) 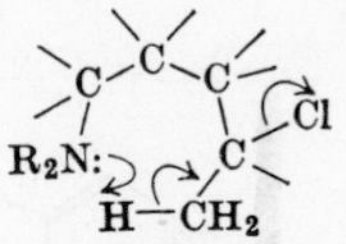   (**21**) 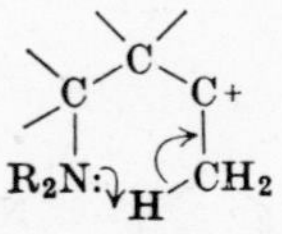   (**22**)

however, that participation occurs after a rate-determining ionization as (**22**), since it was also reported that the compounds with the amino groups

[29a] A. M. Braun, C. E. Ebner, C. A. Grob, and F. A. Jenny, *Tetrahedron Letters*, **1965**, 4733.

yielded terminal alkene exclusively, whereas compound (**17b**) gave 20% of 2-alkene.

A similar, intramolecularly base-catalysed elimination possibly occurs in the conversion of the 6-*O*-unsubstituted 1,2-*O*-isopropylidene-5-*O*-toluene-*p*-sulphonyl-α-D-glucofuranose (**23a**) into the enol ether (**23b**) by sodium methoxide in methanol, since when position 3 is blocked the elimination does not occur.[29b]

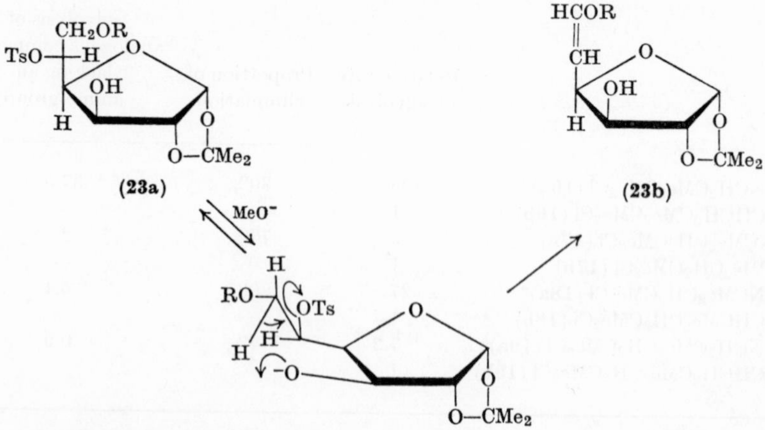

(23a)   (23b)

R = Ph₃C or PhCH₂

Interesting examples of neighbouring-group participation are found in the eliminations of *o*-iodo- and *o*-methylthio-*syn*-benzaldoxime esters into nitriles which proceed 119 and 11,000 times faster than those of the corresponding *para*-compounds. It seems most likely that the neighbouring iodo- and methylthio-groups provide nucleophilic assistance to yield cyclic intermediates [e.g., (**24**)] which then undergo elimination to the nitriles.[29c]

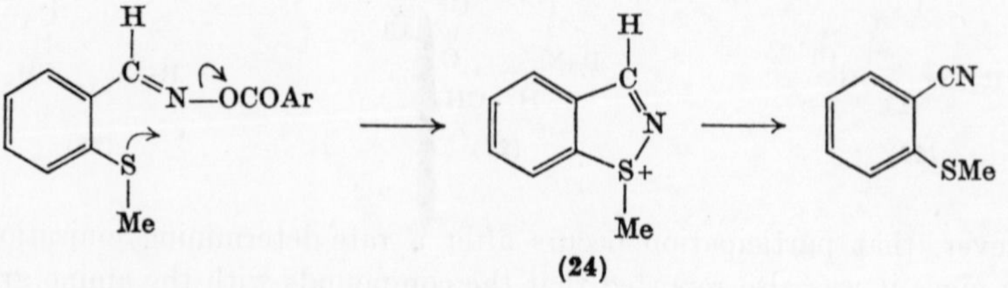

(24)

[29b] J. G. Buchanan and E. M. Oakes, *Carbohydrate Res.*, **1**, 242 (1965).

It has also been suggested that the conversion of 6-*O*-benzoyl-1,2:4,5-di-*O*-isopropylidene-3-*O*-methanesulphonylmannitol (**25a**) into the enol ether (**25c**) involves neighbouring-group participation by the benzyloxy-group to give the seven-membered cyclic ion (**25b**) with a geometry suitable for elimination.[29d]

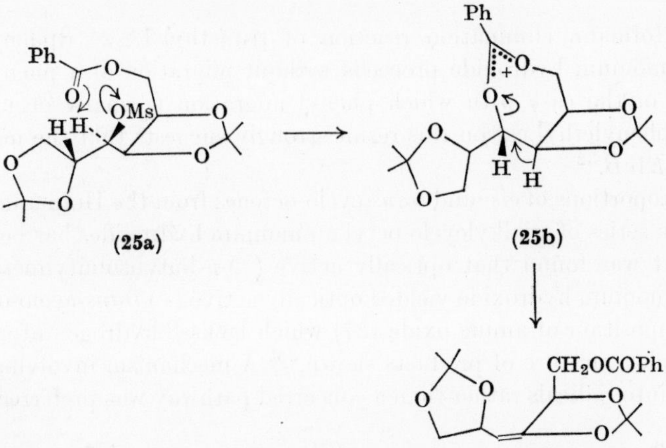

(**25a**)   (**25b**)

(**25c**)

Examples of what are probably *E*2 eliminations with alkoxide ions as leaving groups have been reported to occur when diethylene glycol dimethyl ether is heated to 160° with potassium *tert*-butoxide:[30]

$$(CH_3OCH_2CH_2)_2O \xrightarrow{KOBu^t} CH_2{=}CHOCH_3 + HOCH_2CH_2OCH_3$$

$$(CH_3OCH_2CH_2)O \xrightarrow{KOBu^t} CH_2{=}CHOCH_2{-}CH_2OCH_3 + CH_3OH$$

$$CH_2{=}CHO{-}CH_2{-}CH_2{-}OCH_3 \xrightarrow{KOBu^t} CH_2{=}CHOCH_3 + CH_3CHO$$

The *E*1 elimination of 5α-cholestan-6β-yltrimethylammonium iodide (**26**) in ethanol at 70° proceeds 1.6 times faster than that of its tris(trideuteriomethyl) analogue. It was suggested that this was the result of a "steric" secondary isotope effect arising from the strong non-bonding interactions between the trimethylammonium group and the 19-methyl and 4-methylene groups[31] (see also ref. 97*a*, p. 69).

[29c] R. J. Crawford and C. Woo, *Can. J. Chem.*, **43**, 3178 (1965).

[29d] M. A. Bukhari, A. B. Foster, J. M. Webber, and J. Lehmann, *Carbohydrate Res.*, **1**, 485 (1966).

[30] W. H. Snyder, J. Parascandola, and M. Wolfinger, *J. Org. Chem.*, **31**, 2037 (1966).

[31] G. H. Cooper and J. McKenna, *Chem. Commun.*, **1966**, 734; see also C. Heitner and K. T. Leffek, *Can. J. Chem.*, **44**, 2567 (1966).

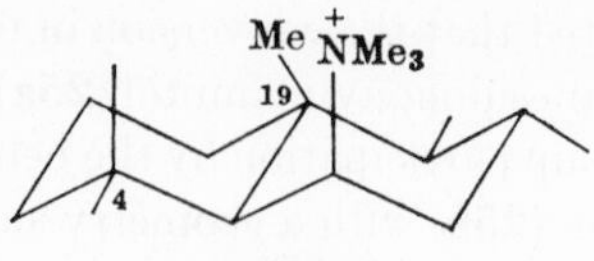

(26)

The Hofmann elimination reaction of trimethyl-1,2,2,-triphenyl[1-^{14}C]-ethylammonium hydroxide proceeds without migration of a phenyl group. In view of the ease with which phenyl migration normally occurs in the 1,2,2-triphenylethyl cation this result strongly suggests that the mechanism is *E*2 or *E*1c*B*.[32]

The proportions of *cis*- and *trans*-cyclo-octenes from the Hofmann eliminations of a series of trialkylcyclo-octyl ammonium hydroxides has been determined. It was found that optically active (—)-*n*-butylisobutylmethylcyclo-octylammonium hydroxide yielded optically active (—)-*trans*-cyclo-octene.[33a]

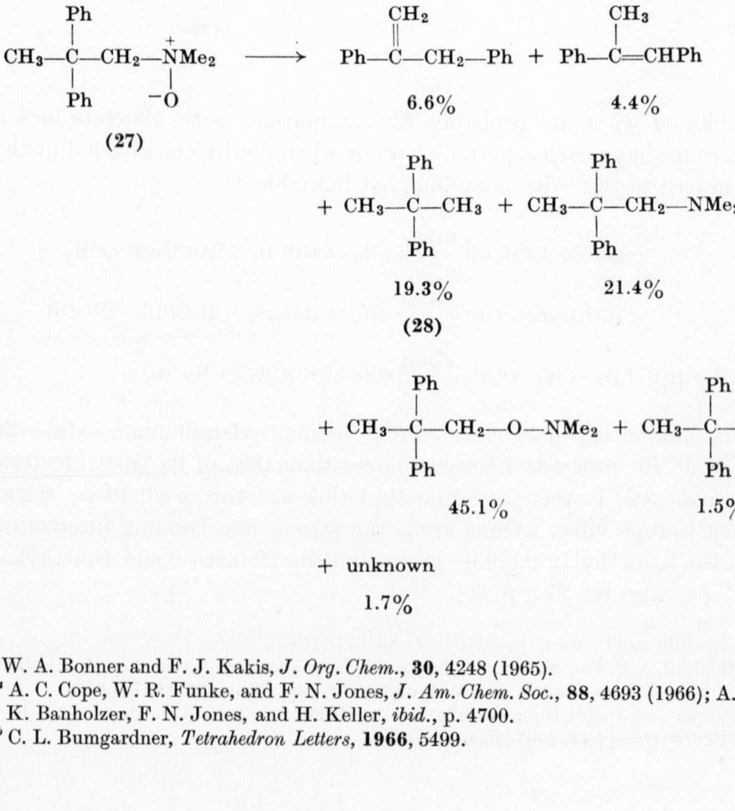

Decomposition of amine oxide (**27**) which lacks *β*-hydrogen atoms yields the complex mixture of products shown.[33b] A mechanism involving decomposition into radicals rather than a concerted pathway was preferred, since it

[32] W. A. Bonner and F. J. Kakis, *J. Org. Chem.*, **30**, 4248 (1965).
[33a] A. C. Cope, W. R. Funke, and F. N. Jones, *J. Am. Chem. Soc.*, **88**, 4693 (1966); A. C. Cope, K. Banholzer, F. N. Jones, and H. Keller, *ibid.*, p. 4700.
[33b] C. L. Bumgardner, *Tetrahedron Letters*, **1966**, 5499.

was considered that the latter could not account for the formation of the alkane (**28**).

Pyrolysis of (*R*)-*trans*-4-methylcyclohexyl *p*-tolyl sulphoxide (**29a**) proceeds with at least 42% stereospecificity, to yield (*R*)-4-methylcyclohexene (**29c**) preferentially.[34] This is consistent with the expected geometries of the transition states, since non-bonding interactions are greater in that (**29d**), leading to (*S*)-4-methylcyclohexene, than in that (**29b**), leading to its (*R*)-isomer. A similar but much smaller stereospecificity has also been observed

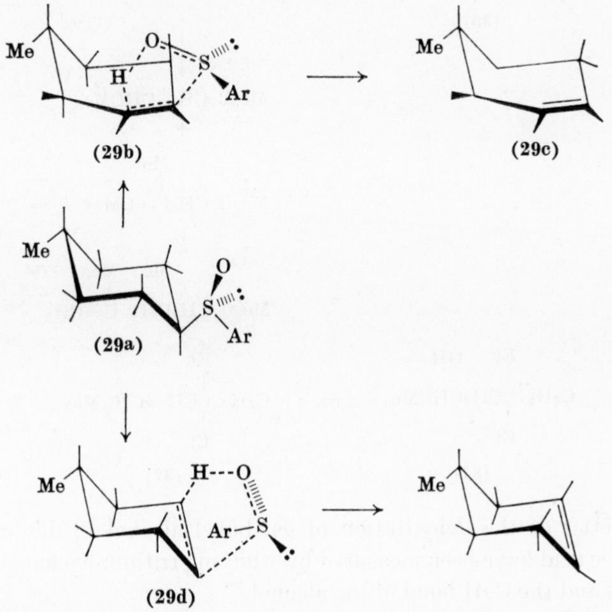

(29b)   (29c)

(29a)

(29d)

in the pyrolyses of the four stereoisomeric 4-methylcyclohexyl hydratropates.[35]

The thermal decomposition of alkyltriphenylphosphonium methoxides proceeds by way of an aromatic nucleophilic substitution to yield alkyldiphenylphosphine and anisole when the alkyl group is primary, but by way of an elimination to yield olefin and triphenylphosphine when it is secondary or tertiary.[36a]

An elimination similar to that of amine oxides occurs in the reaction of alkyl sulphides with sulphinic acids.[36b]

34 S. I. Goldberg and M. S. Sahli, *Tetrahedron Letters*, **1965**, 4441.
35 S. I. Goldberg and Fuk-Luen Lam, *J. Org. Chem.*, **31**, 2336 (1966).
36a C. T. Eyles and S. Trippett, *J. Chem. Soc.*, *C*, **1966**, 67.
36b J. L. Kice, B. R. Toth, D. C. Hampton, and J. F. Barbour, *J. Org. Chem.*, **31**, 848 (1966).

Whereas dehydration of the secondary neopentyl-type alcohol (30) with potassium hydrogen sulphate yields olefins which have been formed with migration of a methyl group, dehydration of the alcohol (31) yields only the unrearranged olefin (32).[37] It was suggested that rearrangement of the carbonium ion formed directly from (31) is prevented because the carbonium ion which would then be formed is even more sterically crowded.

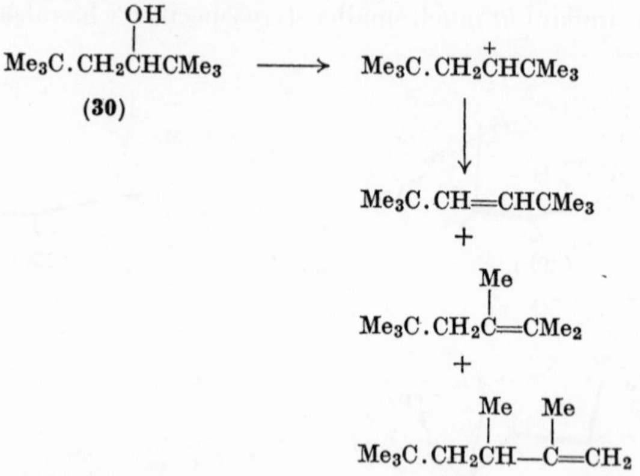

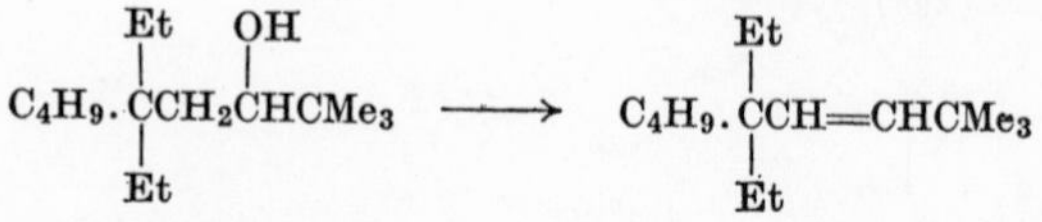

$$
\begin{array}{c}
\underset{(30)}{\overset{\overset{\displaystyle OH}{|}}{Me_3C.CH_2CHCMe_3}} \longrightarrow Me_3C.CH_2\overset{+}{C}HCMe_3
\end{array}
$$

$$
\downarrow
$$

$$
Me_3C.CH{=}CHCMe_3
$$
$$
+
$$
$$
\underset{}{\overset{\overset{\displaystyle Me}{|}}{Me_3C.CH_2C{=}CMe_2}}
$$
$$
+
$$
$$
\overset{\overset{\displaystyle Me}{|}\ \ \overset{\displaystyle Me}{|}}{Me_3C.CH_2CH{-}C{=}CH_2}
$$

$$
\underset{\underset{\displaystyle Et}{|}}{\overset{\overset{\displaystyle Et\ \ \ OH}{|\ \ \ \ |}}{C_4H_9.CCH_2CHCMe_3}} \longrightarrow \underset{\underset{\displaystyle Et}{|}}{\overset{\overset{\displaystyle Et}{|}}{C_4H_9.CCH{=}CHCMe_3}}
$$
$$
(31) \hspace{5cm} (32)
$$

The kinetics of the dehydration of *tert*-butyl alcohol in dilute aqueous hydrochloric acid have been measured by studying tritium-exchange between the solvent and the C–H bond of the alcohol.[38]

The ease of decomposition of some vinyllithium compounds into the corresponding acetylenes decreases in the order:

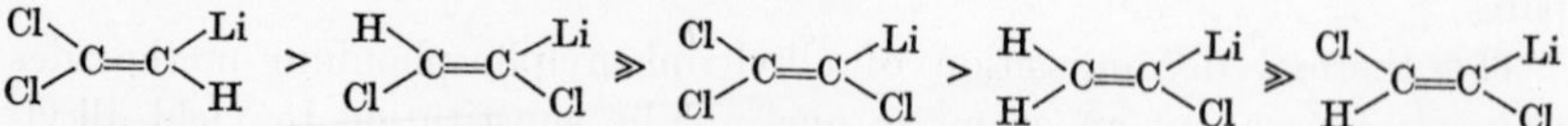

(33)   >   (34)   ≫   (35)   >   (36)   ≫   (37)

From the high reactivity of (33), (34), and (35) it was concluded that a

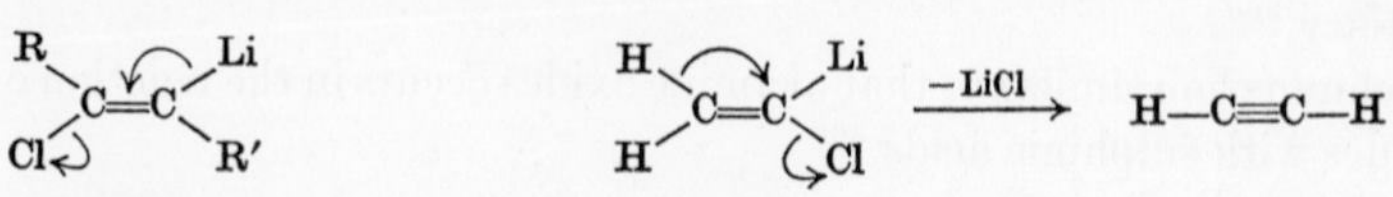

(38)   (39)

[37] N. Rabjohn and C. A. Drake, *J. Am. Chem. Soc.*, **88**, 3154 (1966).
[38] V. Gold and L. C. Gruen, *J. Chem. Soc.*, B, **1966**, 600.

trans-elimination (see **38**) is favoured. The possibility that the decompositions of (**36**) and (**37**) proceeded via carbenes or carbenoid intermediates was excluded by the failure to trap these with a large excess of methyllithium. Instead, a synchronous migration of the β-hydrogen, as shown in (**39**), was favoured.[39]

Dichloromethyllithium decomposes with dimerization to yield 1,2-dichloro-ethylene. It was concluded that this reaction also did not proceed via a carbene since in the presence of cyclohexene only a trace of 7-chloronorcarane was formed. The mechanism of equation (1) was suggested.[40]

$$
\begin{array}{c}
\text{LiCHCl—Cl} \\
\swarrow \searrow \\
\text{Cl}_2\text{CH—Li}
\end{array}
\longrightarrow
\begin{array}{c}
\text{Li} \\
| \\
\text{Cl}_2\text{CH—CH} \\
\backslash \\
\text{Cl}
\end{array}
\longrightarrow
\text{ClCH}{=}\text{CHCl}
\qquad (1)
$$

The decomposition of trichloromethyllithium was also investigated. This compound yields dichlorocyclopropanes in the presence of olefins, but since the rate of decomposition is then increased a synchronous mechanism involving a transition state, as (**40**), was preferred rather than one involving an intermediate carbene or carbenoid species.[36a, 41]

(**40**)

The decomposition of 1-chloro-2,2-diphenylvinylsilver to diphenylacetylene, 1-chloro-2,2-diphenylethylene, and tetraphenylbutatriene was also thought not to involve a carbene, since no cyclopropane was formed in the presence of styrene and cyclohexene although these blocked the formation of the triene. A mechanism involving a radical pair was suggested.[42]

The decomposition of n-butyllithium in decane at 130—150° to give but-1-ene follows the first-order rate law, is accelerated in the presence of lithium butoxide, and on β-deuteration shows an isotope effect k_H/k_D of 3—4. The four-centred transition state (**41**) was proposed.[43] The decomposition of *sec*-butyllithium in octane is kinetically more complex, with order 0.5 in BuLi

[39] G. Köbrich and K. Flory, *Chem. Ber.*, **99**, 1773 (1966).
[40] G. Köbrich and H. R. Merkle, *Chem. Ber.*, **99**, 1782 (1966).
[41] G. Köbrich, K. Flory, and R. H. Fischer, *Chem. Ber.*, **99**, 1793 (1966).
[42] G. Köbrich, H. Fröhlich, and W. Drischel, *J. Organometallic Chem.*, **6**, 194 (1966).
[43] R. A. Finnegan and H. W. Kutta, *J. Org. Chem.*, **30**, 4138 (1965).

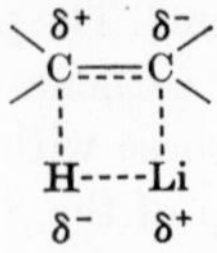

(41)

and 1.0 in added lithium alkoxide.[44] It was suggested that this was owing to the presence of oligomers in the solution and that the reaction could be formulated:

$$\tfrac{1}{2}(RLi)_n + B \underset{Fast}{\overset{\longrightarrow}{\longleftarrow}} (RLi)_{n/2}B$$

$$(RLi)_{n/2}B \longrightarrow Products$$

Decomposition of *sec*-butyllithium in the absence of solvent yields but-1-ene and a mixture of but-2-enes in which the *cis*-isomer predominates.[45] It was suggested that the *sec*-butyllithium group exists in a *cis*-formation in the oligomers of *sec*-butyllithium and that it is this which controls the steric course of the elimination.

An interesting elimination reaction in which the eliminated groups contain boron and nitrogen has been described by Allred, Anderson, and Smith.[46]

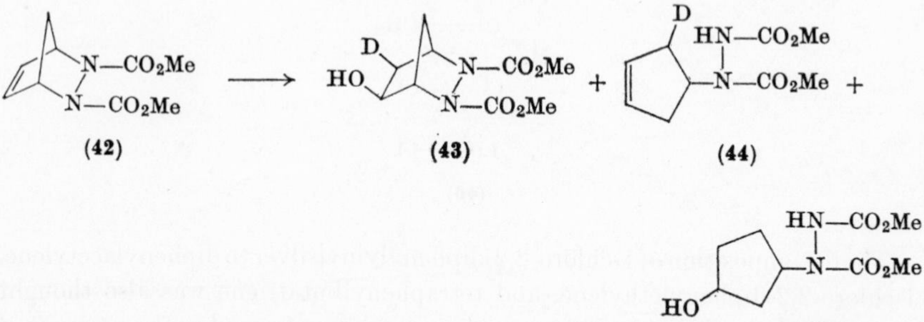

These workers found that hydroboration of compound **(42)** with diborane and deuteriodiborane yielded **(43)**, **(44)**, and **(45)**. The proportion of the

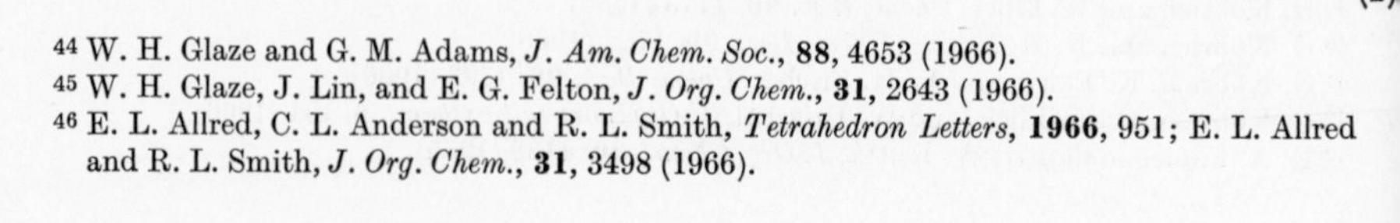

(2)

[44] W. H. Glaze and G. M. Adams, *J. Am. Chem. Soc.*, **88**, 4653 (1966).

[45] W. H. Glaze, J. Lin, and E. G. Felton, *J. Org. Chem.*, **31**, 2643 (1966).

[46] E. L. Allred, C. L. Anderson and R. L. Smith, *Tetrahedron Letters*, **1966**, 951; E. L. Allred and R. L. Smith, *J. Org. Chem.*, **31**, 3498 (1966).

fragmented products (**44**) and (**45**) was very sensitive to the presence of added nucleophiles, especially BH_4^-, and it was suggested that they were formed by an elimination from the intermediate organoborane arising from nucleophilic attack on boron, as shown in equation 2 (see also, p. 74).

If *cis*-β-ethoxystyrene (**46**) is treated with $(n\text{-}C_3H_7)_2BD$ in tetrahydrofuran and the solution left for 1 hour at room temperature, *trans*-β-deuteriostyrene (**47**) is formed by a *cis*-addition and *cis*-elimination. In the presence of acid (BF_3) and base (BuLi) *trans*-elimination took place.[47]

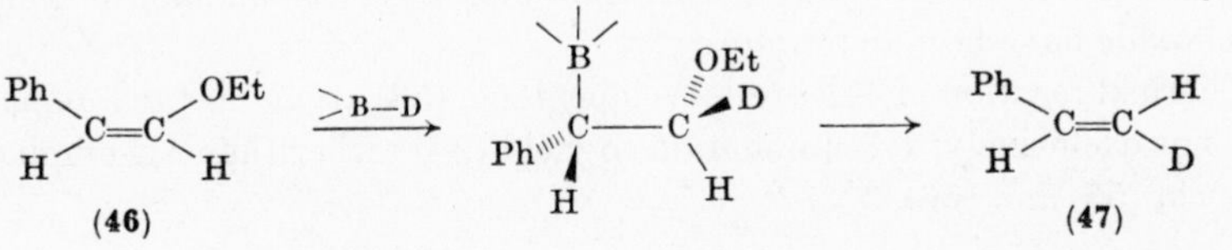

The effect of substituents on the rates of pyrolysis of β-hydroxy-olefins (at 650°) which are thought to involve a cyclic transition state, as shown in Scheme 1, has been investigated by Smith and Yates.[48] Methyl substituents at

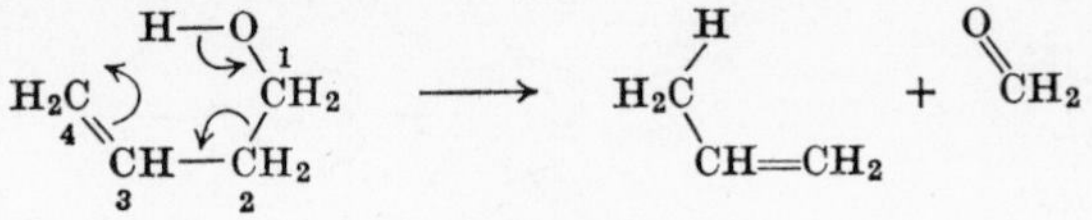

Scheme 1

$C_{(1)}$ cause small increases which may be the result of a more rigid conformation of the tertiary alcohol (i.e., owing to the *gem*-dialkyl effect). A phenyl substituent at $C_{(3)}$ causes a 10-fold increase in rate which may be the result of delocalization of positive charge developed as the π-electrons of the double bond co-ordinate with the hydroxyl-hydrogen, and phenyl at $C_{(4)}$ causes a decrease in rate owing, presumably, to the fact that the double bond is moving out of conjugation.

The pyrolytic gas-phase elimination from isobornyl acetate (**48**) occurs 6.8 times faster than that from bornyl acetate (**49**) at 345.2°.[49] Both reactions yield tricyclene (**50**) and camphene (**51**) as well as 2-bornene (**52**), the proportions of the two former compounds from (**48**) (31.5 and 48.4%) being higher than from (**49**) (23.3% and 14.8%). It was concluded that isobornyl acetate reacts predominantly through a "quasi-non-classical ion transition state", but in our opinion the small differences observed hardly support this.

The proportions of olefins with exocyclic and endocyclic double bonds

[47] D. J. Pasto and R. Snyder, *J. Org. Chem.*, **31**, 2777 (1966).
[48] G. G. Smith and B. L. Yates, *J. Chem. Soc.*, **1965**, 7242.
[49] E. U. Emovon, *J. Chem. Soc.*, B, **1966**, 588.

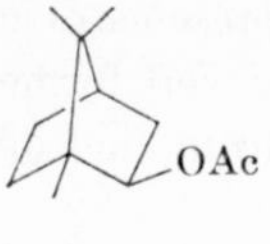

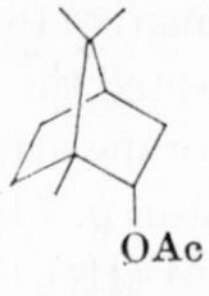

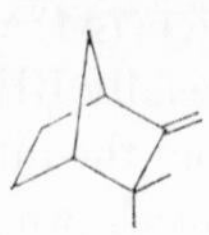

(48)   (49)   (50)   (51)   (52)

arising from the acid-catalysed elimination from a series of 1-acetamido- and
1-acetoxy-1-ethyl cyclohexanes, pyrolytic eliminations from 1-ethyl-1-(ethyl-
sulphinyl)cyclohexanes, and dehydration of 1-alkylcycloalkanol in dimethyl
sulphoxide have been determined.[50]

Thermal reaction of 4-deuteriocyclopentene, (53) at 550° is predominantly,
but not exclusively, 1,4-elimination to yield (54) rather than 1,2-elimination
to yield (55) and (56).[51]

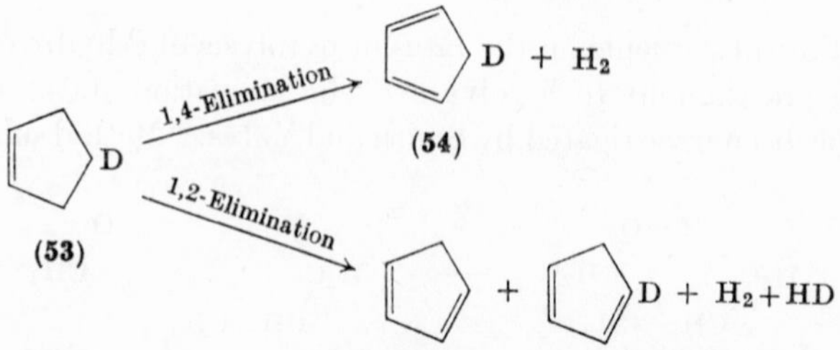

The rates of the gas-phase eliminations of alkyl chlorides, bromides, and
acetates may be correlated by the Taft equation.[52]

The interesting observation has been made, by means of deuterium-
labelling, that electron impact-induced dehydrochlorination of primary alkyl
chlorides involves preferential removal of the hydrogen from $C_{(3)}$ (i.e., via a
five-membered ring) in contrast to the dehydration of the corresponding
alcohols in which the hydrogen at $C_{(4)}$ is removed (i.e., via a six-membered
ring).[53]

There have been theoretical discussions of the stereoelectronic requirements
of $E2$ reactions[54] and of isotope effects in elimination reactions.[55]

[50] G. Gelli, A. Maccioni, and M. Secci, *Ann. Chim.* (*Rome*), **55**, 592 (1965); A. Maccioni and
    M. Secci, *Boll. Sci. Fac. Chim. Ind. Bologna*, **23**, 271 (1965); *Chem. Abs.*, **64**, 17381 (1966).
[51] J. E. Baldwin, *Tetrahedron Letters*, **1966**, 2953.
[52] M. Kraus, *Chem. Ind.* (*London*), **1966**, 1263.
[53] A. M. Duffield, S. D. Sample, and C. Djerassi, *Chem. Commun.*, **1966**, 193.
[54] K. Fukui and H. Fujimoto, *Tetrahedron Letters*, **1965**, 4303.
[55] L. J. Steffa, U.S. At. Energy Comm. NYO-3041-1, p. 1; *Chem. Abs.*, **64**, 9541 (1966); L. Pentz
    and E. R. Thornton, U.S. At. Energy Comm., NYO-3041-1, pp. 6—16 (1965); *Chem. Abs.*,
    64, 9529 (1966); E. M. Hodnett, and W. Dunn, U.S. At. Energy Comm., TID-22251 (1965);
    Chem. Abs., **64**, W. H. Saunders, *Chem. Ind.* (*London*), **1966**, 663; H. Simon and D. Palm,
    Angew. Chem. Intern. Ed. Engl., **5**, 920 (1966).

The following reactions have also been investigated: elimination from alkylamides under the influence of acetic anhydride and sulphosalicylic acid;[56] reaction of alkanesulphonic acids with aqueous sodium hydroxide;[57] thermal decomposition of 1-alkyl-3-pyrroline N-oxides[58] and ethylene episulphoxide;[59] dehydrochlorination of dichloroethane and vinyl chloride over Al_2O_3;[60] catalytic dehydrogenation of butane to butenes;[61] dehydrogenation by organic polymers;[62a] gas-phase hydrogen bromide-catalysed decomposition of trimethylacetic acid;[62b] gas-phase decomposition of *tert*-butyl methyl and ethyl ether catalysed by hydrogen chloride;[63] pyrolyses of isopropyl and n-butyl bromide in the presence of pyrolytic carbon,[64] of salts of α-chlorocinnamic acid,[65] and of esters of 2,2,3-trimethylpentan-3-ol, 2,3,4-trimethylpentan-3-ol and 2-methyl-3-ethylpentan-3-ol;[66] acid-catalysed dehydration of cycloheximide;[67] dehydration of decalols[68] and butanols,[69] tertiary methylbicyclo-octanols,[70] diastereoisomeric 3-hydroxy-(±)-2,3-diphenylpropionic acids,[71] ethanol, propan-1-ol, the butanols,[72] cyclohexanol,[73a] *sec*-pentyl alcohol,[73b] and long-chain alcohols.[73c]

[56] H. Bočková and K. Syhora, *Coll. Czech. Chem. Commun.*, **31**, 3790 (1966).
[57] P. B. Brindley, *J. Chem. Soc., C*, **1966**, 163.
[58] R. Kreher and H. Pawelczyk, *Tetrahedron Letters*, **1966**, 2591.
[59] G. E. Hartzell and J. N. Paige, *J. Am. Chem. Soc.*, **88**, 2616 (1966).
[60] G. L. Shik, T. N. Shakhtakhtinskii, and S. Seidov, *Azerb. Khim. Zh.*, **1965**, 103; *Chem. Abs.*, **64**, 19359 (1966).
[61] Y. S. Khodakov, K. M. Minachev, and O. D. Sterligov, *Pokl. Akad. Nauk. SSSR*, **165**, 344 (1965); *Chem. Abs.*, **64**, 4900 (1965).
[62a] J. Manassen and Sh. Khalif, *J. Am. Chem. Soc.*, **88**, 1943 (1966).
[62b] J. T. D. Cross and V. R. Stimson, *Chem. Commun.*, **1966**, 350.
[63] V. R. Stimson and E. J. Watson, *Australian J. Chem.*, **19**, 393, 401 (1966).
[64] M. R. Bridge and J. L. Holmes, *J. Chem. Soc., B*, **1966**, 713.
[65] G. Köbrich and H. Fröhlich, *Ann. Chem.*, **691**, 68 (1966).
[66] L. Markovec and S. Landa, *Coll. Czech. Chem. Commun.*, **31**, 3758 (1966).
[67] E. R. Garrett and R. E. Notari, *J. Org. Chem.*, **31**, 425 (1966).
[68] F. G. Schappell, and H. Pines, *J. Org. Chem.*, **31**, 1735 (1966); F. G. Schappell, and H. Pines, *ibid.*, p. 1965; H. Pines and J. Manassen, *Adv. Catalysis*, **16**, 49 (1966).
[69] I. I. Pis'man, V. V. Kas'yanov, I. I. Ninalalov, and M. A. Dalin, *Azerb. Khim. Zh.*, **1966**, 77; *Chem. Abs.*, **65**, 8713 (1966).
[70] W. Kraus and R. Dewald, *Ann. Chem.*, **689**, 21 (1965).
[71] C. G. Kratchanov and B. J. Kurtev, *Tetrahedron Letters*, **1966**, 5537.
[72] T.-C. Liu, F. A. Wang, W.-H. Yang, Y.-Z. Lee, B.-K. Lee, and T.-C. Lu, *Acta Chim. Sinica*, **32**, 93 (1966).
[73a] S. Carra, N. Santangelo, and A. Fusi, *Chim. Ind. (Milan)*, **48**, 229 (1966).
[73b] V. Z. Sharf, L. K. Freidlin, A. S. Nekrasov, I. V. Sablina, and A. A. Nazaryan, *Neftekhimiya*, **6**, 407 (1966); *Chem. Abs.*, **65**, 15190 (1966).
[73c] B. Blouri, M. Laroche, and P. Rumpf, *Bull. Soc. Chim. France*, **1966**, 505.

CHAPTER 5

Addition Reactions

Electrophilic Additions

A monograph on electrophilic additions to unsaturated systems has appeared.[1]

Addition of halogens and related reactions. Addition reactions of halogens which accompany electrophilic aromatic substitution,[2] and electrophilic addition to fluoro-olefins,[3] have been reviewed.

The mechanisms of the addition of halogens to olefins in non-polar media is complex and no single consistent mechanism has emerged. In this connection addition to dibenzobicyclo[2.2.2]octatriene (**1**) is of interest since it is known, largely from the work of Cristol, that radical addition gives unrearranged products, *cis-* and *trans-*(**2**), whilst ionic addition gives the rearranged products, *exo-* and *endo-*(**3**). Addition of iodine to (**1**) in non-polar solvents proceeds by

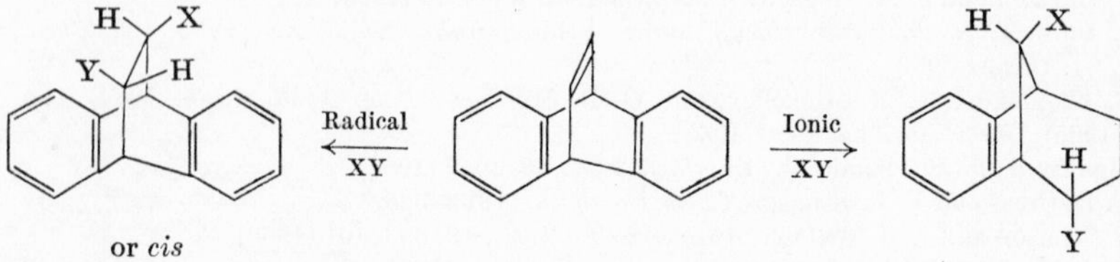

$$
\text{or } cis
$$
$$
(\mathbf{2}) \qquad\qquad (\mathbf{1}) \qquad\qquad (\mathbf{3})
$$

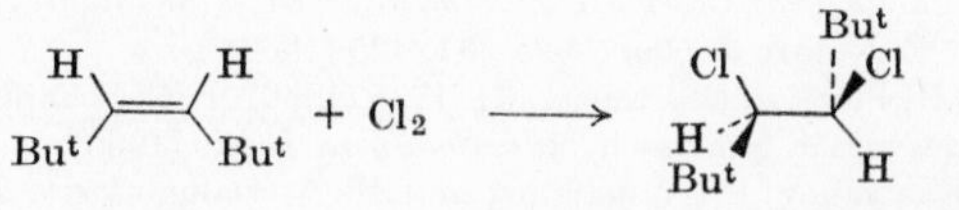

$$
(\mathbf{4})
$$

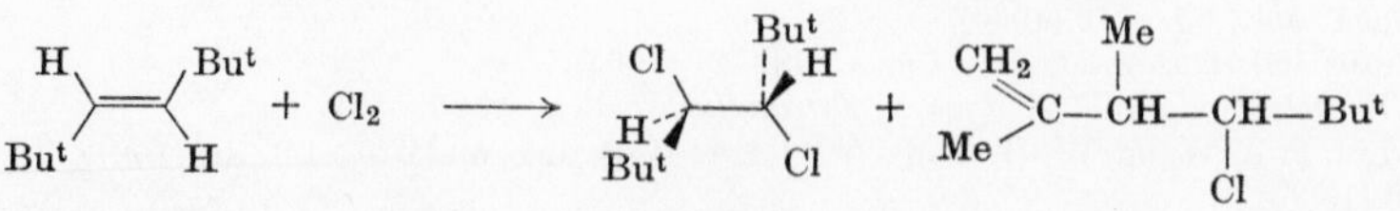

$$
(\mathbf{5}) \qquad (\mathbf{6})
$$

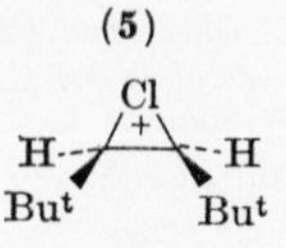

$$
(\mathbf{7})
$$

[1] P. B. D. de la Mare and R. Bolton, "Electrophilic Additions to Unsaturated Systems", Elsevier, London, 1966.
[2] P. B. D. de la Mare, J. S. Lomas, and V. S. Del Olmo, *Bull. Soc. Chim. France*, **1966**, 1157.
[3] B. L. Dyatkin, E. P. Mochalina, and I. L. Knunyants, *Usp. Khim.*, **35**, 979 (1966).

an ionic mechanism to give *endo*-4-*syn*-8-diiodobenzobicyclo[3.2.1]octadiene [(**3**); X = Y = I] solely, though this product slowly isomerizes at room temperature to an equilibrium mixture of starting materials, the *exo-anti*-isomer of [(**3**); X = Y = I] and the more stable isomer, *trans*-[(**2**); X = Y = I]. However, irradiation of a solution of iodine and (**1**) in carbon tetrachloride gave *trans*-[(**2**); X = Y = I] exclusively.[4] The addition of chlorine in carbon tetrachloride, in the presence of oxygen to inhibit radical reactions, to *cis*-di-*tert*-butylethylene gave (±)-3,4-dichloro-2,2,5,5-tetramethylhexane (**4**) without rearranged products; addition to the *trans*-isomer gave the *meso*-dichloride (**5**) and the rearranged product (**6**) resulting from stereospecific shift of a methyl group. The stereospecific *trans*-addition and methyl migration strongly suggest that bridged chloronium ions, e.g., (**7**), and not open carbonium ions are intermediates. *trans*-Addition to the *cis*-olefin provides a striking demonstration of the isomerizational stability of the crowded chloronium ion (**7**); even in the more polar methanol, addition is still stereospecific.[5] The effect of solvent on the stereospecificity of the addition of bromine to *cis*- and *trans*-stilbene has been studied quantitatively for carbon disulphide, carbon tetrachloride, dioxan, trichloroacetonitrile, methyl trichloroacetate, and nitrobenzene. In the first two solvents the addition to both isomers was stereospecific, *cis*-stilbene giving 90% of (±)- and *trans*-stilbene giving 96% of *meso*-dibromide. As the solvent polarity increased the stereoselectivity of addition to both isomers decreased, and this was explained by a change from a bromonium ion intermediate in the non-polar solvents to an open carbonium ion intermediate in the polar solvents.[6] The stereoselectivity for the addition of chlorine, from iodobenzene dichloride, to the same olefins in the same solvents is much lower than for addition of bromine, as expected for a smaller contribution from the chloronium ion structure.[7] By the same token the addition of iodine monochloride is expected to be much more stereospecific and this was shown to be so since in various solvents *cis*-stilbene added iodine chloride to give exclusively *erythro*-1-chloro-2-iodo-1,2-diphenylethane. Formation of the *erythro*-isomer resulted from a fast, catalysed isomerization of *cis*- to *trans*-stilbene before the addition.[8]

In a study[9] of the addition of aqueous bromine to a variety of olefins, rate constants have been obtained for the reactions with molecular bromine and with tribromide ions, and the relative amounts of dibromide and bromohydrin have been determined as a function of bromide ion concentration. From the absence of correlation between product composition and kinetics,

4 D. D. Tanner and B. G. Brownlee, *J. Am. Chem. Soc.*, **88**, 771 (1966).
5 R. C. Fahey, *J. Am. Chem. Soc.*, **88**, 4681 (1966).
6 G. Heublein, *J. Prakt. Chem.*, **31**, 84 (1966); *Chem. Abs.*, **64**, 11064 (1966).
7 G. Heublein and D. Stadermann, *Z. Chem.*, **6**, 147 (1966); *Chem. Abs.*, **65**, 5321 (1966).
8 G. Heublein, *Z. Chem.*, **6**, 186 (1966); *Chem. Abs.*, **65**, 7013 (1966).
9 R. P. Bell and M. Pring, *J. Chem. Soc.*, B, **1966**, 1119.

it was concluded that an intermediate formed in the rate-determining step, by electrophilic attack by bromine or tribromide, reacted rapidly with either bromide ion or water. The reaction of diethyl fumarate, however, appeared to involve simultaneous electrophilic attack by bromine and nucleophilic attack by bromide or water. Some evidence for the bromonium ion structure of the reaction intermediate was obtained by showing that in the reaction of the corresponding epoxides with hydrobromic acid, competition in the ring opening step, between bromide and water for the structurally analogous oxonium ion, was affected similarly by substituents.

The addition of bromine to several acyclic and cyclic olefins in the presence of optically active bases (*Cinchona* alkaloids) gave optically active dibromides; it was suggested[10] that the reactive species was an asymmetric bromine–alkaloid complex which formed preferentially the enantiomer with minimal non-bonded interactions between the alkene and alkaloid substituents during transfer of bromine from nitrogen to carbon. In addition reactions of bromine an "evolutionary charge-transfer complex" is considered to be an intermediate on the reaction path since, for a series of olefins, there was a linear correlation between a spectroscopic parameter, Γ, for Freon 112 as solvent and log k in this and other solvents.[11] The relative equilibrium constants for complexes formed between molecular iodine and a series of olefins (under conditions where addition did not occur) have been determined effectively by measuring the adsorption of gaseous olefin molecules on solid iodine. These were compared with the corresponding equilibrium constant for silver nitrate–olefin complexes, and the variations of both with structure were similar for non-cyclic olefins.[12]

Addition of hypohalous acids to allyl halides is known to proceed with

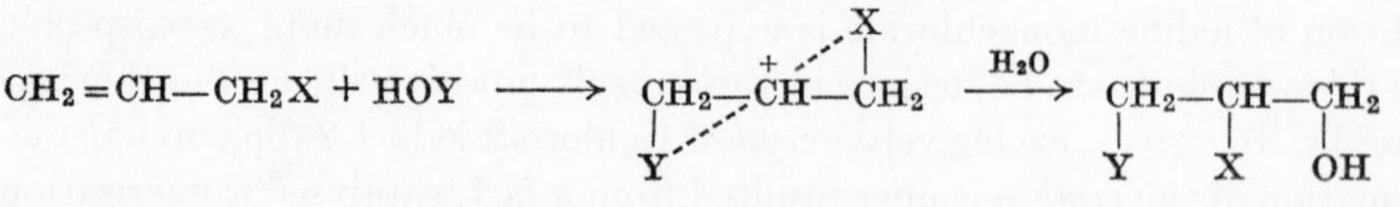

$$CH_2=CH-CH_2X + HOY \longrightarrow CH_2{-}\overset{\overset{X}{|}}{\underset{\underset{Y}{|}}{CH}}{-}CH_2 \overset{H_2O}{\longrightarrow} \overset{}{\underset{Y\ \ X\ \ OH}{CH_2{-}CH{-}CH_2}} \quad (1)$$

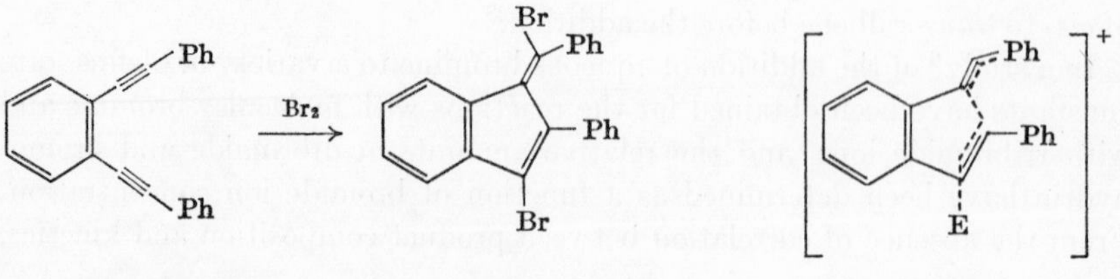

(8)   (9)   (10)

[10] G. Berti and A. Marsili, *Tetrahedron*, **22**, 2977 (1966).
[11] J. E. Dubois and F. Garnier, *Tetrahedron Letters*, **1966**, 3047.
[12] R. J. Cvetanović, F. J. Duncan, W. E. Falconer, and W. A. Sunder, *J. Am. Chem. Soc.*, **88**, 1602 (1966).

(11)   (12)

rearrangement resulting from neighbouring-group participation by halogen [equation (1)]; the amount of rearrangement increases, as expected, as X changes from Cl to Br to I. The extent of rearrangement has now been determined for $X = Y = Br$ by adding hypobromous acid to allyl [^{82}Br]bromide and by adding [^{82}Br]hypobromous acid to allyl bromide; in each case 30% of the 2,3-dibromopropan-1-ol (23% of the total products) resulted from bromine migration.[13] An interesting interaction between the two triple bonds of *o*-di(phenylethinyl)benzene (8) has been demonstrated in electrophilic, nucleophilic, and radical addition reactions. For example, addition of bromine gave the benzofulvene (9), and in competitive bromine addition to a mixture of (8) and tolan, (9) was formed to the exclusion of dibromotolan, showing the much greater reactivity of the di- than of the mono-acetylene. Irradiation of (8) with thiophenol, and reaction of (8) with lithium or with lithium naphthalenide, also gave benzofulvenes. A concerted ring closure via the transition state (10) was tentatively proposed for the reaction with electrophiles[14] (see also, pp. 31 and 98). A similar interaction between two double bonds is provided by the *cis,cis*-diene (11) which does not react with bromine in carbon tetrachloride but does react with bromine in methanol at room temperature, as shown, to give (12) stereospecifically in high yields.[15] In palitantin and the closely related model compound (13) the enhanced reactivity towards iodine (to form a monoiodo-compound) was attributed to the neighbouring-group participation shown, and the decreased reactivity towards maleic anhydride to a corresponding increase in ground-state stabilization.[16] Neighbouring-group participation by sulphinyl-oxygen has also been reported for an electrophilic addition. Methyl 3-*endo*-syn-phenylsulphinylbicyclo-[2.2.1]hept-5-ene-2-*endo*-carboxylate (14), unlike the *anti*-isomer, gave the iodohydrin (15) quantitatively under iodolactonization conditions (iodine–sodium hydrogen carbonate). This abnormal reaction was shown to depend upon the presence and the configuration of the sulphinyl group; this con-

13 C. A. Clarke and D. L. H. Williams, *J. Chem. Soc.*, *B*, **1966**, 1126.
14 H. W. Whitlock and P. E. Sandvick, *J. Am. Chem. Soc.*, **88**, 4525 (1966).
15 R. M. Gipson, H. W. Guin, S. H. Simonsen, C. G. Skinner, and W. Shive, *J. Am. Chem. Soc.*, **88**, 5366 (1966).
16 A. T. Austin and B. Pearson, *Chem. Ind.* (*London*), **1966**, 1228.

figuration was inverted and ^{18}O was incorporated into the sulphinyl group from ^{18}O-enriched water during reaction. The mechanism proposed is shown in Scheme 1[17] (see also p. 66). Participation by neighbouring acetoxy-, ethoxycarbonyloxy-, and phenylcarbamoyl groups in the reaction of cholestenes and androstenes with N-bromosuccinimide has also been observed.[18]

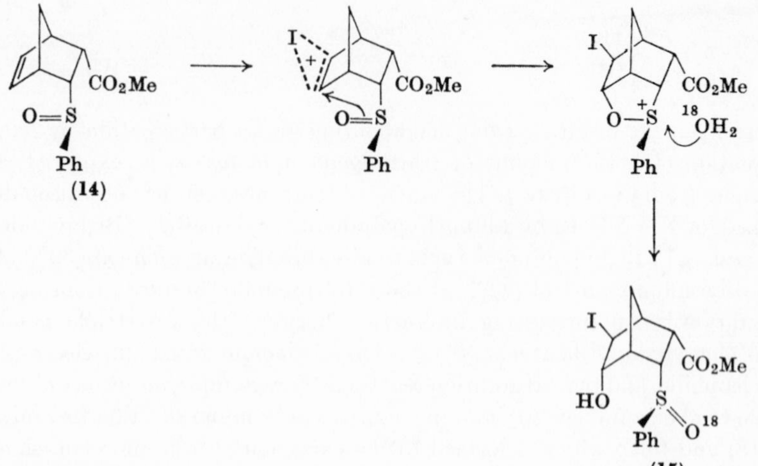

Ionic addition of hydrogen chloride to 2,3-dideuterionorbornene (16) gave ca. 50% of the product of *exo*-cis-addition without rearrangement and ca. 50% of rearranged products, 38% from a 6,2-hydride shift and 12% from a Wagner–Meerwein rearrangement. Results with hydrogen bromide were similar. The ease of dehydrohalogenation of halogenonorbornanes was shown to be in the order *exo-cis* > *trans* > *endo-cis*, and the *exo*-proton was preferentially removed by base[19] (see also, p. 105).

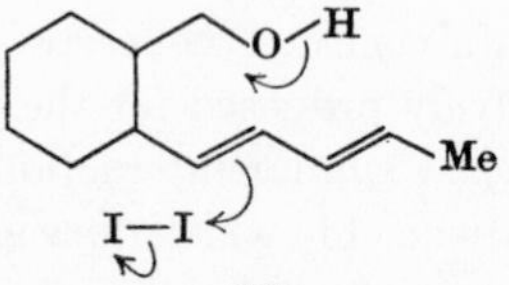

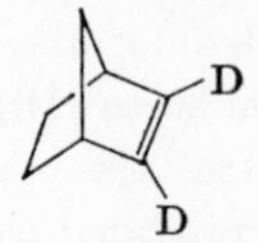

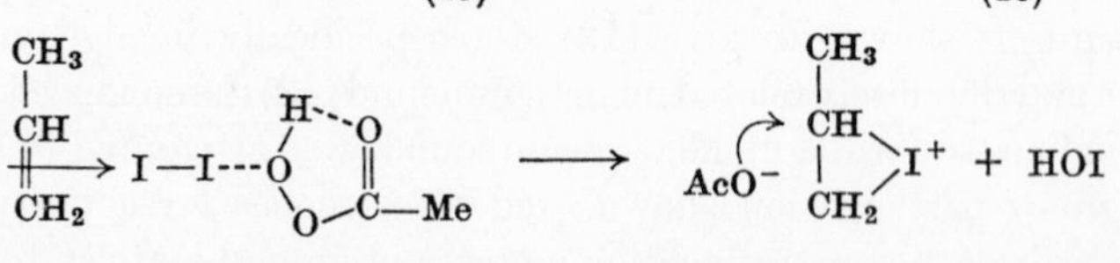

[17] H. Hogeveen, G. Maccagnani and F. Montanari, *J. Chem. Soc., C,* **1966**, 1585.
[18] S. Julia and B. Fürer, *Bull. Soc. Chim. France,* **1966**, 1114.
[19] J. K. Stille, F. M. Sonnenberg, and T. H. Kinstle, *J. Am. Chem. Soc.,* **88**, 4922 (1966).

Elementary fluorine has been added (*cis*) directly to cholest-4-en-3-one and cholesteryl chloride in trichlorofluoromethane at −78°.[20] Rapid stereospecific 1,2-*cis*-addition of chlorine to cyclo-octatetraene has been observed in both polar (acetonitrile) and non-polar (hexane) solvents.[21] The reaction of propene with a mixture of iodine and peracetic acid in acetic acid gave 2-acetoxy-1-iodopropane, and the mechanism shown [equation (2)] involving rate-determining attack of the peracid on an olefin–iodine complex was suggested.[22] When cyclohexene was added at 0° to bromine and silver perchlorate in methyl cyanide an immediate precipitate of silver bromide was formed, together with the nitrilium ion (17) formed by opening of the bromonium ion by the solvent; with aqueous alkali, (17) gave the corresponding amide.[23] Treatment of tri-*O*-acetyl-D-galactal with *N*-bromosuccinimide and hydrofluoric acid in ether at −70° gave the *cis*-bromofluoro-adduct.[24] Bromine chloride, prepared *in situ* from *N*-bromosuccinimide and hydrogen chloride, has been added to a number of alkylcyclohexanes to give mixtures of *trans*-alkylbromochloro-cyclohexanes; the results are explained by *trans*-diaxial opening of a bromonium ion by chloride ion.[25] Nitrosyl formate, generated *in situ* from isopentyl

(17)   (18)

nitrite and formic acid, added readily to olefins to give nitroso formates; addition to norbornane occurred without rearrangement, and nitrosyl chloride in formic acid gave only the nitrosyl chloride adduct. The four-centre mechanism (18) was therefore tentatively proposed.[26]

Other reactions which have been studied are: addition of *N,N*-dibromo-benzenesulphonamide to norbornene, bicyclo[2.2.2]octene, and *endo*-bicyclo-[2.2.1]hept-5-ene-2,3-dicarboxylic anhydride;[27] addition of diboron tetra-chloride to cyclohexa-1,3-diene;[28] reaction of tetranitromethane with olefins;[29] addition of iodine to cyclohexene in dimethylformamide,[30] of

20 R. F. Merritt and T. E. Stevens, *J. Am. Chem. Soc.*, **88**, 1822 (1966).
21 R. Huisgen, G. Boche, W. Hechtl, and H. Huber, *Angew. Chem. Internat. Edn. Engl.*, **5**, 585 (1966).
22 Y. Ogata and K. Aoki, *J. Org. Chem.*, **31**, 1625 (1966).
23 A. Hassner, L. A. Levy, and R. Gault, *Tetrahedron Letters*, **1966**, 3119.
24 P. W. Kent and M. R. Freeman, *J. Chem. Soc.*, *C*, **1966**, 910.
25 H. J. Hageman and E. Havinga, *Rec. Trav. Chim.*, **85**, 1141 (1966).
26 H. C. Hamann and D. Swern, *Tetrahedron Letters*, **1966**, 3303.
27 A. C. Oehlschlager, C. D. Kennedy, and L. H. Zalkow, *J. Org. Chem.*, **31**, 1682 (1966).
28 M. Zeldin and T. Wartik, *J. Am. Chem. Soc.*, **88**, 1336 (1966).
29 R. W. Bradshaw, *Tetrahedron Letters*, **1966**, 5711.
30 G. V. Chernyavskii, G. F. Dvorko, V. A. Shrubovich, and O. M. Grishin, *Ukv. Khim. Zh.*, **32**, 260 (1966); *Chem. Abs.*, **65**, 584 (1966).

hydrogen bromide to cyclohexenecarboxylic acid,[31] of hydrogen chloride to propargyl chloride in the presence of mercuric chloride,[32] of chlorine to olefins and acetylenes in the presence of various nucleophiles to give di-chlorides and the mixed chloride–nucleophile adducts,[33] and of bromine to terminal olefins;[34] the stereochemistry of the addition of nitrosyl chloride, from isopentyl nitrite and hydrochloric acid, to cyclohexene;[35] and addition of hypochlorous acid to dihydropyran and other cyclic vinyl ethers.[36]

Addition of sulphenyl halides. A number of papers on the mechanism of addition of alkane- and arene-sulphenyl halides have appeared this year. The addition of *p*-chlorobenzenesulphenyl chloride to *cis*- and *trans*-but-2-ene is highly stereospecific (*trans*) over a wide range of temperature (−34° to +146°). For this to be explained on an open carbonium ion (19) mechanism it would be necessary for the activation energies for rotation of the carbonium ions and for the attack of these by chloride ions to be identical, and also for the pre-exponential term for the bimolecular step to be extremely high. The generally accepted episulphonium ion (20) mechanism is thus strongly supported.[37] This mechanism for stereospecific *trans*-addition is based largely

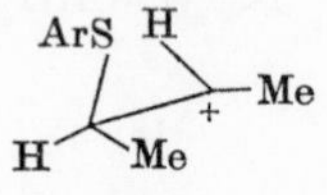

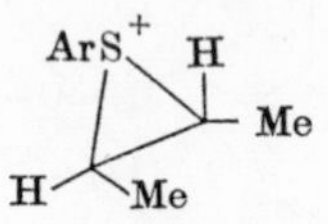

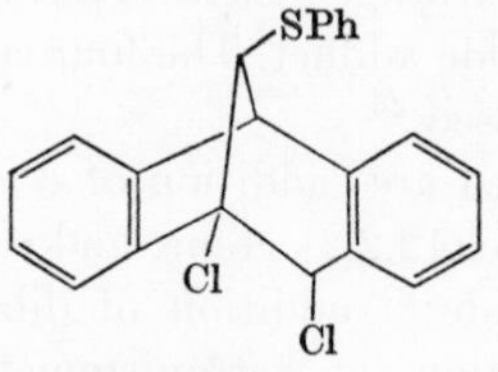

on results with 2,4-dinitrobenzenesulphenyl chloride. Exclusive *trans*-addition has now been confirmed for addition of methane- and benzene-sulphenyl chloride to norbornene and acenaphthalene; ring opening of the bridged ion

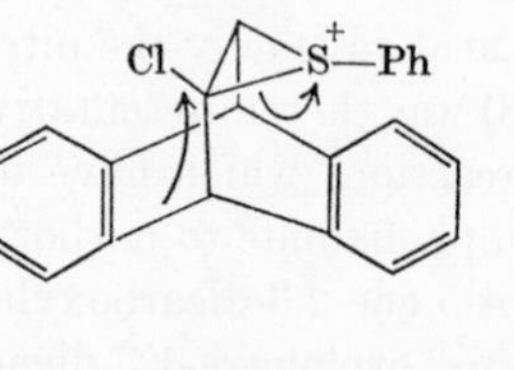

[31] R. Caple and W. R. Vaughan, *Tetrahedron Letters*, **1966**, 4067.
[32] W. Kirmse and M. Kapps, *Chem. Ber.*, **99**, 2869 (1966).
[33] Y. A. Serguchev and E. A. Shilov, *Ukr. Khim. Zh.*, **32**, 34 (1966); *Chem. Abs.*, **65**, 585 (1966).
[34] J. E. Dubois and E. Goetz, *J. Chim. Phys.*, **63**, 780 (1966).
[35] N. S. Zefirov, P. Kadziauskas, Y. A. Ustynyuk, and Y. K. Uur'ev, *Zh. Obshch. Khim.*, **36**, 764 (1966); *Chem. Abs.*, **65**, 8704 (1966).
[36] R. Aguilera and G. Descotes, *Bull. Soc. Chim. France*, **1966**, 3318.
[37] G. H. Schmid and V. M. Csizmadia, *Can. J. Chem.*, **44**, 1338 (1966).

occurs at either carbon atom.[38] Addition of benzenesulphenyl chloride to the 7-chloro-derivative of dibenzobicyclo[2.2.2]octatriene (1) in ethyl acetate proceeded with complete Wagner–Meerwein rearrangement, to give *endo*-4,5-dichloro-*syn*-8-phenylthiodibenzobicyclo[3.2.1]octatriene (21), in contrast to the addition to (1) itself which under similar conditions gave simple 1,2-*trans*-addition. It was suggested that the intermediate episulphonium ion (22) will be less stable than its chlorine-free analogue and will therefore rearrange faster.[39]

In contrast with previous work reporting 1,4-addition of sulphenyl chlorides to certain conjugated dienes, exclusive 1,2-Markovnikov addition of methane- and benzene-sulphenyl chloride to several dienes has now been reported. Some of the methanesulphenyl, but none of the benzenesulphenyl, adducts rearranged on standing to the more stable 1,4-adducts. The episulphonium ion mechanism explains the addition, and also the subsequent rearrangements, when the sulphur is sufficiently nucleophilic; the absence of 1,4-adducts renders the development of an open carbonium ion, which would be allylic, unlikely.[40] 3,3-Dimethylbut-1-ene and 2,4-dinitrobenzenesulphenyl chloride in acetic acid at 25° gave predominantly the anti-Markovnikov product (23), but at higher temperatures increasing amounts of the Markovnikov product were formed; at 100° both isomers gave an equilibrium mixture containing 98% of the Markovnikov adduct. Kinetic measurements showed that the latter formed at 100° must have arisen from (23), presumably by way of the sulphonium intermediate (24). Thus an interesting example is provided of orientation in an electrophilic addition changing with kinetic and thermodynamic control.[41] The addition of 2,4-dinitrobenzenesulphenyl bromide to

$$Me_3C-CH-CH_2Cl \qquad\qquad Me_3C-CH\text{----}CH_2$$

$$| \qquad\qquad\qquad\qquad\qquad\qquad\qquad \overset{+}{S}$$

$$SAr \qquad\qquad\qquad\qquad\qquad\qquad\qquad Ar$$

$$\text{(23)} \qquad\qquad\qquad\qquad\qquad \text{(24)}$$

cyclohexene in carbon tetrachloride was shown to be homogeneous and polar, but kinetically complex, being of the first order in olefin and of higher orders in bromide. This complexity, like that of many electrophilic additions in relatively non-polar solvents, was attributed to solvation of the transition state by molecules of the sulphenyl bromide,[42] and this is supported by the demonstration of catalysis by the product, and by other 1-substituted-2,4-

38 W. H. Mueller and P. E. Butler, *J. Am. Chem. Soc.*, **88**, 2866 (1966).

39 S. J. Cristol and B. B. Jarvis, *J. Am. Chem. Soc.*, **88**, 3091 (1966).

40 W. H. Mueller and P. E. Butler, *Chem. Commun.*, **1966**, 646.

41 G. M. Beverly and D. R. Hogg, *Chem. Commun.*, **1966**, 138.

42 D. S. Campbell and D. R. Hogg, *J. Chem. Soc.*, *B*, **1966**, 109.

dinitrobenzenes.[43] This catalysis increased with electron-release to the 4-nitro-group of the catalyst; this nitro-group is considered to be involved in the solvation of the developing positive charge, in the sulphonium ion-forming transition state, with the mechanism otherwise substantially the same as in polar solvents such as acetic acid.[44]

The orientation of addition of *p*-nitrophenylsulphenyl chloride to phenyl-acetylene depends upon the solvent, being Markovnikov in acetic acid and *anti*-Markovnikov in ethyl acetate.[45] The orientation and rate of addition of benzenesulphenyl chlorides to diphenylacetylenes depend much more on the substituents in the acetylene than on those in the sulphenyl chloride.[46] Sulphenyl chlorides add to the double bond of vinylacetylene very largely in the Markovnikov manner, contrary to earlier reports.[47] The addition of toluene-*p*-sulphenyl chloride to hex-1-yne has also been studied.[48]

Hydrations and related additions. Gold and Kessick have published full details of their work on the effect of substitution of the solvent by deuterium and tritium on the hydration of isobutene in dilute aqueous perchloric acid. A distinction is made between "rate isotope effects" deduced from observed reaction rates in isotopically different systems and "product isotope effects" obtained from the isotopic fractionation detectable in a given reaction. The hydration rate in H_2O is 1.45 times greater than in D_2O, and in mixtures of the two the rates are greater than those calculated by linear interpolation. The abundance of deuterium in the newly formed carbon–hydrogen bond is 3.9 times smaller than in the solvent. For tritium as a tracer the corresponding ratio is 7.1 in H_2O and 1.9 in D_2O. A theoretical treatment was developed that involved fractionation of hydrogen isotopes between hydronium ions and water, and the relative concentrations and reactivities of isotopically different hydronium ions. This gave a satisfactory interpretation of all the experimental results without the postulation of medium effects, such as the secondary solvent isotope effect favoured by Kreevoy. The rate-determining step in the hydration is shown to be transfer to isobutene of one of the group of three equivalent protons of the hydronium ion, not transfer of a proton from the solvation shell; this postulated transfer is nearly complete in the transition state.[49] Schubert and Lamm[50] have also published details of their work on the

[43] D. S. Campbell and D. R. Hogg, *J. Chem. Soc.*, *B*, **1966**, 294.
[44] D. S. Campbell and D. R. Hogg, *J. Chem. Soc.*, **1965**, 5887.
[45] V. Calò, G. Melloni, G. Modena, and G. Scorrano, *Tetrahedron Letters*, **1965**, 4399.
[46] L. Di Nunno, G. Melloni, G. Modena, and G. Scorrano, *Tetrahedron Letters*, **1965**, 4405.
[47] P. E. Butler and W. H. Mueller, *Tetrahedron Letters*, **1966**, 2179.
[48] L. Di Nunno, G. Modena, and G. Scorrano, *Ric. Sci. Rend.*, *Sez. A*, 8, 1423 (1965); *Chem. Abs.*, **65**, 5317 (1966).
[49] V. Gold and M. A. Kessick, *J. Chem. Soc.*, **1965**, 6718; *Discussions Faraday Soc.*, **39**, 84 (1965).
[50] W. M. Schubert and B. Lamm, *J. Am. Chem. Soc.*, **88**, 120 (1966).

hydration of styrene, [α-^{2}H$_1$]styrene, and [β,β-^{2}H$_2$]styrene in aqueous perchloric acid. No isotope effect was found in the hydration of these compounds and there was no isotope exchange during the forward reaction. The dependence of hydration rate on the acidity (intermediate between H_0 and $H_{R'}$) was determined. The simplest mechanism to meet all the experimental requirements is slow proton transfer from the hydronium ion to styrene, giving directly the intermediate carbonium ion [equation (3)]. The hydration

$$\text{PhCH=CH}_2 + \text{H}_3\text{O}^+ \xrightarrow{\text{Slow}} \overset{+}{\text{PhCHMe}} \xrightarrow{\text{Fast}} \underset{\overset{|}{\text{OH}}}{\text{PhCHMe}} \text{ ----- (3)}$$

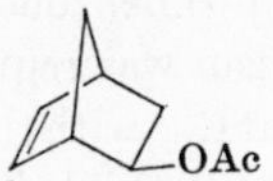

(25) 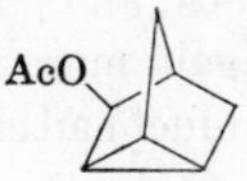   (26)

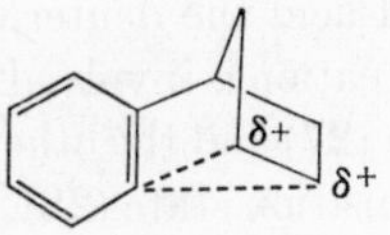

(27) 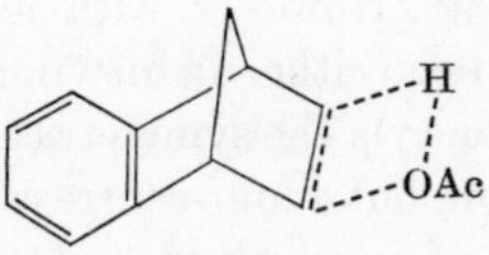   (28)

of a series of *meta*- and *para*-substituted styrenes in aqueous sulphuric acid was first order in styrene and gave linear Hammett acidity-function plots. The transition state appeared to involve two molecules of water for all substituents and resembled the intermediate carbonium ion.[51] Other investigations have been into orientation of the hydration of diacetylenes,[52] hydration of methyl 2-nitrocrotonate in buffer solutions[53] and of dihydronicotinamide–adenine dinucleotide,[54] Wagner–Meerwein rearrangements in the hydration of *trans*-pinocarveol,[55] base-catalysed addition of methanol, and solvolysis of *N*-phenylmaleimide,[56] and hydration of vinylacetylene by cuprous oxide in aqueous sulphuric acid where the rate was said to be proportional to the square root of the cuprous oxide concentration.[57]

51 J.-P. Durand, M. Davidson, M. Hellin, and F. Coussement, *Bull. Soc. Chim. France*, **1966**, 43, 52.
52 E. S. Turbanova, Y. I. Porfir'eva, and A. A. Petrov, *Zh. Org. Khim.*, **2**, 772, 777 (1966); *Chem. Abs.*, **65**, 10480.
53 V. M. Belikov and Y. N. Belokon, *Izv. Akad. Nauk SSSR, Ser. Khim.*, **1966**, 936; *Chem. Abs.*, **65**, 10461 (1966).
54 S. G. A. Alivisatos, F. Ungar, and G. J. Abraham, *Biochemistry*, **4**, 2616 (1965).
55 H. Schmidt, M. Mühlstädt, and P. Son, *Chem. Ber.*, **99**, 2736 (1966).
56 R. A. Finnegan and W. H. Mueller, *J. Pharm. Sci.*, **54**, 1257 (1965).
57 N. G. Karapetyan, A. S. Tarkhanyan, and A. N. Lyubimova, *Izv. Akad. Nauk Arm. SSSR, Khim. Nauki*, **18**, 472 (1965); *Chem. Abs.*, **64**, 11043 (1966).

Cristol and his co-workers[58] have made a detailed study of the catalysed and uncatalysed additions of acetic acid and acetic [^{2}H]acid to norbornadiene, to give *exo*-dehydronorbornyl acetate (25) and nortricyclyl acetate (26). This included the nature of the acid catalysis, salt effects, and medium effects, as shown by reaction rates and by the amounts of homoconjugate addition accompanying normal 1,2-*exo*-addition. The results required the participation of a number of product-determining intermediates and were accommodated by assuming competition between polar cyclic additions and processes involving ion pairs, ion dipoles, and solvated ions as intermediates. The possible mechanisms were discussed in detail.[58] The stereochemistry and skeletal deuterium distribution resulting from polar addition of deuterium chloride and acetic [^{2}H]acid and [^{2}H$_3$]acetic [^{2}H]acid to benzonorbornadiene were also studied, and again more than one mechanism was required. Under kinetic control the DCl adduct had chlorine solely *exo* at $C_{(5)}$ with the deuterium distributed equally between $C_{(6)}$ (*exo*) and $C_{(7)}$ (*syn* to Cl), this being consistent with a symmetrical carbonium ion [non-classical (27) or a rapidly equilibrating pair] as intermediate. However, with acetic [^{2}H]acid the deuterium was not equally distributed and either an unsymmetrical cation is involved or there are two mechanisms, one via the symmetrical cation (27) and the other involving, not a carbonium ion, but a four-centre cyclic transition state (28).[59] The acid-catalysed addition of acetic acid to substituted styrenes has also been investigated.[60]

Peterson and his co-workers[61] have extended their study of the addition of trifluoroacetic acid to 5-substituted pent-1-enes[62] to the corresponding pentynes and other alkynes and have again observed rate enhancements and rearrangements caused by neighbouring-group participation. For example, 5-chloropent-1-yne gave 4-chloropent-4-en-1-yl trifluoroacetate via a chloronium ion (equation 4), and 5-methoxypentyne similarly gave 5-(trifluoroacetoxy)pentan-2-one.[61] In contrast with previous reports,[63] Prins reactions with *cis*- and *trans*-1-phenylpropene, *cis*- and *trans*-β-bromo- and β-chlorostyrene are not stereospecific; that of 1-phenylpropene appears to proceed through a simple symmetrical solvated carbonium ion, though that of the halogen compounds is more complex.[64] A previous suggestion that the acetoxonium ion (29) was an intermediate in the Prins reaction of cyclohexene in acetic acid (formed from cyclohexene and $CH_3CO \cdot OCH_2^+$) has been withdrawn, since (29), generated independently, gave *cis*-2-(acetoxymethyl)cyclo-

[58] S. J. Cristol, T. C. Morrill, and R. A. Sanchez, *J. Org. Chem.*, **31**, 2719, 2726, 2733, 2738 (1966).
[59] S. J. Cristol, and R. Caple, *J. Org. Chem.*, **31**, 2741 (1966).
[60] M. Mollard, B. Torck, M. Hellin, and F. Coussemant, *Bull. Soc. Chim. France*, **1966**, 1186.
[61] P. E. Peterson and J. E. Duddey, *J. Am. Chem. Soc.*, **88**, 2900 (1966).
[62] See *Organic Reaction Mechanisms*, **1965**, 109.
[63] See *Organic Reaction Mechanisms*, **1965**, 110.
[64] L. J. Dolby, C. Wilkins, and T. G. Frey, *J. Org. Chem.*, **31**, 1110 (1966).

hexyl acetate whilst the Prins reaction gives the *trans*-isomer.[65] Evidence has been given for diaxial *trans*-addition in the Prins reaction of 4-*tert*-butylcyclohexene,[66] and the thermal and the Lewis acid-catalysed reactions have been compared.[67] The kinetics of the Ritter reaction between isobutene, acrylonitrile, and sulphuric acid in acetic anhydride have been studied.[68]

$$\cdots \cdots \quad (4)$$

(29) (30) (31)

The stereochemistry and mechanism of the oxymercuration of alkenes has been reviewed.[69] Electrophilic addition to 5-norbornene-2-*endo*-carboxylic acid (30) generally results in lactonization to (31) with *exo*-attack by the electrophile. This *trans*-stereochemistry has now been proved for oxymercuration of (30) with mercuric acetate in methanol, followed by treatment with sodium chloride to give [(31); X = HgCl].[70] Cyclohexene and mercuric acetate in acetic acid at 70° gave the *trans*-(acetoxymercuri)acetate which was stable at this temperature but was converted at 100° into 3-acetoxycyclohexene. A preliminary investigation of the mechanism of this allylic acetoxylation (Treibs reaction) has been reported.[71] The chloromercuration of *o*-allylphenol has also been studied.[72]

From a detailed study of the reaction of 1-phenylpropyne with di-isobutylaluminium hydride it appears that polar factors are more important than steric factors in determining the orientation of addition of both Al–H and Al–C bonds to alkynes.[73] The chloroplatinic acid-catalysed addition of trimethylgermanium hydride to various dienes,[74] and the hydroboration of

[65] L. J. Dolby and M. J. Schwarz, *J. Org. Chem.*, **30**, 3581 (1965).
[66] O. Kovacs and I. Kovari, *Acta Chim. Acad. Sci. Hung.*, **48**, 147 (1966).
[67] C. Agami and C. Prévost, *Compt. Rend., Ser. C*, **263**, 153 (1966).
[68] G. Glikmans, B. Torck, M. Hellin, and F. Coussement, *Bull. Soc. Chim. France*, **1966**, 1383.
[69] N. S. Zefirov, *Usp. Khim.*, **34**, 1272 (1965); *Russian Chem. Rev.*, **1965**, 527.
[70] F. R. Jensen and J. J. Miller, *Tetrahedron Letters*, **1966**, 4861.
[71] S. Wolfe, P. G. C. Campbell, and G. E. Palmer, *Tetrahedron Letters*, **1966**, 4203.
[72] I. I. Vasil'kevich and E. A. Shilov, *Ukr. Khim. Zh.*, **32**, 474 (1965); *Chem. Abs.*, **65**, 5318 (1966).
[73] J. J. Eisch and W. C. Kaska, *J. Am. Chem. Soc.*, **88**, 2213 (1966).
[74] R. H. Fish and H. G. Kuivila, *J. Org. Chem.*, **31**, 2445 (1966).

vinyl halides,[75] of buta-1,3-diene,[76] and of olefins, allene, and acetylenes in the gas phase,[77] have also been studied.

Epoxidations. On the basis of strong similarities between the reactivity parameters and general kinetic characteristics of the epoxidation of olefins with peracids on the one hand and 1,3-dipolar cycloadditions of olefins on the other, Kwart and Hoffman[78] have proposed that the accepted mechanism for epoxidation [equation (5)] should be replaced by a cycloaddition mechanism [equation (6)]. In their mechanism the proposed 1,3-dipole is the peracid tautomer (32); closely related dipoles, generated from molozonides, were also shown to epoxidize olefins. It was also suggested that other epoxidizing agents

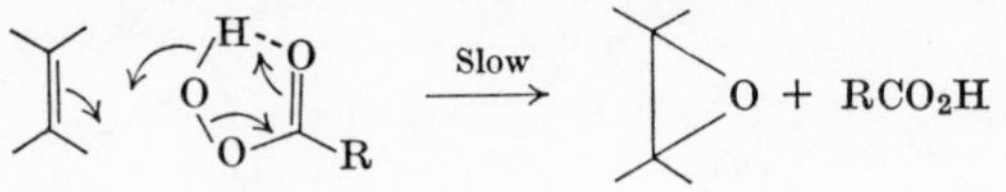

$$\text{----- (5)}$$

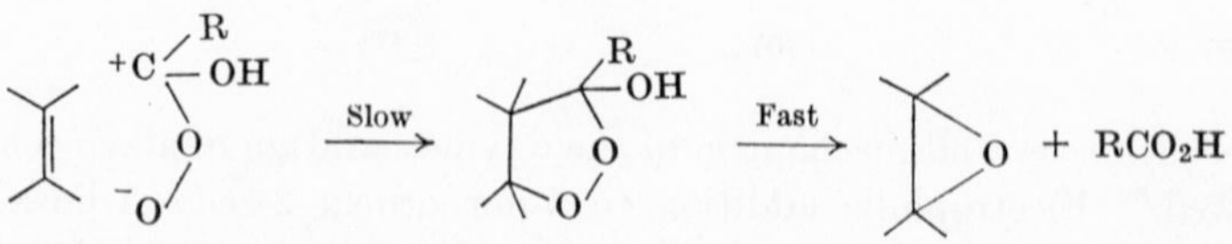

$$\text{----- (6)}$$

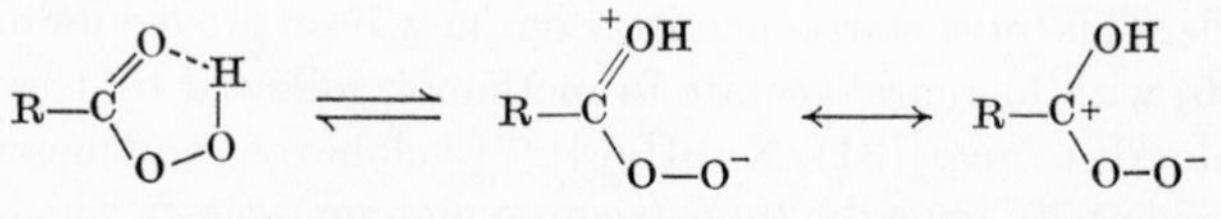

$$\text{(32)}$$

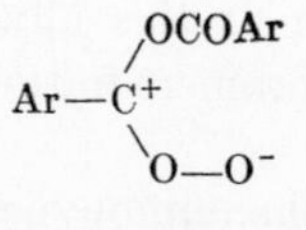

$$\text{(33)} \qquad\qquad \text{(34)}$$

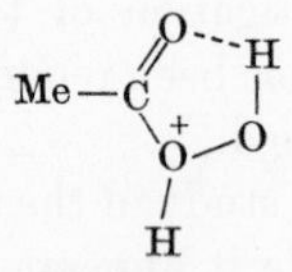

will probably react through similar intermediates, e.g., (33) from diaroyl peroxides which epoxidize highly reactive olefins.[78] However, strong support for the earlier mechanism with a three-membered cyclic transition state, and against the new mechanism with a five-membered transition state, has been given by Bingham, Meakins, and Whitham[79] on the basis that with strained olefins the former should provide little or no relief of strain in the transition

[75] D. J. Pasto and R. Snyder, *J. Org. Chem.*, **31**, 2773 (1966).
[76] B. M. Mikhailov, A. Y. Bezmenov, and L. S. Vasil'ev, *Dokl. Akad. Nauk SSSR*, **167**, 590 (1966); *Chem. Abs.*, **64**, 19338 (1966).
[77] H. H. Lindner and T. Onak, *J. Am. Chem. Soc.*, **88**, 1886 (1966).
[78] H. Kwart and D. M. Hoffman, *J. Org. Chem.*, **31**, 419 (1966).
[79] K. D. Bingham, G. D. Meakins, and G. H. Whitham, *Chem. Commun.*, **1966**, 445.

state whilst the latter should. Thus norbornene is very much more reactive towards 1,3-dipolar addition of azides than is cyclohexene; however, no such difference in reactivity of these two olefins was found in their epoxidation with perlauric acid in chloroform, and therefore dipolar cycloaddition cannot be rate-determining in this reaction.[79] The rates of epoxidation of cyclopentene, cyclohexene, and a series of cholestenes with perbenzoic acid in chloroform were found to vary only ca. 3-fold.[80] poxidation of steroidal olefins with perterephthalic acid was accelerated by the presence of a neighbouring *cis*-hydroxyl group, presumably by bonding between this group and the approaching peracid.[81]

The rate of epoxidation of allyl alcohol *in situ* by peracetic acid has been measured and compared with that for preformed peracetic acid; the rate-determining step was formation of the peracid from acetic acid and hydrogen peroxide.[82]

Acid-catalysis in the epoxidation of allyl chloride with peracetic acid has been measured for mineral, carboxylic, and sulphonic acids, and for boron trifluoride, and has been shown to follow the Brønsted equation. The conjugate acid (34) is considered to be the reactive species.[83] The epoxidation of olefins with hydrogen peroxide and tungstic acid[84] has been further investigated,[85] and the epoxidation of car-2- and -3-ene[86] and *p*-menth-1- and -3-ene[87] has been discussed. The modes of oxidation of alicyclic olefins and stilbenes by permanganate ion and by osmium tetroxide have been compared; electron-withdrawing substituents accelerate the former reaction ($\rho = 0.65$ for the stilbenes in aqueous dioxan) and retard the latter ($\rho = -0.55$ for the stilbenes in dioxan).[88] The first reaction of *cis,trans,trans*-cyclododeca-1,5,9-triene with these and other *cis*-addition reagents occurred preferentially at one of the *trans*-double bonds.[89]

Nucleophilic Additions

The chemistry of α-carbonyl azo-compounds, R–N=N–COR and RCO–N=N–COR, has been reviewed;[90] their reactions include many

[80] R. Cetina, J. L. Mateos, and E. Trabulse, *Bol. Inst. Quim. Univ. Nacl. Auton. Mex.*, **17**, 56 (1965); *Chem. Abs.*, **63**, 18201 (1965).
[81] M. Mousseron-Canet, B. Labeeuw, and J. C. Lanet, *Compt. Rend., Ser. C*, **262**, 1438 (1966).
[82] T. Suzuki and Y. Mizumara, *Kogyo Kagaku Zasshi*, **69**, 434 (1966); *Chem. Abs.*, **65**, 13482 (1966).
[83] V. N. Sapunov and N. N. Lebedev, *Zh. Org. Khim.*, **2**, 225 (1966); *Chem. Abs.*, **65**, 2086 (1966).
[84] See *Organic Reaction Mechanisms*, **1965**, 112.
[85] V. N. Sapunov and N. N. Lebedev, *Zh. Org. Khim.*, **2**, 273 (1966); *Chem. Abs.*, **65**, 2088 (1966).
[86] S. P. Acharya, *Tetrahedron Letters*, **1966**, 4117.
[87] R. M. Bowman, A. Chambers, and W. R. Jackson, *J. Chem. Soc., C*, **1966**, 612.
[88] H. B. Henbest, W. R. Jackson, and B. C. G. Robb, *J. Chem. Soc., B*, **1966**, 803.
[89] M. Ohno, M. Okamoto, and S. Torimitsu, *Bull. Chem. Soc., Japan*, **39**, 316 (1966).
[90] E. Fahr and H. Lind, *Angew. Chem. Internat. Ed. Engl.*, **5**, 372 (1966).

nucleophilic additions to the nitrogen–nitrogen double bond, and very rapid cycloadditions to dienes.

The products of Michael addition are usually those resulting from thermodynamic control; the addition of diethyl malonate to 4-*tert*-butyl-1-cyanocyclohexene has now been studied under conditions of both thermodynamic and kinetic control. In the presence of sodium ethoxide in ethanol at room temperature for 5 days, (35) and (36) were formed in ratio 5:95 whilst in boiling ethanol the ratio was 81:11; base-catalysed equilibration showed that (35) is the more stable. Product (36) is formed when the entering group adopts the equatorial conformation and protonation occurs from the least hindered side.[91] A detailed investigation has been made of the kinetics of addition of nitroform to methyl acrylate to form methyl 4,4,4-trinitrobutyrate (37) and methyl 2-hydroxy-4,4-dinitrobutyrate (38) in 50% dioxan in the

(35)

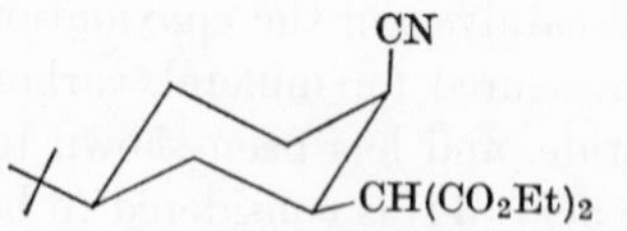

(36)

$(O_2N)_3C \cdot CH_2CH_2CO_2Me$

(37)

$(O_2N)_2CH \cdot CHCO_2Me$
                        |
                       OH

(38)

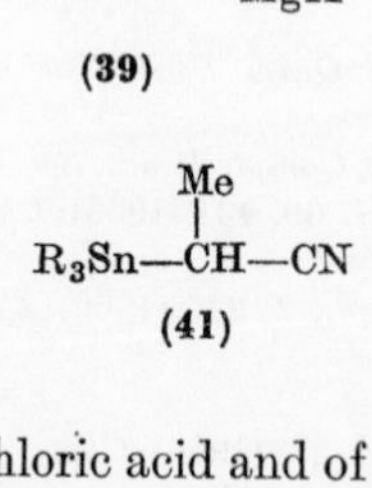

(39)

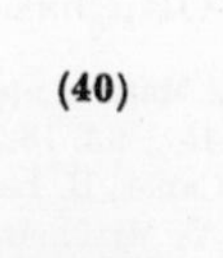

(40)

$$\overset{Me}{\underset{|}{R_3Sn-CH-CN}}$$

(41)

$R_3SnCH_2CH_2CN$

(42)

presence of perchloric acid and of acetate buffers. In acetic acid, formation of (37) involves a rapid and reversible addition of trinitromethyl carbanions to the double bond, followed by rate-determining protonation of the resulting

[91] R. A. Abramovitch and D. L. Struble, *Tetrahedron Letters*, **1966**, 289.

carbanion. In perchloric acid the rate of this protonation gradually increases with acidity until formation of the intermediate carbanion becomes rate-determining.[92] The base-catalysed addition of thiols to maleic anhydride in non-polar solvents is considered to proceed by reversible formation of an ion-pair, from the thiol and base, followed by attack of the double bond by the thiolate end of the ion pair. This provides a convenient reaction for determining the nucleophilicity of thiolate anions, free from complications due to readily formed thiyl radicals. This nucleophilicity paralleled basicity, after correction for the prior acid–base equilibration.[93] Friedman and Wall have continued their investigation[94] of nucleophilic additions of amino-acids and peptides to acrylonitrile and related α,β-unsaturated compounds; they have correlated the wide variation in rates by a four-parameter linear free-energy equation associated with polar and steric factors for each reactant.[95]

Munch-Petersen and his co-workers[96] have suggested two types of mechanism for the addition of Grignard reagents to conjugated esters: the normal Michael carbanion mechanism (39) and the cyclic mechanism (40), the mechanism adopted in a given case depending on the structures of the ester and reagent. The conjugative additions of Grignard reagents to unsaturated ester of sugars have now been rationalized on the basis of these two mechanisms.[97] The kinetically controlled Michael addition of methylmagnesium iodide to 5-methylcyclohex-2-enone gave *trans*-3,5-dimethylcyclohexanone, as predicted from conformational analysis (see p. 334).[98a] Reactive Grignard reagents have been found to add to the double bond of allyl alcohol.[98b] An unusual reversal of stereospecificity has been reported but not yet explained: reaction of 1,2-dicyclohexylethanedione with phenyl-lithium gave the racemic glycol only, and with phenylmagnesium bromide gave the *meso*-glycol only.[99] The addition of nitrosyl fluoride to perfluoropropene in the presence of inorganic fluorides is considered to be a nucleophilic reaction initiated by addition of fluoride ion to the double bond.[100]

Addition of organotin hydrides (hydrostannation) to double bonds has usually been considered to involve a radical mechanism. Leusink and Noltes[101]

92 L. A. Kaplan and D. J. Glover, *J. Am. Chem. Soc.*, **88**, 84 (1966).
93 B. Dmuchovsky, F. B. Zienty, and W. A. Vredenburgh, *J. Org. Chem.*, **31**, 865 (1966).
94 See *Organic Reaction Mechanisms*, **1965**, 113.
95 M. Friedman and J. S. Wall, *J. Org. Chem.*, **31**, 2888 (1966).
96 S. Jacobsen, A. Jart, T. Kindt-Larsen, I. G. K. Andersen, and J. Munch-Petersen, *Acta Chem. Scand.*, **17**, 2423 (1963).
97 M. Kawana and S. Emoto, *Bull. Chem. Soc. Japan*, **39**, 910 (1966).
98a N. L. Allinger and C. K. Riew, *Tetrahedron Letters*, **1966**, 1269.
98b M. Chérest, H. Felkin, C. Frajerman, C. Lion, G. Roussi, and G. Swierczewski, *Tetrahedron Letters*, **1966**, 875.
99 J. H. Stocker, *J. Am. Chem. Soc.*, **88**, 2878 (1966).
100 B. L. Dyatkin, E. P. Mochalina, R. A. Bekker, and I. L. Knunyants, *Izv. Akad. Nauk SSSR, Ser. Khim.*, **1966**, 585; *Chem. Abs.*, **65**, 5320 (1966).
101 A. J. Leusink and J. G. Noltes, *Tetrahedron Letters*, **1966**, 335.

have now shown that hydrostannation of acrylonitrile gives both isomers (**41**) and (**42**), the former resulting from a polar mechanism and the latter from a radical mechanism. The polar mechanism involves nucleophilic attack of the stannane-hydrogen on carbon in the rate-determining step.[101]

Other related topics that have been discussed are: addition of organolithium compounds to vinylphosphines[102] and to tolan;[103] conjugative addition of Grignard reagents to α,β-unsaturated ketones;[104] the stereochemistry of the addition of amines to ethyl propiolate and to several acetylenic sulphones;[105] the stereochemistry of the addition of alcohols and amines to acetylenic esters and dicyanoacetylene;[106] addition (of the amino-group) of amino-alcohols to alkyl acrylates,[107] of nitroform to aqueous acrylic acid,[108] and of thiosulphate anions to acrylic acid and derivatives,[109] the irreversibility of intramolecular addition of a nitrone group to a double bond;[110] Michael additions to 7-hydroxypteridine[111] and to *para*-substituted cinnamoylferrocene derivatives;[112] and addition of hydroiodic acid to methyl propiolate[113] and dimethyl acetylenedicarboxylate.[114]

Radical Additions

Tedder and Walton[115] have elaborated their evidence for the role played by substituents on the carbon atom of a double bond that is actually attacked in a radical-addition process. However, molecular-orbital calculations point to the dominating directing effect of substituents on the β-carbon atom.[116]

[102] D. J. Peterson, *J. Org. Chem.*, **31**, 950 (1966).
[103] J. E. Mulvaney, Z. G. Gardlund, S. L. Gardlund, and D. J. Newton, *J. Am. Chem. Soc.*, **88**, 476 (1966).
[104] J. A. Marshall and N. H. Andersen, *J. Org. Chem.*, **31**, 667 (1966).
[105] W. E. Truce and D. G. Brady, *J. Org. Chem.*, **31**, 3543 (1966).
[106] E. Winterfeldt and H. Preuss, *Chem. Ber.*, **99**, 450 (1966); E. Winterfeldt, W. Krohn and H. Preuss, *ibid.*, p. 2572.
[107] N. Ogata and T. Asahara, *Bull. Chem. Soc. Japan*, **39**, 1486 (1966).
[108] S. S. Novikov and I. S. Ivanova, *Izv. Akad. Nauk SSSR, Ser. Khim.*, **1966**, 1138; *Chem. Abs.*, **65**, 15180.
[109] R. Kerber and J. Starnick, *Tetrahedron Letters*, **1966**, 3007.
[110] N. A. LeBel and T. A. Lajiness, *Tetrahedron Letters*, **1966**, 2173.
[111] A. Albert and J. J. McCormack, *J. Chem. Soc.*, **1965**, 6930.
[112] M. Furdik and S. Toma, *Chem. Zvesti*, **20**, 326 (1966); *Chem. Abs.*, **65**, 7015 (1966).
[113] G. F. Dvorko, T. F. Karpenko, and E. A. Shilov, *Kinetika i Kataliz.*, **6**, 809 (1965).
[114] G. F. Dvorko, T. F. Karpenko, D. F. Mironova, and E. A. Shilov, *Ukr. Khim. Zh.*, **31**, 1177 (1965); G. F. Dvorko and D. F. Mironova, *ibid.*, p. 1289; **32**, 362 (1966); *Chem. Abs.*, **65**, 7014 (1966).
[115] J. M. Tedder and J. C. Walton, *Trans. Faraday Soc.*, **62**, 1859 (1966).
[116] J. B. Flannery, *J. Phys. Chem.*, **70**, 3707 (1966).

Molecular-orbital calculations on additions have also been reported by a second group of workers.[117]

Readio and Skell[118] have examined the radical addition of HBr and thiols to 4-*tert*-butyl-1-chlorocyclohexene. Addition of HBr leads to >95% of the diaxial addition product (**43**) from the reaction at −78° in pentane. This product is formulated as arising from hydrogen-transfer to the bridged intermediate (**44**), in which unsymmetrical bridging is induced by the radical-stabilizing influence of the chlorine atom. Unsymmetrical bridging is discussed at length. The unsymmetrical nature of the bridge coupled with preferred axial attack leads from intermediate (**44**) exclusively to (**43**). The suggestion is made that products from the isomeric intermediate (**45**) are formed in relatively minor yield because (**44**) is more stable than (**45**); this, in turn, is attributed to the

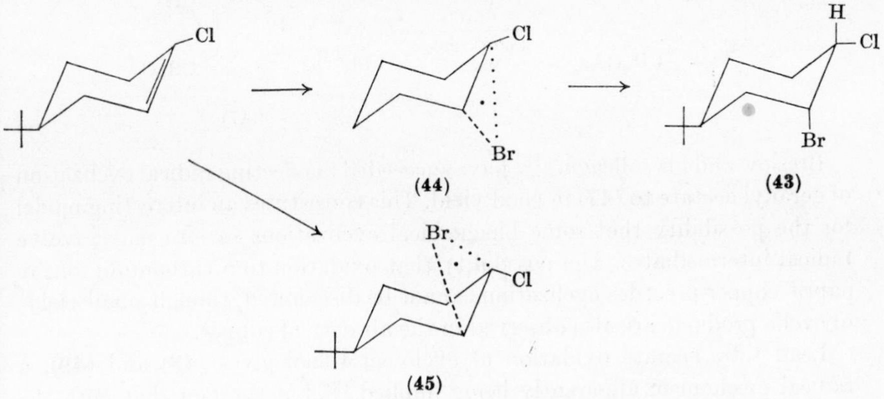

possibility that the unsymmetrical bridged intermediate which has its stronger bond in a pseudo-axial orientation may be the energetically preferred isomer. Similar stereochemical results are obtained for the thiol additions, suggesting the possible importance of sulphur-bridged intermediates.

Some interesting intramolecular additions have been reported. Julia and Maumy[119] have examined the factors determining the ring-size of products resulting from the cyclization of radicals (**46**). Changing from R = H to R = Me increases the proportion of cyclohexane products, and greater stabilization of the radical centre by X and Y appears also to favour cyclohexane formation. For example, with R = Me, X = H, and Y = CN, cyclization leads exclusively to a five-membered ring; but, when R = Me, X = CN, and Y = CO_2Et, only six-membered ring products are observed. Julia has sum-

117 J. E. Bloor, A. C. R. Brown, and D. G. L. James, *J. Phys. Chem.*, **70**, 2191 (1966).
118 P. D. Readio and P. S. Skell, *J. Org. Chem.*, **31**, 753, 759 (1966).
119 M. Julia and M. Maumy, *Bull. Soc. Chim. France*, **1966**, 434.

marized some of his group's results in a report of the Gomberg centenary symposium.[120]

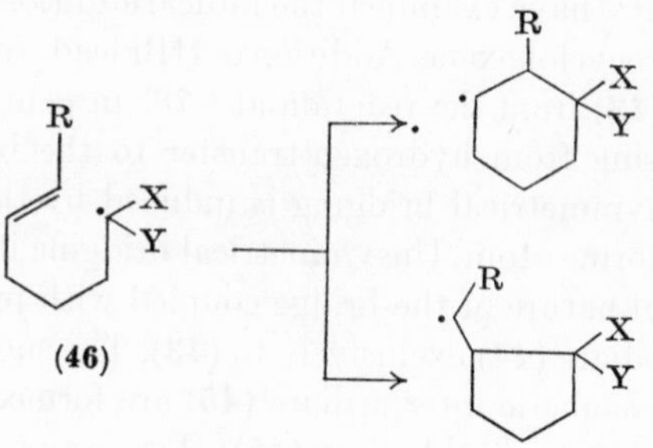

(46)

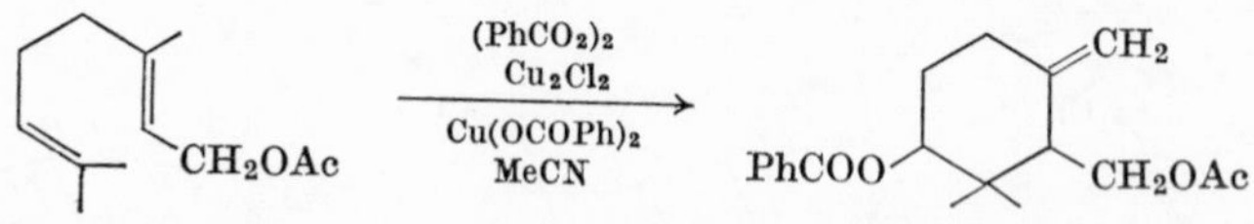

(47)

Breslow and his colleagues[121] have succeeded in effecting radical cyclization of geranyl acetate to (47) in good yield. This constitutes an interesting model for the possibility that some biochemical cyclizations *in vivo* may involve radical intermediates. The possibility that oxidation to a carbonium ion by cupric copper precedes cyclization cannot be discounted, though small yields of cyclic products are also observed in the absence of copper.

Lead tetra-acetate oxidation of cyclo-oct-4-enol gives (48) and (49), a radical mechanism apparently being implied,[122] but the fact that both the norbornenecarboxylic acid (50) and its methyl ester give the same product (51) indicates that in this case there is initial electrophilic addition of

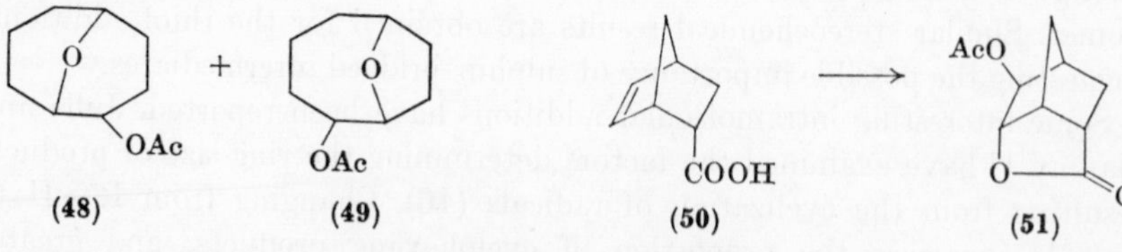

(48)   (49)   (50)   (51)

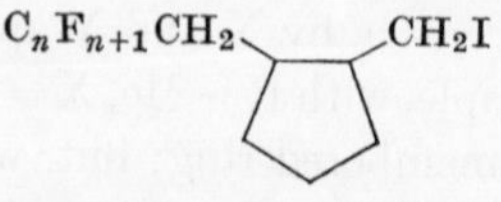

(52)

[120] *Chem. Eng. News*, Oct. 3rd 1966, p. 100.
[121] R. Breslow, J. T. Groves, and S. S. Olin, *Tetrahedron Letters*, 1966, 4717.
[122] S. Moon and L. Haynes, *J. Org. Chem.*, 31, 3067 (1966).

$Pb(OAc)_4$ to the double bond, followed by neighbouring-group participation by carboxyl-oxygen.[123]

Homolytic addition of iodoperfluoroalkanes to hepta-1,6-diene gives (**52**) as a major product, but no cyclization was observed with hexa-1,5-diene or octa-1,7-diene.[124] Some cyclization has also been observed subsequent to abstraction of benzylic hydrogen from ω-phenylalk-1-enes.[125]

Radical additions to longifolene reported last year[126] were accompanied by transannular hydrogen-transfer. The radical addition of formamide apparently occurs without this rearrangement.[127] Other formamide additions have also been studied.[128]

The addition of carbon tetrachloride to *cis*-cyclo-octene does involve a hydrogen-transfer, giving *cis*- and *trans*-1-chloro-4-trichloromethylcyclo-octane.[129] The transannular reaction does not compete effectively with bromine-abstraction from bromotrichloromethane, and with this reagent the principal product is the 1,2-adduct.

The addition of thiols and related compounds to hexachloronorbornadiene has now been reported in full.[130] A new product has been isolated from the cuprous-catalysed reaction of benzonorbornadiene with benzoyl peroxide. 7-Phenylbenzonorbornadiene is probably formed as shown,[131] though it would be of interest to have confirmation that the phenyl group originates from the peroxide and not from the benzene solvent.

Heiba[132] has made some interesting contributions to the free-radical chemistry of allene. In the addition of HBr at $-78°$, Br• adds to both terminal

[123] R. M. Moriarty, H. G. Walsh, and H. Gopal, *Tetrahedron Letters*, **1966**, 4363, 4369.
[124] N. O. Brace, *J. Org. Chem.*, **31**, 2879 (1966).
[125] H. Pines, N. C. Sih, and D. B. Rosenfield, *J. Org. Chem.*, **31**, 2255 (1966).
[126] See *Organic Reaction Mechanisms*, **1965**, 118.
[127] M. Fisch and G. Ourisson, *Bull. Soc. Chim. France*, **1966**, 1325.
[128] J. Rokach, C. H. Krauch and D. Elad, *Tetrahedron Letters*, **1966**, 3253; D. P. Gush, N. S. Marans, F. Wessells, W. D. Addy, and S. J. Olfky, *J. Org. Chem.*, **31**, 3829 (1966).
[129] J. G. Traynham and T. M. Couvillon, *J. Am. Chem. Soc.*, **87**, 5806 (1965).
[130] C. K. Alden, J. A. Claisse, and D. I. Davies, *J. Chem. Soc., C*, **1966**, 1498, 1540; see also p. 159.
[131] M. A. Battiste and M. E. Brennan, *Chem. Ind. (London)*, **1966**, 1496.
[132] E.-A. I. Heiba, *J. Org. Chem.*, **31**, 776 (1966); E.-A. I. Heiba and W. O. Haag, *ibid.*, p. 3814 (1966); see also, *Organic Reaction Mechanisms*, **1965**, 116.

and central carbon atoms in the statistical ratio 2:1. However, terminal addition to give a substituted vinyl radical is reversible, whereas central addition to give a stabilized allyl radical is not. Thus with low HBr concentrations there is little product evidence of terminal addition, but with increased concentrations the limit is reached where products of terminal addition to central addition are in the above-mentioned ratio. Benzenethiyl radicals are slightly more selective at 80°, whilst the more selective and bulky trichloromethyl radical adds exclusively at the terminal carbon.

Additions to acetylenes include the preparation of adipic acid by double addition of acetic acid to acetylene itself,[133] and addition of thiols to enynes.[134] Heptyne with carbon tetrachloride gives the normal adduct together with

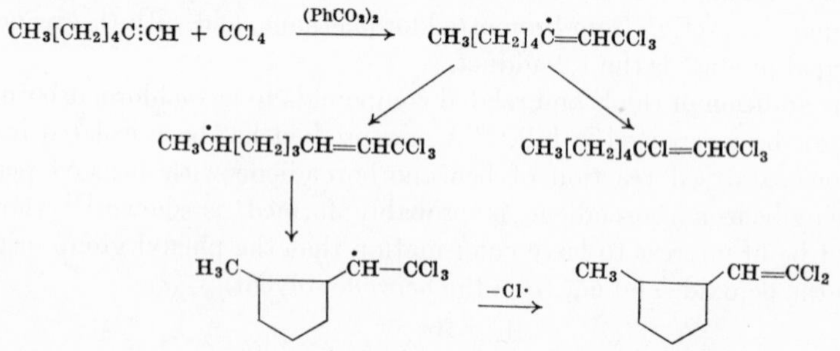

$CH_3[CH_2]_4C:CH + CCl_4$
$(PhCO_2)_2$
$CH_3[CH_2]_4\dot{C}=CHCCl_3$
$CH_3\dot{C}H[CH_2]_3CH=CHCCl_3$
$CH_3[CH_2]_4CCl=CHCCl_3$
H_3C
$\dot{C}H-CCl_3$
$-Cl\cdot$
CH_3
$CH=CCl_2$

(53)

CH_3
CN
RS·
RS
CH_3
CN
SR
CH_3
CN
RSH
SR
CH_3
CN

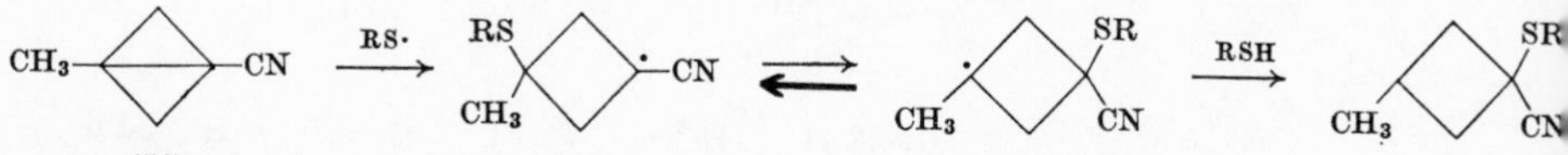

(54) (55) (56) (57)

20% of the vinylcyclopentane (**53**).[135] *trans*-Dichlorobut-1-ene is the major product of addition of chlorine to but-1-yne; traces of allenic products are formed, but the surprising conclusion is drawn that hydrogen-abstraction from the propargylic methylene is appreciably slower per hydrogen atom than that from cyclohexane.[136]

Addition of thiols to the bicyclobutane (**54**) gives predominantly (**57**).[137] To explain the unexpected orientation of the major product, the equilibrium (**55**) ⇄ (**56**) is proposed, chain transfer from the less stable (**56**) being pos-

[133] J. DiPietro and W. J. Roberts, *Can. J. Chem.*, **44**, 2241 (1966).
[134] I. G. Sulimov and A. A. Petrov, *Zh. Org. Khim*, **2**, 767 (1966); *Chem. Abs.*, **65**, 12099 (1966).
[135] E.-A. I. Heiba and R. M. Dessau, *J. Am. Chem. Soc.*, **88**, 1589 (1966).
[136] M. L. Poutsma and J. L. Kartch, *Tetrahedron*, **22**, 2167 (1966).
[137] E. P. Blanchard and A. Cairncross, *J. Am. Chem. Soc.*, **88**, 487, 496 (1966).

tulated as sufficiently rapid to dominate the reaction. Radical intermediates in cycloadditions of (54) are also discussed.

Amongst the many additions to simple olefins are reports that alkyl iodides and bromides add as alkyl group and halogen,[138] but that RCH_2Cl adds to norbornene as [RĊHCl] and [H·].[139a] Hydrogen abstraction α to chlorine has also been noted elsewhere.[139b] The importance of polar effects in the R group in additions of thiols to $RSCH{=}CHCO_2Me$ are reflected by the proportions of α-attack to β-attack.[140] Where $R = CH_3CO$, $\alpha/\beta = 1.1$; $R = Me$, $\alpha/\beta = 4.2$; $R = Ph$, $\alpha/\beta = 53$. These results are clearly unrelated to steric effects.

The results of a detailed analysis of secondary deuterium isotope effects on the polymerization of styrene can be accommodated in terms of the usual explanations of secondary isotope effects.[141] Chain-transfer constants for hydrogen-abstraction from conventional "active methylene" compounds such as acetylacetone have been measured in styrene polymerization. Very little stabilization of the radicals was revealed.[142] Polymerization of certain vinyltriarylcarbinols (58) leads to polymers which, after appropriate manipulation, give the "polyradicals" (59).

In a study of substituent effects on the copolymerization of a series of aryl methacrylates with styrene, there was strong deviation from a Hammett correlation in the case of electron-releasing substituents. This was attributed

$$[{-}CH{-}CH_2{-}]_n \qquad [{-}CH{-}CH_2{-}]_n$$

$$Ar{-}\overset{|}{\underset{Ar}{C}}{-}OH \qquad Ar{-}\overset{|}{\underset{Ar}{C}}{-}OH \qquad Ar{-}\overset{|}{\underset{Ar}{C}}\cdot$$

(58) (59)

$$CH_2{:}C{\overset{\displaystyle Me}{\underset{\displaystyle \overset{|}{\underset{OAr}{C}}{=}O}{\big\langle}}} \quad \longleftrightarrow \quad CH_2{:}C{\overset{\displaystyle Me}{\underset{\displaystyle \overset{+}{\underset{OAr}{C}}{-}O^-}{\big\langle}}}$$

(60)

[138] I. B. Afanas'ev, E. D. Safronenko, and V. Y. Katsobashvili, *Zh. Org. Khim.*, **2**, 423 (1966); *Chem. Abs.*, **65**, 7052 (1966).

[139a] D. J. Trecker and J. P. Henry, *Chem. Commun.*, **1966**, 258.

[139b] T. Migita, M. Kosugi, H. Kono, and Y. Nagai, *Yuki Gosei Kagaku Kyokai Shi*, **24**, 223 (1966); *Chem. Abs.*, **64**, 15684 (1966).

[140] W. H. Mueller, *J. Org. Chem.*, **31**, 3075 (1966).

[141] W. A. Pryor, R. W. Henderson, R. A. Patsiga, and N. Carroll, *J. Am. Chem. Soc.*, **88**, 1199 (1966).

[142] J. I. G. Cadogan, D. H. Hey and J. T. Sharp, *J. Chem. Soc.*, B, **1966**, 933.

to an increased contribution from the polar form (**60**), tending to isolate the double bond from the ester grouping.[143]

Polymerization of 9-vinylcarbazole appears to be initiated by electron-transfer, as shown by the formation of the dimer (**61**) in the presence of a high concentration of ferric salt.[144, 145]

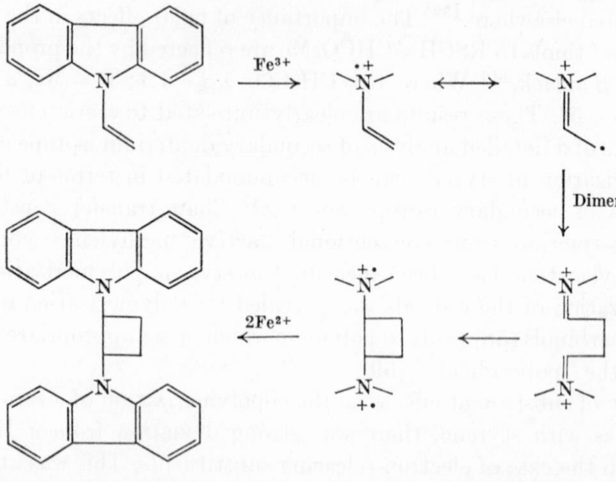

(**61**)

The addition of acetaldehyde to hept-1-ene catalysed by O_2/cobaltous acetate gives a fair yield of nonan-2-one;[146] addition of methyl radicals to crotonaldehyde gives but-2-ene by loss of CHO from the presumed intermediate;[147] and the interesting radical-promoted isomerization $CH_2{=}C(OEt)_2$ $\rightarrow EtCH_2CO_2Et$ is presumably a consequence of the chain-carrying sequence:[148]

$$Et\cdot + CH_2{=}C(OEt)_2 \rightarrow EtCH_2\overset{\cdot}{C}(OEt)_2 \rightarrow EtCH_2CO_2Et + Et\cdot$$

Benzenethiyl radicals add principally to the vinyl group in 4-vinylcyclohexene; the dehydro-dimers resulting from initial allylic abstraction have also been investigated.[149]

Additions of HBr, and HBr-promoted isomerization, have received further attention,[150] and the iodine atom-catalysed isomerization of styrylpyridines

[143] D. Braun and R. J. Faust, *Angew. Chem. Internat. Edn. Engl.*, **5**, 838 (1966).

[144] T. Otu, T. Ito, and M. Imoto, *J. Polymer Sci.*, Pt. A-1, **4**, 733 (1966).

[145] S. McKinley, J. V. Crawford, and Chi-Hua Wang, *J. Org. Chem.*, **31**, 1963 (1966).

[146] G. I. Nikishin, M. G. Vinogradov, and R. V. Kereselidze, *Izv. Akad. Nauk. SSSR, Ser. Khim.*, **1966**, 1122; *Chem. Abs.*, **65**, 12100 (1966).

[147] E. R. Allen and J. N. Pitts, *J. Phys. Chem.*, **70**, 1691 (1966).

[148] E. S. Huyser, R. M. Kellogg, and D. T. Wang, *J. Org. Chem.*, **30**, 4377 (1965).

[149] J. R. Shelton, and J. F. Siuda, *J. Org. Chem.*, **31**, 2028 (1966); J. R. Shelton and A. E. Champ, *ibid.*, **30**, 4183 (1965).

[150] K. T. Wong and D. A. Armstrong, *Chem. Commun.*, **1966**, 353; P. I. Abell, *J. Am. Chem. Soc.*, **88**, 1346 (1966); L. H. Gale, *ibid.*, p. 4661.

has been related to that of the stilbenes.[151] There is some evidence for participation by nitrogen in the case of 2-styrylpyridine.

Peroxide-initiated addition of PCl_3 to olefins is an inefficient process, probably because of competing heterolytic destruction of peroxide. However, quantum yields of 10 or more are obtained in the light-initiated process.[152] Both $RCH(PCl_2)CH_2Cl$ and $RCHClCH_2PCl_2$ were observed. Possibly chain-carrying may be by both Cl· and ·PCl_2, but symmetrical adducts might then be expected, e.g.:

$$RCH{=}CH_2 + \cdot PCl_2 \rightarrow R\dot{C}HCH_2PCl_2 \xrightarrow{PCl_3} \underset{\underset{\cdot PCl_3}{|}}{RCHCH_2PCl_2} \xrightarrow{-Cl\cdot} \underset{\underset{PCl_2}{|}}{RCHCH_2PCl_2}$$

Although no such products were observed, this may have been a consequence of the working-up procedure.

The addition of amino-radicals and radical cations generated from chloramines or related compounds continues to receive attention.[153]

Additions of *N,N*-dichlorourethane,[154] *N*-acetylglycine methyl ester,[155] benzyl radicals,[156] thiyl radicals,[157] carbon tetrachloride,[158] and 3-ethoxypropionitrile[159] have been reported.

Isomers of 1,1,2-trichlorohept-1-ene are obtained on *γ*-radiolysis of *n*-pentane and tetrachloroethylene, the *G*-value for this unusual addition–elimination being >30.[160]

Gas-phase additions which have been studied include those by hydrogen,[161] chlorine,[162] trifluoroacetonitrile,[163] tetrafluorohydrazine,[164] and perfluorodimethylnitroxide.[165]

[151] G. Cauzzo, U. Mazzucato, and G. Aloisi, *Gazz. Chim. Ital.*, **96**, 721 (1966).

[152] J. R. Little and P. F. Hartman, *J. Am. Chem. Soc.*, **88**, 96 (1966).

[153] R. S. Neale, *Tetrahedron Letters*, **1966**, 483; F. Minisci, R. Galli, and M. Cecere, *ibid.*, p. 3163; F. Minisci and R. Galli, *Chim. Ind. (Milan)*, **48**, 268 (1966); F. Minisci, R. Galli, and M. Cecere, *ibid.*, p. 347.

[154] T. A. Foglia and D. Swern, *J. Org. Chem.*, **31**, 3625 (1966).

[155] D. Elad and J. Sinnreich, *Chem. Ind. (London)*, **1966**, 1180.

[156] R. L. Huang, H. H. Lee, and L.-Y. Wong, *J. Chem. Soc.*, **1965**, 6730.

[157] A. A. Oswald and W. Naegele, *J. Org. Chem.*, **31**, 830 (1966).

[158] S. Dolezal, *Coll. Czech. Chem. Commun.*, **31**, 3765 (1966).

[159] S. I. Sadykhzade and S. D. Yul'chevskaya, *Azerb. Khim. Zh.*, **1966**, 29; *Chem. Abs.*, **65**, 7052 (1966).

[160] L. A. Rajbenbach and A. Horowitz, *Chem. Commun.*, **1966**, 769.

[161] M. C. Lin, *Can. J. Chem.*, **44**, 1237 (1966); J. M. Brown, P. B. Coates, and B. A. Thrush, *Chem. Commun.*, **1966**, 843.

[162] C. Vallana, E. Castellano, and H. J. Schumacher, *Z. Physik. Chem. (Frankfurt)*, **46**, 294 (1965); J. H. Knox and J. Riddick, *Trans. Faraday Soc.*, **62**, 1190 (1966); J. H. Knox, *ibid.*, p. 1206; P. B. Ayscough, F. S. Dainton, and B. E. Fleischfresser, *ibid.*, pp. 1838, 1846 (1966).

[163] G. J. Janz and J. B. Flannery, *J. Phys. Chem.*, **70**, 2061 (1966); *J. Am. Chem. Soc.*, **88**, 5097 (1966).

[164] A. J. Dijkstra, J. A. Kerr, and A. F. Trotman-Dickenson, *J. Chem. Soc.*, *A*, **1966**, 582.

[165] R. E. Banks, R. N. Haszeldine, and M. J. Stevenson, *J. Chem. Soc.*, *C*, **1966**, 901.

Finally, mention should be made of two homolytic β-eliminations resulting from the reversibility of thiyl-radical addition. Thiyl radicals abstract hydrogen from a hydroxymethylene group of a β-hydroxy-sulphide:

$$
\begin{array}{ccccc}
\text{OH} & & \text{OH} & & \text{OH} \\
| & & | & & | \\
\text{HC—CH}_2\text{SMe} & \xrightarrow{\text{Me}\dot{\text{S}}} & \cdot\text{C—CH}_2\text{SMe} & \xrightarrow{-\text{Me}\dot{\text{S}}} & \text{C}{=}\text{CH}_2 \rightarrow \text{Me}_2\text{CO} \\
| & & | & & | \\
\text{Me} & & \text{Me} & & \text{Me}
\end{array}
$$

Acetone is reasonably stable in the reaction conditions and, with peroxide initiation, chain lengths of 20—30 were achieved.[166] Similarly, in the reaction between triphenylphenylazomethane and either di-*tert*-butyl sulphide or *tert*-butyl phenyl sulphide, elimination occurs, this time in a non-chain process:

$$\text{PhN}{=}\text{NCPh}_3 \rightarrow \text{Ph}\cdot + \text{N}_2 + \cdot\text{CPh}_3$$
$$\text{Ph}\cdot + \text{Bu}^t\text{SR} \rightarrow \text{PhH} + \text{CH}_2{=}\text{CMe}_2 + \text{RS}\cdot$$
$$\text{RS}\cdot + \cdot\text{CPh}_3 \rightarrow \text{Ph}_3\text{SR}$$

Hydrogen abstraction from the *tert*-butyl group is unusually rapid, suggesting that it may occur in concert with the elimination.[167] In accord with this was the failure to isolate products from the scavenging of intermediate radicals by triphenylmethyl. On the other hand, the ease of abstraction was most pronounced for di-*tert*-butyl sulphide, whereas *tert*-butyl phenyl sulphide would appear to have the better leaving group. An alternative mechanism involving sulphur-bridging was also discussed.

Diels–Alder Reactions

Recent developments with emphasis on preparative aspects,[168] and Diels–Alder reactions with molecular oxygen as dienophile,[169] have been reviewed.

The "ene" synthesis or "indirect" substitutive addition (7) is formally, and probably mechanistically, closely related to the Diels–Alder reaction (8). Berson and his co-workers[170] have now shown that reaction (7), like (8), shows a preference for *endo*-type ("endoid") addition. *cis*-But-2-ene and maleic anhydride in benzene at 225° gave *erythro*- and *threo*-(1-methylalkyl)-succinic anhydrides (62) in a kinetically controlled ratio of ca. 1:4. With *trans*-but-2-ene the stereoselectivity was considerably lower, but it was qualitatively preserved since the *erythro*-isomer was now the major product.

[166] E. S. Huyser and R. M. Kellogg, *J. Org. Chem.*, **31**, 3366 (1966).
[167] J. A. Kampmeier, R. P. Geer, A. J. Meskin, and R. M. D'Silva, *J. Am. Chem. Soc.*, **88**, 1257 (1966).
[168] J. Sauer, *Angew. Chem. Internat. Ed. Engl.*, **5**, 211 (1966).
[169] Y. A. Arbuzov, *Russian Chem. Rev.*, **1965**, 558.
[170] J. A. Berson, R. G. Wall, and H. D. Perlmutter, *J. Am. Chem. Soc.*, **88**, 187 (1966); see also, C. Agami, M. Andrac-Taussig, C. Justin, and C. Prévost, *Bull. Soc. Chim. France*, **1966**, 1195.

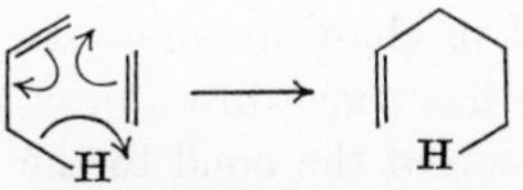

------- (7)

------- (8)

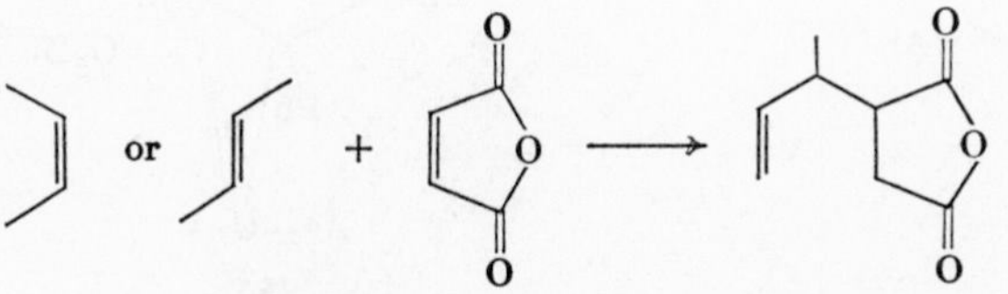

(62)

(63)

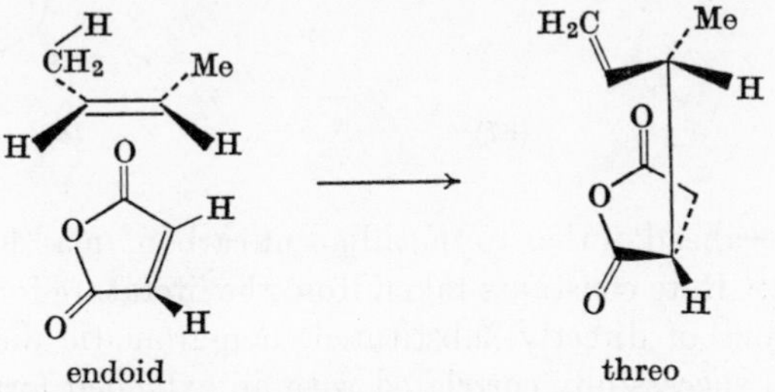

------- (9)

endoid   threo

These isomers (**62**) were not formed on addition of but-1-ene, which gave (**63**), and vice versa, thus excluding a radical-chain mechanism with initiation by abstraction of allylic hydrogen. In the cyclopentene–maleic anhydride ene reaction the *erythro:threo* product ratio was 3.5:1. If the C–C and C–H bond formation in the ene synthesis is concerted, as appears likely, these results indicate a preference for the endoid orientation, favoured by steric and, possibly, electronic factors of the type that control the Diels–Alder addition. This orientation is shown for *cis*-but-2-ene (9).[170]

In the Diels–Alder reaction of tetraphenylcyclopentadienone with methyl arylpropiolates, formation of the bridged adducts (**64**) is rate-determining and since decarbonylation is fast the reaction is irreversible. A normal Hammett plot was curved but became linear when σ^- values, appropriate for direct interaction of the substituent with an electron-rich centre and obtainable from the phenol ionization constants, were used. This, and the small ρ-value

(0.3), were interpreted by a concerted mechanism where the propiolic acid bears a partial negative charge which has some direct interaction with the substituent; this suggests that formation of the bond to the carbon remote

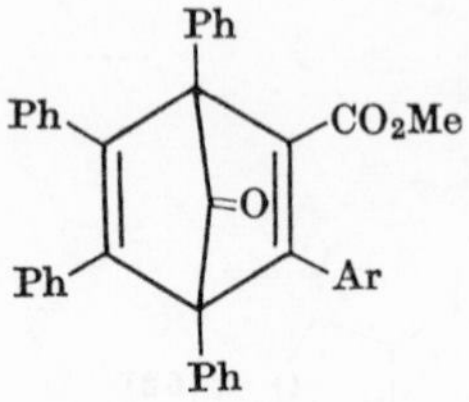

(64) 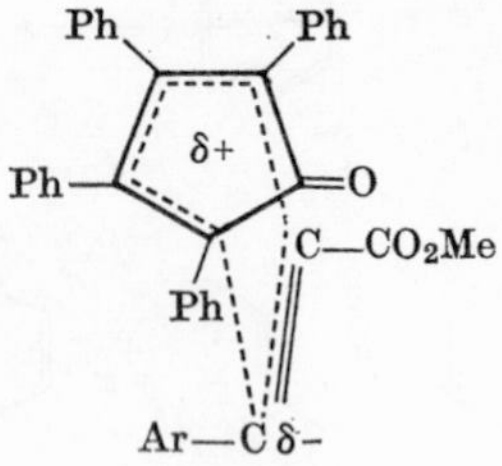   (65)

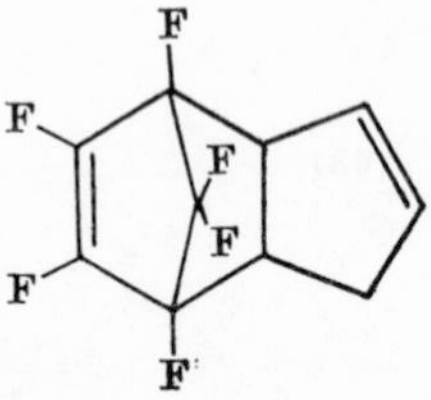

(66) 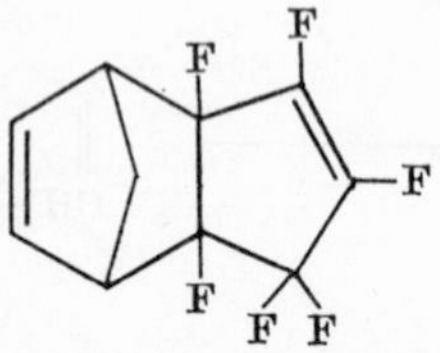   (67) 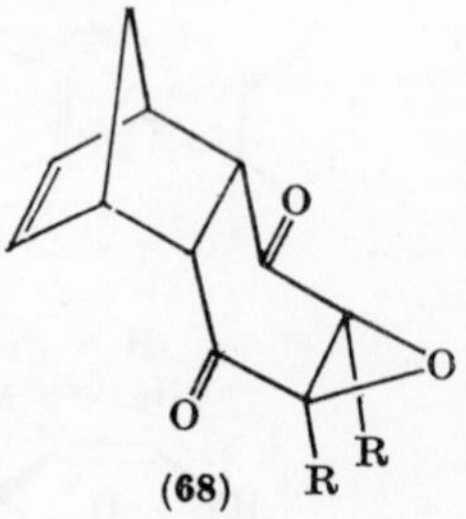   (68)

from the aryl ring runs ahead of that to the adjacent carbon, in a "lopsided" transition state (65).[171] Rate constants taken from the literature for a range of Diels–Alder reactions of directly substituted, non-aromatic dienes and dienophiles have been successfully correlated with an extended form of the Hammett equation; mechanistic deductions from this correlation all point to a concerted process with a transition state resembling reactants more than products.[172] The reaction of equimolecular amounts of cyclopentadiene and its perfluoro-derivative gave a kinetically controlled mixture of adducts (66) and (67), the composition of which was virtually unchanged with change in reaction temperature or solvent. By the argument used by Little last year[173] this was considered to provide good evidence for a reaction involving one transition state leading to a common intermediate, which rapidly collapsed in two different ways to give the observed products.[174]

Further evidence that *endo → exo* isomerization of Diels–Alder adducts proceeds by a simple dissociation–recombination sequence[175] has been

[171] D. N. Matthews and E. I. Becker, *J. Org. Chem.*, **31**, 1135 (1966).
[172] M. Charton, *J. Org. Chem.*, **31**, 3745 (1966).
[173] J. C. Little, *J. Am. Chem. Soc.*, **87**, 4020 (1965); *Organic Reaction Mechanisms*, **1965**, 125.
[174] R. E. Banks, A. C. Harrison, and R. N. Haszeldine, *Chem. Commun.*, **1966**, 338.
[175] See *Organic Reaction Mechanisms*, **1965**, 126.

provided for the cyclopentadiene–maleic anhydride adduct,[176] for dicyclo-pentadiene,[177] and for some cyclopentadiene-1,4-benzoquinone-2,3-epoxide adducts (68).[178] For dicyclopentadiene this was done by labelling one ring specifically with deuterium; it was shown that the monomer molecules could change partners before redimerizing.[177] The cyclopentadiene liberated from (68) could be trapped with tetracyanoethylene.[178]

Catalysed Diels–Alder reactions have also received further attention. The relative rates of the uncatalysed and aluminium chloride-catalysed reactions of methyl acrylate with butadiene, isoprene, and 2,3-dimethylbutadiene, and the proportions of the two adducts (69) and (70) formed in the isoprene reaction were measured. The catalytic reaction was free from the steric complication expected on the one-step mechanism for prior co-ordination of aluminium chloride with the ester group. A heterolytic two-step mechanism was therefore proposed for the catalysed reaction.[179] This view had to be

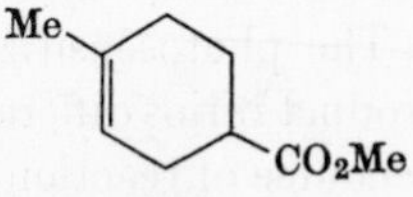

(69) 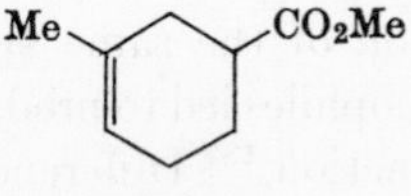   (70) 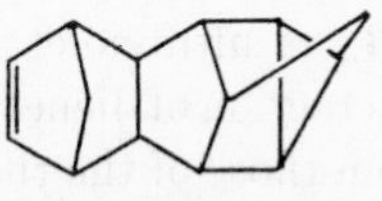   (71)

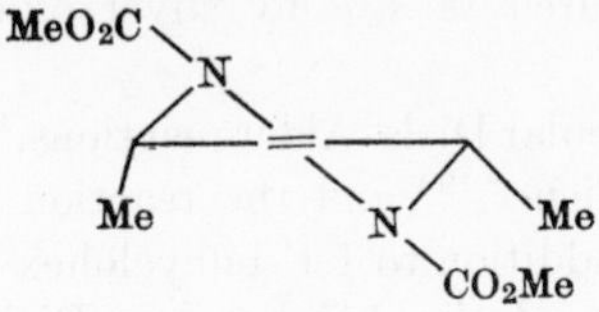

(72) 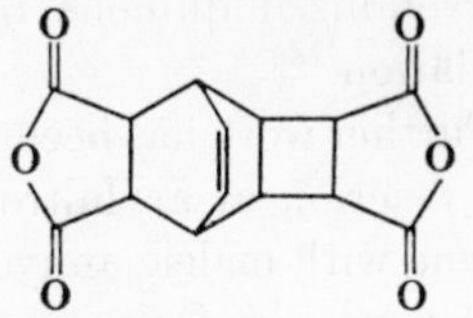   (73)

modified however when it was found that the catalysed reactions of cyclo-pentadiene with methyl acrylate and related dienophiles consistently gave higher proportions of *endo*-adducts than did the uncatalysed reactions. This enhanced stereoselectivity was then explained on a one-step mechanism with larger π-interaction between the unsaturated centres, the dienophile being more electrophilic when complexed with aluminium chloride.[180] Higher proportions of *endo*-adducts were also obtained from cyclopentadiene and methyl or (−)-menthyl acrylate in the presence of a range of Lewis acid catalysts.[181] Similar results have been reported for the isoprene–acrylonitrile reaction catalysed by aluminium chloride and titanium tetrachloride.[182]

176 V. A. Mironov, T. M. Fadeeva, A. U. Stepaniantz, and A. A. Akhrem, *Tetrahedron Letters*, 1966, 5823.
177 J. E. Baldwin, *J. Org. Chem.*, 31, 2441 (1966).
178 M. J. Youngquist, D. F. O'Brien, and J. W. Gates, *J. Am. Chem. Soc.*, 88, 4960 (1966).
179 T. Inukai and T. Kojima, *J. Org. Chem.*, 31, 1121 (1966).
180 T. Inukai and T. Kojima, *J. Org. Chem.*, 31, 2032 (1966).
181 J. Sauer and J. Kredel, *Tetrahedron Letters*, 1966, 731.
182 J.-C. Soula, D. Lumbroso, M. Hellin, and F. Coussemont, *Bull. Soc. Chim. France*, 1966, 2059, 2065.

Rhodium, but not platinum or palladium, on carbon was an effective catalyst for the di- and tri-merization of norbornadiene, giving mainly stereoisomers of the Diels–Alder type (71) rather than the cyclobutanes formed on catalysis by transition-metal complexes.[183]

In the Diels–Alder reaction of *trans,trans*-hexa-2,4-diene with dimethyl azodicarboxylate the diene retains its configuration, to give the product (72), thus implying a similar transition state for this azo dienophile as for an olefinic dienophile.[184] 3-*tert*-Butylcyclopentadienone undergoes self-Diels–Alder condensation at −20° ca. 10^7 times faster than does 2,5-di-*tert*-butyl-cyclopentadienone at 25°; the enormously decreased reactivity of the dibutyl derivative is attributed almost exclusively to steric retardation, and so the rate of dimerization of cyclopentadienone itself may approach that for diffusion control. The origin of the great reactivity of cyclopentadienone has been discussed.[185]

^{60}Co γ-Irradiation of maleic anhydride in benzene gave the same 2:1-adduct (73) as ultraviolet irradiation of the same system.[186] The photosensitized interaction of dienes and dienophiles led to products or product ratios different from those of the thermal reaction.[187] Differences in the course of reaction of *o*-benzoquinone with dienes may be attributable to the use of freshly prepared, recrystallized quinone rather than that prepared *in situ* by silver oxide oxidation.[188]

Further work has been reported on intramolecular Diels–Alder reactions,[189] the reaction of arylnitroso-compounds with dienes,[190] and the reaction of indene with maleic anhydride.[191] Diels–Alder addition to 1,1′-bi(cyclohex-1-ene) gave *endo*-isomers exclusively.[192] A linear relationship between Diels–Alder reactivity and ionization potential in polynuclear hydrocarbons has been reported.[193]

Other Cycloaddition Reactions

Work on 1,3-dipolar cycloadditions has continued and recent advances have been reviewed.[194] Since certain 1,3-dipoles (nitrile ylides, diazoalkanes,

[183] J. J. Mrowca and T. J. Katz, *J. Am. Chem. Soc.*, **88**, 4012 (1966).
[184] R. Daniels and K. A. Roseman, *Tetrahedron Letters*, **1966**, 1335.
[185] E. W. Garbisch and R. F. Sprecher, *J. Am. Chem. Soc.*, **88**, 3433, 3434 (1966).
[186] Z. Raciszewski, *Chem. Ind. (London)*, **1966**, 418.
[187] G. O. Schenck, J. Kuhls, and C. H. Krauch, *Z. Naturforsch.*, **20b**, 635 (1965).
[188] W. M. Horspool, J. M. Tedder, and Z. Ud Din, *Chem. Commun.*, **1966**, 775.
[189] L. H. Klemm, D. H. Lee, K. W. Gopinath, and C. E. Klopfenstein, *J. Org. Chem.*, **31**, 2376 (1966).
[190] G. Kresze and O. Korpiun, *Tetrahedron*, **22**, 2493 (1966); M. Ahmad and J. Hamer, *J. Org. Chem.*, **31**, 2829 (1966).
[191] N. S. Isaacs, *Can. J. Chem.*, **44**, 415 (1966).
[192] R. K. Hill and H. J. Barger, *J. Org. Chem.*, **31**, 2021 (1966).
[193] A. I. Konovalov and V. D. Kiselev, *Zh. Org. Khim.*, **2**, 142 (1966); *Chem. Abs.*, **64**, 14060 (1966).
[194] R. Huisgen, *Bull. Soc. Chim. France*, **1965**, 3431.

azides, etc.) can be written with carbene or nitrene termini, the possibility that 1,3-cycloadducts could be formed by rearrangement of initially formed 1,1-adducts [equation (10)] was considered. This route was, however, discounted for the reactions studied by the independent synthesis of the 1,1-adducts and the demonstration that these do not rearrange significantly in the 1,3-cycloaddition reaction conditions.[195] Evidence has been presented

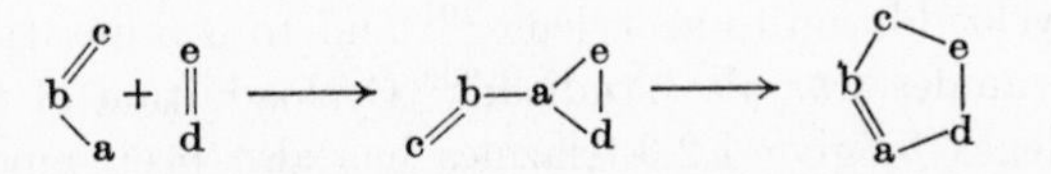

(10)

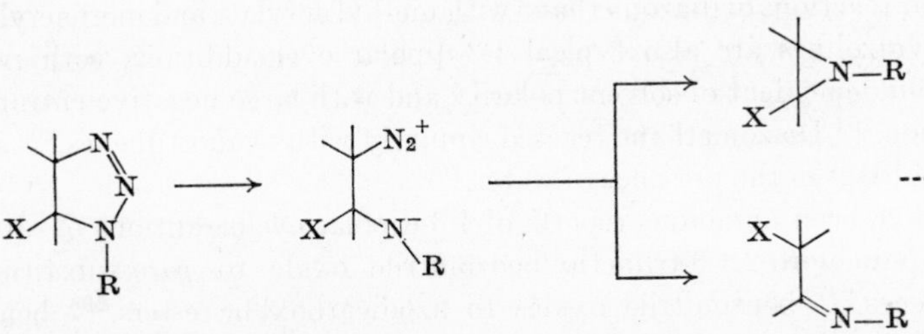

(11)

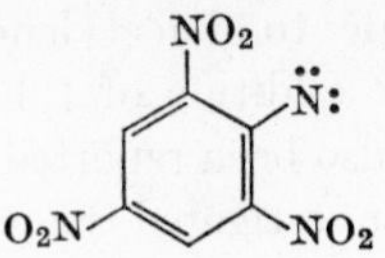

(74) 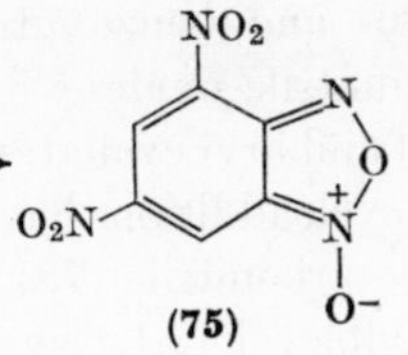   **(75)**

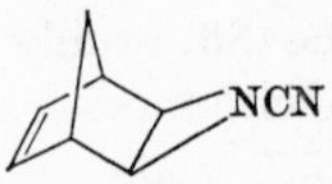

(76) 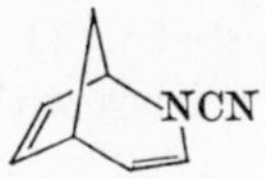   **(77)**

that the reactions of benzenesulphonyl azide[196] and methyl azidoformate[197] with strained olefins proceed through reactive triazolines which decompose via a diazonium intermediate to give aziridines or azomethines [equation (11)]. Further support for this is the high negative entropy of activation ($\Delta S^{\ddagger} = -29$ cal deg^{-1}) for the reaction of norbornene with benzenesulphonyl azide and the comparative insensitivity of rate to solvent polarity.[198] The very reactive picryl azide and olefins also gave unstable triazolines and showed the same kinetic characteristics; in this case any scheme involving prior loss of nitrogen

[195] R. Huisgen, R. Sustmann, and K. Bunge, *Tetrahedron Letters*, **1966**, 3603.
[196] A. C. Oehlschlager and L. H. Zalkow, *J. Org. Chem.*, **30**, 4205 (1965).
[197] A. C. Oehlschlager, P. Tillman, and L. H. Zalkow, *Chem. Commun.*, **1965**, 596.
[198] A. C. Oehlschlager and L. H. Zaldow, *Chem. Commun.*, **1966**, 144.

from the azide to give the nitrene (74) is eliminated since this nitrene would be trapped intramolecularly as the benzofuroxan (75).[199]

Cyanogen azide reacted with norbornadiene at 0° to give two major products (76) and (77) which arise from the labile triazoline cycloadduct.[200] Thermolysis of the triazolines formed from azides and strained olefins was shown to give aziridines and azomethines, whilst photolysis gave aziridines only; the increase in rate of cycloaddition with increase in strain was measured kinetically, and the cycloaddition to acetylenes[201] and to α,β-unsaturated esters, ketones, and cyanides was also studied.[202] Cycloaddition of trimethylsilyl azide to acetylenes to give 1,2,3-triazoles has also been reported.[203] The bimolecular reactions of diazomethane with methyl acrylate and methacrylate to give pyrazolines are also typical 1,3-dipolar cycloadditions with rates essentially independent of solvent polarity and with large negative entropies of activation.[204] Diazomethane reacted similarly with cyanostilbenes,[205] and with Schiff bases in the presence of water.[206]

There have been numerous reports of 1,3-dipolar cycloadditions of nitrile oxides: 3,5-dichloro-2,4,6-trimethylbenzonitrile oxide to *para*-substituted arylacetylenes,[207] benzonitrile oxides to azodicarboxylic esters,[208] benzonitrile oxides to diazomethane,[209] 2,4,6-trimethylbenzonitrile oxide to carbon disulphide,[210] aceto- and benzo-nitrile oxide to diacetylenes.[211] The dimerization of benzonitrile oxides,[212] and the addition of 1,3-dipoles to the C≡N bond of alkyl and aryl cyanates, have also been reported.[213]

A number of 1,2-cycloadditions have been investigated this year. 3-Methylbicyclo[1.1.0]butanecarbonitrile (78) reacted with a series of olefins to give, *inter alia*, 4-methylbicyclo[2.1.1]hexanecarbonitrile (79); diradical intermediates were suggested.[214] Quadricyclane (80) readily added to tetracyanethylene and to acetylenes with electron-withdrawing substituents, to give

[199] A. S. Bailey and J. E. White, *J. Chem. Soc., B*, **1966**, 819.
[200] A. G. Anastassiou, *J. Org. Chem.*, **31**, 1131 (1966).
[201] R. Huisgen, L. Möbius, G. Müller, H. Stangl, G. Szeimies, and J. M. Vernon, *Chem. Ber.*, **98**, 3992 (1965); R. Huisgen, R. Knorr, L. Möbius, and G. Szeimies, *ibid.*, p. 4014.
[202] R. Huisgen, G. Szeimies, and L. Möbius, *Chem. Ber.*, **99**, 475 (1966).
[203] L. Birkofer and P. Wegner, *Chem. Ber.*, **99**, 2512 (1966).
[204] A. Ledwith and D. Parry, *J. Chem. Soc., C*, **1966**, 1408.
[205] J. Jaz and J. Weiler, *Tetrahedron Letters*, **1966**, 273.
[206] P. K. Kadaba, *Tetrahedron*, **22**, 2453 (1966).
[207] P. Beltrame, C. Veglio, and M. Simonetta, *Chem. Commun.*, **1966**, 433.
[208] R. Huisgen, H. Blaschke, and E. Brunn, *Tetrahedron Letters*, **1966**, 405.
[209] K. Nagarajan and P. Rajagopalan, *Tetrahedron Letters*, **1966**, 5525; G. Lo Vecchio, M. Crisafulli, and M. C. Aversa, *ibid.*, p. 1909.
[210] W. O. Foye and J. M. Kauffman, *J. Org. Chem.*, **31**, 2417 (1966).
[211] L. B. Sokolov, L. K. Vagina, V. N. Chistokletov, and A. A. Petrov, *Zh. Org. Khim.*, **2**, 615 (1966); *Chem. Abs.*, **65**, 8890 (1966).
[212] A. Dondoni, A. Mangini, and S. Ghersetti, *Tetrahedron Letters*, **1966**, 4789.
[213] D. Martin and A. Weise, *Chem. Ber.*, **99**, 317 (1966).
[214] A. Cairncross and E. P. Blanchard, *J. Am. Chem. Soc.*, **88**, 496 (1966).

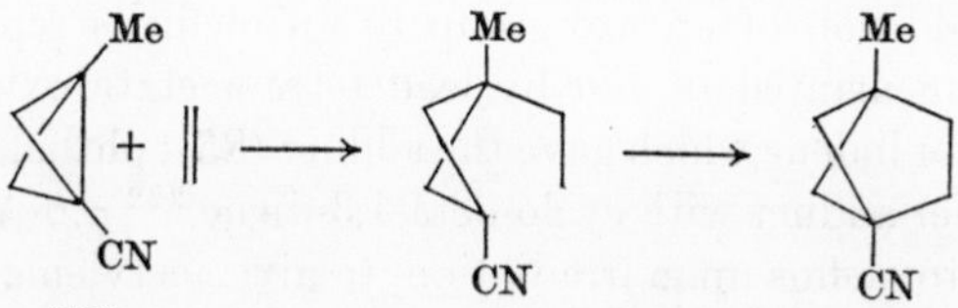

(78) + ⟶ (79)

(80) 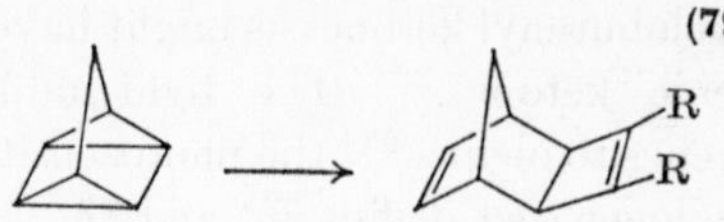 ⟶ (81)

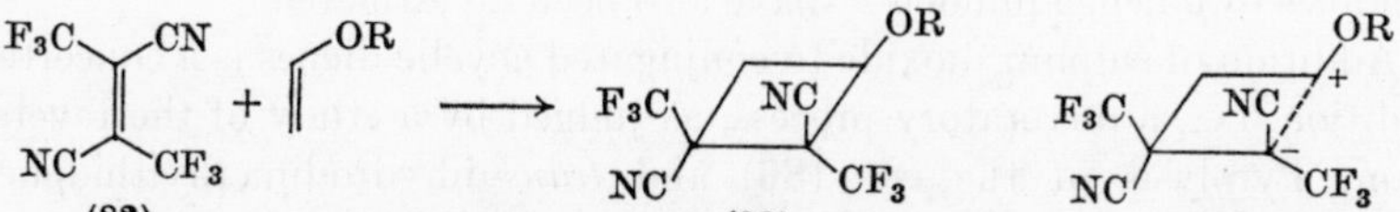

(82) + ⟶ (83) (84)

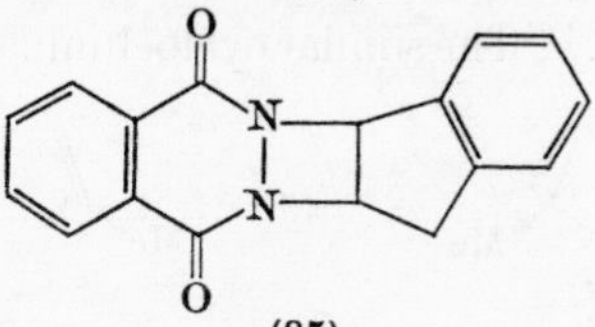

(85)

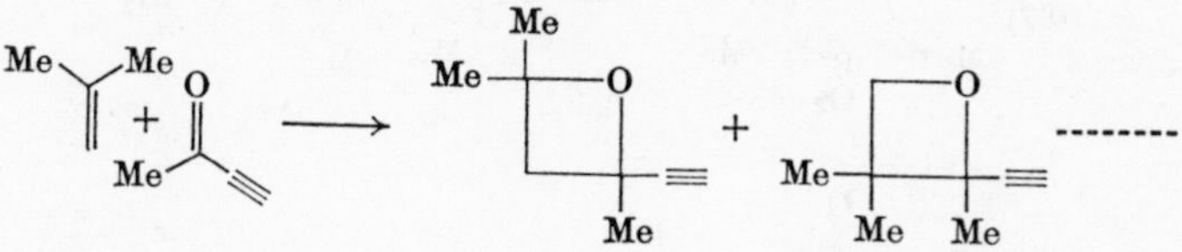

(12)

the *exo*-adducts (**81**) stereospecifically.[215] *cis*- and *trans*(**82**)-1,2-Dicyano-1,2-bis(trifluoromethyl)ethylenes added to electron-rich olefins at room temperature to form 1,2-dicyano-1,2-bis(trifluoromethyl)cyclobutanes (**83**). Although many of these cycloadditions occur with high stereospecificity, the first examples of non-stereospecific cycloadditions of this type were reported. The latter show large rate accelerations in polar solvents and the intermediacy of the dipolar species (**84**) was proposed for these reactions.[216]

Addition of the C–C double bond of ketenes to several olefins has been described. Dimethylketene adds stereospecifically to *cis*- and *trans*-but-1-enyl ethyl ether[217] and to other olefins;[218] dichloroketene adds to cyclopentene and cyclopentadiene[219] and to indene;[220] and diphenylketene adds to

215 C. D. Smith, *J. Am. Chem. Soc.*, **88**, 4273 (1966).
216 S. Proskow, H. E. Simmons, and T. L. Cairns, *J. Am. Chem. Soc.*, **88**, 5254 (1966).
217 J. C. Martin, V. W. Goodlett, and R. D. Burpitt, *J. Org. Chem.*, **30**, 4309 (1965).
218 A. P. Krapcho and J. H. Lesser, *J. Org. Chem.*, **31**, 2030 (1966).
219 L. Ghosez, R. Montaigne, and P. Mollet, *Tetrahedron Letters*, **1966**, 135.
220 R. W. Turner and T. Seden, *Chem. Commun.*, **1966**, 399.

tropone.[221] 1,2-Cycloaddition of an azo-group to an olefin is reported for phthalazine-1,4-dione (generated *in situ* by lead tetra-acetate oxidation of phthalhydrazide) and for indene which gave the adduct (85); phthalazine-1,4-dione gave a Diels–Alder adduct with cyclo-octa-1,3-diene.[222] α,β-Acetylenic ketones add smoothly to olefins upon irradiation, to give acetylenic oxetanes [equation (12)], and not cyclobutenyl ketones as might have been expected by analogy with α,β-ethylenic ketones.[223] The light-induced stereospecific addition of benzocyclobutenes to olefins,[224] the photosensitized cycloaddition of maleic anhydride to halogenated olefins,[225] and the cycloaddition of 3-alkylindoles to *p*-benzoquinone[226] have also been investigated.

1,4-Addition of sulphur dioxide to conjugated acyclic dienes is a concerted *cis*-addition, i.e., a disrotatory process, as judged by a study of the reverse reaction. Pyrolysis of the *cis*- (86) and *trans*-dihydrodimethylthiophen dioxide (87) gave *trans,trans*- and *trans,cis*-hexa-2,4-diene, respectively, with complete stereospecificity.[227] The similar cycloelimination of carbon monoxide

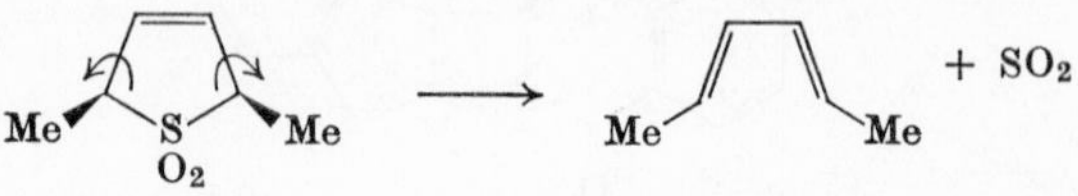

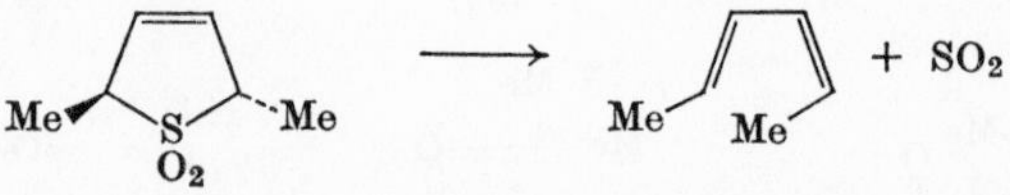

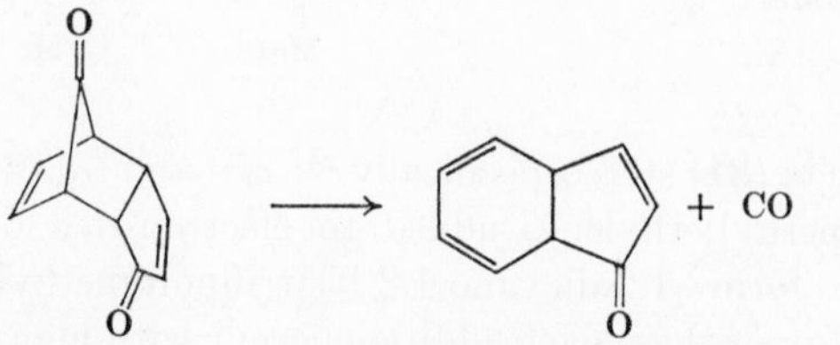

from dicyclopentadiene-1,8-dione (88) to give (89) is necessarily a disrotatory process and is probably also concerted[228] (see also p. 71).

Brief heating of ethyl azepine-1-carboxylate (90) at 200° yields a dimer (92); from orbital-symmetry considerations this (6 + 6)π thermal cyclization is not

[221] C. Jutz, I. Rommel, I. Lengyel, and J. Feeney, *Tetrahedron*, 22, 1809 (1966).
[222] O. L. Chapman and S. J. Dominanni, *J. Org. Chem.*, 31, 3862 (1966).
[223] M. J. Jorgenson, *Tetrahedron Letters*, 1966, 5811.
[224] G. Quinkert, K. Opitz, W. W. Wiesdorff, and M. Finke, *Ann. Chem.*, 693, 44 (1966).
[225] R. Steinmetz, W. Hartmann, and G. O. Schenck, *Chem. Ber.*, 98, 3854 (1965).
[226] W. E. Noland and F. J. Baude, *J. Org. Chem.*, 31, 3321 (1966).
[227] W. L. Mock, *J. Am. Chem. Soc.*, 88, 2857 (1966); S. D. McGregor and D. M. Lemal, *ibid.*, p. 2858.
[228] J. E. Baldwin, *Can. J. Chem.*, 44, 2051 (1966).

allowed in a concerted process; hence a possible intermediate in a multistep process was sought. The $(4 + 6)exo$-adduct (91) was shown to be formed from (90) at lower temperatures and convertible in (92) and is probably this

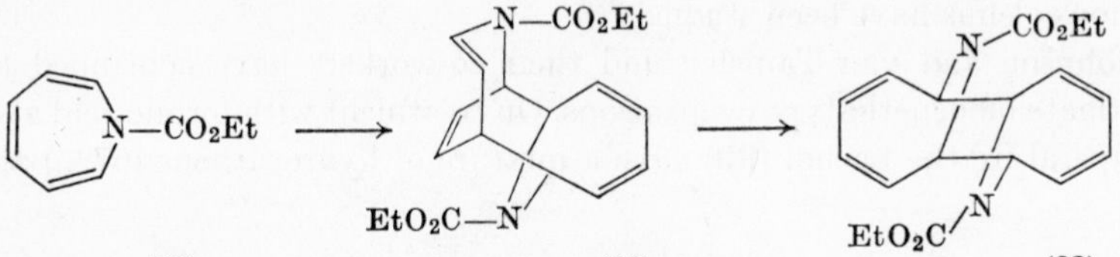

(90)   (91)   (92)

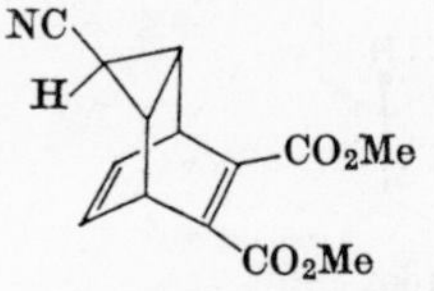

anti-3-exo   (93) 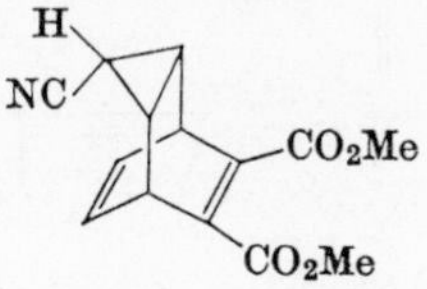   anti-3-endo (94) 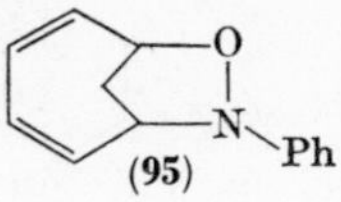   (95)

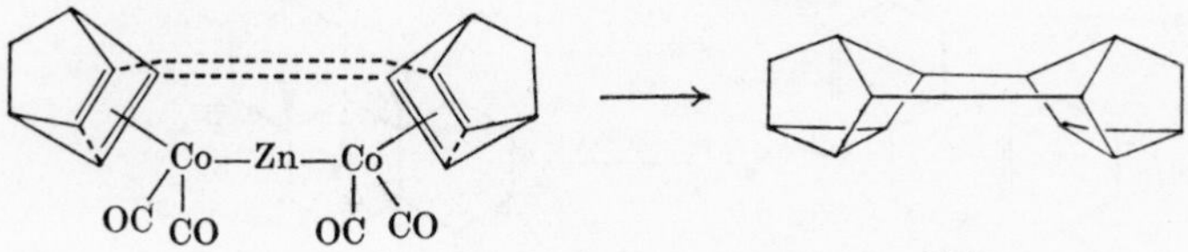

(96)   (97)

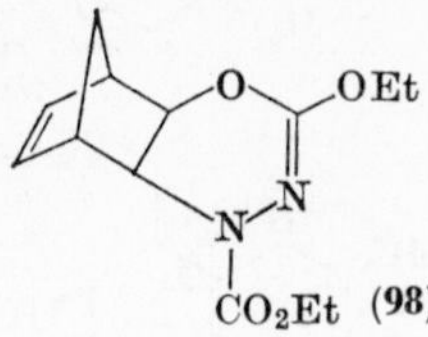

CO2Et (98)

intermediate.[229] 1-Cyano-[230] and 1-methyl-azepine[231] behaved similarly, the latter dimerizing rapidly in ether above 0°.

The stereospecificity of dienophile addition to cycloheptatrienes is well demonstrated by the addition of dimethyl acetylenedicarboxylate to 7-cyano-cyclohepta-1,3,5-triene which has now been shown to give the *anti-3-exo*-adduct (93) and the severely strained *anti-3-endo*-adduct (94) in comparable amounts.[232] Nitrosobenzene and cycloheptatriene react to give the 1,6-addition product (95).[233]

Binuclear carbonyl catalysts such as $Zn[Co(CO)_4]_2$ dimerize norbornadiene stereospecifically via a π-complex intermediate (96) to give the new dimer

229 L. A. Paquette and J. H. Barrett, *J. Am. Chem. Soc.*, **88**, 2590 (1966).
230 A. L. Johnson and H. E. Simmons, *J. Am. Chem. Soc.*, **88**, 2591 (1966).
231 K. Hafner and J. Mondt, *Angew. Chem. Internat. Edn. Engl.*, **5**, 839 (1966).
232 M. J. Goldstein and A. H. Gevirtz, *Tetrahedron Letters*, **1965**, 4417.
233 J. Hutton and W. A. Waters, *Chem. Commun.*, **1966**, 534.

(97); this is termed a "π-complex multicentre process."[234] The structure of the unsaturated adduct obtained from norbornadiene and ethyl azodicarboxylate has been revised to (98), and the corresponding adduct from norbornene to the dihydro-derivative of this.[235] The addition reactions of cinnamaldehyde with various olefins have been studied.[236]

Johnson and van Tamelen and their co-workers have continued to investigate biogenetic-type cyclizations. On treatment with formic acid at room temperature the trienol (99) gave a mixture of hydrocarbons (67%) and an

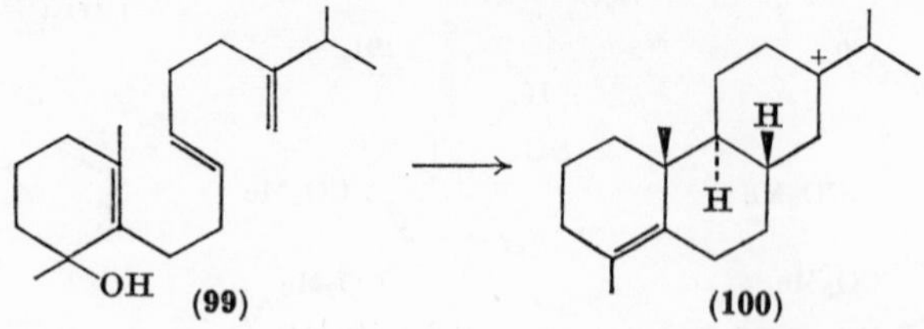

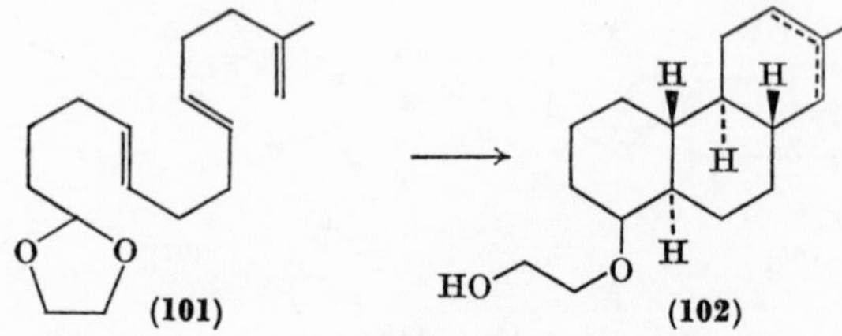

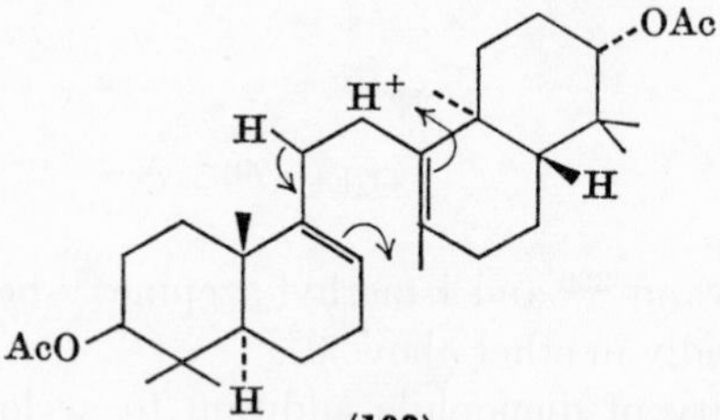

[234] G. N. Schrauzer, B. N. Bastian, and G. A. Fosselius, *J. Am. Chem. Soc.*, **88**, 4890 (1966).
[235] J. J. Tufariello, T. F. Mich, and P. S. Miller, *Tetrahedron Letters*, **1966**, 2293.
[236] M. Mizuta, A. Suzuki, and Y. Ishii, *Kogyo Kagaku Zasshi*, **69**, 77 (1966); *Chem. Abs.*, **65**, 5320 (1966); M. Mizuta, H. Arki, and Y. Ishii, *Kogyo Kakagu Zasshi*, **69**, 79 (1966); *Chem. Abs.*, **65**, 5320 (1966).

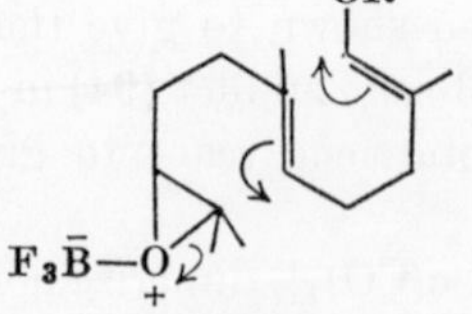

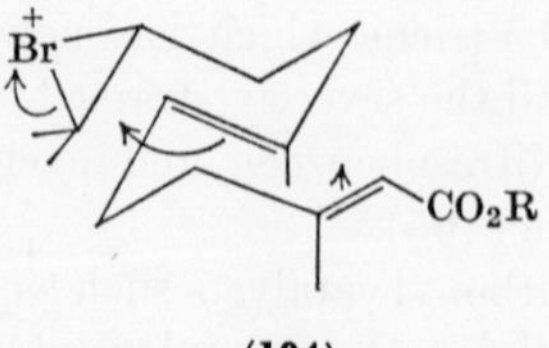

alcohol (28%) derived from the carbonium ion (**100**). This essentially quantitative and stereospecific cyclization appears to be the most efficient non-enzymic cyclization of this kind yet reported.[237] Treatment of the acetal (**101**) in benzene with stannic chloride at 0—5° gave the tricyclic unsaturated alcohols (**102**) in high yield; these appear to be formed stereospecifically with respect to the ring junctions and thus represent the first example of stereoselective production of a tricarbocyclic system of "natural" configuration as the major product of cyclization of a polyolefin.[238] Biogenetic-type oxidation–cyclizations have been put to good use in the total synthesis of triterpenoids,[239] the direct brominative cyclization of methyl farnesate,[240] and the synthesis of farnesiferol A and C[241] typified, respectively, by the processes (**103**),(**104**), and (**105**).

Other cyclizations which have received some mechanistic consideration are those of the unsaturated ketones $MeCO \cdot [CH_2]_n \cdot CH{=}CH_2$ ($n = 5$ or 8) which give the 1-acetyl-2-methyl-cyclohexane and -cyclononane, respectively, on strong heating,[242] the ring closure of 2-(cyclohex-1-enyl)ethylamines with formaldehyde to give *cis*-decahydroisoquinolin-4α-ols,[243] and the acid-catalysed cyclization of 3-isopropenyl-6-oxoheptanoic acid.[244]

[237] W. S. Johnson, N. P. Jensen, and J. Hooz, *J. Am. Chem. Soc.*, **88**, 3859 (1966).
[238] W. S. Johnson and R. B. Kinnel, *J. Am. Chem. Soc.*, **88**, 3861 (1966).
[239] E. E. van Tamelen, M. A. Schwartz, E. J. Hessler, and A. Storni, *Chem. Commun.*, **1966**, 409.
[240] E. E. van Tamelen and E. J. Hessler, *Chem. Commun.*, **1966**, 411.
[241] E. E. van Tamelen and R. M. Coates, *Chem. Commun.*, **1966**, 413.
[242] J. M. Conia, F. Leyendecker, and C. Dubois-Faget, *Tetrahedron Letters*, **1966**, 129.
[243] C. A. Grob and R. A. Wohl, *Helv. Chim. Acta*, **49**, 2175 (1966).
[244] J. Wolinsky and D. Chan, *J. Org. Chem.*, **31**, 2471 (1966).

Addendum to ref. 130 (p. 143): See *Organic Reaction Mechanisms*, **1965**, 119. See also V. F. Bystrov, V. A. Azovskaya, N. P. Petukhova, A. V. Stepanyants, and E. N. Prilezhaeva, *Izv. Akad. Nauk SSSR, Ser. Khim.*, **1966**, 318; *Chem. Abs.*, **64**, 15761 (1966).

CHAPTER 6

Nucleophilic Aromatic Substitution

Compelling evidence for the intermediate-complex mechanism rather than a concerted S_N2 mechanism for nucleophilic substitution in activated aromatic substrates was summarized last year.[1] For example, the kinetic form of sodium hydroxide catalysis in the reaction of 2,4-dinitrophenyl phenyl ether with piperidine in aqueous dioxan was in complete agreement with Scheme 1; either formation or decomposition of the intermediate may be rate-limiting, depending upon the hydroxide ion concentration. Hart and Bourns[2] have now convincingly confirmed this mechanism for the same reaction system by measuring the $^{16}O:^{18}O$ kinetic isotope effect for the ether-oxygen over a range of hydroxide concentration. At low concentrations, return of the intermediate predominates and mainly the step involving C–O bond fission will be rate-determining, so that a primary oxygen isotope effect should result. At high hydroxide ion concentration, most of the intermediate proceeds to products

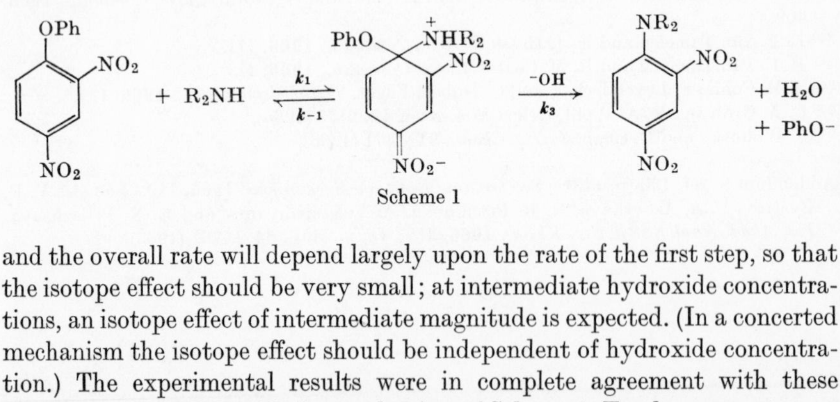

Scheme 1

and the overall rate will depend largely upon the rate of the first step, so that the isotope effect should be very small; at intermediate hydroxide concentrations, an isotope effect of intermediate magnitude is expected. (In a concerted mechanism the isotope effect should be independent of hydroxide concentration.) The experimental results were in complete agreement with these expectations and thus with the mechanism of Scheme 1. Further support came from the solvent isotope effect ($k_3^{H_2O}/k_3^{D_2O}$ = ca. 1.8) which was too large to be accounted for by a mechanism which does not involve proton-transfer in the rate-determining step.[2] Base-catalysis is also well established for some reactions of 1-fluoro-2,4-dinitrobenzene, particularly with piperidine.[1] Pietra and Vitali[3] have now presented evidence for acid-catalysis as well, i.e., for bi-

[1] See *Organic Reaction Mechanisms*, **1965**, 133.
[2] C. R. Hart and A. N. Bourns, *Tetrahedron Letters*, **1966**, 2995.
[3] F. Pietra and D. Vitali, *Tetrahedron Letters*, **1966**, 5701.

functional catalysis in these reactions, analogous to that originally suggested by us a few years ago.[4] Catalytic coefficients, $k_{cat.}$, calculated from:

$$\text{Rate}/[\text{ArF}][\text{Piperidine}] = k_{uncat.} + k_{cat.}[\text{Catalyst}]$$

are shown in Table 1. The concentration used for 2-pyridone is that of the monomeric species. 2-Pyridone is a very much more efficient catalyst than pyridine or phenol, although it is a very much weaker base than the former

Table 1. Catalytic coefficients for some reactions of 1-fluoro-2,4-dinitrobenzene.

Catalyst	Catalytic coefficient, $k_{cat.}$ (mole^{-2} l.^{2} sec^{-1})
2-Pyridone	3200
Piperidine	600
Phenol	220
Pyridine	2
1-Methyl-2-pyridone	0

and a weaker acid than the latter. It therefore presumably acts as a bifunctional catalyst assisting the concerted separation of both proton and fluoride from the intermediate complex in a doubly hydrogen-bonded cyclic transition state (1). The crucial test of the effect of 4-pyridone has unfortunately so far

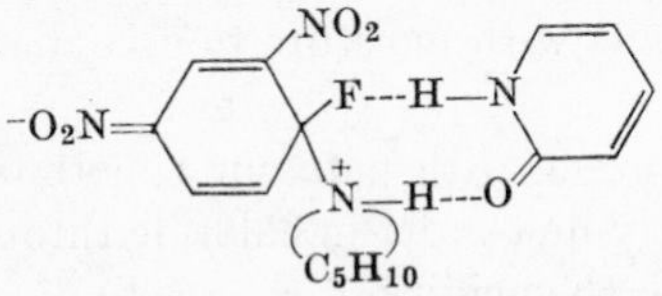

(1) 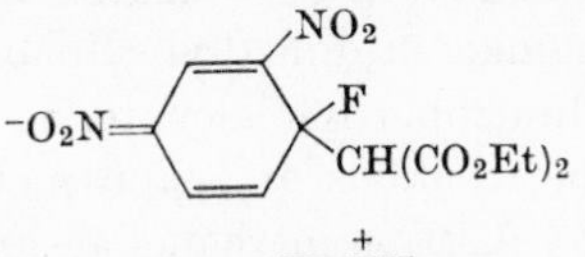   (2)

proved inconclusive. The analogous reaction of 1-chloro-2,4-dinitrobenzene shows no such catalysis since formation of the tetrahedral complex is rate-determining in this case.[3] Pietra has corrected and extended his work[1] with 1-chloro- and 1-fluoro-2,4-dinitrobenzene and piperidines in benzene to include *cis*- and *trans*-2,6-dimethylpiperidine. Although the relative rates vary very widely with the different nucleophiles the reactivity ratio ArF/ArCl is still found not to depend greatly on their steric requirement.[5] In contrast, the relative rates of the reactions of *p*-fluoronitrobenzene with piperidine,

[4] B. Capon and C. W. Rees, *Ann. Reports Chem. Soc. (London)*, **60**, 279 (1963).
[5] F. Pietra and F. Del Cima, *Tetrahedron Letters*, **1966**, 1925.

6

2-methylpiperidine, and *cis*-2,6-dimethylpiperidine in the "faster" solvent, dimethyl sulphoxide, were said to be very much smaller.[6] Pietra and Del Cima[7] have, however, been unable to reproduce Suhr's rate constants and suggest that his 2,6-dimethylpiperidine may have contained highly nucleophilic impurities; they find a wide spread of reactivity for the various piperidines, not drastically different from their results with 1-fluoro-2,4-dinitrobenzene.

A primary isotope effect in the reactions of 2,4-dinitrophenyl phenyl ether with piperidine was reported last year;[1] replacing piperidine by deuteriopiperidine slowed the reaction in benzene 1.27-fold. A similar isotope effect, $k_H/k_D = 1.2$, has now been observed in the overall second-order reactions of the same nucleophiles in the same solvent for the displacement of chlorine from 4-chloro-3-nitrobenzotrifluoride. The variation in rate constants with nucleophile concentration again fits the Bunnett two-step mechanism (Scheme 1), with heterolysis of the N–H or N–D bond rate-determining in the base-catalysed pathway. It was suggested that earlier failure to observe kinetic isotope effects in these reactions resulted from a study of too narrow a range of nucleophile concentration.[8] Full details have now appeared for the catalysis of the reaction of 1-fluoro-2,4-dinitrobenzene with piperidine in benzene by methanol, pyridine, piperidine, and 1,4-diazabicyclo[2.2.2]-octane.[9] Reaction of the same fluoride with diethyl malonate in the presence of triethylamine gave an intensely red product considered to be the triethylammonium salt of the *aci*-nitrocyclohexadienate anion (2) with fluorine and the malonyl residue bound to the same aromatic carbon—the postulated intermediate in the aromatic substitution. The salt (2) is stable in dry dimethylformamide or dimethyl sulphoxide but reacts with moisture to give diethyl 2,4-dinitrophenylmalonate.[10]

The reactions of *o*- and *p*-chloronitrobenzene with potassium methoxide (1.45—5.3M) in methanol at 20° were strictly first-order in chloride throughout; the rate constants varied linearly with the acidity of the medium, H_M, but exponentially with methoxide concentration. The ratio k_p/k_o also varied with H_M and became inverted at 3.05M-potassium methoxide, thus giving the reverse of the normal reactivity for reactions with alkoxide ions. This reversal may be associated with the decrease in the concentration of free methanol, which would favour reaction of the *ortho*-isomer if participation of solvent molecules in the transition state for this reaction is less important than with the *para*-isomer.[11]

[6] H. Suhr, *Ann. Chem.*, **689**, 109 (1965).
[7] F. Pietra and F. Del Cima, *Tetrahedron Letters*, **1966**, 4453.
[8] R. L. Toranzo, R. V. Caneda, and J. A. Brieux, *J. Am. Chem. Soc.*, **88**, 3651 (1966).
[9] C. Bernasconi and H. Zollinger, *Helv. Chim. Acta*, **49**, 103 (1966).
[10] P. Baudet, *Helv. Chim. Acta*, **49**, 545 (1966).
[11] F. Terrier, *Compt. Rend.*, **261**, 1001 (1965).

The interesting observation has been made that 1-bromo-2-naphthol reacts with aniline and with piperidine at 100° to give the 1-amino-compounds, whilst its O-methyl ether does not; and 1-bromo-2-naphthol is much more reactive towards these nucleophiles than is 1-bromonaphthalene. Furthermore, 1-bromo-2-naphthol reacted with aniline and with piperidine at the same rate, and must therefore be reacting through its keto-form.[12]

Extensive rate data for the $S_N Ar$ reactions of azide, thiocyanate, and thiophenoxide ions with 1-halogeno-2,4-dinitrobenzenes and *p*-halogeno-nitrobenzenes, and of $S_N 2$ reactions of azide, thiocyanate, and pyridine with methyl and butyl halides in the protic solvent methanol and the dipolar aprotic solvent dimethylformamide, have been presented and compared. Changes in Arrhenius parameters on changing solvent are quite different for the $S_N Ar$ and $S_N 2$ reactions, as are their respective transition states, the two-step mechanism for the former being favoured over the synchronous nature of the latter. Analysis of nucleophilicities and leaving-group mobilities shows that they depend on so many factors that correlations of relative reactivities have very limited application. Nucleophilicity, for example, is very much a function of "external" factors such as solvent, the type of carbon being attacked, and the group being displaced.[13] On the other hand, the individual reactivities and irregular patterns of reactivity in the reactions of similar nucleophiles with *p*-fluoro- and *p*-iodo-nitrobenzene and with 1-fluoro- and 1-iodo-2,4-dinitrobenzene are shown[14] to be quantitatively predictable by calculations[15] based on thermochemical data and the two-step mechanism; changes in halogen mobility arise when formation of the first changes to formation of the second transition state as rate-determining.

Some interesting examples of acid and electrophilic catalysis in the $S_N Ar$ reaction of 1-fluoro-2,4-dinitrobenzene have been described. The reaction with potassium iodide in methanol is negligibly slow but that with hydriodic acid is ca. 5×10^5 times faster; the reaction with thiocyanate is very slow but is 2×10^3 times faster in the presence of an equimolar amount of thorium nitrate. In contrast, the uncatalysed reaction with azide ions is very much faster and is decelerated by thorium ions. This pattern of catalysis is said to be as expected from Miller's calculations and is considered to provide strong evidence for the two-step mechanism.[16] A modified Hückel molecular-orbital treatment of the one- and two-step mechanism has been presented, and correlations between experimental and calculated activation energies have been found for the

[12] M. Foa, A. Ricci, P. E. Todesco, and P. Vivarelli, *Boll. Sci. Fac. Chim. Ind. Bologna*, **23**, 233 (1965).
[13] B. O. Coniglio, D. E. Giles, W. R. McDonald, and A. J. Parker, *J. Chem. Soc.*, B, **1966**, 152; see also p. 51.
[14] K. C. Ho, J. Miller, and K. W. Wong, *J. Chem. Soc.*, B, **1966**, 310.
[15] D. L. Hill, K. C. Ho, and J. Miller, *J. Chem. Soc.*, B, **1966**, 299.
[16] K. B. Lam and J. Miller, *Chem. Commun.*, **1966**, 642.

reactions of nitro-activated aryl halides with amines and methoxide ion.[17] π-Electron densities calculated by the simple LCAO-MO Hückel method correlated roughly with the logarithm of the rate constant for alkaline methoxylation of various activated aromatic substrates.[18]

The influence of pressure on the reaction of hydroxide ions with 1-fluoro-2,4-dinitrobenzene in water, and on the product ratios and rate constants for concurrent hydrolysis and methanolysis in aqueous methanol, has been determined. The variation of rate constants was small, suggesting that the hydroxide–methoxide equilibrium is largely independent of pressure and that the rate-determining transition states are loose structures with little transfer of charge from the nucleophile and hence little change in solvation.[19] The dependence of rate constant on the leaving group for the reactions of 1-X-2,4-dinitrobenzene with hydroxide in water has been studied where X is a range of alkoxy- and aryloxy-groups, chlorine, or nitro. Log k varies inversely with the pK_a of HX.[20] A similar relationship holds for the same reaction of several alkyl and aryl picryl ethers; the hydrolysis of picryl fluoride and chloride and of 1,2,4,6-tetranitrobenzene,[21] and the reactions of picryl fluoride with hydroxide and alkoxide ions and with water and alcohols,[22] have also been studied.

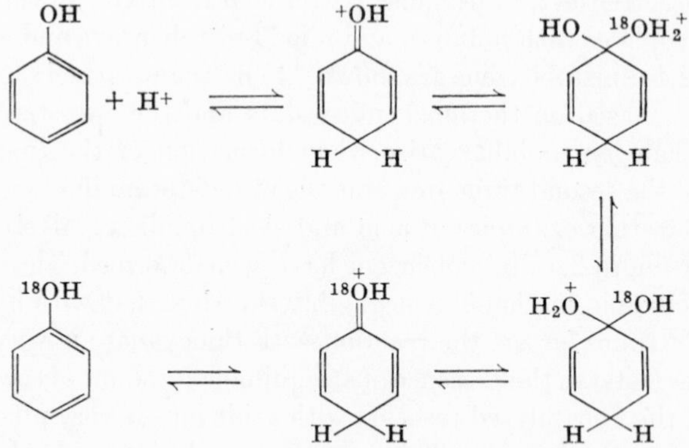

Scheme 2

The acid-catalysed oxygen-exchange reactions of a number of phenols in ^{18}O-enriched aqueous acid under various conditions has been investigated and the mechanism shown (Scheme 2), or that involving the corresponding *o*-

[17] S. Carrà, M. Raimondi, and M. Simonetta, *Tetrahedron*, **22**, 2673 (1966).
[18] J. Murto, *Suomen Kemistilehti, B*, **38**, 246 (1965).
[19] J. Murto and M. Kiuttu, *Suomen Kemistilehti, B*, **39**, 14 (1966).
[20] J. Murto and M.-L. Murto, *Acta Chem. Scand.*, **20**, 297 (1966).
[21] J. Murto, *Acta Chem. Scand.*, **20**, 310 (1966).
[22] J. Murto, *Acta Chem. Scand.*, **20**, 303 (1966).

quinonoid intermediates, has been proposed.[23] Similar evidence leads to the same type of mechanism for the acid-catalysed reactions of phenol with ethanol and propan-1-ol to give the ethyl and *n*-propyl (but no isopropyl) ether, respectively.[24]

In the reactions of activated aromatic halides with piperidine and alkoxide ions, changes in composition of aqueous-alcohol solvents in the region near 100% alcohol caused small changes in second-order rate constants. These usually increased with addition of water, as expected on the Hughes–Ingold theory of solvent action, for the piperidine reactions but not for the alkoxide ion reactions. This result for the latter is also opposite to that expected for the equilibrium replacement of alkoxide ions by the less reactive hydroxide ions, and it was explained by the progressive dissociation, with increase of water, of metal–alkoxide ion pairs to the more reactive solvated anions.[25] Reaction of *p*-fluoronitrobenzene in methanol with piperidine, morpholine, and the weak nucleophile diisopropylamine gave 7.7, 10.4, and 97.7%, respectively, of *p*-nitroanisole as a result of the equilibrium:[26]

$$R_2NH + MeOH \rightleftarrows R_2NH_2^+ + MeO^-$$

The kinetics of the reactions of 18 primary[27] and 19 secondary[28] amines with *p*-fluoronitrobenzene in dimethyl sulphoxide have been measured, and the sequence of amine reactivity has been found to parallel those for a variety of other activated aromatic and heteroaromatic substrates.[29] The reactions of a series of 1-fluoro-3-X-5-nitrobenzene with methoxide in methanol vary very widely in rate, with the large ρ value 5.28, showing that the reactions are particularly sensitive to the electronic effects of *meta*-substituents.[30] A fluorine atom *ortho* or *para* to one of a wide range of mildly activating groups such as acyl, cyano, trifluoromethyl, and methoxycarbonyl is readily displaced by aliphatic and alicyclic amines in dimethylformamide or dimethyl sulphoxide.[31] The use of boiling dimethylformamide as solvent for the reaction of *p*-chloronitrobenzene, but not the bromo- or iodo-analogue, with arylamines can lead to the preferential replacement of chlorine by the dimethylamino-group.[32]

The S_N2 mechanism depicted (3) is proposed for the gas-phase decomposition of aryl fluoroformates into aryl fluorides.[33] A number of direct nucleophilic

23 S. Oae, R. Kiritani, and W. Tagaki, *Bull. Chem. Soc. Japan*, **39**, 1961 (1966).
24 S. Oae and R. Kiritani, *Bull. Chem. Soc., Japan*, **39**, 611 (1966).
25 R. G. Burns and B. D. England, *J. Chem. Soc., B*, **1966**, 864.
26 H. Suhr, *Tetrahedron Letters*, **1966**, 5871.
27 H. Suhr, *Ann. Chem.*, **687**, 175 (1965).
28 H. Suhr, *Ann. Chem.*, **689**, 109 (1965).
29 H. Suhr and H. Grube, *Ber. Bunsenges. Physik. Chem.*, **70**, 544 (1966); *Chem. Abs.*, **65**, 7008 (1966).
30 C. W. L. Bevan, J. Hirst, and S. J. Una, *Chem. Ind. (London)*, **1966**, 341.
31 H. Bader, A. R. Hansen, and F. J. McCarty, *J. Org. Chem.*, **31**, 2319 (1966).
32 R. S. Asquith, W. M. Lord, A. T. Peters, and F. Wallace, *J. Chem. Soc., C*, **1966**, 95.
33 K. O. Christe and A. E. Pavlath, *J. Org. Chem.*, **30**, 4104 (1965).

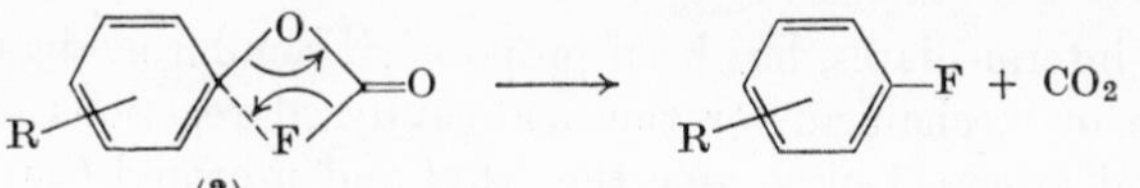

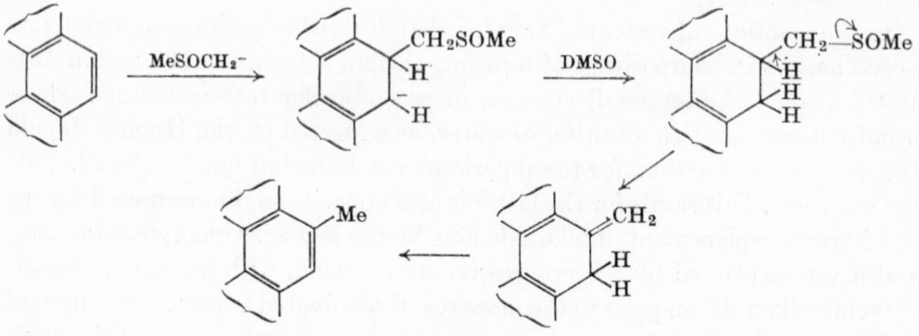

Scheme 3

methylations of reactive aromatic substrates have been reported recently. Thus, when heated with the methylsulphinyl carbanion, $MeSOCH_2^-$, anthracene, phenanthrene, and acridine gave the 9-methyl derivatives, and quinoline and isoquinoline gave, respectively, the 4- and 1-methyl derivatives. 9-Deuteriophenanthrene lost ca. 50% of its deuterium on methylation, and the mechanism in Scheme 3 was suggested.[34] A similar direct methylation of unsubstituted polycyclic hydrocarbons has been achieved with dimethylsulphonium methylide, $Me_2S^+-CH_2^-$; the product distribution agrees with the nucleophilic nature of the process and correlates with π-electron density calculations.[35] Dimethyloxosulphonium methylide, $Me_2\overset{+}{S}\overset{-}{O}CH_2$, reacted with nitrobenzene to give o- and p-nitrotoluenes (35%) with the *ortho*-isomer predominating; many derivatives of nitrobenzene were methylated similarly.[36]

Phosphoro- and phosphono-thiolates reacted rapidly with 1-fluoro-2,4-dinitrobenzene in the presence, but not in the absence, of tertiary bases, to give the corresponding fluoridates and the phenyl sulfide (Scheme 4). Reaction of the thiolate with the tetrahedral intermediate (4) was proposed.[37] Triethyl phosphite reacted with o-dinitrobenzene to give diethyl o-nitrophenylphosphonate and ethyl nitrite; the simplest mechanism would be as shown (5), presumably after initial nucleophilic displacement of a nitro-group by triethyl phosphite since these nitro-groups are known to be reactive towards nucleophilic displacement.[38]

[34] H. Nozaki, Y. Yamamoto, and R. Noyori, *Tetrahedron Letters*, **1966**, 1123; see also, P. A. Argabright, J. E. Hofmann, and A. Schriesheim, *J. Org. Chem.*, **30**, 3233 (1965).
[35] B. M. Trost, *Tetrahedron Letters*, **1966**, 5761.
[36] V. J. Traynelis and J. V. McSweeney, *J. Org. Chem.*, **31**, 243 (1966).
[37] A. Bebbington and R. V. Ley, *J. Chem. Soc.*, C, **1966**, 1410.
[38] J. I. G. Cadogan, D. J. Sears, and D. M. Smith, *Chem. Commun.*, **1966**, 491.

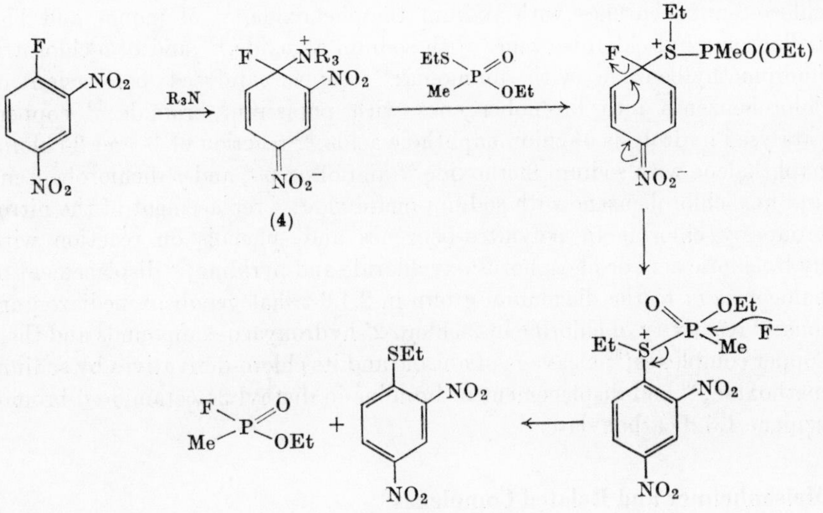

F—NO$_2$ ... NO$_2$

$\xrightarrow{R_3N}$

F, $\overset{+}{N}R_3$, NO$_2$ ... NO$_2^-$

(4)

$\text{EtS}\diagdown\underset{\text{Me}}{\overset{\text{O}}{P}}\diagup\text{OEt}$

F, $\overset{+}{S}$—PMeO(OEt), Et ... NO$_2^-$

$\underset{\text{Me}}{\overset{\text{O}}{\text{F—P—OEt}}}$ + SEt—NO$_2$ ... NO$_2$

$\longleftarrow$

$\overset{\text{O}}{\underset{\text{Me}}{\text{Et—}\overset{+}{\text{S}}\diagdown\text{P}\diagup\overset{\text{OEt}}{\text{F}^-}}}$ —NO$_2$ ... NO$_2$

Scheme 4

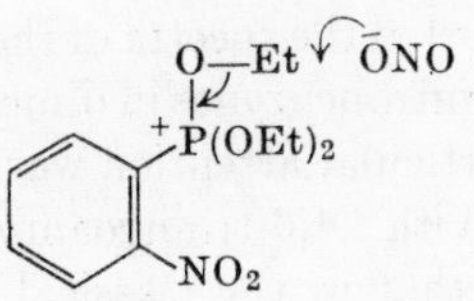

O—Et $\curvearrowleft$ $^-$ONO

$\overset{+}{\text{P}}(\text{OEt})_2$

NO$_2$

(5)

The kinetics of the reactions of 1-chloro-2,4-dinitrobenzene with sodium azide in methanol and ethanol,[39] with pyridine to give the pyridinium chloride,[40] with *p*-aminophenol,[41] and with 3- and 4-substituted benzylamines,[42] of picryl chloride with methanol[43] and with aromatic anils,[44] and of other chloronitrobenzenes with reactive methylene compounds[45] and ammonia[46] have also been studied. Other nucleophilic aromatic substitutions that have been investigated are: reactions of 4-, 5-, and 6-substituted 1-

[39] S. Patai and Y. Gotshal, *Israel J. Chem.*, **3**, 223 (1966).
[40] M. Vagaonescu, G. Niac, and M. Ionescu, *Rev. Roumaine Chim.*, **10**, 537 (1965).
[41] A. N. Roseira and A. S. Alvarez, *Anais Assoc. Brasil. Quin.*, **22**, 57 (1963); *Chem. Abs.*, **64**, 15691 (1966).
[42] A. Fischer, R. S. H. Hickford, G. R. Scott, and J. Vaughan, *J. Chem. Soc.*, B, **1966**, 466.
[43] V. A. Sokolenko, *Reaktsionnaya Sposobnost Organ. Soedin, Tartusk. Gos. Univ.*, **2**, 208 (1965); *Chem. Abs.*, **64**, 1915 (1966).
[44] V. I. Minkin, E. A. Medyantseva, and A. P. Olekhnovich, *Zh. Obshch. Khim.*, **35**, 1962 (1965).
[45] J. Bourdais and C. Mahieu, *Compt. Rend., Ser. C.*, **263**, 84 (1966).
[46] L. A. Kozorez, S. M. Shein, and N. N. Vorozhtsov, *Zh. Obshch. Khim.*, **36**, 424 (1966); *Chem. Abs.*, **65**, 2084 (1966); S. M. Shein, L. A. Kozorez, and N. N. Vorozhtsov, *Izv. Sibirsk. Otd. Akad. Nauk. SSSR, Ser. Khim. Nauk*, **1965**, 105; *Chem. Abs.*, **64**, 19347 (1966).

chloro-2-nitrobenzenes with sodium thiophenoxide,[47a] of mono- and bis-trifluoromethyl chlorobenzenes with sodium alkoxide,[47b] and of *o*-chlorotrifluoromethylbenzene with ammonia;[48] copper-catalysed conversion of chlorobenzenes into bromobenzenes with potassium bromide;[49] copper-catalysed hydrolysis of chloronaphthoic acids;[50] reaction of 1- and 2-chloronaphthalene with sodium methoxide,[51] and of *o*-, *m*-, and *p*-dichlorobenzene and hexachlorobenzene with sodium methoxide;[52] replacement of the nitro-group by chlorine in polynitro-benzenes and -phenols on reaction with hydrochloric acid or phosphorus oxychloride and pyridine;[53] displacement of halogen *para* to the diazonium group in 2,4,6-trihalogenobenzenediazonium ions;[54] reactivity of chlorine in 2-chloro-2'-hydroxyazo-compounds and their copper complexes;[55] cleavage of anisole and its chloro-derivatives by sodium methoxide;[56] and displacement of bromine in diethyl 2-acetamido-6-bromo-azulene-1,3-dicarboxylate.[57]

Meisenheimer and Related Complexes [58]

Meisenheimer and related compounds have been extensively reviewed.[59] NMR spectroscopy has proved particularly useful recently in studying their structures. Servis[60] has reported the spectra of the anions obtained on treating some 1-substituted 2,4,6-trinitrobenzenes in dimethyl sulphoxide with sodium methoxide in methanol; particular attention was paid to the spectra obtained immediately after mixing. With 2,4,6-trinitroanisole the initially formed anion has structure (6) and not that of the classical Meisenheimer complex (7); (6) is unstable, however, and rapidly ($k_1 \approx 4 \times 10^{-3}$ sec^{-1}) changes to (7). *N*-Methyl-2,4,6-trinitroaniline gave a mixture of two anions [(8); R = Me, and

[47a] A. M. Porto, L. Altieri, A. J. Castro, and J. A. Brieux, *J. Chem. Soc., B*, **1966**, 963.
[47b] S. M. Shein and M. I. Krasnosel'skaya, *Zh. Obshch. Khim.*, **35**, 1952 (1965); *Chem. Abs.*, **64**, 7987 (1966); *J. Gen. Chem. USSR*, **35**, 1944 (1965).
[48] S. M. Shein, L. A. Kozorez, and N. N. Vorozhtsov, *Izv. Sibirsk. Otd. Akad. Nauk SSSR, Ser. Khim. Nauk*, **1965**, 85; *Chem. Abs.*, **64**, 1917 (1966).
[49] V. D. Shteingarts, G. G. Furin, G. G. Yakobson and N. N. Vorozhtsov, *Zh. Org. Khim.*, **2**, 701 (1966); *Chem. Abs.*, **65**, 8703 (1966).
[50] V. N. Lisitsyn and L. A. Didenko, *Zh. Org. Khim.* **2**, 1063 (1966); *Chem. Abs.*, **65**, 15178 (1966).
[51] S. M. Shein and V. A. Ignatov, *Zh. Org. Khim.*, **2**, 704 (1966); *Chem. Abs.*, **65**, 8702.
[52] S. M. Shein and V. A. Ignatov, *Zh. Org. Khim.*, **2**, 1070 (1966); *Chem. Abs.*, **65**, 15177 (1966).
[53] G. M. Shutov, V. L. Zbarskii, V. F. Zhilin, and E. Y. Orlova, *J. Gen. Chem. USSR*, **35**, 1363 (1965).
[54] B. Lamm and B. Andersson, *Arkiv Kemi*, **25**, 367 (1966); *Chem. Abs.*, **65**, 7003 (1966).
[55] B. A. Korolev and B. I. Stepanov, *Tr. Mosk. Khim. Tekhnol. Inst.* No. 48, 132 (1965); *Chem. Abs.*, **65**, 15179 (1966).
[56] V. A. Ignatov and S. M. Shein, *Zh. Org. Khim.*, **1**, 1951 (1965); *Chem. Abs.*, **64**, 9533 (1966).
[57] M. Tada, *Bull. Chem. Soc., Japan*, **39**, 1954 (1966).
[58] See *Organic Reaction Mechanisms*, **1965**, 137.
[59] R. Foster and C. A. Fyfe, *Rev. Pure Appl. Chem.*, **16**, 61 (1966).
[60] K. L. Servis, *J. Am. Chem. Soc.*, **87**, 5495 (1965).

(**9**); R = Me]; *N*-phenyl-2,4,6-trinitroaniline gave a single anion [(**9**); R = Ph]; 2,4,6-trinitroaniline gave two anions [(**8**); R = H, and (**9**); R = H], with the former predominant. Thus, of these compounds, only trinitroanisole gave a

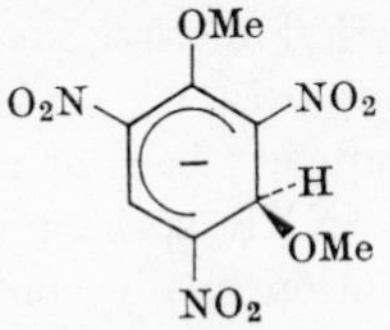

(6)

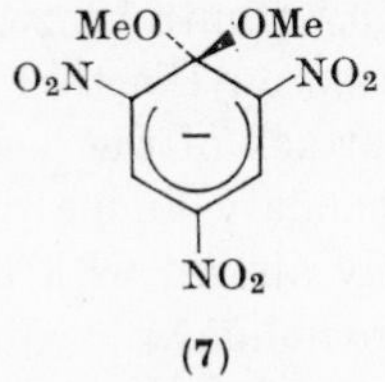

(7)

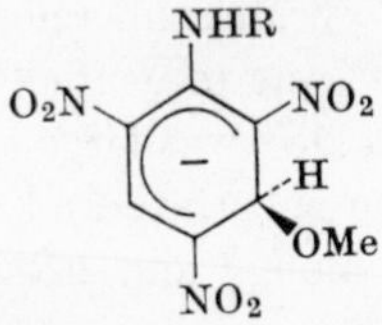

(8)

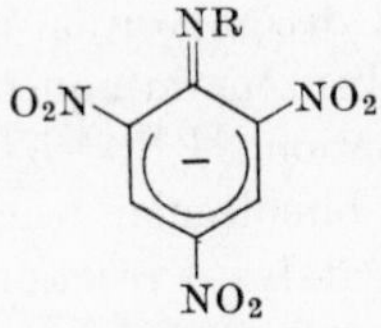

(9)

Meisenheimer complex. If the present results can be extrapolated to other solvent systems many apparent complexities in earlier work are readily rationalized.[60] Full details of an NMR investigation of the interaction of a series of di- and tri-nitrobenzene derivatives with methoxide ions in methanol–dimethyl sulphoxide have appeared. Methoxide adds to a nuclear position carrying hydrogen or to a substituted nuclear position or removes a proton from an amino-substituent. More than one of these processes may be observed with a given substrate; in agreement with Servis, attack at an unsubstituted nuclear position tends to be faster than at a substituted position, but the latter gives the more stable product.[61] A study of the rate of tritium-exchange with $H_{(2)}$ in *m*-dinitrobenzene as a function of the basicity of the medium has shown that proton loss is not the cause of the colour formed; colour probably results from a reversible methoxide addition to $C_{(4)}$, to give the anion (**10**) which is unreactive in tritium-exchange.[62] Hydrogen-exchange

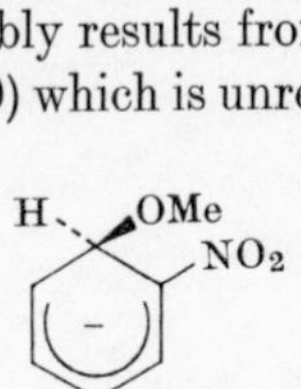

(10)

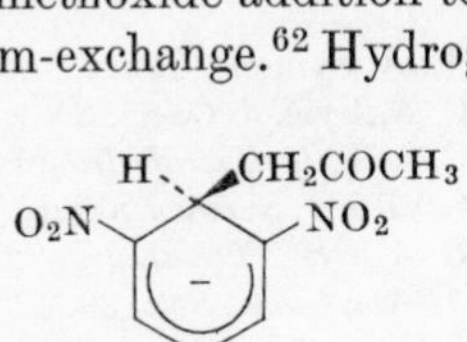

(11)

[61] M. R. Crampton and V. Gold, *J. Chem. Soc., B*, **1966**, 893.
[62] M. R. Crampton and V. Gold, *J. Chem. Soc., B*, **1966**, 498.

has also been observed with 1,3,5-trinitrobenzene in 9:1 dimethylformamide–D_2O 0.01M in NaOD; the importance of the solvent in controlling the competition between proton abstraction and formation of Meisenheimer complexes is briefly discussed.[63] The deep red species produced by the addition of tertiary amines to 1,3,5-trinitrobenzene in acetone, ethyl methyl ketone, diethyl ketone, and isopropyl methyl ketone are σ-complexes, e.g., (11), formed by nucleophilic attack of the benzene by the conjugate base of the ketone.[64] With the secondary amine diethylamine, the NMR spectrum of the red solution slowly altered with time and the solution finally contained N,N-diethyl-p-nitroaniline.[65]

The influence of pressure on the rates of the uncatalysed and hydrogen ion-catalysed decomposition of the 1,1-diethoxy Meisenheimer complex of 1,3,5-trinitrobenzene in aqueous solution at 0° was measured. For the uncatalysed reaction $\Delta V^* = -5.6$ cm³ mole⁻¹ and ΔS^* was large and negative, suggesting a bimolecular reaction between the substrate and water, while for the acid-catalysed reaction $\Delta V^* = 18$ cm³ mole⁻¹ and ΔS^* was slightly positive, suggesting an A-1 mechanism.[66]

In the alkoxy Meisenheimer complexes of 1,3,5-trinitrobenzene the alkoxy-groups were readily replaced by the acetonyl group in acetone solution.[67] Full details of the reactions[58] of 2,4-dinitro- and 2,4,6-trinitro-anisole with sodium methoxide in methanol have appeared.[68] The results are best explained by a symmetrical two-step mechanism, with formation of the intermediate fast for the trinitro-case and for the same reaction of 4-methoxypyridine 1-oxide.[68]

Other reactions which have been studied are: formation of complexes from 2,4,6-trinitro-anisole and -phenetole;[69] decomposition of complexes formed from alkyl picryl ethers and alkoxide ions in water;[70] interaction of alkali and aromatic dinitro-compounds, which was followed by ESR measurements;[71] the Janovsky reaction;[72] formation of a cyclic Meisenheimer complex from glycol picryl ether;[73] and reaction of aqueous and alcoholic alkali with 1,2,3,5-tetranitrobenzene.[74]

[63] E. Buncel and E. A. Symons, *Can. J. Chem.*, **44**, 771 (1966).
[64] R. Foster and C. A. Fyfe, *J. Chem. Soc., B*, **1966**, 53.
[65] R. Foster and C. A. Fyfe, *Tetrahedron*, **22**, 1831 (1966).
[66] J. Murto and A. Viitala, *Suomen Kemistilehti, B*, **39**, 138 (1966).
[67] R. Foster and C. A. Fyfe, *Tetrahedron*, **21**, 3363 (1965).
[68] J. H. Fendler, *J. Am. Chem. Soc.*, **88**, 1237 (1966).
[69] J. Murto and E. Kohvakka, *Suomen. Kemistilehti, B*, **39**, 128 (1966).
[70] J. Murto and J. Vainionpää, *Suomen Kemistilehti, B*, **39**, 133 (1966).
[71] B. I. Shapiro, V. M. Kazakova, and Y. K. Syrkin, *Dokl. Akad. Nauk. SSSR*, **165**, 619 (1965); *Chem. Abs.*, **64**, 4882 (1966).
[72] M. Kimura, M. Kawata, and M. Nakadate, *Chem. Ind. (London)*, **1965**, 2065.
[73] J. Murto, *Suomen Kemistilehti, B*, **38**, 255 (1965).
[74] J. Murto, *Suomen Kemistilehti, B*, **38**, 251 (1965).

Substitution in Polyfluoro-aromatic Compounds

Burdon[75] has presented a useful summary and rationalization of the orientations and reactivities recently found in nucleophilic displacements in aromatic polyfluoro(and polychloro)-compounds, many of which were reported last year.[76] The problem of orientation in the nucleophilic displacement of fluorine in C_6F_5X is, of course, analogous to that of electrophilic substitution in C_6H_5X; the results are similarly explained by considering the relative stabilities of the possible tetrahedral intermediates. The assumptions are made that *para*-quinonoid structures (**12**) are more important than *ortho*-

(**12**)   (**13**)

N = Nucleophile

quinonoid structures (**13**) and that the halogens are electron-releasing in π-systems. The halogens appear to destabilize a negative charge on the adjacent carbon atom in the order $F > Cl > Br > I \sim H$, which is the opposite of their normal electron-attracting behaviour. This sequence of electron-release by the halogens in π-systems (I_π repulsion) is explained by Coulombic repulsion between their p-electrons and the π-electrons on adjacent carbon atoms. When ground-state stabilities, which will increase with electron-releasing power of X in C_6F_5X, are considered, relative reactivities may also be rationalized.[75] On the basis of these arguments it was predicted that 1,2,3,4-tetrafluoro-5- and 1,2,3,5-tetrafluoro-4-halogenobenzenes would react with nucleophiles mainly at the position *para* to hydrogen; this has now been observed with sodium methoxide and, for the first compound, with dimethylamine; the second compound reacted with dimethylamine predominantly *para* to halogen when this was Br or I, and this was attributed to a primary steric effect.[77] Pentafluorohalogenobenzenes react mainly at the position *para* to halogen, and the minor *ortho* replacement decreases with halogen size; and this was explained similarly.[78]

The results of an extensive kinetic study of substituent effects in nucleophilic displacements by hydroxide and methoxide ions in the compounds C_6F_5X, including C_6F_6, where X ranges from strongly activating to strongly deactivating groups, have been presented and analysed.[79] On passing from

[75] J. Burdon, *Tetrahedron*, **21**, 3373 (1965).
[76] *Organic Reaction Mechanisms*, **1965**, 139.
[77] J. Burdon, D. R. King, and J. C. Tatlow, *Tetrahedron*, **22**, 2541 (1966).
[78] J. Burdon, P. L. Coe, C. R. Marsh, and J. C. Tatlow, *Tetrahedron*, **22**, 1183 (1966).
[79] K. C. Ho and J. Miller, *Australian J. Chem.*, **19**, 423 (1966).

C_6F_6 to C_6F_5X both orientation and rate changes can be simply and reliably predicted by considering the structural change as made up of two components: $C_6F_6 \rightarrow C_6F_5H \rightarrow C_6F_5X$. The same applies to results with the polychloro-compounds with which the polyfluoro results are compared. The greater reactivity of hexafluorobenzene than of hexachlorobenzene is considered to result solely from the greater mobility of fluorine, the C_6Cl_5 group actually being slightly more electron-withdrawing than C_6F_5.[79]

Pentafluoropyridine and pentafluoronitrobenzene (but not the less reactive hexafluorobenzene) react with heptafluoroisopropyl carbanions (from hexafluoropropene and potassium fluoride) to give *o*- and *p*-mono- and di-substituted perfluoroisopropyl derivatives; this may be regarded as a nucleophilic equivalent of the Friedel–Crafts reaction.[80] Competition for sodium methoxide in methanol at 0° showed the overall reactivities of pentafluoropyridine and pentafluoronitrobenzene to be about the same and slightly greater than that of tetrafluoro-4-nitropyridine. With the last compound substantial displacement of the nitro-group, activated by the ring-nitrogen atom, accompanied displacement of fluorine by both methoxide and ammonia.[81] The 4-fluorine atom of perfluoropyridazine[82] and, more slowly, the 2-fluorine atom of perfluoropyrazine[83] are preferentially replaced by ammonia.

Heterocyclic Systems

The extended Hückel molecular orbital theory (EHT) recently developed by Hoffmann,[84] in which σ- and π-electron distributions are calculated simultaneously, has been applied by Adam and Grimison[85] to calculating the position of nucleophilic attack in pyridine, quinoline, and isoquinoline. The total σ- and π-electron densities clearly show that $C_{(2)}$ in pyridine and quinoline and $C_{(1)}$ in isoquinoline should be the most reactive towards nucleophiles; the calculated difference between $C_{(2)}$ and $C_{(4)}$ in pyridine, which is small when only π-electrons are considered, is now found to be significant and to be mainly a σ-electron effect. The energies of the intermediate σ-complexes calculated for the localization of a hydride ion at each carbon in turn, are readily calculated by the EHT method and, with the same set of parameters, agree with the above calculations and with experiment.

The position of attack of pyridinium ions by nucleophiles has previously

[80] R. D. Chambers, R. A. Storey, and W. K. R. Musgrave, *Chem. Commun.*, **1966**, 384.

[81] R. D. Chambers, J. Hutchinson, and W. K. R. Musgrave, *J. Chem. Soc.*, *C*, **1966**, 220.

[82] R. D. Chambers, J. A. H. MacBride, and W. K. R. Musgrave, *Chem. Ind.* (*London*), **1966**, 904.

[83] R. D. Chambers, J. A. H. MacBride, and W. K. R. Musgrave, *Chem. Ind.* (*London*), **1966**, 1721.

[84] R. Hoffmann, *J. Chem. Phys.*, **39**, 1397 (1963).

[85] W. Adam and A. Grimison, *Tetrahedron*, **21**, 3417 (1965).

been related[86] to the intermediacy of a "charge-transfer complex," the formation of such a complex leading to a 1,4-dihydropyridine instead of the more usual 1,2-dihydro-product. It has now been shown[87] that, in the reaction of a cyanide ion with a number of pyridinium ions (14), initial attack is predominantly at $C_{(2)}$ to give (15) which are slowly converted into an equilibrium mixture consisting of the more stable 1,4-dihydro-derivatives (16). Thus the cyanide reaction differs from those giving 1,2-dihydro-derivatives only in being reversible and with cyanide, at least, there is no need to postulate

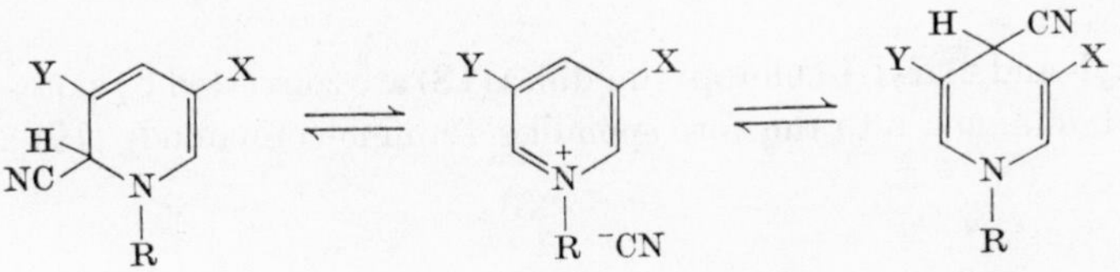

(15)　　　　　　(14)　　　　　　(16)

Y = H, Br; X = CO_2Et, PhCO, MeCO, CN, $CONH_2$;
R = Me, $PhCH_2$, $2,6\text{-}Cl_2C_6H_3CH_2$.

two different mechanisms. The reactions of the pseudo-base derived from 1-cyanoquinolinium hydroxide have been studied.[88]

The kinetics of the reactions of a series of halogeno- and nitro-pyridine *N*-oxides with sodium ethoxide[89] and with piperidine[90] in ethanol have been measured. With sodium ethoxide the reaction rates, and the entropies and energies of activation for nitro-group displacement, all decrease in the order 2 > 4 > 3, and for bromine displacement the entropies and energies decrease in the order 4 > 2, the reverse of the reaction rate. Methyl groups adjacent to the leaving group retard the reactions of 4-chloro- and 4-nitro-3,5-diethyl-pyridine 1-oxide. The results could be rationalized in terms of steric and electronic effects of substituents in the ground and transition states. Thus the relatively high activation entropy for the reaction of 2-nitropyridine 1-oxide with ethoxide is attributed to increased freedom of rotation of the nitro-group in the transition state compared with the restriction imposed upon it by the *N*-oxide-oxygen in the ground state; the relatively low activation energy for the reaction of this compound with piperidine is attributed to the high ground-state energy caused by repulsion between the nitro- and the *N*-oxide groups and to stabilization of the transition state by hydrogen-bonding.

86 E. M. Kosower, *J. Am. Chem. Soc.*, **78**, 3497 (1956).
87 R. E. Lyle and G. J. Gauthier, *Tetrahedron Letters*, **1965**, 4615.
88 B. J. Huckings and M. D. Johnson, *J. Chem. Soc.*, B, **1966**, 63.
89 R. M. Johnson, *J. Chem. Soc.*, B, **1966**, 1058.
90 R. M. Johnson, *J. Chem. Soc.*, B, **1966**, 1062.

In the reactions of 4-nitropyridine 1-oxide with hydroxide ion in dimethyl sulphoxide–water mixtures the rate increases greatly with increasing dimethyl sulphoxide concentration, as expected, though considerably less than is found for other nucleophilic displacements. This is attributed to a decrease in hydrogen bonding of the N-oxide group to water (17) and hence a compensating decrease in the effective positive charge on the activating group.[91] Second-order rate constants for the reaction of piperidine with 22 substituted 2- and 4-chloroquinolines have been measured, linear free-energy correlations have been discussed[92] and the effect of substituents on $C_{(8)}$ has been investigated.[93]

2-Alkyl- and 2-aryl-4-chloropyrimidines (18) are converted by potassamide in liquid ammonia into the corresponding 4-amino-compounds (19) and, by

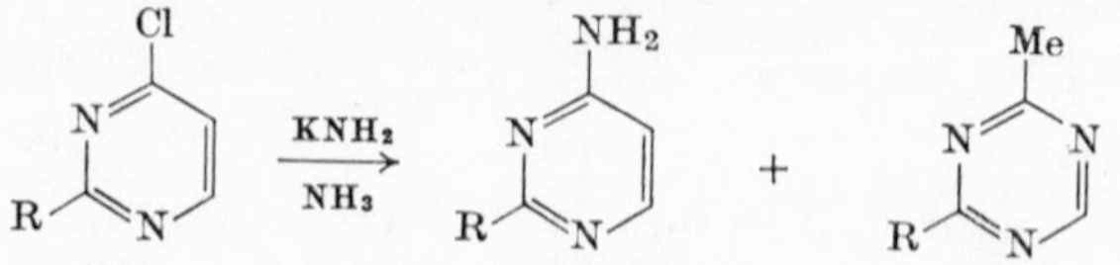

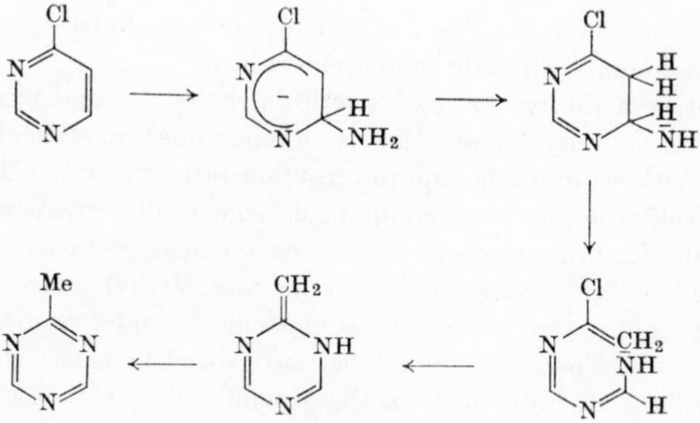

Scheme 5

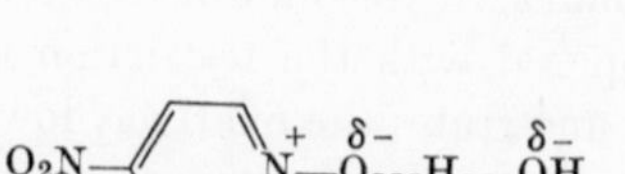

(17) 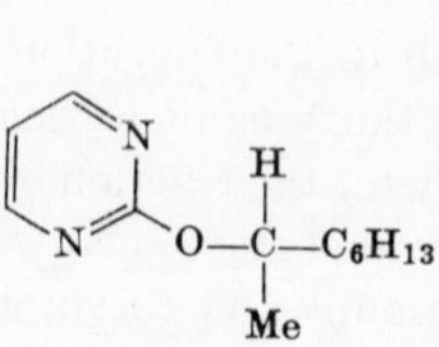   (21)

[91] J. Murto and L. Kääriäinen, *Suomen Kemistilehti, B*, **39**, 40 (1966).

[92] G. Illuminati and G. Marino, *Ric. Sci. Rend., Sez A*, **8**, 449 (1965); *Chem. Abs.*, **63**, 17840 (1965).

[93] G. Illuminati, P. Linda, and G. Marino, *Atti Accad. Nazl. Lincei, Rend. Classe Sci. Fis. Mat. Nat.*, **38**, 389 (1965).

an interesting rearrangement, into 2-alkyl- and 2-aryl-4-methyl-1,3,5-triazines (**20**).[94] The former are not intermediates in the formation of the latter and there is no evidence for pyrimidines. The proposed mechanism, similar to that for the conversion of 2,6-dihalogenopyridines into 4-amino-2-methyl-pyrimidines,[95] is shown for the simplest case in Scheme 5. Cleavage of (+)-2-(1-methylheptyloxy)pyrimidine (**21**) in aqueous-ethanolic phosphoric acid gave 2-pyrimidone and racemic octan-2-ol; an $S_N 1$ heterolysis of ring-protonated (**21**), giving the 1-methylheptyl carbonium ion, is therefore proposed, in contrast with the bimolecular mechanism for acid cleavage of 2-methoxypyrimidine.[96] First-order rate constants for the reaction of 2- and 4-alkoxy- and -alkylthio-pyrimidines with an excess of butylamine show that the 4-substituted compounds are more reactive than the 2-isomers, the alkoxy-compounds are more reactive than their alkylthio-analogues, and all are much less reactive than the corresponding chloropyrimidines.[97] Second-order rate constants calculated for the reactions of 2-chloro-4,6- and 4-chloro-2,6-dimethylpyrimidine with mono- and di-alkylamines in the absence of solvent were found[98] to be quite similar to those for dilute ethanolic solutions. Methyl and phenyl groups in positions 4 and 6 of 2-chloropyrimidine decrease the rate of displacement of chlorine by sodium methoxide in methanol[99] and by piperidine in ethanol.[100] Some nucleophilic displacements in 4-arylamino-2,5,6-trichloropyrimidines have been studied.[101]

In the reactions of 3-, 4-, 5-, and 6-chloropyridazine 1-oxides with piperidine or sodium ethoxide the order of positional reactivity was $5 > 3 > 6 > 4$.[102] Several nucleophilic reactions of fluoropyrazine, which is more reactive than chloropyrazine, have been investigated semi-quantitatively;[103] 2,3-difluoroquinoxaline is very susceptible to nucleophilic attack by water, giving 2,3-dihydroxyquinoxaline almost quantitatively on steam-distillation.[104] The kinetics of the reactions of 2-chlorobenzimidazoles with piperidine,[105] of

[94] H. C. Van Der Plas, B. Haase, B. Zuurdeeg, and M. C. Vollering, *Rec. Trav. Chim.*, **85**, 1101 (1966).

[95] H. J. den Hertog, H. C. van der Plas, M. J. Pieterse, and J. W. Streef, *Rec. Trav. Chim.*, **84**, 1569 (1965).

[96] R. Daniels, L. T. Grady, and L. Bauer, *J. Org. Chem.*, **31**, 1790 (1966).

[97] D. J. Brown and R. V. Foster, *Australian J. Chem.*, **19**, 1487 (1966).

[98] D. J. Brown and J. M. Lyall, *Australian J. Chem.*, **18**, 1811 (1965).

[99] S. M. Shein, V. P. Mawaev, O. A. Zagulyaeva, and A. I. Shvets, *Reaktsionnaya Gos. Univ.*, **2**, 65 (1965); *Chem. Abs.*, **65**, 10461 (1966).

[100] V. P. Mamaev, O. A. Zagulyaeva, S. M. Shein, and A. I. Shvets, *Reaktsionnaya Sposobnost Organ. Soedin. Tartusk. Gos. Univ.*, **2**, 61 (1965); *Chem. Abs.*, **65**, 10461 (1966).

[101] H. Ackermann, *Helv. Chim. Acta*, **49**, 454 (1966).

[102] S. Sako and T. Itai, *Chem. Pharm. Bull.* (*Tokyo*), **14**, 269 (1966); *Chem. Abs.*, **64**, 19346 (1966).

[103] H. Rutner and P. E. Spoerri, *J. Heterocyclic Chem.*, **2**, 492 (1965).

[104] J. Hamer, *J. Heterocyclic Chem.*, **3**, 244 (1966).

[105] A. Ricci and P. Vivarelli, *Boll. Sci. Fac. Chim. Ind. Bologna*, **23**, 409 (1965); *Chem. Abs.*, **65**, 5347 (1966).

2-halogenoselenophens with various nucleophilies,[106] of 2-chlorobenzoxazoles with thiophenoxide ions,[107] of mono- and di-chlorotriazine reactive dyes towards hydrolysis,[108] and of phosphonitrile chloride trimer and various butoxy-derivatives with alkoxide ions[109] have also been reported.

8-Azapurines, though not purines with electron-withdrawing substituents in position 8,[110] have been shown to undergo covalent hydration in water,[111] and the rates for addition and removal of water have been measured.[112] Covalent hydration of pteridine has been studied further, and reactions previously attributed to reversible ring-opening on the basis of ultraviolet measurements are now shown, by NMR, to involve a change in hydration site only.[113] Covalent hydration of many quinazoline cations has been studied.[114]

Diazonium Decomposition

Over the last few years Lewis and his co-workers[115] have presented evidence that the decomposition of arenediazonium ions involves reactive intermediates such as (22) in which the nitrogen atoms become equivalent and which can revert to the diazonium ion. Thus the rearrangement

$$Ar—^{15}N{\equiv}N^+ BF_4^- \rightarrow Ar—N{\equiv}^{15}N^+ BF_4^-$$

was shown to occur at 1.4% and 2.9% of the rate of hydrolysis to the phenol when Ar was Ph and *p*-tolyl, respectively. Bose and Kugajevsky[116] have now repeated the aqueous decomposition of benzene[α-^{15}N]diazonium fluoroborate under Insole and Lewis's conditions; their method of analysis was to reduce the residual diazonium ion, after partial hydrolysis, to phenylhydrazine and to condense this with benzaldehyde to give the hydrazone (23a) or to couple the diazonium ion with ethyl acetoacetate to give the hydrazone (24a). Any randomization of the label would result in formation of the hydrazones (23b) and (24b), respectively. These should be differentiated in the NMR by the sharp doublet expected for ^{15}N–H and the single broad peak for ^{14}N–H.

[106] L. Chierici, C. Dell'Erba, and D. Spinelli, *Ann. Chim.*, (*Rome*), **55**, 1069 (1965); *Chem. Abs.* **64**, 9670 (1966).

[107] M. Foa, A. Ricci, P. E. Todesco, and P. Vivarelli, *Boll. Schi. Fac. Chim. Ind. Bologna*, **23**, 89 (1965).

[108] P. Rys and H. Zollinger, *Helv. Chim. Acta*, **49**, 749, 761 (1966); A. Datynev, P. Rys, and H. Zollinger, *ibid.*, p. 755.

[109] M. F. Sorokin and V. K. Latov, *Kinetika i Kataliz*, **7**, 42 (1966); *Chem. Abs.*, **64**, 19348 (1966).

[110] A. Albert, *J. Chem. Soc.*, *B*, **1966**, 438.

[111] A. Albert, *J. Chem. Soc.*, *B*, **1966**, 427.

[112] J. W. Bunting and D. D. Perrin, *J. Chem. Soc.*, *B*, **1966**, 433.

[113] A. Albert, T. J. Batterham, and J. J. McCormack, *J. Chem. Soc.*, *B*, **1966**, 1105.

[114] W. L. F. Armarengo and J. I. C. Smith, *J. Chem. Soc.*, *C*, **1966**, 234.

[115] E. S. Lewis and J. E. Cooper, *J. Am. Chem. Soc.*, **84**, 3847 (1962); J. M. Insole and E. S. Lewis, *ibid.*, **85**, 122 (1963); *ibid.*, **86**, 32, 34 (1964).

[116] A. K. Bose and I. Kugajevsky, *J. Am. Chem. Soc.*, **88**, 2325 (1966).

From the areas under these curves Bose and Kugajevsky found no evidence for scrambling of the diazonium-nitrogen atoms during hydrolysis, reduction, or coupling, and attributed the earlier results to the large limits of error

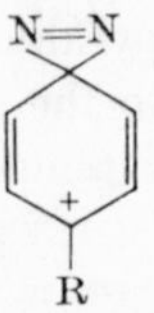

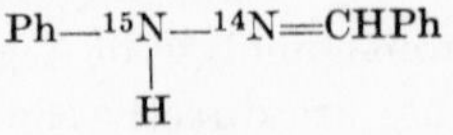

inherent in the analytical method. Lewis and Holliday,[117] however, have now repeated and extended the earlier results and claim to have substantiated them fully. They explain the discrepancy between the two sets of results by the possibility that the NMR signal for $^{14}N–H$ in the hydrazones (**23b**) and (**24b**) may not be the same as that for the isotopically normal hydrazones, as Bose and Kugajersky had assumed, but sufficiently split by the neighbouring ^{15}N for the ^{14}N-proton absorption not to overlap, hence vitiating the comparison of signal areas.

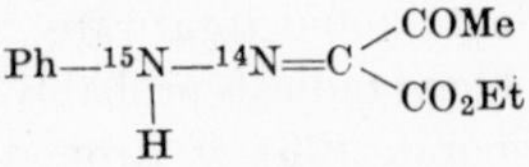

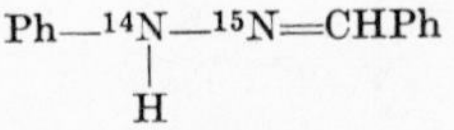

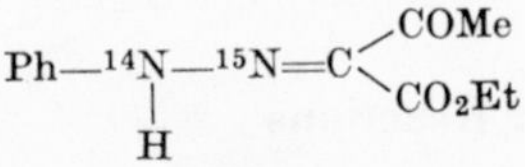

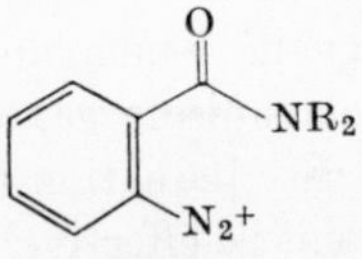

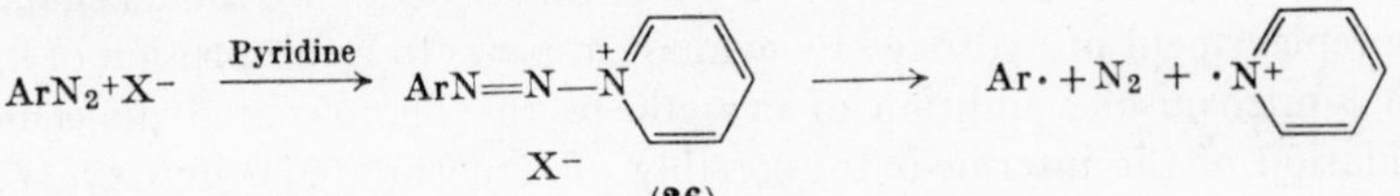

Further evidence has been provided for the decomposition of the same arenediazonium salts by different mechanisms depending upon the reaction conditions.[118] The yields of the various products of diazonium group replacement, ring-closure, and hydrogen-transfer from diazotized *N,N*-dialkyl-*o*-aminobenzamides (**25**)[119] can all be explained by the intermediacy of the aryl cation in the thermal decompositions and the aryl radical in the copper-catalysed decompositions. The role of cuprous ions in the latter reactions are

117 E. S. Lewis and R. E. Holliday, *J. Am. Chem. Soc.*, **88**, 5043 (1966).
118 A. H. Lewin, A. H. Dinwoodie, and T. Cohen, *Tetrahedron*, **22**, 1527 (1966).
119 See *Organic Reaction Mechanisms*, **1965**, 143.

discussed and cuprous oxide is found to be very effective in promoting the homolytic decomposition. Phenylation of aromatic substrates by the decomposition in them of benzenediazonium fluoroborate with one equivalent of pyridine is shown to involve free phenyl radicals by the similarity of partial rate factors and total rate ratios to those obtained with benzoyl peroxide. The phenyl radicals probably arise from homolysis of *N*-phenylazopyridinium fluoroborate (26).[120] Aromatic amines are directly converted into the aryl chloride or bromide by the complex $CuCl_2 \cdot NO$ or $CuBr_2 \cdot NO$ at room temperature; a tentative mechanism is briefly discussed.[121]

Other Reactions

Further interesting photoinduced substitutions of aromatic nitro-compounds have been reported this year, mostly by Havinga and by Letsinger and their co-workers. Brief irradiation of *p*-nitroanisole and potassium cyanide in the presence of oxygen in aqueous *tert*-butyl alcohol gave 2-cyano-4-nitroanisole in good yield [equation (1)]. Similar treatment of *m*-nitroanisole gave *m*-cyanonitrobenzene but oxygen was unnecessary in this case [equation (3)]. Thus a group *meta* to nitro has been displaced and when this is, effectively, a hydride ion an oxidant is required. From kinetic evidence the mechanism for the replacement of hydrogen by cyanide appears to be absorption of light by the *p*-nitroanisole, addition of cyanide to the photoexcited molecule, and oxidation of the intermediate, possibly of structure (27), by oxygen.[122] In contrast, it is the methoxyl group of *p*-nitroanisole that is readily displaced from the photoexcited molecule by methylamine or dimethylamine to give the corresponding *p*-nitroaniline in good yield [equation (2)]. Comparison with earlier results[123] also underlines the importance of the nucleophile in determining the reaction course.[124] Aromatic nitro-compounds also react with concentrated hydrochloric acid when irradiated with ultraviolet light of wavelength > 290 mμ; the nitro-group is reduced and the ring is polychlorinated, as shown in equation (4).[125] The photohydrolysis of *m*-nitroanisole in alkaline media has been shown by kinetic and ^{18}O-tracer measurements to be a bimolecular nucleophilic displacement at the methoxyl-bearing carbon. Formation of a σ-complex between ^-OH and photoexcited *m*-nitroanisole was proposed.[126] Aryl chlorides with electron-withdrawing *para*-groups liberate chloride ions readily on irradiation in methanol.[127]

[120] R. A. Abramovitch and J. G. Saha, *Tetrahedron*, **21**, 3297 (1965).
[121] W. Brackman and P. J. Smit, *Rec. Trav. Chim.*, **85**, 857 (1966).
[122] R. L. Letsinger and J. H. McCain, *J. Am. Chem. Soc.*, **88**, 2884 (1966).
[123] See *Organic Reaction Mechanisms*, **1965**, 145.
[124] M. E. Kronenberg, A. van der Heyden, and E. Havinga, *Rec. Trav. Chim.*, **85**, 56 (1966).
[125] R. L. Letsinger, and G. G. Wubbels, *J. Am. Chem. Soc.*, **88**, 5041 (1966).
[126] R. O. De Jongh and E. Havinga, *Rec. Trav. Chim.*, **85**, 275 (1966).
[127] T. Latowski, *Roczniki Chem.*, **40**, 231 (1966).

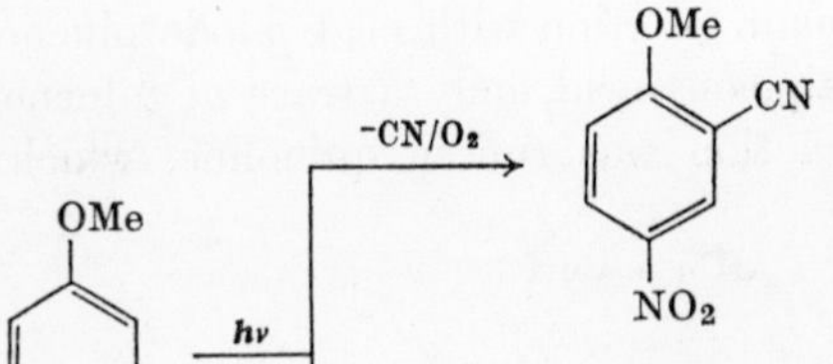

(1)

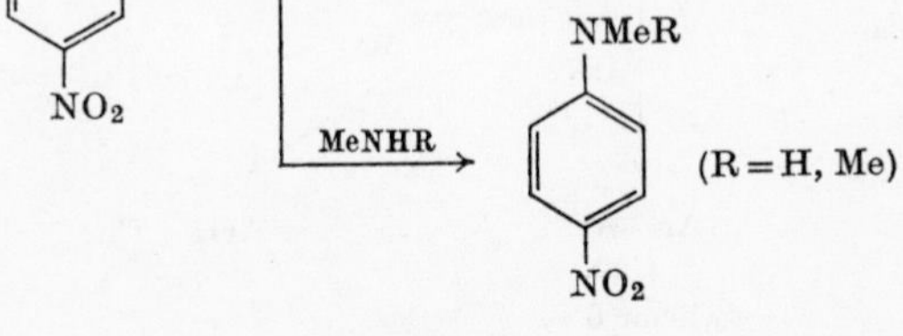

(2)

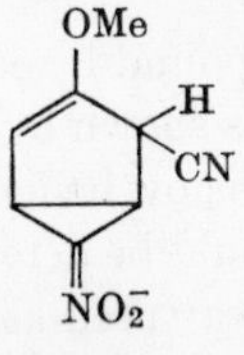

(27)

(3)

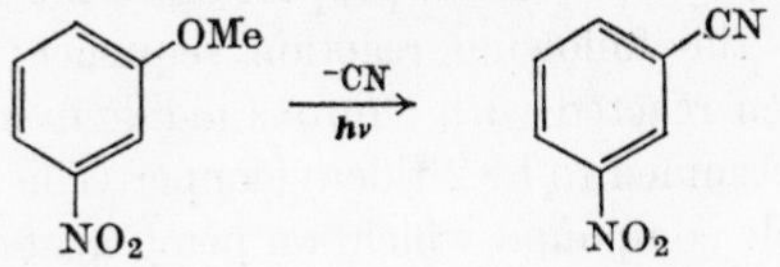

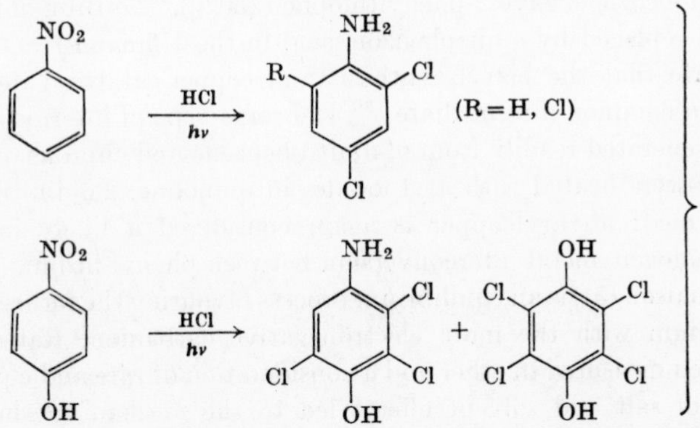

(4)

Lewin and Cohen[128] have proposed that the formation of an organometallic intermediate, probably an arylcopper, is the key step in the Ullmann biaryl synthesis, as shown in Scheme 6. Formation of the arylcopper is normally likely to be rate-determining and it would not accumulate during

[128] A. M. Lewin and T. Cohen, *Tetrahedron Letters*, **1965**, 4531; see also p. 255.

the reaction. Thus, when an Ullmann reaction with neat *p*-iodotoluene was interrupted and quenched with aqueous acid, only a trace of toluene was detected. However, when the reaction was run in quinoline, which was

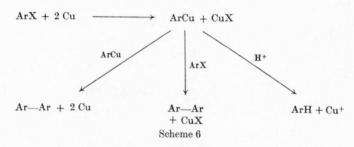

Scheme 6

expected to stabilize the organocopper compound by complex formation, the intermediate did accumulate (up to 43%), as shown by treatment of portions with acid. It appears that the intermediate is now being formed relatively fast and decomposed slowly. No intermediate could be detected in this way when the non-complexing 1-methylnaphthalene was used as solvent. Many of the characteristic features of the Ullmann reaction could be rationalized on the basis of the mechanism of Scheme 6.[128] Support for the proposed intermediacy of an arylcopper was provided by the following reaction sequence: the Grignard reagent from 2-iodothiophen reacted with cuprous iodide in ether to give an air-sensitive compound, presumed to be 2-thienylcopper. This was changed by quinoline to a more stable compound which, on being heated in quinoline with iodobenzene, gave 2-phenylthiophen (50%).[129] *o*-Bromonitrobenzene has been replaced by *o*-nitrobenzoic acid in the Ullmann reaction; the results indicate that the biaryl synthesis and copper-catalysed decarboxylation share a common intermediate.[130] The same type of intermediate also seems to be generated readily from *m*-dinitrobenzene and cuprous oxide since, when these were heated with aryl iodides in quinoline, 2,6-dinitrobiphenyls were formed; an arylcopper is again considered a likely intermediate.[131] The halogen–metal interconversion between phenyl-lithium and aryl bromides [equation (5)] is an equilibrium process favouring the formation of the organolithium with the more electronegative carbanion. Rates of exchange have been measured in ether and a consideration of rate and equilibrium data and of salt and solvent effects led to the mechanism shown [equation (6)] as the most likely.[132]

$$\text{PhLi} + \text{ArBr} \rightleftarrows \text{PhBr} + \text{ArLi} \qquad (5)$$

[129] M. Nilsson, *Tetrahedron Letters*, **1966**, 679.
[130] M. Nilsson, *Acta Chem. Scand.*, **20**, 423 (1966).
[131] C. Björklund and M. Nilsson, *Tetrahedron Letters*, **1966**, 675.
[132] H. J. S. Winkler and H. Winkler, *J. Am. Chem. Soc.*, **88**, 964, 969 (1966).

$$(PhLi)_2 + ArBr \underset{Slow}{\xrightleftharpoons} (PhLiLiAr) + PhBr \left.\begin{array}{c} \\ \\ \end{array}\right\} \quad (6)$$

$$(PhLiLiAr) + ArBr \underset{Slow}{\xrightleftharpoons} (ArLi)_2 + PhBr$$

Studies of the hydrated electron[133] have continued[134] and a monograph on solvated electrons has appeared.[135]

Benzyne and Related Intermediates

Benzynes have been briefly reviewed.[136]

Much work has been stimulated this year by the search for parallels between the pyrolytic decomposition of suitable aromatic molecules and their fragmentation in the mass spectrometer. Full details have been given for the pyrolysis at 500–800° of indanetrione, which eliminates carbon monoxide in successive steps, finally giving benzyne which is detected by its reactions with benzene and chlorobenzene and by its di- and tri-merization. The main pyrolytic decomposition does closely parallel the mass-spectral fragmentation.[137] The pyrolysis of phthalic anhydride and substituted phthalic anhydrides in silica at 450—1100° gave biphenylene and derivatives thereof, presumably via the aryne, in rather low yields.[138] Vapour-phase pyrolysis of phthalic anhydride and its tetrachloro-derivative over a Nichrome coil at ca. 800° gave biphenylene and octachlorobiphenylene; tetrabromobenzyne and 2,3-pyridyne, formed similarly, did not dimerize.[139]

The pyrolysis of a number of aromatic and heterocyclic anhydrides in pyridine at 690° gave carbon monoxide, carbon dioxide, and the aryne; this was detected by its insertion and 1,2- and 1,4-addition to pyridine, followed by aromatization by loss of hydrogen cyanide or acetylene.[140] The products of pyrolysis of phthalic anhydride in each of the dichlorobenzenes at 690° suggests that under these conditions 1,4-addition of benzyne is preferred to 1,2-addition.[141] Benzyne generated similarly in thiophen gives products which also appear to be derived largely from 1,4-addition; some 1,2-addition

[133] See *Organic Reaction Mechanisms*, **1965**, 144.
[134] E. J. Hart, S. Gordon, and E. M. Fielden, *J. Phys. Chem.*, **70**, 150 (1966); M. Anbar, *Chem. Commun.*, **1966**, 416; M. Anbar and D. Meyerstein, *ibid.*, p. 57; S. R. Logan and P. B. Wilmot, *ibid.*, p. 558; W. V. Sherman, *J. Am. Chem. Soc.*, **88**, 1567 (1966).
[135] "Solvated Electron," Advances in Chemistry Series, No. 50 A.C.S., Washington D.C., ed. R. F. Gould.
[136] R. W. Hoffmann, *Naturwissenschaften*, **24**, 655 (1965).
[137] R. F. C. Brown and R. K. Solly, *Australian J. Chem.*, **19**, 1045 (1966).
[138] R. F. C. Brown, D. V. Gardner, J. F. W. McOmie, and R. K. Solly, *Chem. Commun.*, **1966**, 407.
[139] M. P. Cava, M. J. Mitchell, D. C. DeJongh, and R. Y. Van Fossen, *Tetrahedron Letters*, **1966**, 2947.
[140] E. K. Fields and S. Meyerson, *J. Org. Chem.*, **31**, 3307 (1966).
[141] S. Meyerson and E. K. Fields, *Chem. Ind. (London)*, **1966**, 1230.

and some intermolecular transfer of hydrogen (28) from thiophen to benzyne to give 2,3-thiophyne is also proposed.[142]

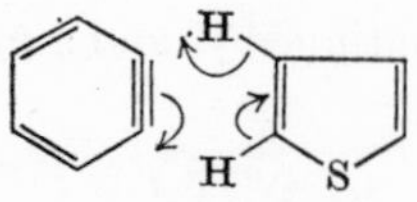

(28)

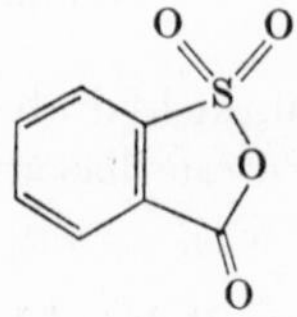

(31)

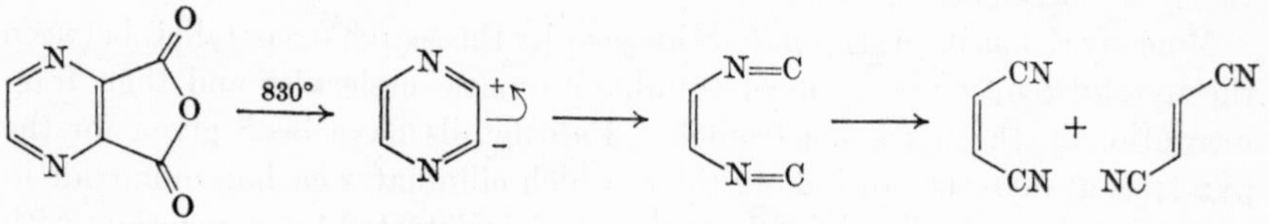

(29)   (30)

Pyrolysis of the anhydride (29) at 830° gave 80% of a 1:1 mixture of maleonitrile and fumaronitrile, possibly by rearrangement of the di-iso-cyanide (30) as shown.[143] *o*-Sulphobenzoic anhydride (31) also gave products derived from benzyne when pyrolysed at 690°.[144] The possibility of intra-molecular *ortho*-dehydrogenation of benzene to benzyne was considered, to explain the formation of a small amount of naphthalene in the pyrolysis of benzene.[145] The pyrolysis of chlorobenzene at 690° to give very small amounts of naphthalene, chloronaphthalenes, and biphenylene was also explained by intramolecular loss of hydrogen chloride.[146] Peaks attributable to arynes were observed in the mass spectra of 2,1,3-benzoselenadiazoles.[147]

The Diels–Alder addition of benzyne to a variety of dienes has been reported. Thus with 1-methyl-2-pyridone, but not with 2-pyridone, the adduct (32) was obtained.[148] Benzyne reacted with styrene to give 9,10-dihydro-9-phenylphenanthrene (33), possibly by Diels–Alder addition followed by phenylation,[149] and with the substituted styrenes isoeugenol methyl ether and isosafrole benzyne yielded the normal 1:1-adducts in each case.[150] Addition to *tert*-butyl pyrrole-1-carboxylate, followed by acid cleavage of the protecting group, gave 7-azabenzonorbornadiene (34),[151] and

[142] E. K. Fields and S. Meyerson, *Chem. Commun.*, 1966, 708.
[143] R. F. C. Brown, W. D. Crow, and R. K. Solly, *Chem. Ind. (London)*, 1966, 343.
[144] S. Meyerson and E. K. Fields, *Chem. Commun.*, 1966, 275.
[145] E. K. Fields and S. Meyerson, *J. Am. Chem. Soc.*, 88, 21 (1966).
[146] E. K. Fields and S. Meyerson, *J. Am. Chem. Soc.*, 88, 3388 (1966).
[147] N. P. Buu-Hoï, P. Jacquignon, and M. Mangane, *Chem. Commun.*, 1965, 624.
[148] L. Bauer, C. L. Bell, and G. E. Wright, *J. Heterocyclic Chem.*, 3, 393 (1966).
[149] W. E. Dilling, *Tetrahedron Letters*, 1966, 939.
[150] S. F. Dyke, A. R. Marshall, and J. P. Watson, *Tetrahedron*, 22, 2515 (1966).
[151] L. A. Carpjno and D. E. Barr, *J. Org. Chem.*, 31, 764 (1966).

addition of benzyne and 4-substituted benzynes to 6,6-dimethylfulvene gave the hydrocarbon (35).[152]

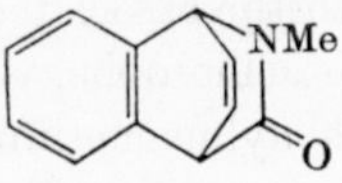

(32)

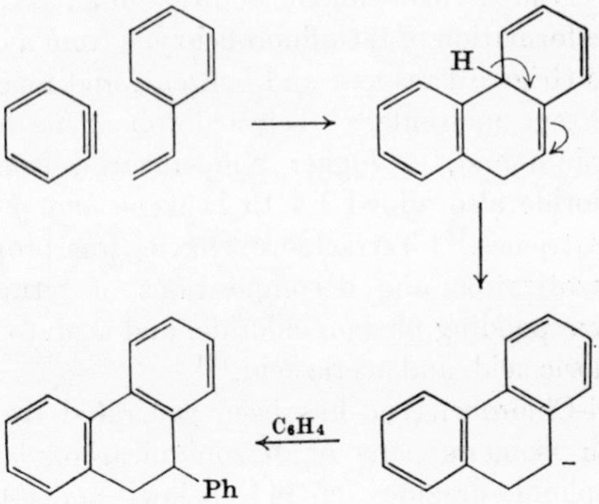

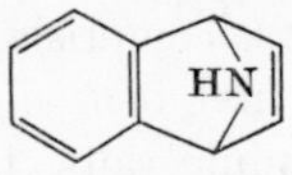

(34)

(33)

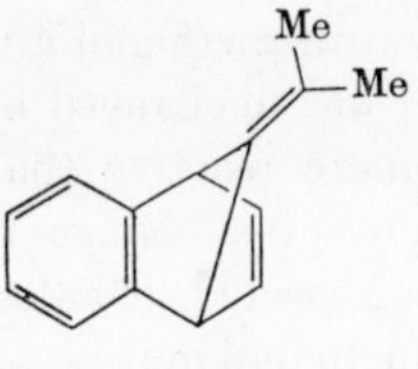

(35) 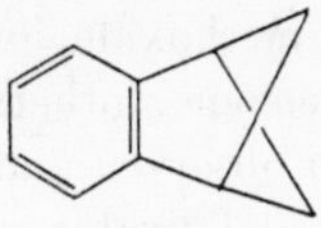   (36) 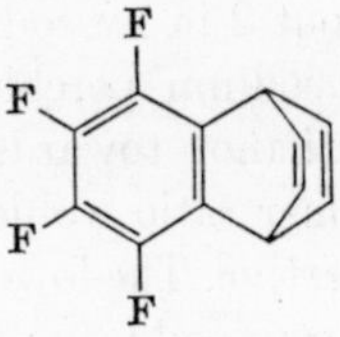   (37)

Further additions of benzyne to pyrroles to give stable 1,4-epimino-1,4-dihydronaphthalenes [cf. (34)] have been reported.[153] Benzyne, generated from *o*-benzenediazoniumcarboxylate, adds 1,2 to acrylonitrile and ethyl acrylate to give the 1-cyano- and the 1-ethoxycarbonyl derivative of benzocyclobutene,[154] to diazoketones to give 3-acylindazoles in good yield,[155] to bicyclobutane (about as readily as to olefins) to give 3-phenylcyclobutene and benzobicyclo[2.1.1]hexene (36),[156] and to cyclohexyl isocyanide.[157]

Tetrafluorobenzyne, from pentafluorophenyl-lithium, rapidly gave good yields of adducts with 1-methylpyrrole, durene, and thiophen; the last reaction, which gave tetrafluoronaphthalene since the bridged intermediate was unstable, is the first Diels–Alder addition to thiophen.[158] The same

152 R. Muneyuki and H. Tanida, *J. Org. Chem.*, **31**, 1988 (1966).
153 E. Wolthuis, W. Cady, R. Roon, and B. Weidenaar, *J. Org. Chem.*, **31**, 2009 (1966).
154 T. Matsuda and T. Mitsuyasu, *Bull. Chem. Soc. Japan*, **39**, 1342 (1966).
155 W. Ried and M. Schön, *Ann. Chem.*, **689**, 141 (1965).
156 M. Pomerantz, *J. Am. Chem. Soc.*, **88**, 5349 (1966).
157 R. Knorr, *Chem. Ber.*, **98**, 4038 (1965).
158 D. D. Callander, P. L. Coe, and J. C. Tatlow, *Chem. Commun.*, **1966**, 143.

benzyne, from pentafluorophenylmagnesium chloride or bromide, added
1,4 to benzene to give (37) in 33% and 44% yield, respectively. These relatively high yields, for the addition of an aryne to benzene, were attributed to
the formation of tetrafluorobenzyne from a charge-transfer complex between
the Grignard reagent and benzene, and reaction thereof with the associated
benzene molecule.[159] Tetrachlorobenzyne formed from pentachlorophenyl-
lithium and, at higher temperatures, from pentachlorophenylmagnesium
chloride also added 1,4 to benzene and mesitylene, to give benzobicyclo-
octatrienes.[160] Tetrachlorobenzyne was proposed as an intermediate in the
diazotization and decompositions of tetrachloranthranilic acid since the
corresponding phenol, chloride, and acetate were formed with water, hydrochloric acid, and acetic acid.[161]

4-Chlorobenzyne has been generated from eight precursors, comprising
four isomeric pairs of diazoniumcarboxylates, *o*-halogenophenyl benzenesulphonhydrazides [cf. (41) below], and *o*-bromophenyldiazonium salts. It
added methanol and methoxide ions to form *m*- and *p*-chloroanisole. The
p/m ratio was substantially the same for a given isomeric pair but differed
with the methoxide concentration, being about 5 in neutral methanol and
about 2 in 2M-sodium methoxide. The ratio in methanol was unchanged by
2M-sodium perchlorate. The methoxide ion must be more reactive than
methanol towards 4-chlorobenzyne, otherwise no appreciable change in
isomer ratio would have been observed and, as is to be expected, it is less
selective. The lower reactivity and greater selectivity of methanol indicates a
stepwise addition via the transition states (38) and (39), and the isomer ratio
follows from the greater stabilization by chlorine of a *meta*- than of a *para*-
substituted phenyl anion. These transition states are the conjugate acids of
those for methoxide ion addition.[162] The ratio of the rates of proton capture by,
and bromide ion loss from, *o*-bromophenyl anions (40) was increased by both
electron-attracting (Cl, CF_3) and electron-releasing (Me, MeO) substituents.
This parallels earlier results for *o*-chlorophenyl anions[163] and is explained in
the same way. The anions were generated from the benzenesulphonhydrazides
(41) and sodium methoxide rather than from *o*-deuterio-compounds, and the
results are thus independent of kinetic isotope effects.[164] The puzzling
preferential formation of 3-pyridyne over 2-pyridyne from 3-chloropyridine
and bases has now been related to the much greater rate of hydrogen exchange

[159] J. P. N. Brewer and H. Heaney, *Tetrahedron Letters*, **1965**, 4709.
[160] H. Heaney and J. M. Jablonski, *Tetrahedron Letters*, **1966**, 4529.
[161] R. Howe, *J. Chem. Soc.*, *C*, **1966**, 478.
[162] J. F. Bunnett, D. A. R. Happer, M. Patsch, C. Pyun, and H. Takayama, *J. Am. Chem. Soc.*,
      88, 5250 (1966); J. F. Bunnett, D. A. R. Happer, and H. Takayama, *Chem. Commun.*,
      1966, 367.
[163] See *Organic Reaction Mechanisms*, **1965**, 148.
[164] J. F. Bunnett and D. A. R. Happer, *J. Org. Chem.*, **31**, 2369 (1966).

at $C_{(4)}$ than at $C_{(2)}$. No exchange at $C_{(2)}$ could be detected with 3-chloropyridine and sodium methoxide in deuteriomethanol or with 2-deuterio-3-chloropyridine and sodamide in ammonia, although it was not clear why $H_{(4)}$ should

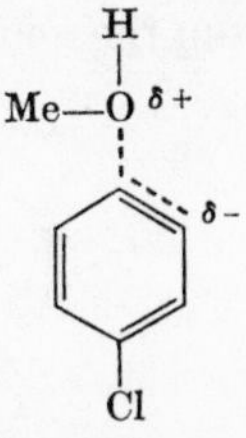

(38) 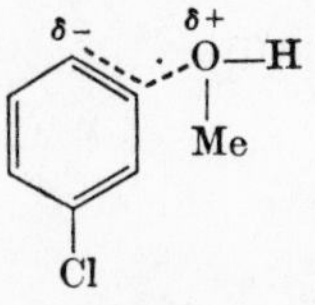   (39)

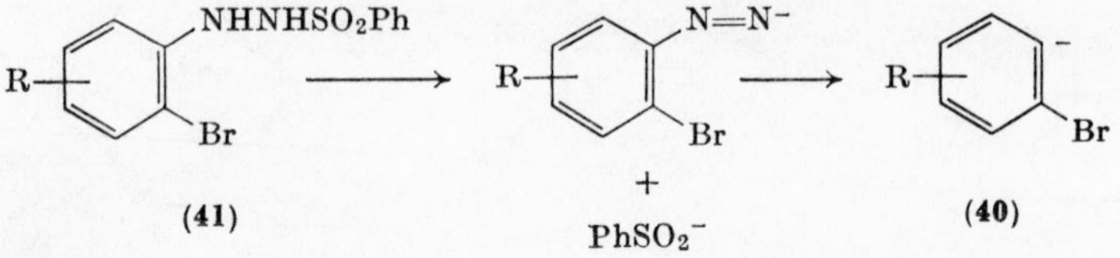

(41)   (40)

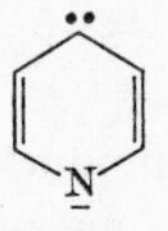

(42) 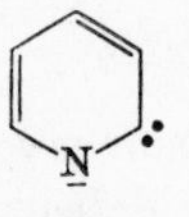   (43)

exchange so much faster than $H_{(2)}$.[165] We suggest that this is related to the stabilization of the pyridyl anions by contributions from the carbenoid structures (42) and (43) with negative charge on nitrogen. Greater stabilization is then to be expected from the *para*- than from the *ortho*-quinonoid structure by analogy with the corresponding tetrahedral intermediates in the nucleophilic reactions of 4- and 2-halogenopyridines. The preference for 3-pyridyne formation, where possible, was also shown by the course of amination reactions of the dibromopyridines with potassamide in ammonia: these complex reactions can be explained by nucleophilic addition to the various substituted pyridynes.[166]

In addition to those already mentioned, a number of other routes to benzyne have been described or proposed. Benzyne was generated by the aprotic diazotization of o-aminophenylboronic acid with isopentyl nitrite in refluxing methylene chloride, by the decomposition shown (44).[167] The 2,5-di-*tert*-butylphenyl cation (45), generated by diazotization of the corresponding

[165] J. A. Zoltewicz and C. L. Smith, *J. Am. Chem. Soc.*, **88**, 4766 (1966).
[166] J. W. Streef and H. J. Den Hertog, *Rec. Trav. Chim.*, **85**, 803 (1966).
[167] L. Verbit, J. S. Levy, H. Rabitz, and W. Kwalwasser, *Tetrahedron Letters*, **1966**, 1053.

aniline, loses a proton to give the di-*tert*-butylbenzyne in substantial amounts in competition with solvolysis since abstraction of the *ortho*-proton is presumably less hindered than attack on carbon.[168] The decomposition of *o*-iodo-*N*-nitrosobenzanilide[169] and acetanilide[170] in benzene gave small amounts of benzyne, possibly by loss of iodine from the *o*-iodophenyl radical.

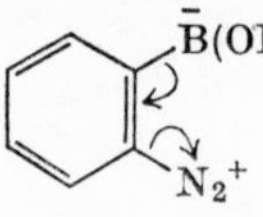

(44) 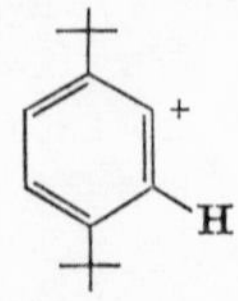   (45) 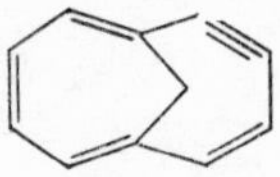   (49)

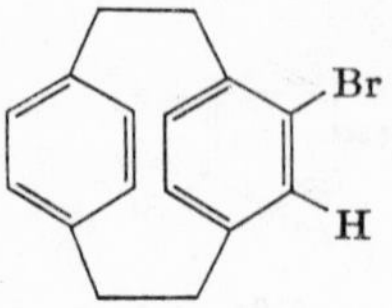

(46) 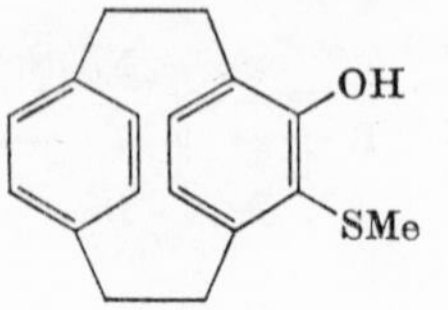   (47) 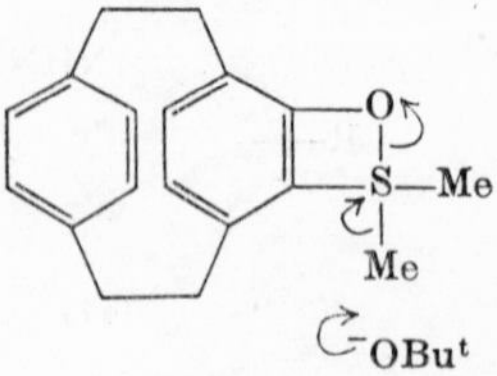   (48)

Chlorobenzene vapour gave a complex mixture of products in a radiofrequency glow discharge, and benzyne was proposed as one of the possible inter-mediates.[171] 4-Methyl- and 4-nitro-benzyne have been prepared from the corresponding pairs of substituted benzothiadiazole dioxides.[172]

Treatment of 4-bromo[2.2]paracyclophane (46) with potassium *tert*-butoxide in dimethyl sulphoxide at 120° gave the 4-*tert*-butyl ether, the 4-phenol, and, unexpectedly, the sulphide (47). An aryne intermediate was proposed, (47) being formed from it by addition of solvent, followed by demethylation as shown (48).[173] 2,3-Dehydro-1,6-methano[10]annulene (49), formed from the 2-bromo-compound with potassium *tert*-butoxide in dioxan, can be trapped with tetracyclone and also reacts with nucleophiles pre-dominantly at $C_{(3)}$, thus providing a route to the 3-substituted derivatives.[174] Contrary to many suggestions, however, the fusion of sodium benzene-sulphonate with potassium hydroxide at 320—350° has been shown by $^{14}C_{(1)}$-labelling and ^{18}O-labelling of the hydroxide to proceed, without

[168] R. W. Franck and K. Yanagi, *Tetrahedron Letters*, **1966**, 2905.
[169] J. A. Kampmeier and A. B. Rubin, *Tetrahedron Letters*, **1966**, 2853.
[170] D. L. Brydon and J. I. G. Cadogan, *Chem. Commun.*, **1966**, 744.
[171] J. K. Stille, and C. E. Rix, *J. Org. Chem.*, **31**, 1591 (1966).
[172] G. Wittig and G. Vargas, *Rev. Fac. Quim. Univ. Nacl. Mayor San Marios (Lima)*, **17**, 49 (1965); *Chem. Abs.*, **65**, 12197 (1966).
[173] D. J. Cram and A. C. Day, *J. Org. Chem.*, **31**, 1227 (1966).
[174] W. A. Böll, *Angew. Chem. Internat. Edn. Engl.*, **5**, 733 (1966).

rearrangement, by a simple S_N2 mechanism and not to involve benzyne;[175] the same applies to the fusion of diphenylsulphone at 300°.[176]

Triphenylenes are formed via benzyne intermediates in a number of reactions of o-dihalogenobenzenes with metals. Concerted trimerization of benzyne is extremely unlikely to be significant and it has now been shown that benzyne does not add to biphenylene to give triphenylene. A stepwise mechanism, involving reaction of benzyne with the o-organometallic species to give a 2,2'-biphenylylene organometallic compound which again reacts with benzyne to give a 2,2''-triphenylylene organometallic compound, which then cyclizes, was proposed and supported by the incorporation into the triphenylene formed of a substituted biphenyl.[177]

Benzyne reacted with dimethylaniline to give N-methyl- and N-ethyl-diphenylamine, probably via the betaine (50) and the ylid (51).[178] The intermediacy of benzyne and cleavage by it of a polyphosphine ring have been

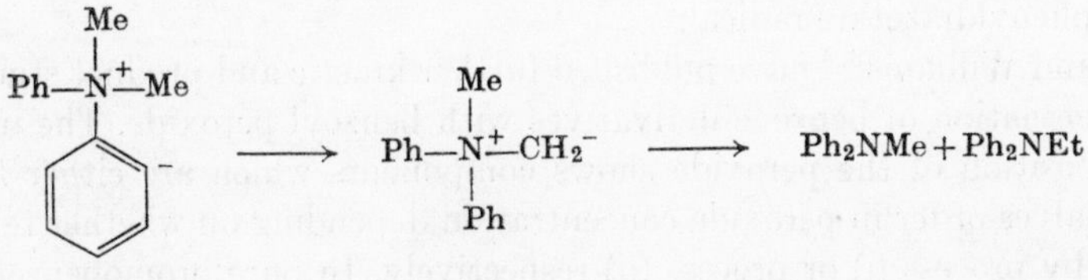

Me
|
Ph—N^{+}—Me $\longrightarrow$ Me
| Ph—N^{+}—CH$_2$$^{-}$ $\longrightarrow$ Ph$_2$NMe + Ph$_2$NEt
                                        |
                                        Ph

(50)   **(51)**

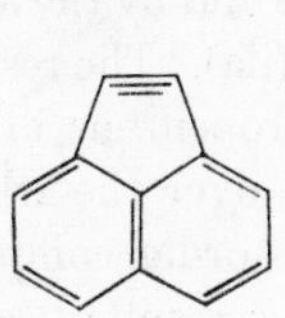

(52)

proposed to explain the formation of some novel cyclophosphines.[179] Several attempts to generate acenaphthyne (**52**) were unsuccessful.[180]

[175] S. Oae, N. Furukawa, M. Kise, and M. Kawanishi, *Bull. Chem. Soc. Japan*, **39**, 1212 (1966)
[176] S. Oae and N. Furukama, *Bull. Chem. Soc. Japan*, **39**, 2260 (1966).
[177] K. D. Bartle, H. Heaney, D. W. Jones, and P. Lees, *Tetrahedron*, **21**, 3289 (1965).
[178] A. R. Lepley, A. G. Giumanini, A. B. Giumanini, and W. A. Khan, *J. Org. Chem.*, **31**, 2051 (1966).
[179] F. G. Mann and M. J. Pragnall, *J. Chem. Soc., C*, **1966**, 916.
[180] K. Rasheed, *Tetrahedron*, **22**, 2957 (1966).

CHAPTER 7

Radical and Electrophilic Aromatic Substitution

Radical Substitution

Rüchardt's mechanisms for the Gomberg reaction and for arylation with nitrosoacetanilide discussed last year[1] were based on the supposed relatively high stability of the phenyldiazotate radical (PhN:N–O·). ESR studies[2] have now confirmed the formation of a relatively stable radical species in the nitrosoacetanilide reaction, and the spectrum obtained has been ascribed to the phenyldiazotate radical.

Gill and Williams[3,4] have published further kinetic and product studies on the phenylation of benzene derivatives with benzoyl peroxide. The induced decomposition of the peroxide shows components which are either first or three-halves order in peroxide concentration depending on whether termination is by process (i) or process (ii) respectively. In pure bromobenzene, the importance of process (i) is revealed both by the kinetics and by the low yields of products of high molecular weight arising from path (iia).[3] The results with nitrobenzene and with benzene containing 1% of nitrobenzene are closely similar. Both show first-order induced decomposition over the whole concentration range studied, together with a three-halves order component at initial peroxide concentrations below 0.06 molar. These results bear on the "nitro-group effect" mentioned last year.[5] Phenylcyclohexadienyl radicals are considered to be intercepted by nitrobenzene, and the resulting adduct is then thought to induce the decomposition of a peroxide molecule. The importance of electron-transfer in the induced decomposition of the peroxide is discussed in terms of the conclusions of Tokumaru and Simamura.[6]

The pyrolysis of benzenediazonium fluoroborate in aromatic solvents gives, in addition to fluorobenzene, low yields of phenylated products. With nitrobenzene as solvent, the predominant isomer (ca. 80%) was 3-nitrobiphenyl, consistent with attack, not by Ph·, but Ph⁺.[7]

[1] See *Organic Reaction Mechanisms*, **1965**, 154.
[2] G. Binsch and C. Rüchardt, *J. Am. Chem. Soc.*, **88**, 173 (1966).
[3] G. B. Gill and G. H. Williams, *J. Chem. Soc.*, **1965**, 7127.
[4] G. B. Gill and G. H. Williams, *J. Chem. Soc.*, *B*, **1966**, 880.
[5] See *Organic Reaction Mechanisms*, **1965**, 156.
[6] K. Tokumaru and O. Simamura, *Bull. Chem. Soc. Japan*, **36**, 333 (1963).
[7] R. A. Abramovitch and J. G. Saha, *Can. J. Chem.*, **43**, 3269 (1965).

Homolytic arylation by aryl radicals obtained in the photolysis of aryl bromides[8] and in the lead tetra-acetate oxidation of 1,3-diaryltriazens[9] has been noted. Phenylation by phenyl radicals from phenyldi-imide, generated

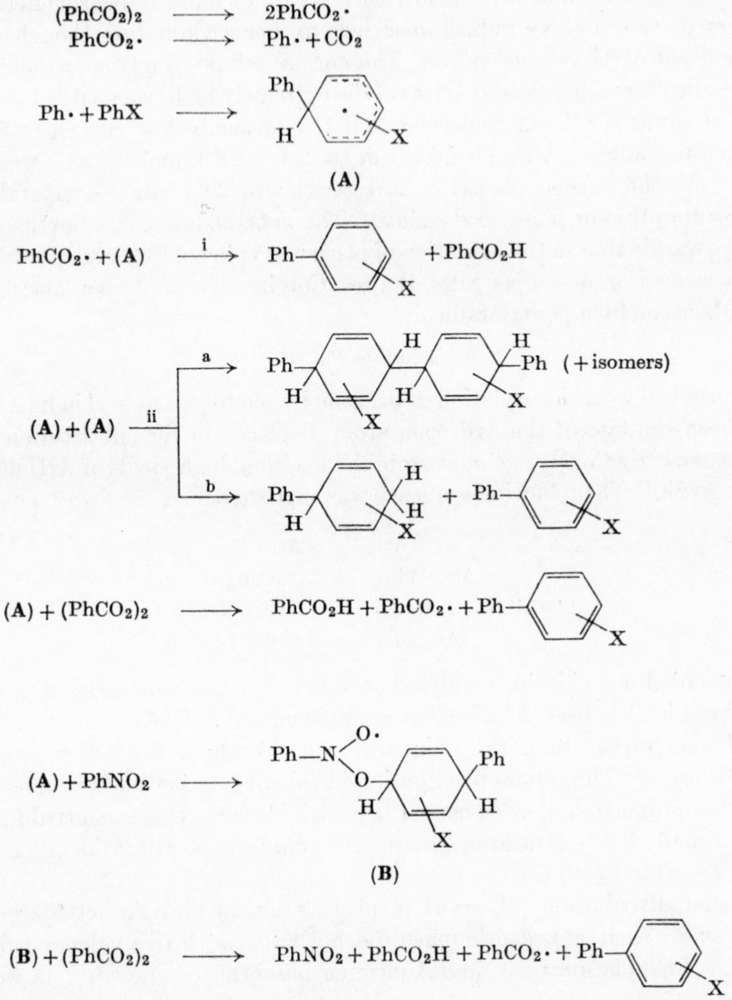

$$(PhCO_2)_2 \longrightarrow 2PhCO_2\cdot$$
$$PhCO_2\cdot \longrightarrow Ph\cdot + CO_2$$

$$Ph\cdot + PhX \longrightarrow \quad \text{(A)}$$

(A)

$$PhCO_2\cdot + \textbf{(A)} \xrightarrow{\;i\;} Ph\text{—}\bigcirc\text{—}X + PhCO_2H$$

$$\textbf{(A)} + \textbf{(A)} \xrightarrow{\;ii\;}$$

a → Ph—(...)—(...)—Ph (+ isomers)

b → Ph—(...) + Ph—(...)—X

$$\textbf{(A)} + (PhCO_2)_2 \longrightarrow PhCO_2H + PhCO_2\cdot + Ph\text{—}\bigcirc\text{—}X$$

$$\textbf{(A)} + PhNO_2 \longrightarrow$$

(B)

$$\textbf{(B)} + (PhCO_2)_2 \longrightarrow PhNO_2 + PhCO_2H + PhCO_2\cdot + Ph\text{—}\bigcirc\text{—}X$$

by ferric ion-catalysed methanolysis of *N*-phenyl-*N*′-benzoyldi-imide has also been observed.[10]

When aryl radicals are formed in an aromatic solvent in the presence of

[8] T. Matsuura and K. Omura, *Bull. Chem. Soc. Japan*, **39**, 944 (1966); N. Kharasch, R. K. Sharma, and H. B. Lewis, *Chem. Commun.*, **1966**, 418.

[9] C. M. Camaggi, M. Tiecco, and A. Tundo, *Boll. Sci. Fac. Chim. Ind. Bologna*, **24**, 49 (1966).

[10] J. Nicholson and S. G. Cohen, *J. Am. Chem. Soc.*, **88**, 2247 (1966).

oxygen, phenol formation competes with substitution. The interaction of aryl radicals with oxygen has been reported to be an abnormally slow process;[11] however, this has now been refuted by Starnes,[12] who has studied the cobalt-catalysed oxidation of aroic acids. In the case of o-phenylbenzoic acid, the intermediate aroyloxy-radical cyclized to benzocoumarin, though more generally decarboxylation occurs. The normal failure of oxygen to intercept aryl radicals was discussed in terms of the extremely high reactivity of the aryl radical towards solvent molecules and the normally low concentration of oxygen in solution. A rate constant of ca. 2.4×10^7 l. mole^{-1} sec^{-1} was estimated for the oxygen–phenyl radical reaction at 25°; this is comparable to figures for alkyl or polystyryl radicals. The unorthodox suggestion has been put forward[13] that in the oxidation of benzene to phenol by oxygen, catalysed by aqueous iron or copper salts, the reaction involves hydrogen abstraction from benzene by a peroxy-radical:

$$PhOO\cdot + PhH \rightarrow PhOOH + Ph\cdot$$

A problem with the arylation of benzene by photolysis of aryl iodides (ArI) has been the fate of the hydrogen atom displaced in the substitution step. If oxygen is rigorously excluded from the reaction, high yields of ArH accompany ArPh.[14] The following sequence was suggested:

$$ArI \xrightarrow{h\nu} Ar\cdot + I\cdot$$
$$Ar\cdot + PhH \longrightarrow [ArC_6H_6]\cdot$$
$$[ArC_6H_6]\cdot + I\cdot \ (\text{or } I_2) \longrightarrow ArPh + HI \ (\text{or } I\cdot)$$
$$Ar\cdot + HI \longrightarrow ArH + I\cdot$$

The cobaltous chloride-catalysed reaction of a Grignard reagent with an aryl bromide has been employed as a source of aryl radicals (principally from the halide rather than the Grignard reagent) which will effect aromatic substitution.[15] The isomer distribution in substituted benzenes is unusual in that the proportion of *ortho*-isomer is invariably low. This was attributed to an unusually bulky attacking species, as would be expected if the aryl radical were associated with the metal.

Isomer distributions observed in phenylation of bicyclic heteroaromatic compounds such as benzothiophen did not agree with free-valency calculations.[16] Phenylation of 3- and 4-picoline has been examined,[17] as well as

[11] G. F. Russell and R. F. Bridger, *J. Am. Chem. Soc.*, **85**, 3765 (1963); K. Tokumaru, K. Horie, and O. Simamura, *Tetrahedron*, **21**, 867, (1965).
[12] W. H. Starnes, *J. Org. Chem.*, **31**, 1436 (1966).
[13] H. Hotta, N. Suzuki, and T. Abe, *Bull. Chem. Soc., Japan*, **39**, 417 (1966).
[14] N. Kharasch and R. K. Sharma, *Chem. Commun.*, **1966**, 106. Cf., however, addendum on p. 208.
[15] D. I. Davies, D. H. Hey, and M. Tiecco, *J. Chem. Soc.*, **1965**, 7062.
[16] H. J. M. Dou and B. M. Lynch, *Compt. Rend., Ser. C*, **262**, 1537 (1966).
[17] R. A. Abramovitch and M. Saha, *Can. J. Chem.*, **44**, 1765 (1966).

methylation of thiazole by lead tetra-acetate,[18] and a further report on radical substitution in the ferricinium ion has appeared.[19]

Photolysis of iodothiophens or iodopyridines generates aryl radicals which show normal behaviour in aromatic substitution.[20] The photolysis of tri-methylsilane in hexafluorobenzene gives (1), but trichlorosilane gives (2), possibly by the 1,2-fluorine shift mechanism shown.[21] Neither reaction gives hydrogen fluoride.

$$C_6F_5SiMe_3 \qquad C_6F_6 \xrightarrow{\cdot SiCl_3} \qquad \xrightarrow{-Cl\cdot}$$

(1)   (2)

The decomposition of *tert*-butyl peroxide in cyclohexane–benzene results in cyclohexylation of the benzene.[22] In homolytic substitution reactions the cyclohexyl radical is more selective than phenyl; for instance, benzonitrile is cyclohexylated 27 times faster than is benzene. Alkylations by methyl, ethyl, and *n*-butyl radicals from photolysis of the corresponding alkylmercuric iodide have also been studied.[23]

Aminations by ferrous salt-catalysed reactions of chloramines and related compounds have received attention.[24—26] The aminating species shows electrophilic behaviour, but this is much more pronounced with hydroxyl-amine-*O*-sulphonic acid than with hydroxylamine hydrochloride as reagent; this is consistent with the hypothesis that the first reaction involves $NH_3\cdot^+$, the second $NH_2\cdot$.[25] The reaction has also been applied as a cyclization procedure, as shown.[26] A competing fragmentation is analogous to that mentioned for the Hoffman–Loeffler reaction (p. 395).

Homolytic hydroxylation, as well as hydrogen-atom addition, shows a modest Hammett correlation with the substituent constant (σ) in a series of

[18] H. J. M. Dou, *Bull. Soc. Chim. France*, **1966**, 1678.
[19] A. L. J. Beckwith and R. J. Leydon, *Australian J. Chem.*, **19**, 1853 (1966).
[20] L. Benati and M. Tiecco, *Boll. Sci. Fac. Chim. Ind. Bologna*, **24**, 45 (1966).
[21] J. M. Birchall, W. M. Daniewski, R. N. Haszeldine, and L. S. Holden, *J. Chem. Soc.*, **1965**, 6702.
[22] J. R. Shelton and C. W. Uzelmeier, *J. Am. Chem. Soc.*, **88**, 5222 (1966).
[23] G. E. Corbett and G. H. Williams, *J. Chem. Soc., B*, **1966**, 877.
[24] H. Bock and K.-L. Kompa, *Chem. Ber.*, **99**, 1357, 1961 (1966); F. Minisci, R. Bernardi, L. Grippa, and V. Trabucchi, *Chim. Ind. (Milan)*, **48**, 264 (1966); F. Minisci, R. Galli, and R. Bernardi, *Tetrahedron Letters*, **1966**, 699.
[25] F. Minisci, R. Galli, and M. Cecere, *Tetrahedron Letters*, **1965**, 4663.
[26] F. Minisci and R. Galli, *Tetrahedron Letters*, **1966**, 2531.

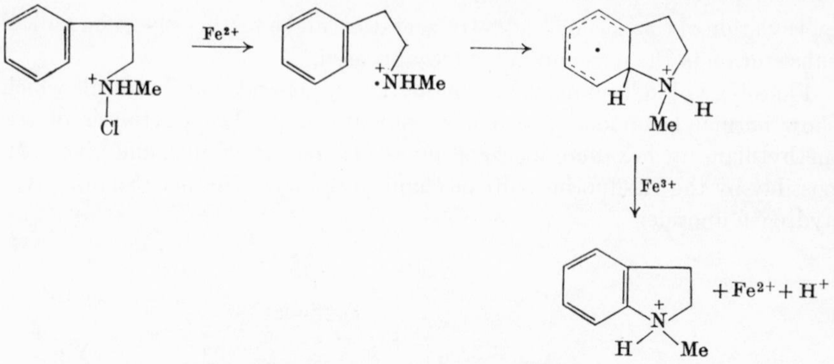

substituted benzenes.[27] The relationship between certain enzymic hydroxylations and those effected by hydrogen peroxide and ferric ions in the presence of catechol has been briefly discussed.[28] Oxidation of phenol to phenoxyradical by $OH\cdot$ has been found to involve hydroxylation followed by elimina-

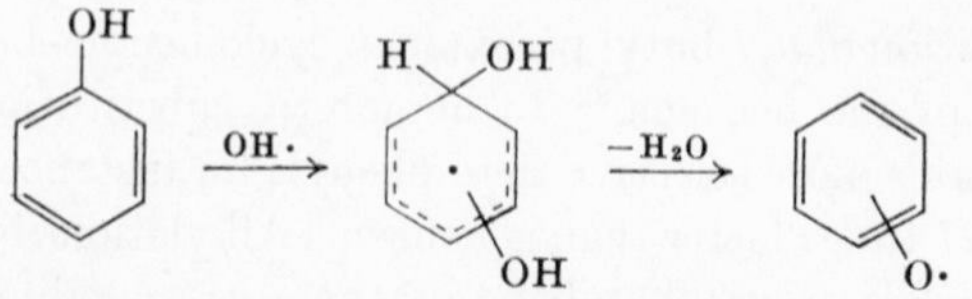

tion of water,[29] and the Baudisch reaction—the conversion of benzene to *o*-nitrosophenol by hydrogen peroxide, hydroxylamine hydrochloride, and cupric ion—also involves an initial hydroxylation.[30]

It was mentioned last year[31] that anodic acetoxylation of naphthalene was not a radical substitution. New polarographic results[32] suggest a two-electron oxidation of the hydrocarbon followed by combination with acetate and

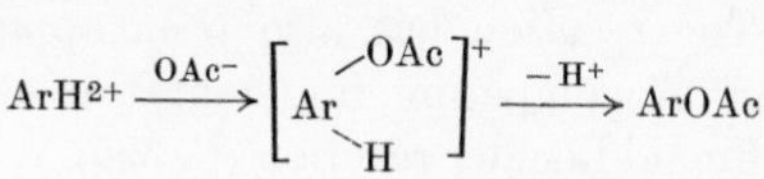

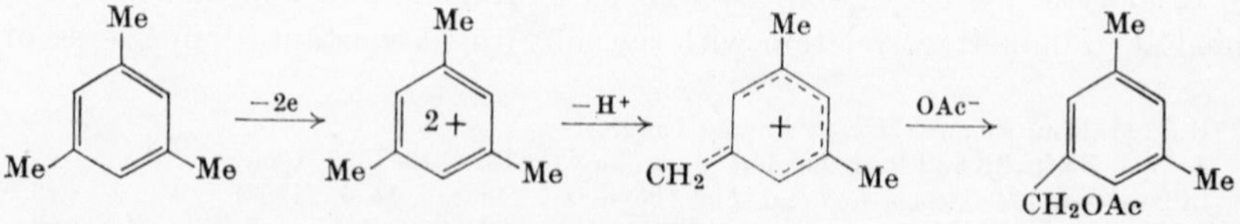

$$ArH^{2+} \xrightarrow{OAc^-} \left[Ar \begin{matrix} OAc \\ H \end{matrix} \right]^+ \xrightarrow{-H^+} ArOAc$$

[27] M. Anbar, D. Meyerstein, and P. Neta, *J. Phys. Chem.*, **70**, 2660 (1966); *Nature*, **209**, 1348 (1966).
[28] G. A. Hamilton, J. P. Friedman, and P. M. Campbell, *J. Am. Chem. Soc.*, **88**, 5266 (1966); G. A. Hamilton, J. W. Hanifin, and J. P. Friedman, *ibid.*, p. 5269.
[29] G. E. Adams, B. D. Michael, and E. J. Land, *Nature*, **211**, 293 (1966).
[30] K. Maruyama, I. Tanimoto, and R. Goto, *Tetrahedron Letters*, **1966**, 5889.
[31] See *Organic Reaction Mechanisms*, **1965**, 212.
[32] L. Eberson and K. Nyberg, *J. Am. Chem. Soc.*, **88**, 1686 (1966).

proton loss. Side-chain acetoxylation can also occur. Anodic benzoyloxylation of anisole has also been found.[33] This gives only *ortho–para*-substitution, and it was suggested that it involves benzoyloxy-radicals stabilized at the electrode. At a higher temperature, benzoyl peroxide also gives *ortho–para*-benzoyloxylation (reflecting the electrophilic character of the benzoyloxy-radical), together with much phenylation, in its reaction with anisole. The failure to observe phenylation in the electrolysis could be due to much reduced decarboxylation of the radical at the lower temperature. The ionization potentials of anisole and benzoate anion would also be pertinent to this study. Acetoxylation of anisole was also observed, and two other cases of non-decarboxylating acetoxy-radicals have been claimed.[34]

Electrophilic Substitution

Reports of papers given at a 1964 symposium in honour of Sir Christopher Ingold have appeared,[35] as has a monograph dedicated to Sir Christopher.[36] The former include reviews of the use of isotope effects in studying electrophilic substitution,[35a] substituent effects of positive poles in nitration,[35b] and methods of changing orientation in substitution;[35c] the monograph contains an instructive essay on nitration mechanisms in organic solvents.[37] Other pertinent reviews[38] include a general one on secondary hydrogen isotope effects,[38a] one on positive halogenating agents,[38b] and one on kinetics of nitration on a commercial scale.[38c]

In last year's report, mention was made[39] of an objection to the experimental procedure on which rested Olah's arguments for π-complex formation as the rate-controlling step for nitronium fluoroborate nitrations in sulpholan. This objection, by Tolgyesi, appears itself to have been based on unsound experimental technique, and indeed Olah and Overchuk[40] were not only unable to reproduce Tolgyesi's findings, but were able to amass considerable evidence suggesting that in his critical dilute-solution experiments Tolgyesi's solvents contained sufficient impurity (either water or dihydrosulpholane or both) to destroy completely the nitronium fluoroborate as the effective

33 K. Koyama, K. Yoshida, and S. Tsutsumi, *Bull. Chem. Soc., Japan*, **39**, 516 (1966).
34 T. W. Martin, J. M. Burk, and A. Henshall, *J. Am. Chem. Soc.*, **88**, 1097 (1966); S. Murai and S. Tsutsumi, *Bull. Chem. Soc. Japan*, **39**, 198 (1966).
35 *J. Tennessee Acad. Sci.*, **40** (1965); (a) G. A. Olah, p. 77; (b) J. H. Ridd, p. 92; (c) D. E. Pearson, p. 97.
36 "Studies on Chemical Structure and Reactivity", J. H. Ridd, ed., Methuen, London, 1966, p. 133.
37 J. H. Ridd in ref. 36, p. 133.
38 (a) P. Laszlo and Z. Welvart, *Bull. Soc. Chim. France*, **1966**, 2412; (b) E. Berliner, *J. Chem. Educ.*, **43**, 124 (1966); (c) C. Hanson, J. G. Marsland, and G. Wilson, *Chem. Ind.* (*London*), **1966**, 675.
39 See *Organic Reaction Mechanisms*, **1965**, 160.
40 G. A. Olah and N. A. Overchuk, *Can. J. Chem.*, **43**, 3279 (1965).

nitrating agent. Tolgyesi suggested that the low substrate selectivity observed by Olah in these nitrations, and used by him as evidence for rate-controlling π-complex formation was due to inefficient mixing of reactants for a process whose rate approaches that of diffusion control. One factor supporting this, which perhaps was not adequately answered by Olah,[40] was the extensive dinitration that was observed—more even than would have been expected for a quite indiscriminate reagent. If this were due to successive attack at the point of mixing with the reagent solution, then the effect might be greatly enhanced if the second nitration were not repressed by the nitro-group already present. In experiments reported by Ridd[37] this was tested by nitration of bibenzyl under comparable conditions. The result was that the major nitration product was a mixture of dinitrobibenzyls, apparently emphasizing the occurrence of reaction at the point of mixing. On the other hand, similar nitration of biphenyl gives very little dinitro-derivative.[41] Clearly much remains to be understood about these reactions.

The nitration of biphenyl mentioned above constituted part of a study of the variations in *ortho–para*-ratio observed on nitration of this compound. Relatively high values were obtained in cases (including $NO_2^+BF_4^-$) where a π-complex (1) could be formed from a reagent NO_2X, by nucleophilic displacement of X^-. Subsequent σ-complex formation is then postulated to involve electrophilic attack by the bonded NO_2-group on to the electrons of the adjacent ring, as shown.[41, 42]

(1)

Rate-determining π-complex formation has also been invoked to explain the low substrate selectivity in Friedel–Crafts alkylations in nitromethane. Olah and Overchuk[43] have now measured the rates of such reactions (catalysed by $AlCl_3$ or $SnCl_4$) under identical conditions for both toluene and benzene and have found that the rate ratios compare very favourably with those obtained by product analysis in competition experiments (see Table 1). It is perhaps pertinent to question what is the rate-controlling step in such very fast processes of low substrate selectivity; could it, for example, be π-complexing between the aromatic compound and the Lewis acid? Such

[41] R. Taylor, *Tetrahedron Letters*, **1966**, 6093.
[42] R. Taylor, *J. Chem. Soc.*, B, **1966**, 727.
[43] G. A. Olah and N. A. Overchuk, *J. Am. Chem. Soc.*, **87**, 5786 (1965).

complexing has recently been measured for hydrogen halides[44] and aluminium bromide,[45] although it would not be expected to be important in nitromethane. Evidence against this suggestion comes from observation[46,47] of similar rate ratios (Table 1) in competition experiments in which the alkyl cation is generated by deamination of the appropriate amine in nitromethane. Although this could be effected by alkyl nitrite, nitrosonium hexafluorophosphate ($NO^+PF_6^-$) was the reagent of choice.[46] *n*-Alkyl groups appear to suffer very little isomerization in such alkylations.[47]

Table 1. Relative rates of alkylation of toluene and benzene in nitromethane.

Alkyl group	$RCl + AlCl_3$		$RNH_2 + NO^+PF_6^-$
	Separate rate measurement	Competition	Competition
Et			1.52
iso-Propyl	1.65	2.03	2.52
tert-Butyl	13.1	16.6	
PhCH$_2$	3.45	3.20	3.52

Nakane and Natsubori[48] have now examined the decomposition of the oriented π-complex[49] formed from toluene, *tert*-butyl chloride, and boron trifluoride at low temperature. At $-78°$ boron trifluoride is lost with regeneration of toluene, together with a little *tert*-butyltoluene; but, if the decomposition occurs in the presence of an excess of *tert*-BuCl–BF$_3$ complex, more butylation occurs, and this is exclusively at the *para*-position. A high substrate selectivity was also observed in competition experiments, and the results were discussed in terms of σ-complex formation as the rate-determining process, the attacking electrophile being the weakly electrophilic *tert*-BuCl–BCl$_3$ complex.

Rates of aroylation of toluene catalysed by AlCl$_3$ in chlorobenzene have been measured for a series of aroyl chlorides bearing substituents stable to the reaction conditions. These were shown to exhibit isokinetic behaviour, and to give a fairly good σ^+ correlation, consistently with ArCO$^+$ being the reactive species.[50] Variation in reactivities of compounds RCOCl in acylation, as a function of R, have been measured for several widely differing acyl groups,

44 H. C. Brown and J. J. Melchiore, *J. Am. Chem. Soc.*, **87**, 5269 (1965).
45 S. U. Choi, W. C. Firth, and H. C. Brown, *J. Am. Chem. Soc.*, **88**, 4128 (1966); S. U. Choi and H. C. Brown, *ibid.*, p. 903.
46 G. A. Olah, N. A. Overchuk, and J. G. Lapierre, *J. Am. Chem. Soc.*, **87**, 578£ (1965).
47 A. T. Jurewicz, J. H. Bayless, and L. Friedman, *J. Am. Chem. Soc.*, **87**, 5788 (1965).
48 R. Nakane and A. Natsubori, *J. Am. Chem. Soc.*, **88**, 3011 (1966).
49 See *Organic Reaction Mechanisms*, **1965**, 161.
50 P. J. Slootmaekers, A. Rasschaert, and W. Janssens, *Bull. Soc. Chim. Belg.*, **75**, 199 (1966).

and a range of mechanistic behaviour with varying extent of ionization $(RCOCl–AlCl_3 \rightarrow RCO^+AlCl_4^-)$ hinted at.[51] The pressure-dependence of the rate of benzoylation has been studied.[52] No variation in isomer distribution was found. Kinetics of intermolecular alkyl migrations in Friedel–Crafts systems have been reported,[53] and the rearrangements occurring in the alkylation of benzene with neophyl chloride (**2a**) discussed.[54]

$$Me_2CPhCH_2Cl \xrightarrow{\text{PhH/AlCl}_3} Me_2CPhCH_2Ph + Me_2CHCHPh_2 + MeCHPhCHPhMe$$

  (**2a**)

The interesting intramolecular catalysis of acylation shown below is observed as a result of treating hydroborated acenaphthylene with acetic

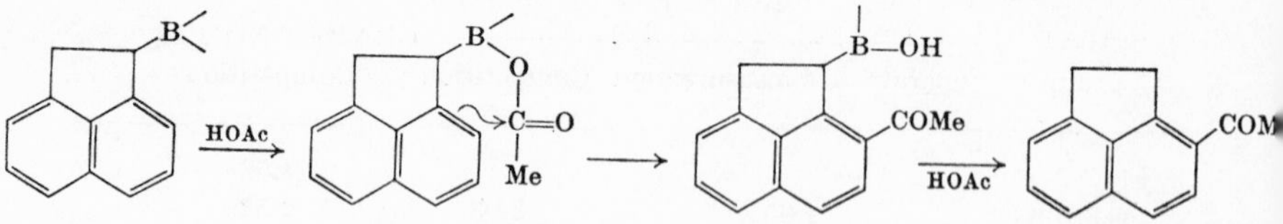

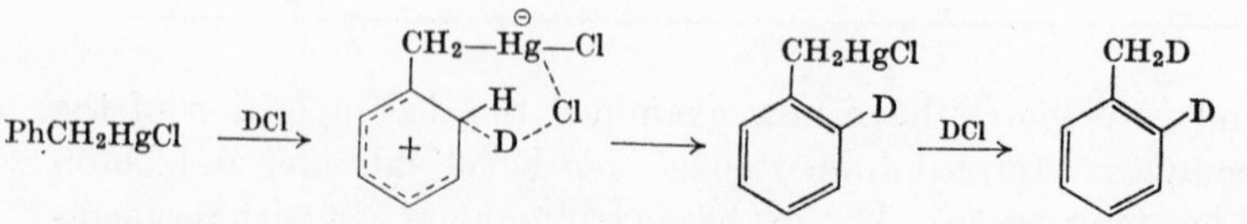

acid.[55] A related intramolecular catalysis of hydrogen exchange is observed during the demetallation of benzylmercuric chloride.[56] Isomerization of

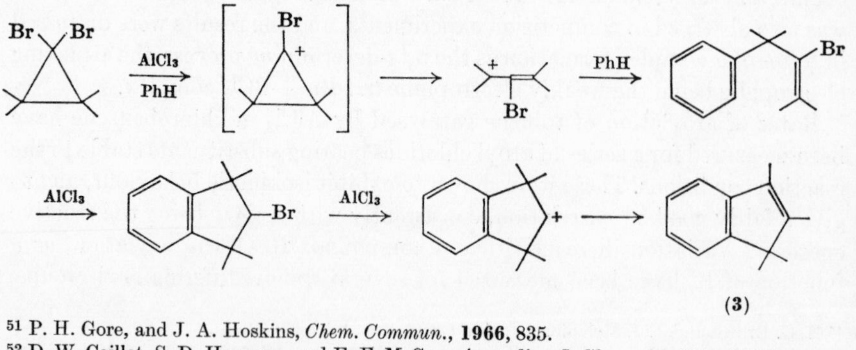

(3)

[51] P. H. Gore, and J. A. Hoskins, *Chem. Commun.*, **1966**, 835.
[52] D. W. Coillet, S. D. Hamann, and E. F. McCoy, *Australian J. Chem.*, **18**, 1911 (1965).
[53] M. M. Oreshin and N. N. Lebedev, *Tr. Mosk. Khim.-Tekhnol. Inst.*, No. 48, 79 (1965); *Chem. Abs.*, **65**, 15180 (1966).
[54] A. A. Khalaf and R. M. Roberts, *J. Org. Chem.*, **31**, 926 (1966).
[55] H. W. Whitlock, C-Y. Hsu, and K. Sundaresan, *Tetrahedron Letters*, **1965**, 4821.
[56] Y. G. Bundel, N. D. Antonova, and O. A. Reutov, *Dokl. Akad. Nauk SSSR*, **166**, 1103 (1966); *Chem. Abs.*, **64**, 15684 (1966).

1,3,5- to 1,2,4-tri-isopropylbenzene is considered to precede alkylation with propene to give 1,2,4,5-tetraisopropylbenzene.[57] Alkylation of benzene with 1,1-dibromotetramethylcyclopropane gives the tetramethylindene (3), presumably by the sequence illustrated.[58]

The question of alkylation and acylation of benzene by ethyl and vinyl acetate has been discussed.[59] A plausible initial reaction is:

$$MeCO_2R + AlCl_3 \rightarrow MeCOR \xrightarrow{AlCl_3} MeCOAlCl_2 + RCl$$

$$\begin{array}{ccc} \| & & \| \\ O^+ & & {}^+O \\ | & & | \\ {}^-AlCl_3 & & {}^-AlCl_3 \end{array} \qquad \begin{array}{c} (R=Et \ or \\ vinyl) \end{array}$$

Rates of reaction of trityl perchlorate with phenol and aryl ethers in nitromethane have been measured, the rates falling in the order PhOMe > PhOH > PhOEt > PhOPr^i.[60] The position of phenol in this series was attributed to electron-release from the hydrogen resulting from hydrogen-bonding to solvent. This effect becomes dominant in the catechol monoalkyl ethers, where the hydrogen-bonding is intramolecular.[61]

Several new reports of the effect of solvent, notably nitrobenzene, on isomer distribution in Friedel–Crafts acylations have been published.[62]

Acetylation[63] and tritylation[64] of ferrocene have received attention. Electron-transfer in the reaction of trityl fluoroborate with ferrocene is shown by spectral identification of the ferricinium ion.[64] Trityl radicals may then attack the ferricinium ion.

$$Ph_3C^+ + Fc \rightleftarrows Fc^+ + Ph_3C\cdot$$

No evidence for electron-transfer could be adduced for the intramolecular acylation of ferrocene which occurs when compounds (4) and (5) are treated with trifluoroacetic anhydride in methylene chloride.[65] A small rate difference (ca. 5) favouring the *exo*-isomer (5) seemed inconsistent with initial participation of the iron.

In cycloalkylation processes, compounds of general formula $Ar(C)_nCl$ cyclize preferentially to give six-membered rather than five- or seven-membered rings when aluminium chloride is used as catalyst. For example,

[57] I. M. Kolesnikov, E. P. Babin, and V. P. Marshtupa, *Zh. Fiz. Khim.*, **39**, 3063 (1965); *Chem. Abs.*, **64**, 9535 (1966).

[58] L. Skattebøl and B. Boulette, *J. Org. Chem.*, **31**, 81 (1966).

[59] J. M. Pepper and B. P. Robinson, *Can. J. Chem.*, **44**, 1809 (1966).

[60] G. Chuchani, H. Diaz, and J. Zabicky, *J. Org. Chem.*, **31**, 1573 (1966).

[61] N. Barroeta, G. Chuchani, and J. Zabicky, *J. Org. Chem.*, **31**, 2330 (1966).

[62] R. B. Girdler, P. H. Gore, and J. A. Hoskins, *J. Chem. Soc.*, *C*, **1966**, 181, 518; G. E. Lewis, *J. Org. Chem.*, **31**, 749 (1966).

[63] S. P. Gubin, I. P. Shepilov, and A. N. Nesmeyanov, *Izv. Akad. Nauk SSSR, Ser. Khim*, **1966**, 384; *Chem. Abs.*, **64**, 17373 (1966).

[64] P. L. Pauson, M. A. Sandhu, and W. E. Watts, *J. Chem. Soc.*, *C*, **1966**, 251.

[65] M. Rosenblum and F. W. Abbate, *J. Am. Chem. Soc.*, **88**, 4178, 1966.

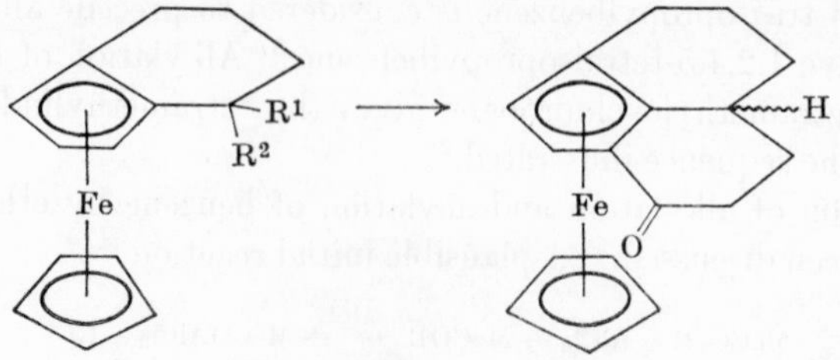

(4) $R^1 = H$
     $R^2 = CH_2CH_2CO_2H$
(5) $R^1 = CH_2CH_2CO_2H$
     $R^2 = H$

five-membered rings are formed only from tertiary carbonium ions [e.g. (6)], whereas six-membered ones may be obtained from primary carbonium ions (albeit accompanied by rearrangement products).[66] An example of this appears to be the conversion of (7) into (8) by $AlCl_3/HCl$. Polyphosphoric acid gives (9), thought to be the kinetically controlled product.[67]

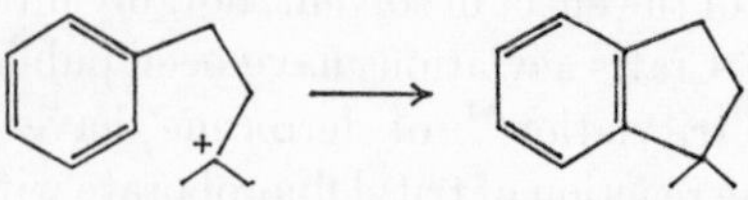

(6)

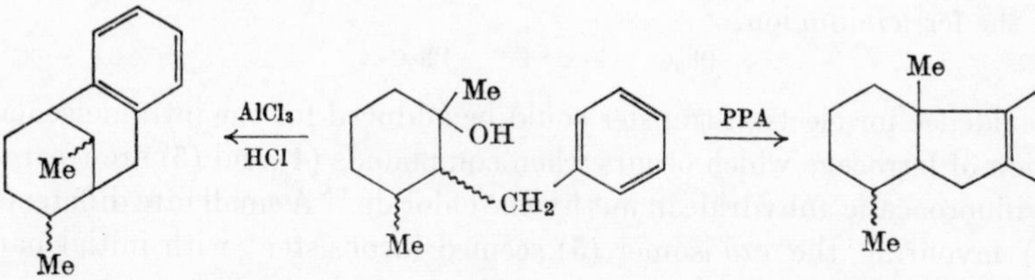

(8)   (7)   (9)

The aluminium chloride-catalysed oxygenation of aromatic compounds with peresters continues to receive attention; initial formation of mixed

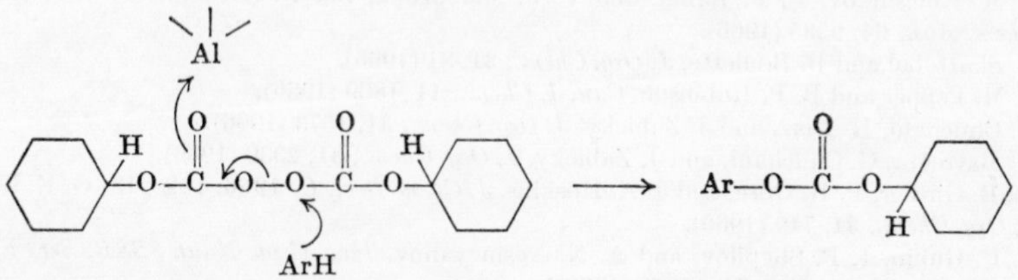

[66] A. A. Khalaf and R. M. Roberts, J. Org. Chem., 31, 89 (1966).
[67] V. R. Ghatak and J. Chakravarty, Tetrahedron Letters, 1966, 2449.

carbonates is involved in the case of secondary alkyl peroxydicarbonates,[68,69] and initial *tert*-butoxylation is considered responsible in the reaction with percarbonate (**10**).[70] Substitution patterns are typically electrophilic in these cases.

$$\text{Bu}^t\text{---OOC---OCH} \quad \begin{array}{c} \overset{\displaystyle O}{\overset{\|}{\ }} \quad \overset{\displaystyle Me}{\overset{|}{\ }} \\ | \\ Me \end{array}$$

(**10**)

Rather different isomer ratios, though again characteristically electrophilic, are obtained in oxygenations catalysed by iron[71] and copper salts.[72] In these instances, acyloxy-radical intermediates are, it is tentatively suggested, oxidized to acyloxy-cations, which then give rise to substitution products. In our opinion, in view of the known electrophilic behaviour of a

$$R\overset{\overset{\displaystyle O}{\|}}{-}C-O\cdot \xrightarrow{Cu^{2+}} R\overset{\overset{\displaystyle O}{\|}}{-}C-O^+ + Cu^+$$

range of oxygen-centred radicals, oxidation could equally probably occur after the attack on the aromatic substrate.

$$\overset{\overset{\displaystyle O}{\|}}{RCO}\cdot + ArH \rightarrow \left[\overset{\overset{\displaystyle O}{\|}}{RCO}\underset{\underset{\displaystyle H}{|}}{-}Ar\right]^{\cdot} \xrightarrow{Cu^{2+}} \left[\overset{\overset{\displaystyle O}{\|}}{RCOAr}\underset{\underset{\displaystyle H}{|}}{\ }\right]^{+} \xrightarrow{-H^+} RCO_2Ar$$

A related, though uncatalysed, substitution for which a polar mechanism is tentatively advanced, based solely on isomer distributions, is the sulphonyloxylation effected by decomposing nitrobenzenesulphonyl peroxides.[73]

$$(m\text{-}O_2NC_6H_4SO_2O)_2 \xrightarrow[heat]{ArH} m\text{-}O_2NC_6H_4SO_3H + m\text{-}O_2NC_6H_4SO_3Ar$$

In addition to their work with catalysed perester reactions, Kovacic's group have extended their study of σ-substitution.[74] The results substantiate the mechanisms outlined last year.[75] The reaction has also been extended to

[68] G. A. Razuvaev, N. A. Kartashova, and L. S. Boguslavskaya, *Zh. Organ. Khim.*, **1**, 1927 (1965); *Chem. Abs.*, **64**, 9544.
[69] P. Kovacic and M. E. Kurz, *J. Org. Chem.*, **31**, 2011 (1966).
[70] P. Kovacic and M. E. Kurz, *J. Org. Chem.*, **31**, 2459 (1966).
[71] P. Kovacic and M. E. Kurz, *Chem. Commun.*, **1966**, 321.
[72] P. Kovacic and M. E. Kurz, *Tetrahedron Letters*, **1966**, 2689; *J. Am. Chem. Soc.*, **88**, 2068 (1966).
[73] R. L. Dannley and G. E. Corbett, *J. Org. Chem.*, **31**, 153 (1966).
[74] P. Kovacic, J. A. Levisky, and C. T. Goralski, *J. Am. Chem. Soc.*, **88**, 100 (1966); P. Kovacic and J. A. Levisky, *ibid.*, p. 1000; P. Kovacic and J. F. Gormish, *ibid.*, p. 3819; V. L. Heasley, P. Kovacic, and R. M. Lange, *J. Org. Chem.*, **31**, 3050 (1966).
[75] See *Organic Reaction Mechanisms*, **1965**, 146, 169.

the use of mono- and di-chloramines, but in no instance is the nature of the nitrogen species which attacks the initial σ-complex clear. Some of the results are incorporated in the reaction scheme shown here for fluorobenzene. Fluorine is displaced (in path a) more readily than is chlorine or bromine, in accord with the normal sequence of reactivities in nucleophilic aromatic displacements.

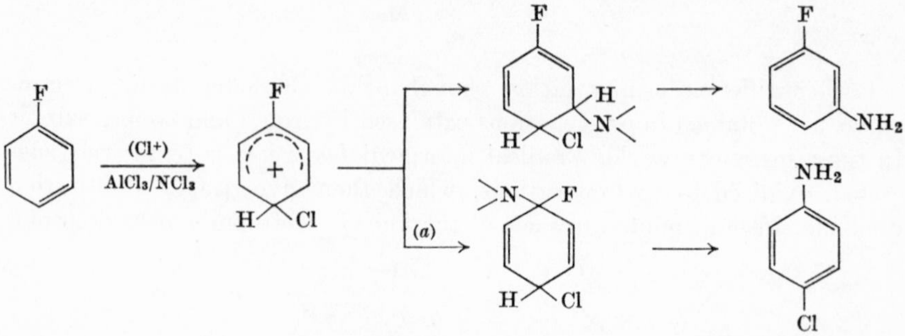

Among studies of hydrogen transfer is a further observation of *para*-C-protonation of anisole in non-aqueous media,[76] as well as inconclusive[77] and erroneous[78] data on its protonation in aqueous acid.

Further work on hydrogen exchange in azulenes has appeared.[79,80] The exchange with the base pyrrolidine was discussed[80] in terms of initial nucleophilic addition, as shown (deuterium labelling is shown as appropriate to the initial forward reaction).

Rates of exchange at the starred positions of the diarylethylenes (11) correlate with σ^+ for the X-substituent ($\rho = -2.6$). The reactions were run in concentrated D_2SO_4, and the results imply the intermediacy of dications (12).[81] Examination of the hydrogen-exchange behaviour of various aromatic compounds in moderately concentrated perchloric and sulphuric acids has established general acid-catalysis involving HSO_4^- and H_2SO_4 for the latter system.[82]

The thermodynamic parameters for exchange by substituted dimethyl-anilines in concentrated acid give an unsatisfactory isokinetic plot; however, replotting the "external" components of the enthalpy and entropy terms

[76] D. M. Brouwer, E. L. Mackor, and C. MacLean, *Rec. Trav. Chim.*, **85**, 109, 114 (1966).
[77] B. G. Ramsey, *J. Am. Chem. Soc.*, **88**, 5358 (1966).
[78] A. J. Kresge and L. E. Hakka, *J. Am. Chem. Soc.*, **88**, 3868 (1966).
[79] B. C. Challis and F. A. Long, *Discussions Faraday Soc.*, **39**, 67 (1965); C. Weiss, W. Engewald, and H. Müller, *Tetrahedron*, **22**, 825 (1966).
[80] C. Weiss, *Tetrahedron*, **22**, 145 (1966).
[81] C. A. Kingsbury, *Tetrahedron Letters*, **1966**, 2539.
[82] A. J. Kresge, L. E. Hakka, S. Mylonokis, and Y. Saton, *Discussions Faraday Soc.*, **39**, 75 (1965).

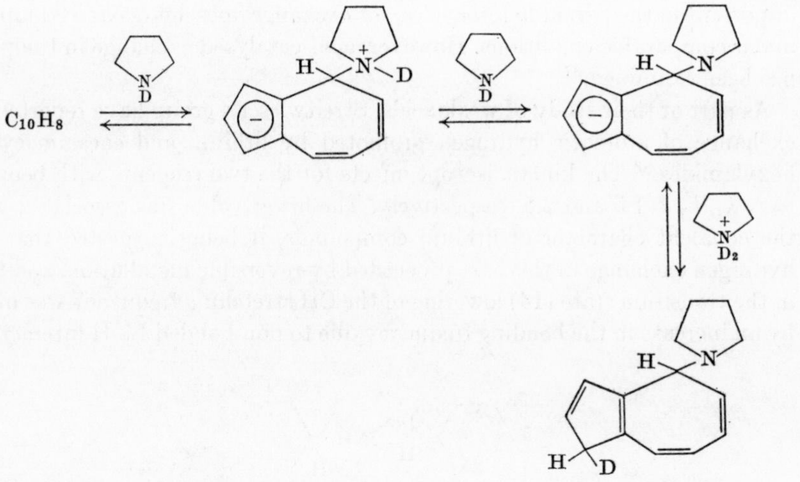

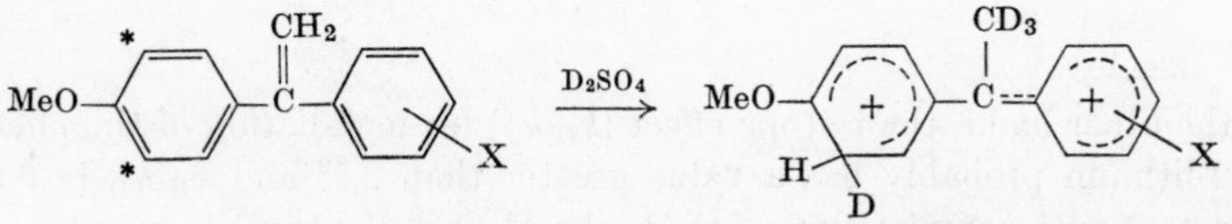

(11)   (12)

gave a much better correlation, and this was discussed in terms of the solvation changes occurring during protonation.[83] The exchange was shown to proceed through the free base.

Base-catalysed exchange in azolium salts has received further study,[84] and the importance of d–σ overlap has been emphasized in stabilizing the anion (13) from thiazolium salts.[85] This is also reflected in the base-catalysed

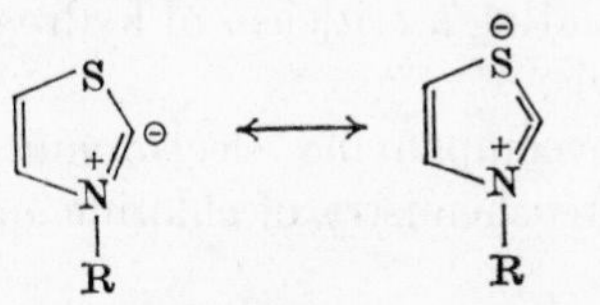

(13)

exchange of protons adjacent to sulphur in thiazole and isothiazole[86] (though at a rate 10^{-5} times that of the salts). Inductive withdrawal by nitrogen is

[83] I. Lee and F. H. Kendall, *J. Am. Chem. Soc.*, **88**, 3813 (1966).
[84] H. A. Staab, H. Irngartinger, A. Mannschreck, and M.-T. Wu, *Ann. Chem.*, **695**, 55 (1966).
[85] R. A. Olofson and J. M. Landesberg, *J. Am. Chem. Soc.*, **88**, 4263 (1966).
[86] R. A. Olofson, J. M. Landesberg, K. N. Houk, and J. S. Michelman, *J. Am. Chem. Soc.*, **88**, 4265 (1966).

7*

important in the parent heterocycles, for exchange does not occur in thiophen under comparable conditions. However, acid-catalysed exchange in thiophen has been examined.[87]

As part of their study of weak acids, Streitwieser's group have reported on exchange of aromatic hydrogen promoted by lithium and caesium cyclo-hexylamides.[88] The kinetic isotope effects for the two reagents with benzene were $k_D/k_T = 1.5$ and 2.5, respectively. The lower value was associated with the covalent character of lithium compounds, it being suggested that the hydrogen exchange in this case proceeded by reversible metallation, and that in the transition state (14) lowering of the CH stretching frequency was offset by an increase in the bending frequency due to non-bonded Li–H interaction.

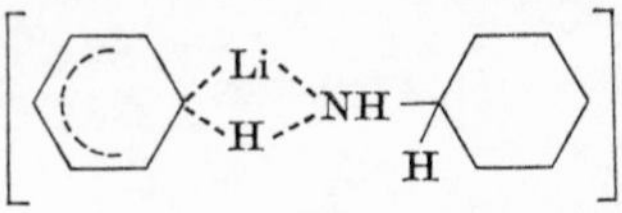

(14)

On the other hand, the isotope effect (k_D/k_T) for metallation of thiophen by alkyl-lithium probably has a value greater than 2,[89] and k_H/k_D (= 6.6) is consistent with complete loss of C–H vibrations in the transition state.

The isomerization of methylbiphenyls is not effected by trifluoroacetic acid at 70°.[90] Hence in the lifetime of species (15) no aryl migration occurs under

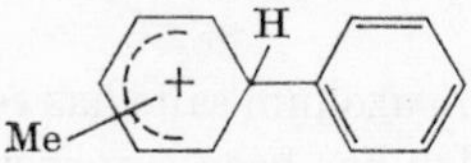

(15)

these conditions, invalidating a criticism of hydrogen-exchange experiments with the methylbiphenyls.

Addition reactions accompanying electrophilic substitution have been reviewed,[91] and the stereochemistry of chlorine adducts of naphthalene has been elucidated.[92]

[87] A. I. Shatenstein, A. G. Kamrad, I. O. Shapiro, Y. I. Ranneva, and E. N. Zvyagintseva, *Dokl. Akad. Nauk SSSR*, 168, 364 (1966).

[88] A. Streitwieser, R. G. Lawler, and C. Perrin, *J. Am. Chem. Soc.*, 87, 5383 (1965); A. Streitwieser and R. G. Lawler, *ibid.*, p. 5388; A. Streitwieser and R. A. Caldwell, *ibid.*, p. 5394; A. Streitwieser, R. A. Caldwell, R. G. Lawler, and G. R. Ziegler, *ibid.*, p. 5399.

[89] D. A. Shirley and K. R. Barton, *Tetrahedron*, 22, 515 (1966).

[90] C. Eaborn and G. A. Skinner, *J. Chem. Soc.*, B, 1966, 619.

[91] P. B. D. de la Mare, J. S. Lomas, and V. S. Del Olmo, *Bull. Soc. Chim. France*, 1966, 1157.

[92] P. B. D. de la Mare, M. D. Johnson, J. S. Lomas, and V. Sanchez del Olmo, *J. Chem. Soc.*, B, 1966, 827.

Chlorination of ArH by $MoCl_5$ or VCl_4 is unusually selective; it gives low *ortho*-substitution, consistent with relatively unreactive and bulky reagents.[93] Bromination of 1,3,5-trimethoxybenzene shows no isotope effect, but for introduction of a second and third bromine k_H/k_D is 4 and 5, respectively, reflecting a steric buttressing effect which renders the initial bromine addition significantly reversible.[94] The same effect was reported earlier for trimethoxytoluene.[95] Trimethoxybenzaldehyde and trimethoxyacetophenone suffer chlorodeacylation on reaction with sulphuryl chloride.[96]

Chlorination of *N*-methylaniline by calcium hypochlorite in carbon tetrachloride[96] has been found to give the *N*-chloroamine.[97] Filtered solutions of the chloroamine (which was not isolated) give exceptionally high *ortho–para*-ratios of *C*-chlorinated products on standing, active halogen being completely lost over a period of ca. 24 hours.

Also studied were the iodination of deactivated benzenes in oleum;[98] the reactions of iodine monochloride with aniline[99] and with polymethylbenzenes;[100] iodine exchange of 4-iodo-2,3-dimethyl-1-phenylpyrazoline with iodine (as a function of added nitrobenzene);[101] bromination of phenols;[102] and the additivity of substituent effects in chlorination.[103] The kinetics of bromination of *N,N*,2-trimethylaniline in aqueous perchloric acid show an h_0 dependence indicative of reaction with the free base.[104]

In 98% sulphuric acid, aniline and its mono- and di-*N*-methyl derivatives are nitrated almost exclusively by nitronium ion attack on the conjugate acid. Comparison of the nitration of these three cations with that of the *N,N,N*-trimethylanilinium ion reveals 38, 30, 22 and 11%, respectively, of *para*-substitution, with a factor of 200 between the rates of *para*-substitution in anilinium, and the less reactive trimethylanilinium cations.[105] Greater solvation is the probable cause of the lower deactivation by $-NH_3^+$. Evidently in these compounds the inductive deactivation is conveyed to the *meta*-position only slightly more than to the *para*, whilst conjugative deactivation

[93] P. Kovacic and R. M. Lange, *J. Org. Chem.*, **30**, 4251 (1965).
[94] E. Helgstrand and A. Nilsson, *Acta Chem. Scand.*, **20**, 1463 (1966).
[95] E. Helgstrand, *Acta Chem. Scand.*, **19**, 1583 (1965).
[96] J. Strating, L. Thijs, and B. Zwanenburg, *Rec. Trav. Chim.*, **85**, 291 (1966).
[97] P. Haberfield and D. Paul, *J. Am. Chem. Soc.*, **87**, 5502 (1965).
[98] J. Arotsky, R. Butler, and A. C. Darby, *Chem. Commun.*, **1966**, 650.
[99] F. M. Vainshten, E. I. Tomilenko and E. A. Shilov, *Kinetika i Kataliz*, **7**, 33 (1966); *Chem. Abs.*, **64**, 17373 (1966).
[100] R. M. Keefer and L. J. Andrews, *J. Org. Chem.*, **31**, 541 (1966).
[101] E. Koros, L. Ladanyi, M. Orban, and L. Pataki, *Magy. Kem. Folyoirat*, **71**, 546 (1965).
[102] J. Rajaram and J. C. Kuriacose, *Current Sci. (India)*, **35**, 306 (1966); K. V. Seshadri and R. Ganesan, *ibid.*, p. 408.
[103] O. M. H. el Dusouqui and M. Hassan, *J. Chem. Soc.*, B, **1966**, 374.
[104] R. P. Bell and B. Ninkov, *J. Chem. Soc.*, B, **1966**, 720.
[105] M. Brickman and J. H. Ridd, *J. Chem. Soc.*, **1965**, 6845; M. Brickman, J. H. P. Utley, and J. H. Ridd, *J. Chem. Soc.*, **1965**, 6851.

in nitrobenzene makes the *para*-position very much less reactive than the *meta*. These results seem to contradict the commonly held view that both types of deactivation are dominant at *ortho*- and *para*-positions.

It has also been pointed out that the commonly regarded deactivation by a fluorine substituent does not hold for the *para*-position of fluorobenzene which is slightly activated with respect to benzene.[106]

The rate of nitration of N-methyl-N-nitrosoaniline by anhydrous nitric acid in carbon tetrachloride shows third-order dependence on acid, and first-order on amine. The results were rationalized by the following scheme:[107]

$$HNO_3 + PhNMeNO \rightleftharpoons PhNMeH + N_2O_4$$
$$N_2O_4 + 2HNO_3 \rightleftharpoons NO^+ \cdot 2HNO_3 \cdot NO_3^- \ (X)$$
$$(X) + PhNMeH \rightarrow ONC_6H_4NMeH + 3HNO_3$$
$$ONC_6H_4NMeH + HNO_3 \rightarrow O_2NC_6H_4NMeH + HNO_2$$
$$HNO_2 + HNO_3 \rightarrow N_2O_4 + H_2O$$
$$O_2NC_6H_4NMeH + N_2O_4 \rightarrow O_2NC_6H_4NMeNO + HNO_3$$

Also examined have been the effect of solvent[108] and temperature[109] on the *ortho–para*-ratio in nitrations by acetyl nitrate; the effect of ammonium sulphate on rates of nitration in anhydrous sulphuric acid[110]—this is very similar to the effect of adding water; and the use of boron trifluoride as a catalyst for nitration.[111a] The rates of nitration of 2,6-dialkylphenols have been related to the variation in stability of dienones (16) as a function of

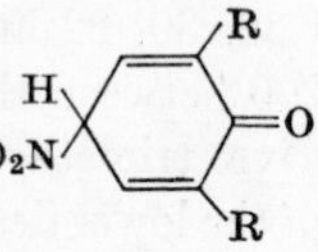

(16)

R.[111b] Partial rate factors for nitration of nitrobenzene have been redetermined,[112] and mechanisms of nitrosation of phenols studied.[113]

[106] A. Ault, *J. Chem. Educ.*, **43**, 329 (1966).
[107] T. G. Bonner, R. A. Hancock, R. L. Williams, and J. C. Wright, *Chem. Commun.*, **1966**, 109; T. G. Bonner and R. A. Hancock, *J. Chem. Soc.*, B, **1966**, 972.
[108] A. K. Sparks, *J. Org. Chem.*, **31**, 2299 (1966).
[109] A. A. Spryskov and I. K. Barvinskaya, *Zh. Organ. Khim.*, **1**, 1941 (1965); *Chem. Abs.*, **64**, 9534 (1966).
[110] T. G. Bonner and F. Brown, *J. Chem. Soc.*, B, **1966**, 658.
[111a] Z. Csuros, L. Fenichel, G. Deak, and L. Torok, *Magy. Kem. Lapja*, **21**, 333 (1966); *Chem. Abs.*, **65**, 13474 (1966).
[111b] G. A. Zlobina and V. V. Ershov, *Izv. Akad. Nauk SSSR, Ser. Khim.* **1966**, 189; *Chem. Abs.*, **64**, 12484 (1966).
[112] A. D. Mésure and J. G. Tillett, *J. Chem. Soc.*, B, **1966**, 669.
[113] H. Schmid, G. Muhr, and P. Riedl, *Monatsh. Chem.*, **97**, 781 (1966).

The steric hindrance to complex-formation by 2,6-di-*tert*-butylpyridine permits study of electrophilic sulphonation of the pyridine ring by reaction with sulphur trioxide in sulphur dioxide. The 3-sulphonic acid is formed at a rate comparable to that of nitrobenzene-3-sulphonic acid under the same conditions.[114] 2,6-Lutidine gives only an addition complex in this reaction. The conclusion that the unprotonated pyridine-nitrogen thus has a deactivating effect comparable to a nitro-group apparently does not take into account the very large steric effect of a *tert*-butyl group in sulphonation. For example, under either kinetic or thermodynamic control, no *ortho*-isomer is detected in the products of sulphonation of *tert*-butylbenzene.[115]

A small hydrogen isotope effect has been determined for the sulphonation of benzene.[116] Sulphonation of phenol by chlorosulphonic acid,[117] and that of benzene in dimethyl sulphate as solvent,[118] have been examined. The concurrent formation of both acyl and sulphonic acid derivatives from hydrocarbons by treatment with acyl halides in sulphuric acid has been attributed to reactions of complexes (17).[119] Such complexes were isolated on reaction of benzoyl halides with sulphuric acid.

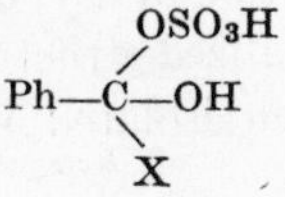

$$\begin{array}{c} OSO_3H \\ / \\ Ph-C-OH \\ \backslash \\ X \end{array}$$

(17)

X = F, Cl, or Br

Dealkylation was observed during sulphonation of *tert*-butylbenzene,[115] and this has also been detected in the iron-catalysed bromination of *p*-di-*tert*-butylbenzene.[120] It is not clear to what extent these reactions involve bromodealkylation (or sulphodealkylation) or dealkylation and subsequent bromina-

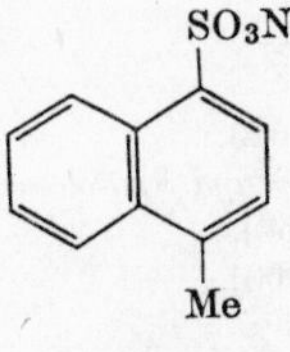

(18)

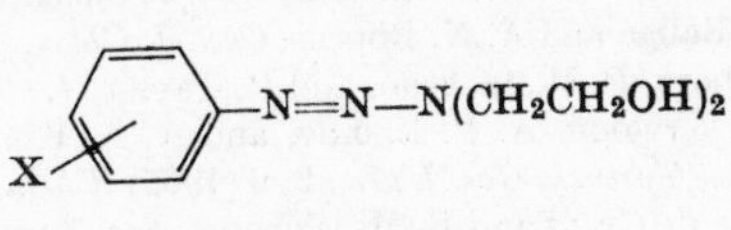

(19)

114 H. C. Brown and B. Kanner, *J. Am. Chem. Soc.*, 88, 986 (1966).
115 J. M. Arends and H. Cerfontain, *Rec. Trav. Chim.*, 85, 93 (1966); H. Cerfontain and J. M. Arends, *ibid.*, p. 358.
116 H. Cerfontain and A. Telder, *Rec. Trav. Chim.*, 84, 1613 (1965).
117 A. A. Spryskov and B. G. Gnedin, *Zh. Organ. Khim.*, 1, 1946 (1965).
118 O. I. Kachurin, *Izv. Vysshikh Uchebn. Zavedenii, Khim. i Khim. Tekhnol.*, 8, 945 (1965); *Chem. Abs.*, 64, 1737 (1966).
119 R. Corriu, C. Coste, and G. Dubosi, *Compt. Rend.*, 261, 3632 (1965).
120 J. M. A. Baas and B. M. Wepster, *Rec. Trav. Chim.*, 85, 457 (1966).

tion (or sulphonation). The sulphur isotope effect k_{32}/k_{34} has been measured for bromodesulphonation of (18).[121] The results combine with kinetic data to establish a normal addition–elimination mechanism with the σ-complex advancing to product at a much greater rate than that at which it reverts to starting material. Primary isotope effects in bromination,[122] detritiation,[123] and desilylation[123] reactions have also been measured.

The acid-promoted cleavage of compounds (19) correlates with σ^+; $\rho = -4 \cdot 0$ at 40°.[124]

Miscellaneous observations of orientation in electrophilic substitution include the following: Nitration of *o*-di-*tert*-butylbenzene gives a surprisingly high proportion (13%) of the 3-nitro-derivative.[125] A neopentyl and a methyl substituent have but slightly different orienting effects.[126] A cyclopropyl substituent activates the benzene ring appreciably more than does cyclobutyl or isopropyl.[127] The acetylation of phenanthrene,[128] sulphonation of phenanthrene and anthracene,[129] bromination of 2,7-di-*tert*-butylnaphthalene[130] and of 2-bromo-4-fluoro-1-naphthylamine,[131] benzoylation of isomeric bromofluorobenzenes,[132] and chlorination of tetrahydropyrene[133] have been examined. Electrophilic substitution of acyl derivatives of pentatriafulvalene (20) appear to support the delocalized structure assigned to this molecule;[134] intermediate adducts have been isolated in the bromination of (21).[135]

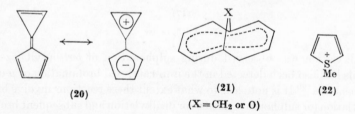

(20)   (21)   (22)
(X = CH₂ or O)

[121] B. T. Baliga and A. N. Bourns, *Can. J. Chem.*, **44**, 363 (1966).
[122] B. T. Baliga and A. N. Bourns, *Can. J. Chem.*, **44**, 379 (1966).
[123] C. Eaborn, P. M. Jackson, and R. Taylor, *J. Chem. Soc.*, *B*, **1966**, 613.
[124] V. K. Kruglov, A. P. Ershov, and A. A. Kharkhavov, *Reaktsionnaya Sposobnost Organ. Soedin.*, *Tartusk. Gos. Univ.*, **2**, 9 (1965); *Chem. Abs.*, **64**, 3331 (1966).
[125] B. Van de Graaf and B. M. Wepster, *Rec. Trav. Chim.*, **85**, 619 (1966).
[126] D. F. Gurka and W. M. Schubert, *J. Org. Chem.*, **31**, 3416 (1966).
[127] Y. S. Shabarov, N. A. Donskaya, L. D. Sychkova and R. Y. Levina, *Vestn. Mosk. Univ. Ser. II, Khim.*, **20**, 73 (1965); *Chem. Abs.*, **64**, 4890.
[128] N. P. Buu-Hoi, P. Mabille and Do-Cao-Thang, *Bull. Soc. Chim. France*, **1966**, 180.
[129] V. M. Bednov and G. N. Mochalova, *Zh. Prikl. Khim.*, **39**, 880 (1966).
[130] L. Erichomovitch, M. Ménard, F. L. Chubb, Y. Pépin, and J. C. Richer, *Can. J. Chem.*, **44**, 2305 (1966).
[131] W. Adcock, M. J. S. Dewar, and G. R. Johnson, *Tetrahedron Letters*, **1966**, 5307.
[132] Bui-Khac-Diep, *Compt. Rend.*, *Ser. C*, **263**, 145 (1966).
[133] P. B. D. de la Mare, E. A. Johnson, and J. S. Lomas, *J. Chem. Soc.*, **1965**, 6893.
[134] A. S. Kende, P. T. Izzo, and W. Fulmor, *Tetrahedron Letters*, **1966**, 3697.
[135] E. Vogel, W. A. Boell and M. Biskup, *Tetrahedron Letters*, **1966**, 1569.

2-Protonated thiophen has been observed by NMR spectroscopy, and the possibility that initial attack in alkylation is on sulphur is discredited by the failure of the S-alkylated species (22) to rearrange.[136] Bromination of thiophen and its derivatives,[137] and alkylation of pyrrole derivatives,[138] have also been recorded. Preferred electrophilic attack on compounds (23) to (28) occurs in the positions indicated.[139-144] The borazaroisoquinoline (29) is reported to be brominated and nitrated at the position marked;[145] however, the sulphur analogue (30) is attacked in the boron–nitrogen ring.[146] The acidity depend-

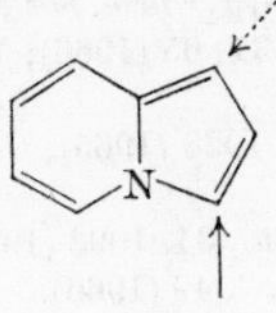

(23) 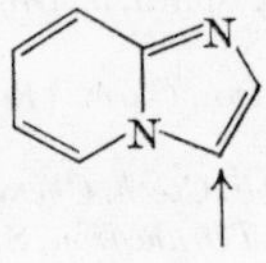   (24) 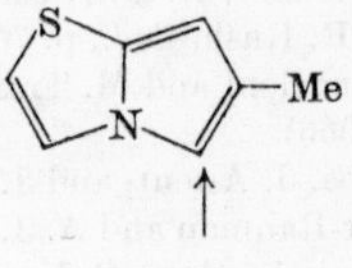   (25)

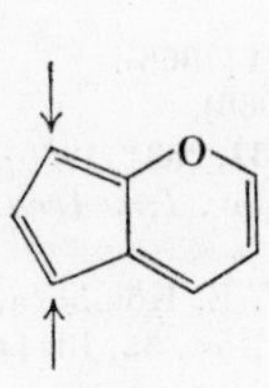

(26) 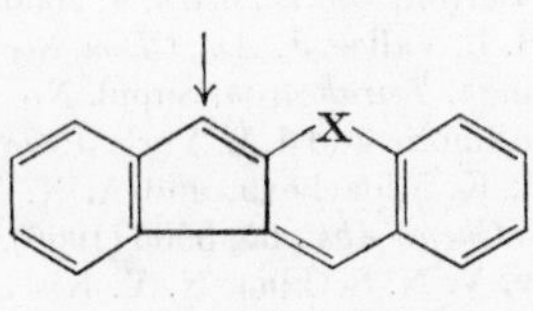   (27)   (28)
           (X = O or NMe)

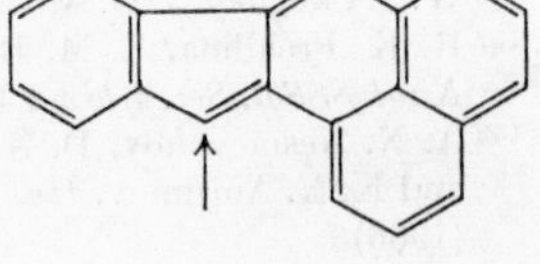

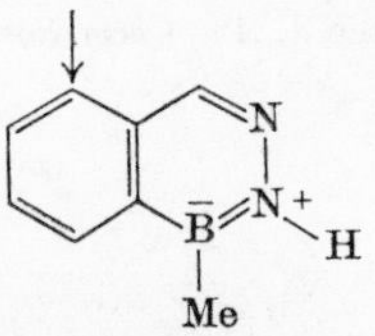

(29) 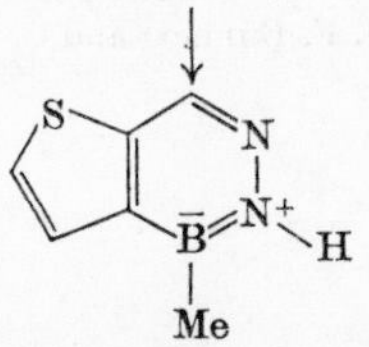   (30)

136 H. Hogeveen, *Rec. Trav. Chim.*, 85, 1072 (1966).
137 G. Marino, *Atti Accad. Nazl. Lincei, Rend. Classe Sci. Fis. Mat. Nat.*, 38, 700 (1965); *Chem. Abs.*, 64, 1917 (1966).
138 H. J. Anderson and L C. Hopkins, *Can. J. Chem.*, 44, 1831 (1966).
139 M. Fraser, S. McKenzie, and D. H. Reid, *J. Chem. Soc., B*, 1966, 44; W. L. F. Armarego, *ibid.*, p. 191.
140 J. P. Paolini and R. K. Robins, *J. Org. Chem.*, 30, 4085 (1965); W. W. Paudler and H. L. Blewitt, *ibid.*, p. 4081.
141 S. McKenzie, B. B. Malloy, and D. H. Reid, *J. Chem. Soc., C*, 1966, 1908.
142 G. V. Boyd and A. W. Ellis, *J. Chem. Soc., B*, 1966, 349.
143 C. Weiss and D. Schönfeld, *Tetrahedron*, 22, 2511 (1966).
144 W. Bonthrone and D. H. Reid, *J. Chem. Soc., B*, 1966, 91.
145 M. J. S. Dewar and J. L. Von Rosenberg, *J. Am. Chem. Soc.*, 88, 358 (1966).
146 S. Gronowitz and J. Namtvedt, *Tetrahedron Letters*, 1966, 2967.

ence of nitration of pyridine N-oxide and 2,6-lutidine N-oxide indicates
nitration of the unprotonated species; however, isoquinoline N-oxide is
nitrated in the carbocyclic ring of the conjugate acid.[147] Substitutions have
also been examined for the indole,[148] benzofuran,[149] benzimidazole,[150]
anthranil,[151] and carbazole[152] systems. Iodination[153] and nitration of tyro-
sine,[154] iodination of histidine,[155] and substitution in porphyrins[156] have also
been noted, as well as substitution reactions of cyclopentadienyl derivatives
of zirconium,[157] manganese,[158] and rhenium.[158]

[147] J. Gleghorn, R. B. Moodie, K. Schofield, and M. J. Williamson, *J. Chem. Soc., B,* **1966**, 870.

[148] W. E. Noland, K. R. Rush and L. R. Smith, *J. Org. Chem.,* **31**, 65 (1966); W. E. Noland, and K. R. Rush, *ibid.,* p. 70.

[149] A. S. Angeloni and M. Tramontini, *Ann. Chim. (Rome),* **55**, 1028 (1965); *Chem. Abs.,* **64**, 5028 (1966).

[150] V. Stěrba, J. Arient, and J. Slosar, *Coll. Czech. Chem. Commun.,* **31**, 1093 (1966).

[151] Altar-ur-Rahman and A. J. Boulton, *Tetrahedron,* Suppl. No. 7, 49 (1966).

[152] P. B. D. de La Mare, O. M. H. El Dusouqui, and E. A. Johnson, *J. Chem. Soc., B,* **1966**, 521.

[153] W. E. Mayberry, J. E. Rall, and D. Bertoli, *Biochemistry,* **4**, 2606 (1965).

[154] J. F. Riordan, M. Sokolovsky, and B. L. Vallee, *J. Am. Chem. Soc.,* **88**, 4104 (1966).

[155] L. Schutte, P. P. Kluit, and E. Havinga, *Tetrahedron,* Suppl. No. 7, 295 (1966).

[156] W. S. Caughey, J. O. Alben, W. Y. Fujimoto, and J. L. York, *J. Org. Chem.,* **31**, 2631 (1966).

[157] R. K. Freidlina, E. M. Brainina, M. K. Minacheva, and A. N. Nesmeyanov, *Izv. Akad. Nauk SSSR, Ser. Khim.,* **1964**, 1417; *Chem. Abs.,* **65**, 3905 (1966).

[158] A. N. Nesmeyanov, D. N. Kursanov, V. N. Setkina, N. V. Kislyakova, N. E. Kolobova, and K. N. Anisimov, *Izv. Akad. Nauk SSSR, Ser Khim ,* **1966**, 944; *Chem Abs.,* **65**, 10444 (1966)

Addendum: In connexion with the subject of ref. 14, the importance of competing iodine
abstraction in arylation of aryl iodides has been emphasized [D. L. Brydon and J. I. G.
Cadogan, *Chem. Commun.,* **1966**, 744; J. A. Kampmeier and A. B. Rubin, *Tetrahedron
Letters,* **1966**, 2853; J. F. Bunnett and C. C. Wamser, *J. Am. Chem. Soc.,* **88**, 5534 (1966)].

CHAPTER 8

Molecular Rearrangements

Aromatic Rearrangements

Extension of the Claisen rearrangement to systems where the oxygen atom is replaced by other groups, X, has met with little success. The rearrangement has been observed[1] for X = NH, and the case of X = S is mentioned below. The elusive carbon analogue (X = CH$_2$) [equation (1)] has now been realized by Doering and Bragole.[2] Success depended upon appreciating that the

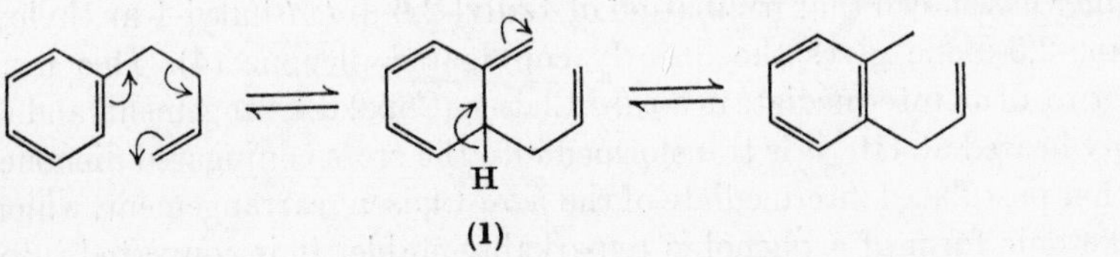

$$(1)$$

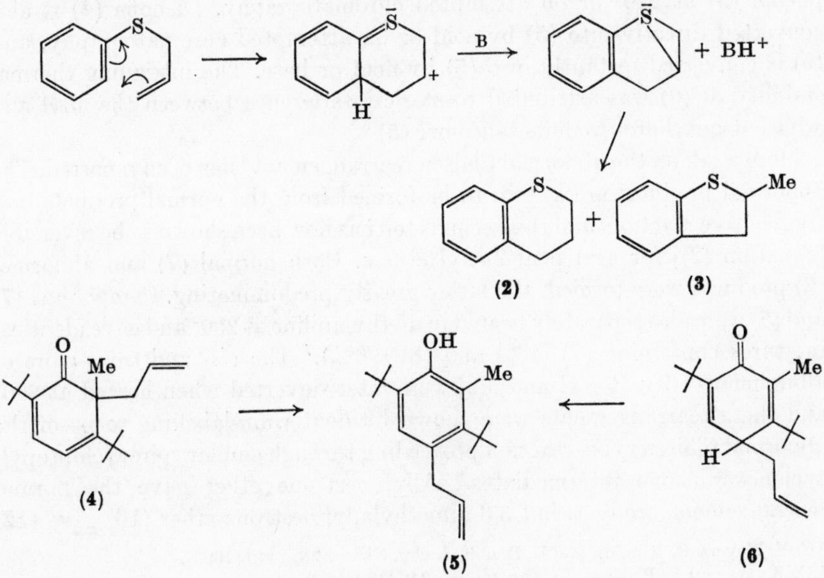

Scheme 1

[1] S. Marcinkiewicz, J. Green, and P. Mamalis, *Tetrahedron*, **14**, 208 (1961).
[2] W. von E. Doering and R. A. Bragole, *Tetrahedron*, **22**, 385 (1966).

energetically difficult step would be removal of the proton in the rearomatiza-
tion step (1) which in the "oxy-Claisen" rearrangement is greatly facilitated
by the carbonyl group. In *tert*-butyl alcohol containing potassium *tert*-butoxide
at 350° (24 hours) the five isomeric 1-phenylbutenes, which are very rapidly
pre-equilibrated under these conditions, were converted into the thermodynamic equilibrium mixture with the three isomeric 1-(*o*-tolyl)propenes.[2]
The "thio-Claisen" rearrangement, X = S, of allyl phenyl sulphide gave
nearly equal amounts of the thiachroman (2) and thiacoumaran (3); *o*-allyl-
thiophenol gave the same products but in the ratio 4:1. Compounds (2) and
(3) are not interconvertible under the rearrangement conditions. Thus an
earlier mechanism[3] is ruled out and was replaced by that shown in Scheme 1
involving a thiiran intermediate. The effect of methyl substitution in the ring
and in the side chain was shown to be very much greater than in the normal
Claisen rearrangement.[4]

Miller has shown that irradiation of 4-allyl-2,6-di-*tert*-butyl-4-methylcyclo-
hexane-2,5-dione gives the linearly conjugated dienone (4). This has the
structure of an intermediate in a *para*-Claisen (Cope) rearrangement, and when
briefly heated at 110° it is transformed into the cross-conjugated dienone (6),
another postulated intermediate of the *para*-Claisen rearrangement, which for
the ketonic form of a phenol is remarkably stable. It is converted into the
phenol (5) at 220° or on attempted chromatography. Dienone (4) is also
converted directly into (5) by acid or on attempted chromatography, and
(6) is converted instantly into (5) by acid or base. The intriguing thermal
stability of (6) was attributed to steric interference between the allyl and
adjacent butyl groups in its tautomer (5).[5]

More work on the abnormal Claisen rearrangement[6] has been reported. The
abnormal products are known to be formed from the normal products in a
consecutive reaction, and this second step has now been shown to be reversible
[equation (2)] for aryl pent-2-enyl ethers. Both normal (7) and abnormal
(8) products were formed, the latter greatly predominating. Compounds (7)
and (8) were also separately heated in diethylaniline at 200° and gave identical
mixtures containing (7) (4%) and (8) (96%).[7] The *cis*- and *trans*-pairs of
allylphenols [(9); R = H and Me] were interconverted when heated at 200°
and these rearrangements were shown by deuterium-labelling to be of the
abnormal Claisen type, reaction proceeding through similar spirocyclopropyl-
cyclohexadienone intermediates.[8] Allyl oestrone ether gave the normal
rearrangement product, but 3,3-dimethylallyl oestrone ether (10) gave (12)

[3] C. Y. Meyers, C. Rinaldi, and L. Bonoli, *J. Org. Chem.*, **28**, 2440 (1963).
[4] H. Kwart and E. R. Evans, *J. Org. Chem.*, **31**, 413 (1966).
[5] B. Miller, *J. Am. Chem. Soc.*, **87**, 5515 (1965).
[6] See *Organic Reaction Mechanisms*, **1965**, 173.
[7] R. M. Roberts and R. G. Landolt, *J. Org. Chem.*, **31**, 2699 (1966).
[8] G. Fráter and H. Schmid, *Helv. Chim. Acta*, **49**, 1957 (1966).

through the normal product (**11**). Compound (**11**) could not be isolated in the rearrangement but could be trapped as its butyric ester with butyric anhydride; (**11**) was shown to give (**12**) under rearrangement conditions.[9] Abnormal Claisen rearrangements have also been observed with but-2-enyl

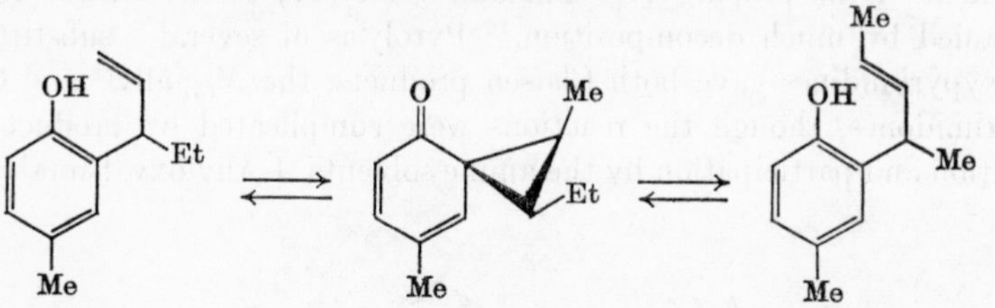

(2)

(7)   (8)

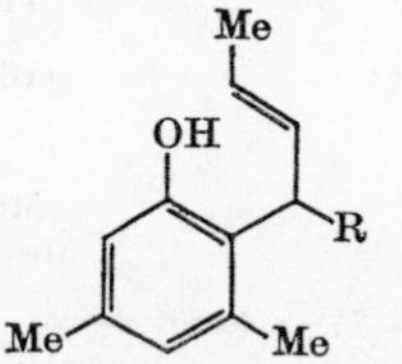

and *cis*

(9)

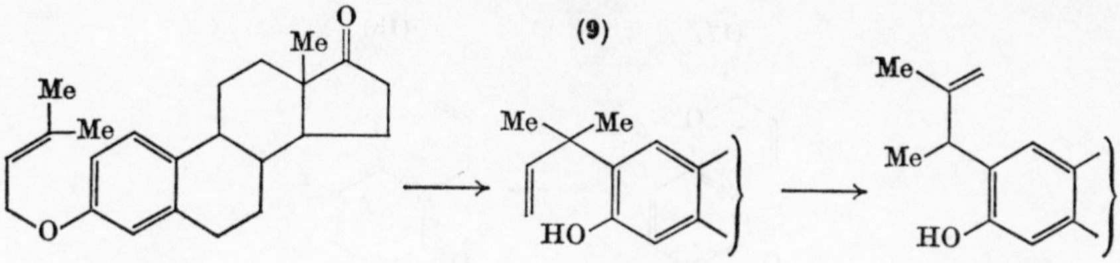

(10)   (11)   (12)

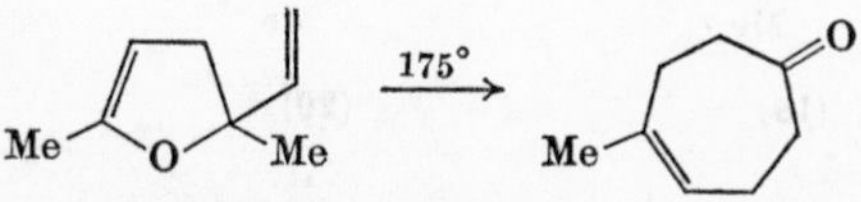

(13)   (14)

tocopheryl ethers.[10] When the allyl vinyl ether, 2,3-dihydro-2,5-dimethyl-2-vinylfuran (**13**) was heated alone or in *n*-decane at 175° for 24 hours it did not undergo a Claisen rearrangement, presumably because of the steric restraint imposed by the 3-methylene group bridging the diallyl system. Instead, 4-methylcyclohept-4-enone (**14**) was formed almost quantitatively; possible mechanisms were suggested and are under investigation.[11]

[9] A. Jefferson and F. Scheinmann, *Chem. Commun.*, **1966**, 239.
[10] D. McHale, S. Marcinkiewicz, and J. Green, *J. Chem. Soc., C*, **1966**, 1427.
[11] S. J. Rhoads and C. J. Brandenburg, *J. Am. Chem. Soc.*, **88**, 4294 (1966).

The Claisen rearrangement of propargyl vinyl ethers (15) to allenic aldehydes (16) requires higher than normal temperatures; the reaction is accelerated by methyl substitution and this was considered to provide evidence for one-electron shifts in the cyclic transition state. The analogous Cope rearrangement of the propargylvinylmalonic ester (17) to the allene (18) is accompanied by much decomposition.[12] Pyrolysis of several 2-substituted 4-allyloxypyrimidines gave both Claisen products, the $N_{(3)}$-allyl- and $C_{(5)}$-allyl-pyrimidones, though the reactions were complicated by product decomposition and participation by the amine solvents. 4-Allyloxy-4-methyl-2-

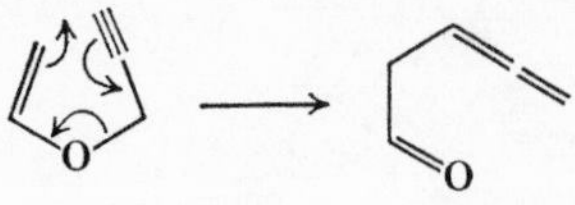

(15)   (16)

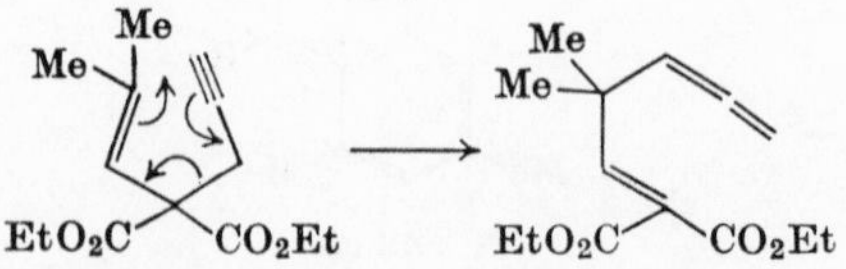

(17)   (18)

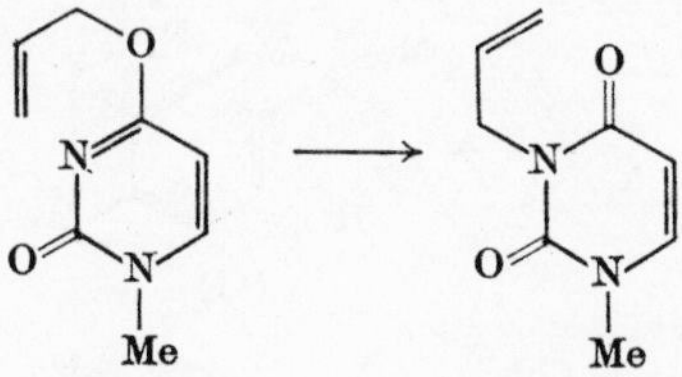

(19)   (20)

pyrimidone (19), however, gave exclusive rearrangement to 3-allyl-1-methyl-pyrimidine-2,4-dione (20), as expected from bond orders. The corresponding alkylthio- and alkylamino-compounds did not undergo Claisen rearrangement.[13] Rearrangement of allyl 2,6-dichlorophenyl ether occurred during gas–liquid chromatographic analysis; such analyses of rearrangement mixtures containing starting ether must, therefore, be interpreted with care.[14]

2-Methylallyl vinyl ether gave *trans*-hex-4-enal quantitatively at 423—461°

[12] D. K. Black and S. R. Landor, *J. Chem. Soc.*, 1965, 6784.
[13] H. J. Minnemeyer, P. B. Clarke, and H. Tieckelmann, *J. Org. Chem.*, 31, 406 (1966).
[14] M. J. Baldwin and R. K. Brown, *Can. J. Chem.*, 44, 1743 (1966).

in a unimolecular reaction probably proceeding through a six-membered cyclic transition state.[15]

Fukui and Fujimoto[16] have described a theoretical approach to the problem of relative stabilities of the chair-like and boat-like transition states for the Claisen and Cope type of double allylic rearrangements. The method is based on differences in "overlap stabilization" of molecular orbitals in the transition state, and provides an alternative to that based on molecular-orbital symmetry relationships. A preliminary report[17] has also been given of a new quantitative approach to the geometry of the Cope rearrangement which agrees with earlier calculations in favouring the chair form for the transition state in the re-arrangement of hexa-1,5-dienes. The method is an extension of Hendrickson and Wiberg's calculations of the conformational energies of cycloalkanes. The variation of energy along the reaction path is calculated as a sum of terms for bond-angle bending strain, torsional strain, steric repulsion, π-delocaliza-tion, compression of the σ-bonds, and the making and breaking of σ-bonds. Calculations of energy and entropy of activation were possible and, in the examples quoted, were of the right order of magnitude.[17]

Banthorpe and his colleagues have continued work on the nitramine rearrangements and provided further evidence for the "cartwheel" mechan-ism.[18] The kinetics of the rearrangement of N-nitro-1-naphthylamine, and its N-methyl and 2,4-dideuterio-derivatives, to the 2- and 4-nitro-isomers were measured at various acidities. The kinetic form, type of product, intra-molecularity, lack of detectable radical intermediates, nature of the side reactions, and occurrence and size of isotope effects were all very similar to the results with N-nitroaniline and were considered to be best accommodated by the same mechanism, with the C-nitrite intermediates formed directly form the N-nitro-compounds. The radical-cage and π-complex mechanisms were again shown to explain the data less satisfactorily.[19] The thermal (100°) and photochemical (20°) rearrangements of N-methyl-N-nitro-1-naphthylamine in various solvents have also been studied. Although these reactions are more complex than in aqueous acid, no evidence for a radical mechanism was obtained from ESR measurements or from polymerization and trapping experiments, and a similar intramolecular "cartwheel" mechanism was suggested.[20]

Štěrba and Vecera have critically discussed the roles of the first and the second proton in the benzidine rearrangement; as a result of a study of the effect of the medium on the reaction rate and activation parameters they

15 H. M. Frey and B. M. Pope, *J. Chem. Soc.*, *B*, **1966**, 209.
16 K. Fukui and H. Fujimoto, *Tetrahedron Letters*, **1966**, 251.
17 M. Simonetta and G. Favini, *Tetrahedron Letters*, **1966**, 4837.
18 See *Organic Reaction Mechanisms*, **1965**, 176.
19 D. V. Banthorpe and J. A. Thomas, *J. Chem. Soc.*, **1965**, 7149.
20 D. V. Banthorpe and J. A. Thomas, *J. Chem. Soc.*, **1965**, 7158.

conclude, in disagreement with Banthorpe, Hughes, and Ingold,[21] that the concentration of the diprotonated species is decisive for the overall reaction rate. The influence of salt effects on the rate also suggests that the transition state is much less polar than assumed by Ingold and his co-workers.[22] In the hydrochloric acid-catalysed rearrangement of hydrazobenzene in aqueous ethanol at 0—80°, it has been shown that the amounts of benzidine and of 2,4'-diaminobiphenyl formed were dependent upon the solvent composition, but the ratio of these two products was almost constant (3:2) and independent of solvent composition, acid concentration, and reaction temperature.[23] Rakušan and Allan[24] have shown that acid reduction of 2-ethylaminoazo-benzene (**20a**) gave 3,4'-diamino-4-ethylaminobiphenyl (**20b**), the product of benzidine rearrangement to a *meta*-position, under the activating influence of the ethylamino-group. This was considered to provide evidence for the Dewar mechanism which can most readily accommodate rearrangement to the *meta*-position.[24] The dimeric cyclic hydrazobenzene derivatives (**21**) have been rearranged with acid to give benzidines when $n = 5$—8; similar rearrangement of the hydrazobenzene (**22**) occurred only with $n = 16$.[25] The rate of acid-catalysed rearrangement of hydrazobenzene has been measured by four electrochemical techniques: step-reversal chronopotentiometry, reverse-ramp

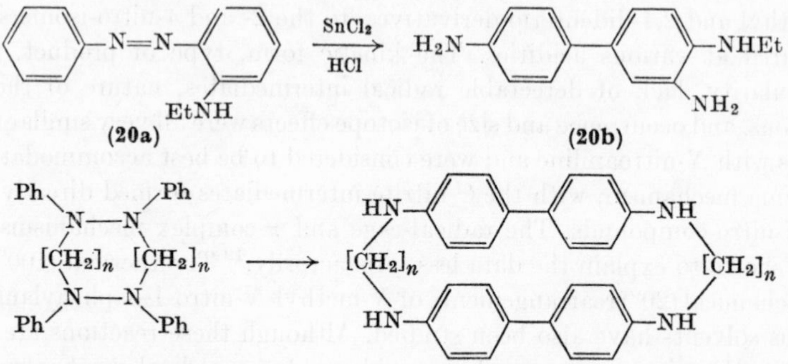

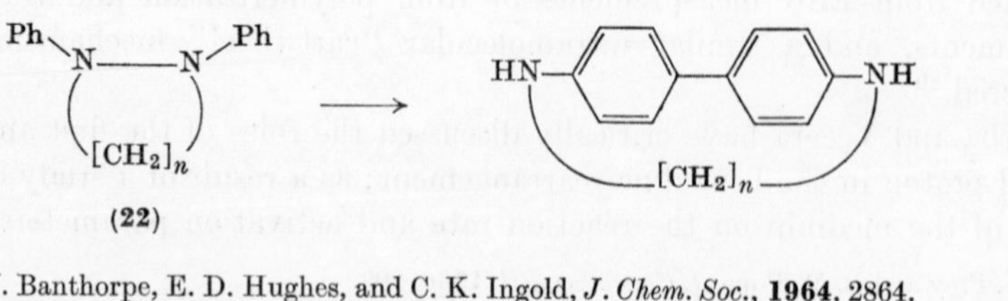

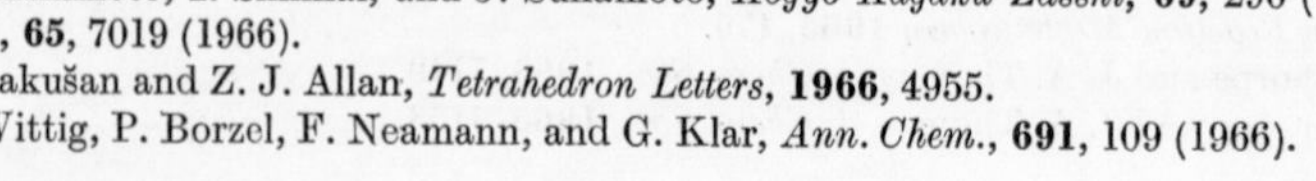

[21] D. V. Banthorpe, E. D. Hughes, and C. K. Ingold, *J. Chem. Soc.*, **1964**, 2864.
[22] V. Štěrba and M. Verčeřa, *Coll. Czech. Chem. Commun.*, **31**, 3486 (1966).
[23] S. Hashimoto, I. Shinkai, and J. Sunamoto, *Kogyo Kagaku Zasshi*, **69**, 290 (1966); *Chem. Abs.*, **65**, 7019 (1966).
[24] J. Rakušan and Z. J. Allan, *Tetrahedron Letters*, **1966**, 4955.
[25] G. Wittig, P. Borzel, F. Neamann, and G. Klar, *Ann. Chem.*, **691**, 109 (1966).

current, thin-layer chronopotentiometry, and thin-layer potential step electrolysis.[26] Other work on the benzidine rearrangement has been reported.[27]

Rearrangement of [1-^{14}C]azoxybenzene to 4-hydroxyazobenzene by hot concentrated sulphuric acid (Wallach rearrangement), followed by location of the label, showed that oxygen had migrated to both *para*-positions of the original azoxybenzene. This agreed with earlier ^{15}N-labelling experiments and with the participation of a symmetrical intermediate.[28]

For the Jacobsen rearrangement of polyalkylbenzenesulphonic acids in sulphuric acid two mechanisms have been considered: (i) direct rearrangement of the sulphonic acid, and (ii) desulphonation, rearrangement of the hydrocarbon, and resulphonation. This rearrangement has now been studied[29] with durenesulphonic acid in polyphosphoric acid, which appears to give very similar results to sulphuric acid. The nature and amounts of the resulting hydrocarbons and sulphonic acids favour the first type of mechanism, i.e., protonation of the sulphonic acid followed by reversible 1,2-methyl migrations and then deprotonation.

Treatment of [2.2]paracyclophane (**23**) in methylene chloride with hydrogen chloride and aluminium chloride at 0° gave [2.2]metaparacyclophane (**24**).[30] In the water-promoted aluminium chloride-catalysed isomerization of the isomeric halogenocumenes, the fluorocumenes isomerize by exclusive migration of the isopropyl group, the chlorocumenes by predominant migration of the isopropyl group, and the bromocumenes by migration of isopropyl and bromine as positively polarized species.[31] Precisely the same trend is found for the

(**23**)   (**24**)

halogeno-*tert*-butylbenzenes.[32] 2-, 3-, and 4-Methylbiphenyl each gave the same equilibrium mixture of methylbiphenyls on treatment with aluminium chloride, by intramolecular 1,2-methyl shifts.[33] Isomerization of the dichloro-

[26] D. M. Oglesby, J. D. Johnson, and C. N. Reilly, *Anal. Chem.*, **38**, 385 (1966).
[27] Z. J. Allan and J. Rakušan, *Coll. Czech. Chem. Commun.*, **31**, 3555 (1966).
[28] L. C. Behr and E. C. Hendley, *J. Org. Chem.*, **31**, 2715 (1966); cf. *Organic Reaction Mechanisms*, **1965**, 177.
[29] E. N. Marvell and B. M. Graybill, *J. Org. Chem.*, **30**, 4014 (1965).
[30] D. J. Cram, R. C. Helgeson, D. Lock, and L. A. Singer, *J. Am. Chem. Soc.*, **88**, 1324 (1966).
[31] G. A. Olah, J. C. Lapierre, and G. J. McDonald, *J. Org. Chem.*, **31**, 1262 (1966).
[32] G. A. Olah, J. C. Lapierre, and U. H. Schreier, *J. Org. Chem.*, **31**, 1268 (1966).
[33] G. A. Olah and J. C. Lapierre, *J. Org. Chem.*, **31**, 1271 (1966).

benzenes has also been studied.[34] Both inter- and intra-molecular migration of the trityl group was observed in the acid-catalysed rearrangement of *N*-tritylaniline and of *O*-tritylphenol in the presence of highly reactive aromatic substrates.[35]

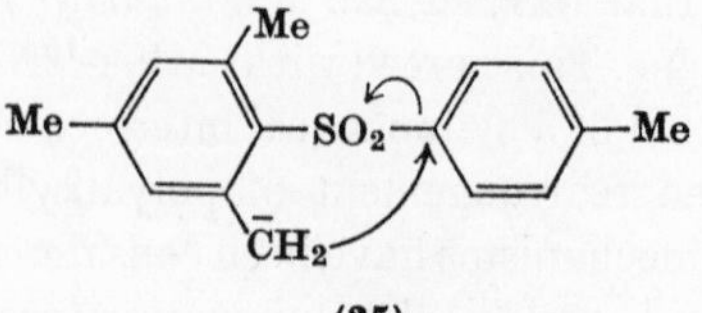

(25)

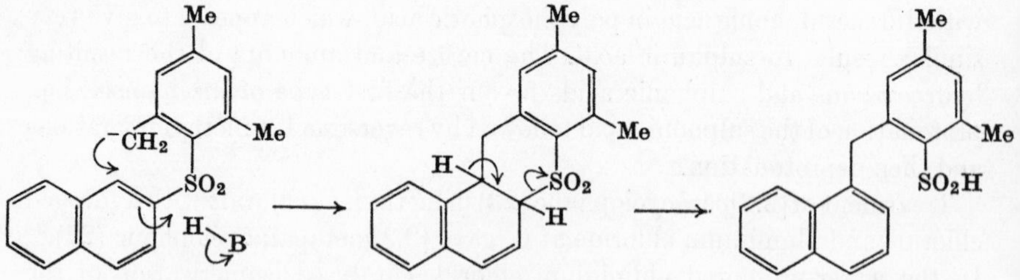

Scheme 2

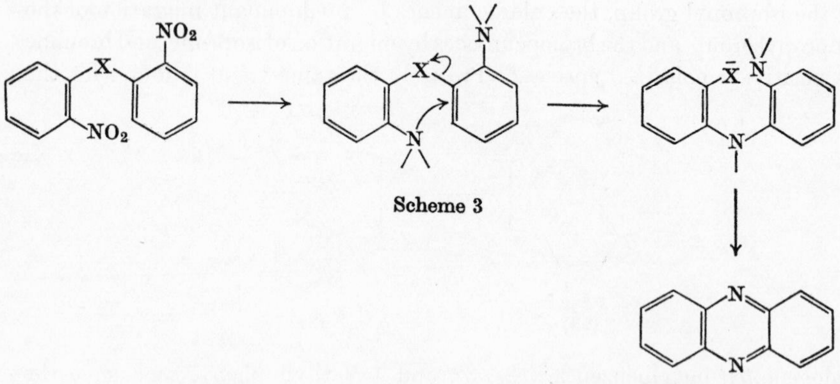

Scheme 3

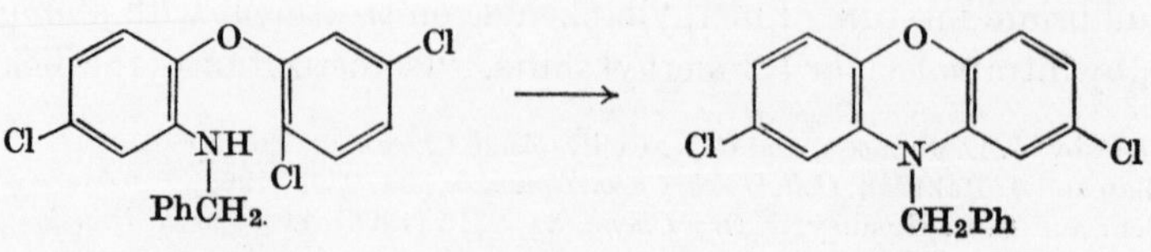

(26)   (27)

[34] V. A. Koptyug and I. S. Isaev, *Izv. Sibirsk. Otd. Akad. Nauk. SSSR, Ser. Khim. Nauk.*, 1966, 146; *Chem. Abs.*, **65**, 10475 (1966).
[35] G. Chuchani and V. Rodriguez-Uzcanga, *Tetrahedron*, **22**, 2665 (1966).

An interesting difference in the mechanism of strong base-catalysed rearrangement of mesityl naphthyl sulphones and mesityl phenyl sulphones has been reported. Rearrangement of mesityl *p*-tolyl sulphone gave 3,4',5-trimethyldiphenylmethane-2-sulphinic acid resulting from attack of the carbanion at the sulphone-bearing carbon (**25**). However, rearrangement of the corresponding 1- and 2-naphthyl sulphones involves attack at carbon adjacent to the sulphone, as shown, for example, in Scheme 2, presumably because of the greater reactivity of naphthalene towards the initial addition reaction.[36] Reduction of 2,2'-dinitrodiaryl sulphides, sulphoxides, and sulphones with zinc and sodium hydroxide in aqueous dioxan gave, *inter alia*, phenazines. Substituent-labelling showed that they were formed by intramolecular nucleophilic rearrangement of partially reduced species, followed by loss of the sulphur group, as shown diagrammatically in Scheme 3. Related reactions have also been studied, including the rearrangement (**26**) → (**27**) with potassium carbonate in dimethylformamide, which is a Smiles rearrangement where the nucleophilic displacement is activated only by chlorine atoms.[37] Another investigation of a Smiles rearrangement has been reported.[38]

Other rearrangements studied include: cadmium oxide-catalysed isomerization of potassium phthalate to terephthalate;[39] benzilic acid rearrangement of 5α-cholestane-3,4-dione;[40] acid-catalysed decomposition of peroxydienones derived from 2,6-di-*tert*-butylphenol;[41] a new type of aromatization involving a dienimine–aniline rearrangement with oxidation–reduction;[42] and some acid-catalysed rearrangements of anhydrocryptopine[43] and of diazotized *o*-aminophenylcarbinols.[44]

Cope[45] and Related Rearrangements: Valence-bond Isomerization

Berson and Willcott have published full details of the thermally induced skeletal rearrangements of 7,7-dimethylcycloheptatrienes reported last year,[46] and have reviewed[47] these reactions generally. After careful consideration of alternative mechanisms, the most satisfactory was still considered to be Cope

[36] W. E. Truce, C. R. Robbins, and E. M. Kreider, *J. Am. Chem. Soc.*, **88**, 4027 (1966).

[37] M. F. Grundon and B. T. Johnston, *J. Chem. Soc., B*, **1966**, 255; M. F. Grundon, B. T. Johnston, and W. L. Matier, *ibid.*, p. 260; M. F. Grundon and W. L. Matier, *ibid.*, p. 266.

[38] V. N. Drozd, *Dokl. Akad. Nauk SSSR*, **169**, 107 (1966); *Chem. Abs.*, **65**, 13646 (1966).

[39] T. Sukeno, M. Murayama, and K. Morikawa, *Kogyo Kagaku Zasshi*, **68**, 1582 (1965); *Chem. Abs.*, **64**, 4983 (1965).

[40] J. Levisalles and I. Tkatchenko, *Bull. Soc. Chim. France*, **1966**, 1287.

[41] W. H. Starnes, *J. Org. Chem.*, **31**, 3164 (1966).

[42] M. Dvolaitzky and A. S. Dreiding, *Helv. Chim. Acta*, **48**, 1988 (1965).

[43] D. W. Brown and S. F. Dyke, *Tetrahedron Letters*, **1966**, 3975.

[44] A. J. Sisti and R. L. Cohen, *Can. J. Chem.*, **44**, 2580 (1966).

[45] See also, pp. 210, 213.

[46] See *Organic Reaction Mechanisms*, **1965**, 179.

[47] J. A Berson and R. Willcott, *Record Chem. Progr.*, **27**, 139 (1966).

rearrangement forming a 1,6-bond followed by stepwise migration of the sopropylidene group around the quasi-aromatic ring.[48]

Photolysis of bicyclo[2.2.2]octatriene gave a compound (28) lacking one of bullvalene's three ethylenic bridges, and called "semibullvalene." This is in rapid equilibrium with its degenerate valence tautomer, (28a) ⇌ (28b), since the NMR spectrum showed only three types of hydrogen in the ratio 2:4:2 for the equivalent hydrogens $(4 + 8){:}(1 + 3 + 5 + 7){:}(2 + 6)$.[49] When bullvalene

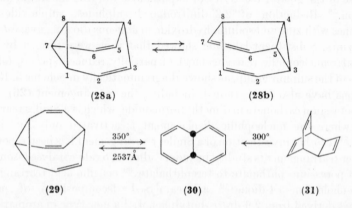

(28a)	(28b)

(29)	(30)	(31)

(29) was heated at 350° in a flow system, 9,10-dihydronaphthalene (30) was formed; at higher temperatures 1,2- and 1,4-dihydronaphthalene and naphthalene were obtained. Irradiation of (30) gave a mixture containing bullvalene; (30) was formed by heating (300°) Nenitzescu's hydrocarbon (31).[50] In the NMR spectrum of solid bullvalene the line width begins to decrease as the temperature is raised above 0°; thus the valence isomerism observed in solution may be occurring in the solid state.[51] A single-crystal X-ray structure analysis of a new bullvalene–silver complex, $(C_{10}H_{10})_3 \cdot AgBF_4$, shows only one tautomeric form of bullvalene suggesting that in this complex its structural fluctuation has been effectively "frozen".[52] A new synthesis of the bullvalene system has been given.[53]

On being heated to 200—220°, the diene (32) undergoes Cope rearrangement to an equilibrium mixture of [(33a), (b), and (c)]; the proportion of (33c) increases with temperature and on stronger heating this rearranges stereospecifically to (34); these reactions give very high yields. A similar sequence

[48] J. A. Berson and M. R. Willcott, *J. Am. Chem. Soc.*, 88, 2494 (1966).
[49] H. E. Zimmerman and G. L. Grunewald, *J. Am. Chem. Soc.*, 88, 183 (1966).
[50] W. von E. Doering and J. W. Rosenthal, *J. Am. Chem. Soc.*, 88, 2078 (1966).
[51] J. D. Graham and E. R. Santee, *J. Am. Chem. Soc.*, 88, 3453 (1966).
[52] M. G. Newton and I. C. Paul, *J. Am. Chem. Soc.*, 88, 3161 (1966).
[53] E. Vogel, W. Grimme, W. Meckel, H. J. Riebel, and J. F. M. Oth, *Angew. Chem. Internat Edn. Engl.*, 5, 590 (1966).

of transformations has been demonstrated for the allylisopulegones (**35**) and for allyl vinyl ketones generally (Scheme 4); some structural limitations to the final cyclization have been reported and discussed.[54] Valence isomerization

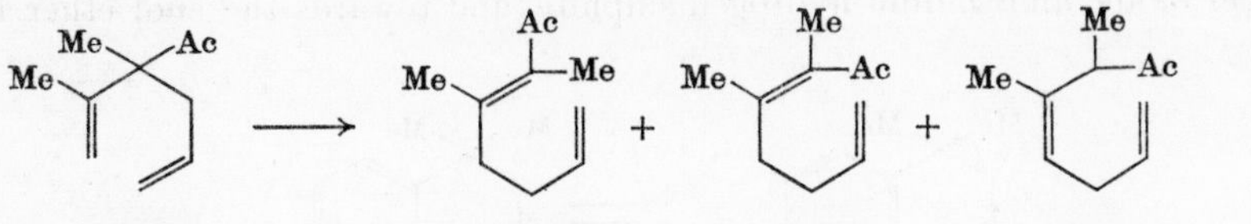

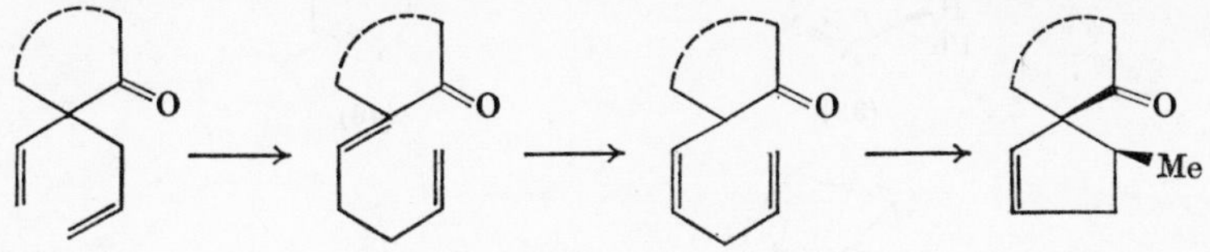

Scheme 4

between a *cis*-dienone and a $2H$-pyran has been clearly established for the first time for *cis*-β-ionone (**36**) and the pyran (**37**),[55] and for the interconversion of 1-dimethylaminopenta-2,4-dienes (**38**).[56] Oxidation of the *N,N'*-dihydro-derivative of (**39**) with lead tetra-acetate gave *trans*-stilbene (89%), possibly by the concerted mechanism shown.[57] Cope rearrangement of hexa-1,5-diene-3,4-diols [e.g., (**40**)] to 1,6-diketones has been demonstrated.[58] The very rapid isomerization of *cis*-1,2-divinylcyclopropanes was reported last year,[59] including that of a relatively stable bicyclic compound where one double bond

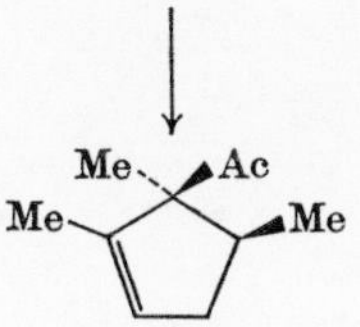

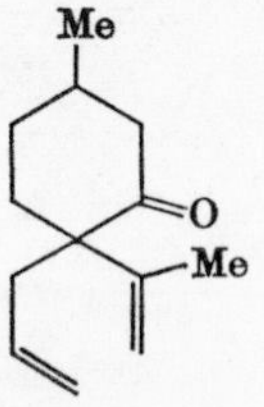

[54] J.-M. Conia and P. Le Perchec, *Bull. Soc. Chim. France*, **1966**, 273, 278, 281, 287.
[55] E. N. Marvell, G. Caple, T. A. Gosink, and G. Zimmer, *J. Am. Chem. Soc.*, **88**, 619 (1966).
[56] H.-W. Bersch and D. Schon, *Tetrahedron Letters*, **1966**, 1141.
[57] M. Rosenblum, A. Longroy, M. Neveu, and C. Steel, *J. Am. Chem. Soc.*, **87**, 5716 (1965).
[58] J. Chuche and J. Wiemann, *Compt. Rend., Ser. C*, **262**, 567 (1966).
[59] See *Organic Reaction Mechanisms*, **1965**, 181, 183.

was part of a fused cyclopentene ring; an oxa-analogue of this has now been reported. *endo*-Bicyclo[3.1.0]hex-2-ene-12-carboxaldehyde (**41**) and 2-oxa-bicyclo[3.2.1]octa-3,6-diene (**42**) exist in rapid reversible equilibrium (7:3) which is displaced towards the aldehyde with lithium aluminium hydride, silver oxide, and sodium hydrogen sulphite, and towards the enol ether by

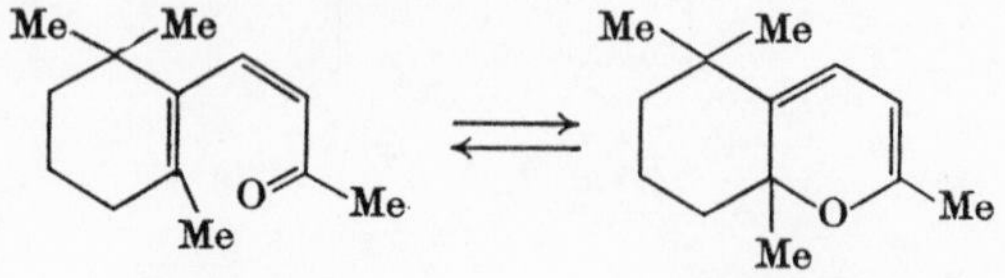

(36)   (37)

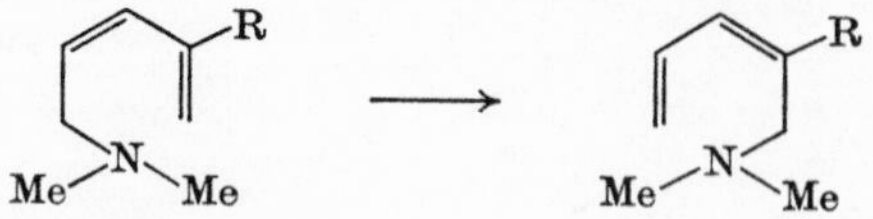

(38)

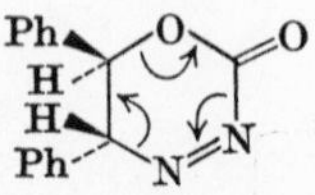

(39) 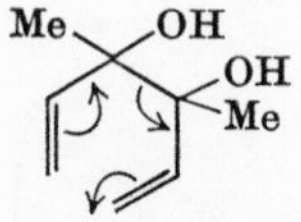   (40)

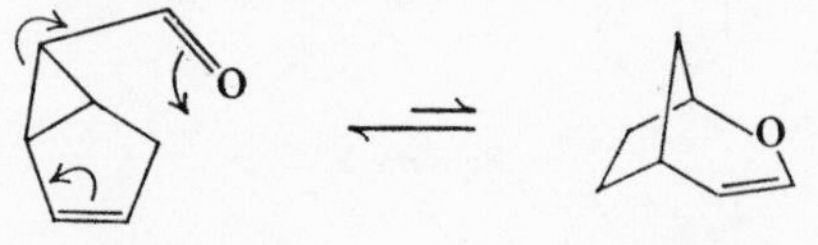

(41)   (42)

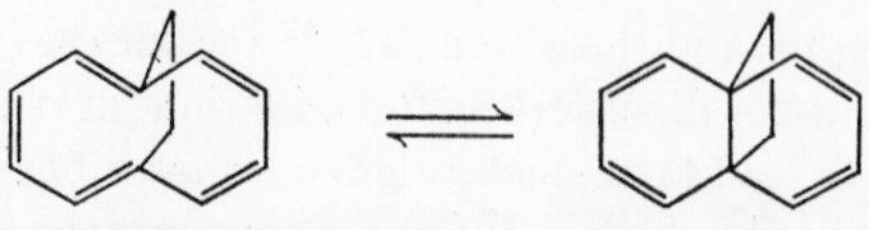

(43)   (44)

cycloaddition with tetracyanoethylene. Decomposition of the bisulphite complex gave the 7:3 mixture.[60] The valence bond isomerization of 1,6-ethanodecapentaene (**43**) and 9,10-dihydro-9,10-ethanonaphthalene (**44**) has been studied; at temperatures above 150° (**44**) did equilibrate with (**43**) but it lost ethylene to give naphthalene.[61]

[60] M. Rey and A. S. Dreiding, *Helv. Chim. Acta*, **48**, 1985 (1965).
[61] E. Vogel, W. Maier, and J. Eimer, *Tetrahedron Letters*, **1966**, 655.

There have been several reports on valence tautomerism in metal–olefin complexes.[62]

Many thermal isomerizations of small-ring hydrocarbons have been reported, and those in the gas phase have been reviewed by Frey.[63] Jefford and Medary[64] have shown that the addition of chlorocarbene to norbornene probably gives all four possible adducts, [(45)—(48)]; (45) and (46) were stable to silver ions and up to 150°, but (47) and (48) were thermally unstable and rearranged to the allyl chlorides shown. They also reacted rapidly with silver nitrate to give *exo*-bicyclo[3.2.1]oct-2-en-3-ol. Isomers (47) and (48) have exactly the geometry required for disrotatory cyclopropyl-to-allyl rearrangement, thus agreeing with the Hoffmann and Woodward predictions. The degenerate scrambling rearrangement of spiropentane [equation (3)] has been shown not to occur under conditions (355°) where much is decomposed to allene and ethylene. Such a rearrangement was observed, however, with methylenecyclobutane in which the exocyclic methylene group mixes with the allylic methylenes [equation (4)]. The activation energy of this reaction was determined and the energetics discussed in detail.[65]

2-*exo*-Deuteriobicyclo[1.1.0]butane (49) rearranges to buta-1,3-diene at 200°, giving the equilibrium mixture of deuterium-labelled *cis*- and *trans*-isomers. The activation energy is considerably less than the calculated enthalpy change for opening to a diradical and it was assumed that the rearrangement is a concerted process with both carbon–carbon bonds partially cleaved in the transition state; in agreement with this is evidence that the Woodward–Hoffmann rules for electrocyclic reactions are obeyed.[66] Heating the dimethyl *exo,exo*- (50) and *exo,endo*(51)-1,3-diphenylbicyclobutane-2,4-dicarboxylate gave the butadienes shown.[67] Bicyclo[1.1.1]pentane rearranged to penta-1,4-diene at about 300°.[68]

The known thermal rearrangement of methylenecyclopropanes [equation (5)] has been extended to alkenylidenecyclopropanes [e.g., equation (6)]. A similar mechanism involving planar delocalized intermediates such as (52) was proposed.[69]

1-Methyl-3-isopropylidenecyclobutene (53) rearranged at temperatures

[62] C. G. Kreiter, A. Maasbol, F. A. L. Anet, H. D. Kaesz, and S. Winstein, *J. Am. Chem. Soc.*, **88**, 3444 (1966); E. B. Fleischer, A. L. Stone, R. B. K. Dewar, J. D. Wright, C. E. Keller, and R. Pettit, *ibid.*, p. 3158; C. E. Keller, B. A. Shoulders and R. Petit, *ibid.*, p. 4760; F. A. Cotton, J. W. Faller, and A. Musco, *ibid.*, p. 4506; F. A. Cotton, A. Davison, and J. W. Faller, *ibid.*, p. 4507.

[63] H. M. Frey, *Adv. Phys. Org. Chem.*, **4**, 147 (1966).

[64] C. W. Jefford and R. Medary, *Tetrahedron Letters*, **1966**, 2069, 2792.

[65] W. von E. Doering and J. C. Gilbert, *Tetrahedron*, Suppl. 7, 397 (1966).

[66] K. B. Wiberg and J. M. Lavanish, *J. Am. Chem. Soc.*, **88**, 5272 (1966).

[67] I. A. D'yakonov, V. V. Razin, and M. I. Komendantov, *Tetrahedron Letters*, **1966**, 1135.

[68] K. B. Wiberg and D. S. Connor, *J. Am. Chem. Soc.*, **88**, 4437 (1966).

[69] J. K. Crandall and D. R. Paulson, *J. Am. Chem. Soc.*, **88**, 4302 (1966).

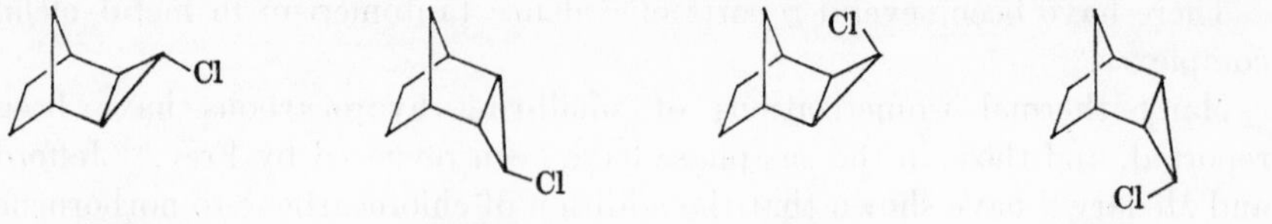

(45)   (46)   (47)   (48)

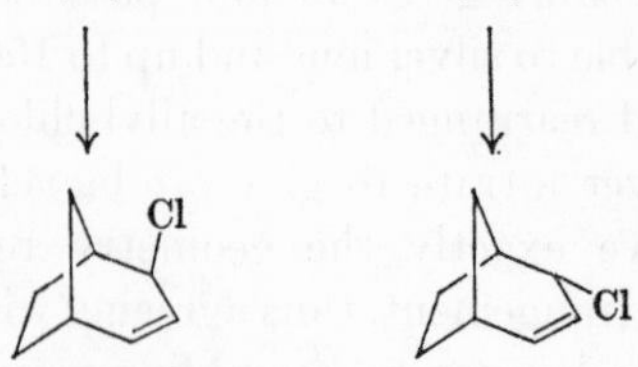

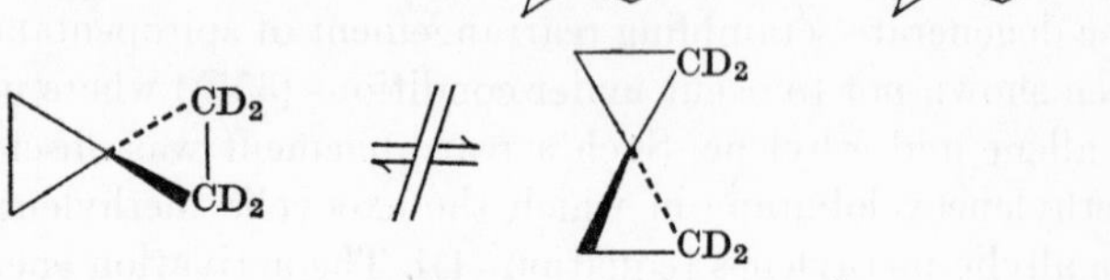

(3)

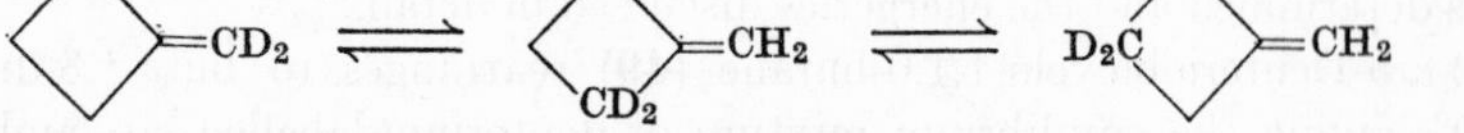

(4)

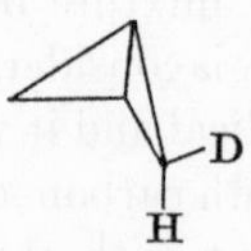

(49)

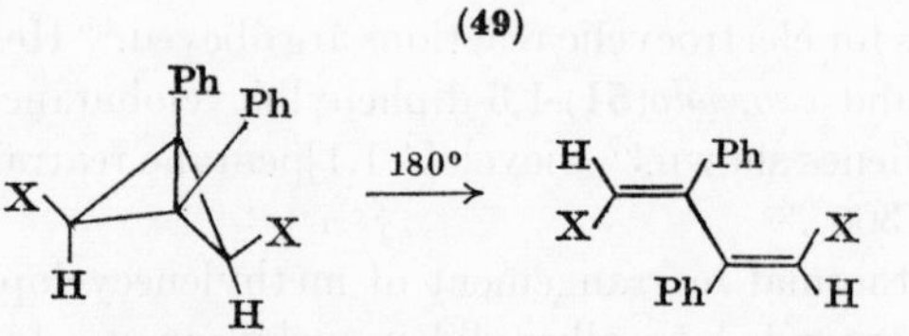

180°

(50)

X = CO$_2$Me   140°

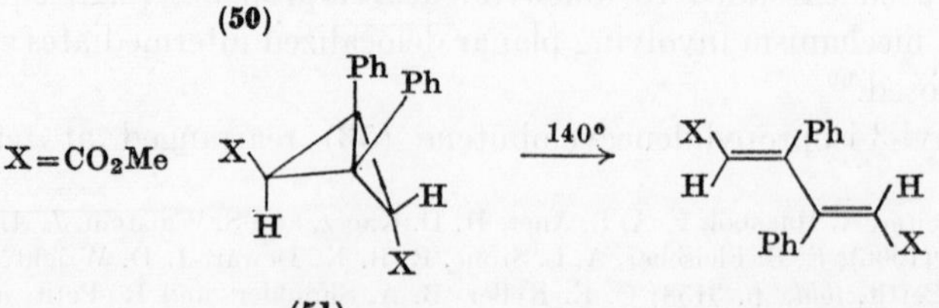

(51)

above 175° to 2,5-dimethylhexa-1,3,4-triene;[70] the rate of isomerization of 1,2-diphenylcyclobutene to 2,3-diphenylbuta-1,3-diene has been measured.[71] A theoretical treatment has been given of the pressure-dependence of the

[70] F. T. Bond, *J. Org. Chem.*, **31**, 3057 (1966).
[71] M. A. Battiste and M. E. Burns, *Tetrahedron Letters*, **1966**, 523.

unimolecular rate constants for the thermal isomerization of cyclobutene and
1- and 3-methylcyclobutene.[72] In the gas phase *cis*- and *trans*-tetramethyl-
cyclobutene isomerize to *cis,trans*- and *trans,trans*-3,4-dimethylhexa-2,4-diene,

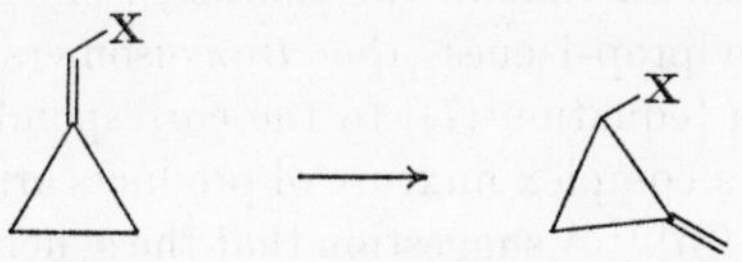

(5)

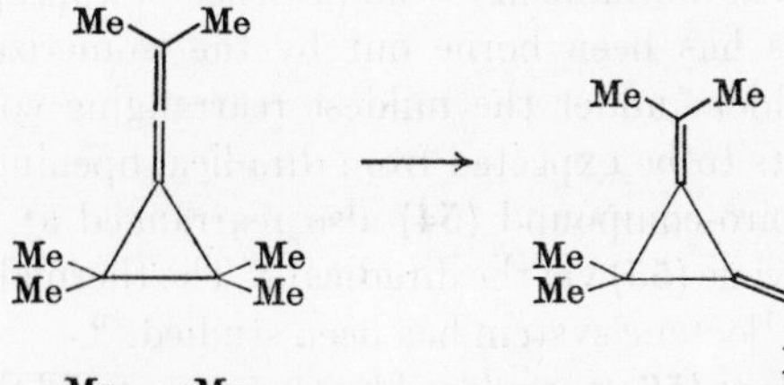

(6)

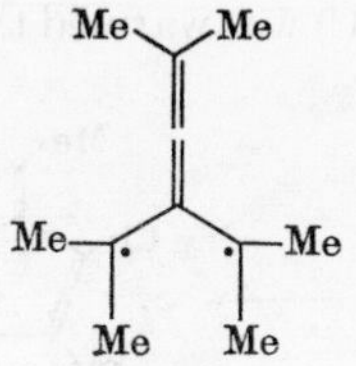

(52)

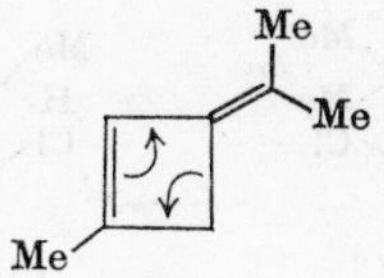

(53)

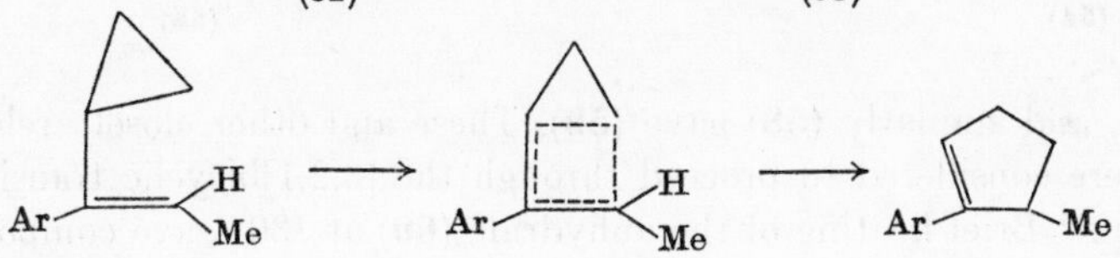

(7)

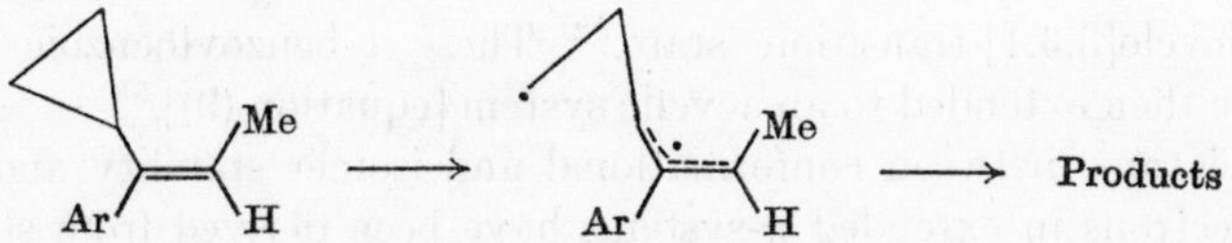

(8)

respectively, and bicyclo[4.2.0]oct-7-ene isomerizes to cycloocta-1,3-diene;
in the first and last of these, steric factors make conrotatory opening highly
unfavourable and, since biradicals are thought not to be involved, disrotatory
opening of the cyclobutene ring is required.[73] Further support for this comes
from a study of the thermal isomerization of bicyclo[3.2.0]hept-6-ene which
gave cyclohepta-1,3-diene exclusively by a disrotatory process, conrotation

[72] C. S. Elliot and H. M. Frey, *Trans. Faraday Soc.*, **62**, 895 (1966).
[73] G. R. Branton, H. M. Frey, and R. F. Skinner, *Trans. Faraday Soc.*, **62**, 1546 (1966).

being impossible.[74] Thermal interconversion of decafluoro-1,2-dimethylcyclo-butene and decafluoro-2,3-dimethylbutadiene has also been studied,[75] and the conversion of 1,1-dicyclopropylethylene into a cyclopentene and thence into bicyclo[3.3.0]oct-1-ene, reported last year, has been reinvestigated.[76] Evidence has been presented that in the thermal isomerization of *cis*- and *trans*-1-aryl-1-cyclopropylprop-1-enes the *trans*-isomers rearrange by a synchronous mechanism [equation (7)] to the corresponding cyclopentenes, and the *cis*-isomers give a complex mixture of products arising from diradical intermediates [equation (8)].[77] A suggestion that the synchronous mechanism might become a diradical mechanism in the presence of appropriate radical-stabilizing substituents has been borne out by the isomerization of some dichloro-derivatives which, under the mildest rearranging conditions, give exclusively the products to be expected from diradical opening of the cyclo-propane ring.[78] The spiro-compound (54) also rearranged at relatively low temperatures to the fulvene (55) via the diradical.[79] The thermal isomerization of the tricyclo[3.2.1.0^{2,4}]octene system has been studied.[80]

When compound (56) or (56; S replaced by C) was warmed the ψ-ester (57)

(54)   (55)

was formed, and similarly (58) gave (59). These and other closely related reactions were considered to proceed through the [3.2.1]bicyclic transition states shown.[81] Brief heating of the anhydride (60) at 130° gave compound (61), and this and closely related rearrangements were thought to involve the analogous bicyclo[3.3.1]-transition state.[82] These *o*-benzoylbenzoic acid reactions were then extended to an acyclic system [equation (9)].[83]

Some correlations between conformational and isomer stability and the number of electrons in extended π-systems have been derived from simple

[74] G. R. Branton, H. M. Frey, D. C. Montague, and I. D. R. Stevens, *Trans. Faraday Soc.*, 62, 659 (1966).
[75] J. P. Chesick, *J. Am. Chem. Soc.*, 88, 4800 (1966).
[76] G. R. Branton and H. M. Frey, *J. Chem. Soc., A*, 1966, 1342.
[77] A. D. Ketley, A. J. Berlin, and L. P. Fisher, *J. Org. Chem.*, 31, 2648 (1966).
[78] A. D. Ketley, A. J. Berlin, E. Gorman, and L. P. Fisher, *J. Org. Chem.*, 31, 305 (1966).
[79] E. T. McBee, J. A. Bosoms, and C. J. Morton, *J. Org. Chem.*, 31, 768 (1966).
[80] H. Prinzbach, W. Eberbach, M. Klaus, G. von Veh, and V. Scheidegger, *Tetrahedron Letters*, 1966, 1681; H. Kriegev and J. Montin, *Suomen Kemistilehti, B*, 39, 201 (1966).
[81] M. S. Newman and C. Courduvelis, *J. Am. Chem. Soc.*, 88, 781 (1966).
[82] M. S. Newman and S. Mladenovic, *J. Am. Chem. Soc.*, 88, 4523 (1966).
[83] M. S. Newman, N. Gill, and B. Darré, *J. Org. Chem.*, 31, 2713 (1966).

molecular orbital-arguments and more detailed extended Hückel molecular-orbital calculations.[84] Zimmerman has given a new treatment of molecular-orbital correlation diagrams for Hückel and Möbius systems.[85]

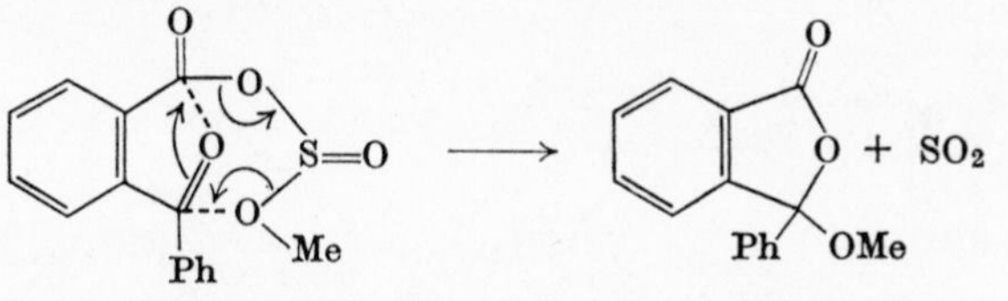

(56) ⟶ (57) + SO_2

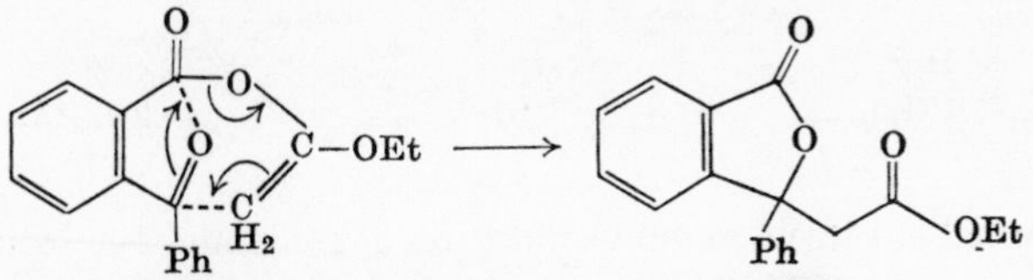

(58) ⟶ (59)

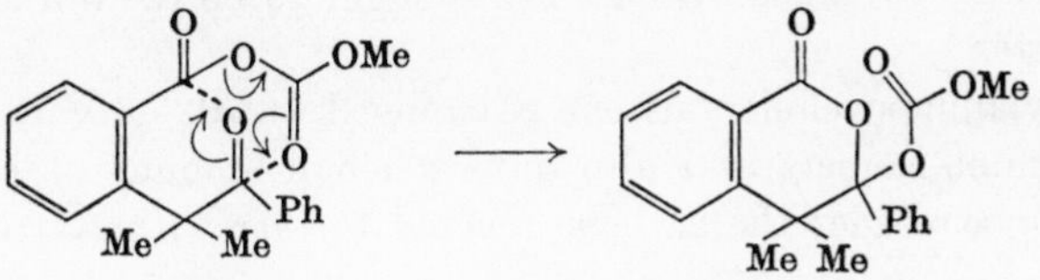

(60) ⟶ (61)

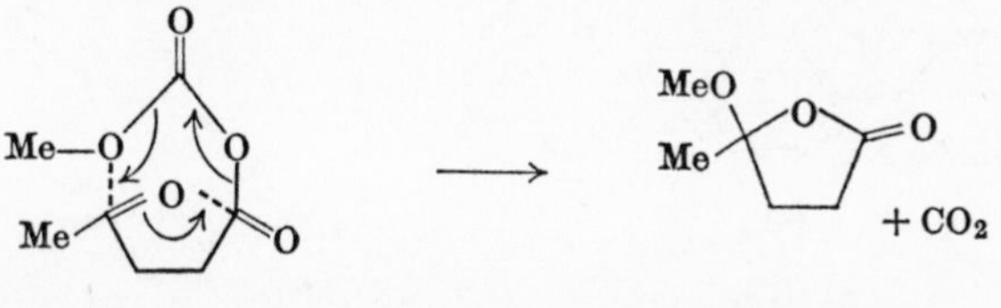

(9)

Intramolecular Hydrogen Migrations and Related Reactions

Intramolecular hydrogen migrations have been reviewed.[86] Winstein and his co-workers have given a general discussion of the energetics and transition states for intramolecular dienyl and homodienyl 1,5-hydrogen shifts, with particular reference to ring size in cyclic dienes [equations (10) and (11)]. For the case where $n = 8$ reaction rates were measured by NMR spectroscopy, with deuterium-labelling for reaction (10) starting with 5-deuteriocyclo-octa-1,3-diene, and Arrhenius parameters were calculated. It was found that the dienyl and homodienyl shifts had very similar energies and entropies of

[84] R. Hoffmann and R. A. Olofson, *J. Am. Chem. Soc.*, **88**, 943 (1966).
[85] H. E. Zimmerman, *J. Am. Chem. Soc.*, **88**, 1564, 1566 (1966).
[86] W. R. Roth, *Chimia (Aarau)*, **20**, 229 (1966).

8

activation and these were also quite similar to the values for dienyl and homodienyl 1,5-shifts in the cyclo-octatrienes and their monomethylene adducts and for acyclic and other cyclic systems.[87] Norbornadienes with 7-alkoxy- or 7-phenyl substituents rearrange at a lower temperature (170°)

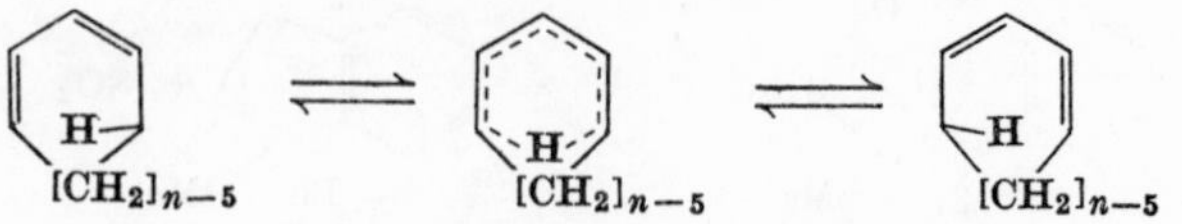

(10)

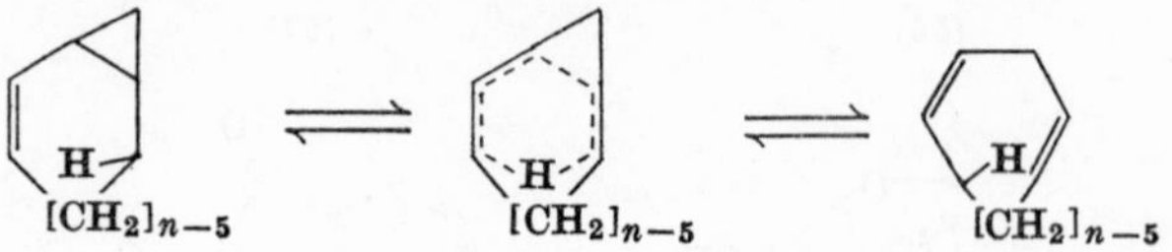

(11)

than norbornadiene itself, and give mixtures of 2-, 3-, and 4-substituted cycloheptatrienes unaccompanied by aromatic and other decomposition products; the 1-substituted cycloheptatrienes are thought to be the initial rearrangement products.[88]

7-Dimethylaminocycloheptatriene rearranged at 70—110° to the 1- and 3-dimethylamino-isomers and also gave a small amount of benzene and dimethylaminocarbene; the carbene reacted further with starting material

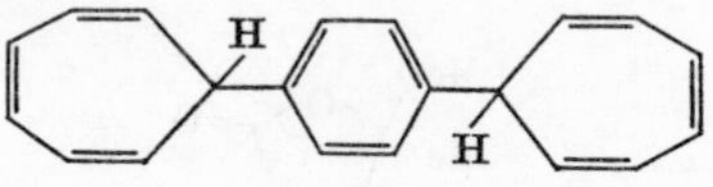

(62)

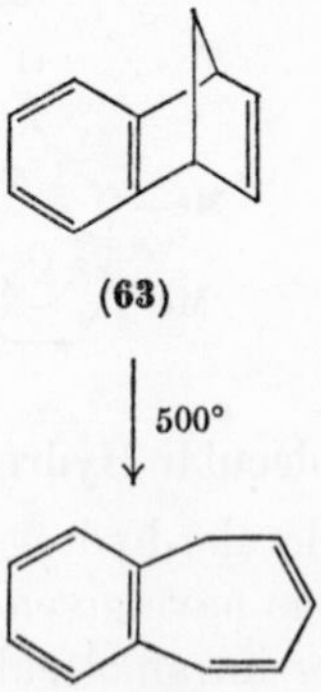

(63)

500°

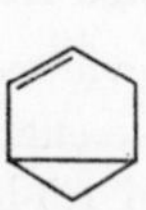

(65)

(64)

and its isomers.[89] Thermal and photochemical sigmatropic reactions of 1,4-di(cycloheptatrienyl)benzene (62) and its isomers have been investigated; in agreement with the Woodward–Hoffmann rules, heating caused a sequence

[87] D. S. Glass, R. S. Boikess, and S. Winstein, *Tetrahedron Letters*, **1966**, 999.
[88] R. K. Lustgarten and H. G. Richey, *Tetrahedron Letters*, **1966**, 4655.
[89] A. P. Ter Borg, E. Razenberg, and H. Kloosterziel, *Rec. Trav. Chim.*, **85**, 774 (1966).

of 1,5-hydrogen shifts whilst ultraviolet irradiation caused 1,7-shifts selectively.[90] Pyrolysis (500°) of benzonorbornadiene (63) gave 1,2-benzocycloheptatriene (64) with small amounts of 1- and 2-methylnaphthalene; at higher temperatures, (64) gave mainly the methylnaphthalenes. The rearrangements are analogous to those without the benzene ring, though here (63) → (64) requires hydrogen transfer, and the mechanism is not yet known.[91]

Thermal isomerization of bicyclo[3.1.0]hex-2-ene (65) at 313—347° to 1,2- and 1,4-dihydrobenzene is a homogeneous first-order reaction that probably involves breaking the common bond to give a diradical, followed by hydrogen transfer.[92] Further work on 1,3-hydrogen shifts in indenes[93] has been reported,

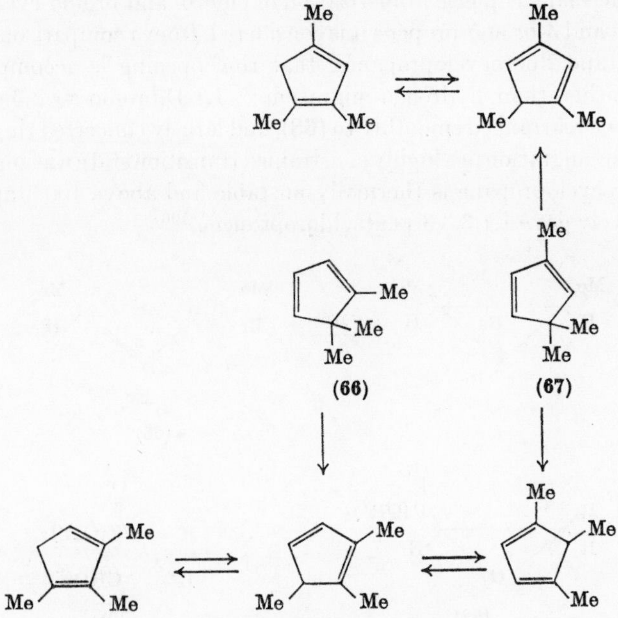

Scheme 5

as have hydrogen shifts in allylbenzene catalysed by deuteriotetracarbonylcobalt,[94] in tricarbonylcycloheptatrienemolybdenum,[95] and in octenes catalysed by phosphine complexes of iridium(III).[96]

[90] R. W. Murray and M. L. Kaplan, *J. Am. Chem. Soc.*, **88**, 3527 (1966).
[91] S. J. Cristol and R. Caple, *J. Org. Chem.*, **31**, 585 (1966).
[92] R. J. Ellis and H. M. Frey, *J. Chem. Soc.*, A, **1966**, 553.
[93] L. Ohlsson, I. Wallmark, and G. Bergson, *Acta Chem. Scand.*, **20**, 750 (1966).
[94] L. Roos and M. Orchin, *J. Am. Chem. Soc.*, **87**, 5502 (1965).
[95] W. R. Roth and W. Grimme, *Tetrahedron Letters*, **1966**, 2347.
[96] R. S. Coffey, *Tetrahedron Letters*, **1965**, 3809.

When 1,5,5-trimethylcyclopenta-1,3-diene (66) was heated (350—400°), 1,2,3-trimethylcyclopentadiene and its tautomers were formed; similarly, when 2,5,5-trimethylcyclopentadiene (67) was heated (300—350°), 1,2,3- and 1,2,4-trimethylcyclopentadiene and their tautomers were formed (see Scheme 5). These isomerizations were not occurring by a chain reaction involving methyl radicals since first-order kinetics were obeyed and products with pentadienylic hydrogen atoms would be expected to act as chain inhibitors; the presence of (67), which rearranges faster than (66), did not alter the rate of rearrangement of (66); and di-*tert*-butyl peroxide and propene had no effect on the rates. Therefore intramolecular thermal 1,5-shifts of methyl groups are proposed.[97]

In the thermal gas-phase isomerization of chloro- and bromo-cyclopropane to 3-chloro- and 3-bromo-propene it is considered, from a comparison of results with alkyl and fluorocyclopropanes, that ring opening is accompanied by halogen- rather than hydrogen-migration.[98] 1,1-Dibromo-*cis*-2,3-dimethyl-cyclopropane rearranged smoothly to (68), and largely concerted ring-opening and bromine-migration in a highly constrained transition state was suggested.[99] Pentachlorocyclopropane is thermally unstable and above 100° rapidly and quantitatively gave 1,1,3,3,3-pentachloropropene.[100]

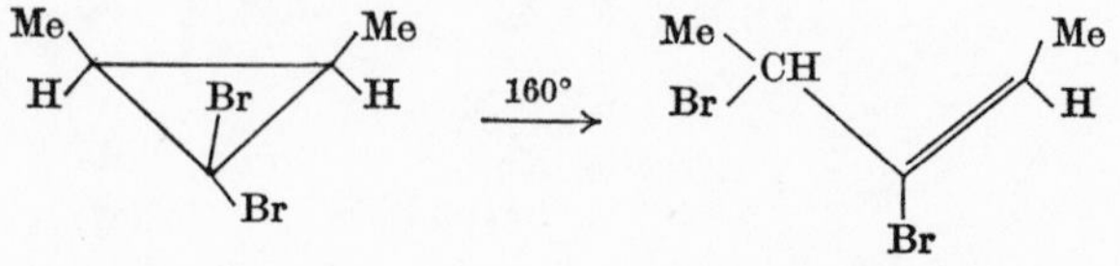

(68)

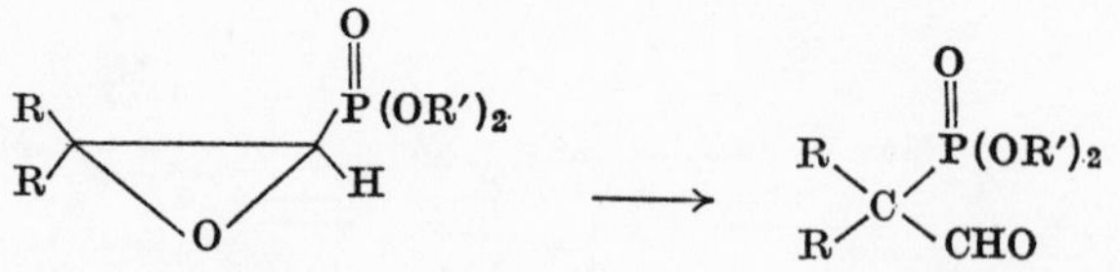

(69)   (70)

Thermal isomerization of hexachlorocyclopropane at 300—400° gave hexachloropropene with no evidence of polymer formation.[101] Oxiranyl-phosphonates (69) rearranged at 200—300° to the 1-formylalkylphosphonates (70).[102]

[97] J. W. de Haan and H. Kloosterziel, *Rec. Trav. Chim.*, **84**, 1594 (1965).
[98] R. C. S. Grant, and E. S. Swinbourne, *Chem. Commun.*, **1966**, 620.
[99] D. C. Duffey, J. P. Minyard, and R. H. Lane, *J. Org. Chem.*, **31**, 3865 (1966).
[100] S. W. Tobey and R. West, *J. Am. Chem. Soc.*, **88**, 2478 (1966).
[101] W. F. Hale, *Can. J. Chem.*, **44**, 1100 (1966).
[102] R. H. Churi and C. E. Griffin, *J. Am. Chem. Soc.*, **88**, 1824 (1966).

Radical Rearrangements

Amongst studies of aryl migrations in free-radical systems,[103—106] it has been found possible to intercept the 2,2,2-triphenylethyl radical before its rearrangement by triphenylstannane.[103] Raising the reaction temperature, or limiting the excess of hydride, leads to increased rearrangement. Migration from oxygen to carbon is observed in the gas phase, the phenoxymethyl radical being transformed into benzaldehyde by ejection of a hydrogen atom.[104]

Phenyl migration has been investigated as a function of ring size in the radicals (71) ($n = 2$—6) obtained by decarbonylation of the corresponding aldehydes. With $n = 2$, the major product is 2-phenylbut-1-ene; products of phenyl migration are also found. With $n = 3$, ring-opening and phenyl migration are accompanied by an apparent alkyl-radical migration that gives products arising from the 1-phenylcyclopentyl radical (72); however, this is probably formed through the ring-opened intermediate shown.

Cycloalkylcarbonyl radicals have also received attention in a different context in the work of Neckers and his colleagues.[107] Hydrogen-abstraction from α-(2-methylcyclopropyl)benzyl alcohol, or H-atom transfer from an α-hydroxyalkyl radical to the corresponding ketone, gave the radical (73).[108] Both processes produce the same proportions of ring-opened ketones (valerophenone and isovalerophenone; 9.25:1). This disallows an alternative mechanism open to the ketonic precursor, although this was earlier suggested for reactions between α-hydroxyalkyl radicals and ketones in photochemical reactions. This alternative involves initial electron-transfer to give the ketyl radical anion. This ketyl radical species, generated independently, was found to give much higher proportions of the isovalerophenone, as expected. The remaining possibility, that electron transfer was succeeded by rapid proton-transfer, before rearrangement, seems to be excluded by comparing the rates of hydrogen-transfer to cyclopropyl phenyl ketone, and to certain cyclopropyl-substituted derivatives. It was found, for example, that the compounds with either *cis*- or *trans*-2-phenyl substituents on the cyclopropane ring accepted hydrogen more than 10 times as readily as cyclopropyl phenyl ketone itself, indicating that hydrogen-transfer and ring-opening are concerted. Further evidence consistent with concerted hydrogen-transfer and ring-opening in the cyclopropyl phenyl ketone comes from a comparison with the relative rates of hydrogen-transfer to the corresponding cyclobutyl,

103 L. Kaplan, *J. Am. Chem. Soc.*, **88**, 4531 (1966).
104 M. F. R. Mulcahy, B. G. Tucker, D. J. Williams, and J. R. Wilshurst, *Chem. Commun.*, **1965**, 609.
105 J. W. Wilt, J. F. Zawadzki, and D. G. Schultenover, *J. Org. Chem.*, **31**, 876 (1966).
106 J. W. Wilt, L. L. Maravetz, and J. F. Zawadzki, *J. Org. Chem.*, **31**, 3018 (1966).
107 See *Organic Reaction Mechanisms*, **1965**, 187.
108 D. C. Neckers, A. P. Schaap, and J. Hardy, *J. Am. Chem. Soc.*. **88**, 1265 (1966).

cyclopentyl, and isopropyl phenyl ketones. The four relative rates are 36, 11, 1.8, and 1.0, respectively.[109] Ring-opened products are observed in the cyclobutyl case.

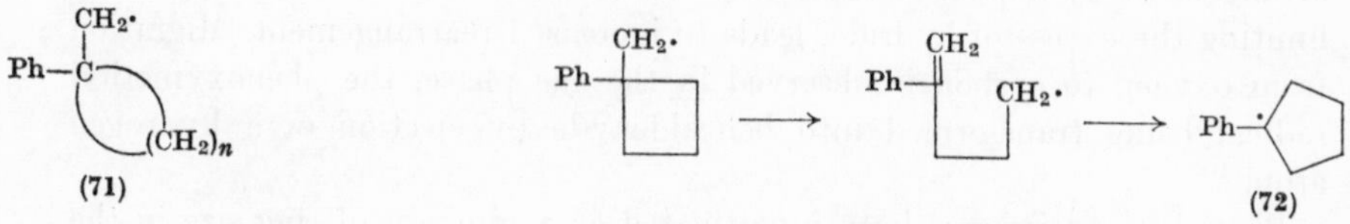

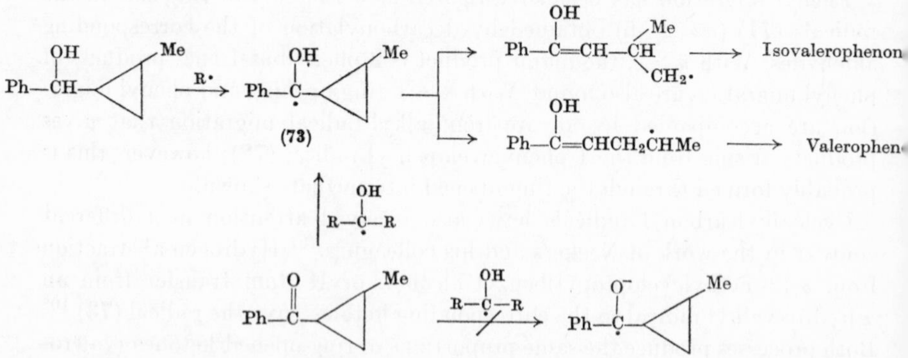

1-Substituted cyclopropanols similarly suffer ring-opening on oxidation; thus the cyclopropanone hemiacetal (74) gives adipic ester.[110] The related ring-opening of radical (75) has been used to obtain cyclodecane derivatives,[111]

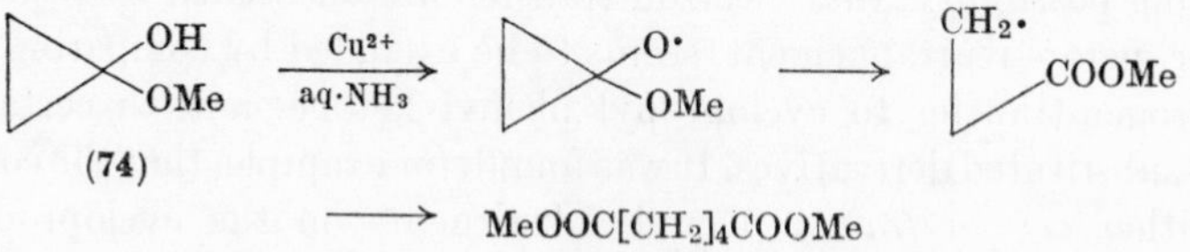

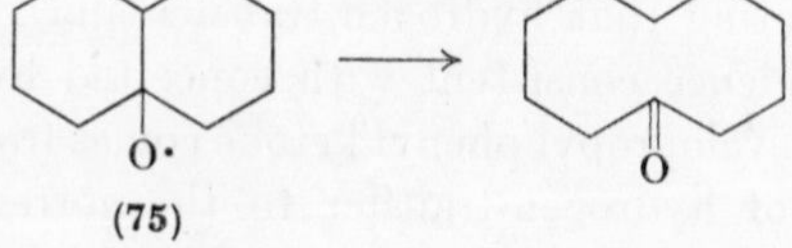

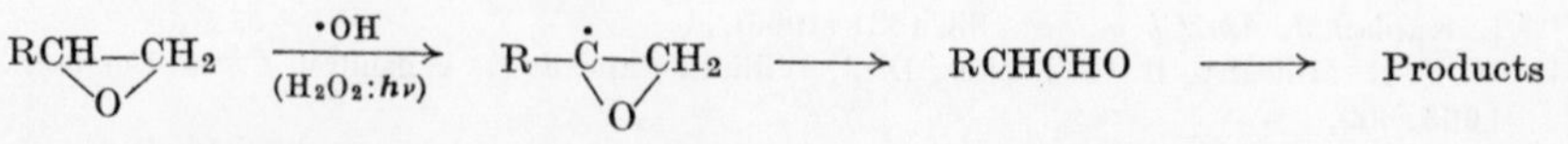

[109] D. C. Neckers, J. Hardy, and A. P. Schaap, *J. Org. Chem.*, **31**, 622 (1966).
[110] S. E. Schaafsma, H. Steinberg, and T. J. de Boer, *Rec. Trav. Chim.*, **85**, 70, 73 (1966).
[111] M. Akhtar and S. Marsh, *J. Chem. Soc., C*, **1966**, 937.

and products from the ring-opening of several epoxides have been observed by Razuvaev's group.[112]

Two groups of workers[113, 114] have approached the norbornenyl–nortricyclyl radical equilibrium from both sides. In neither instance was there any evidence for non-classical behaviour. The vinyl group migration involved finds analogy

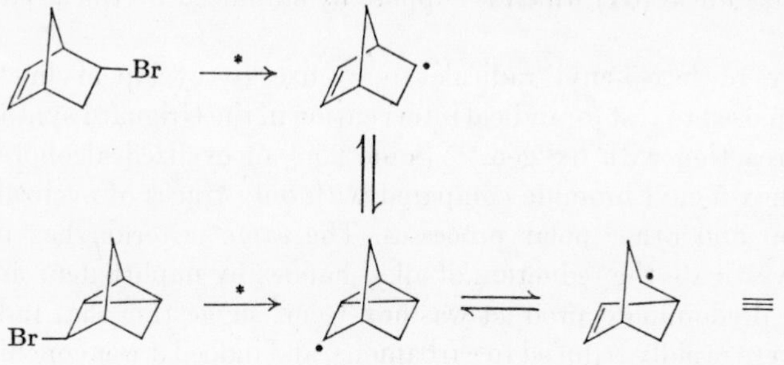

*Et_2O; $RMgBr$; $CoCl_2$[113]; Bu_3SnH[114].

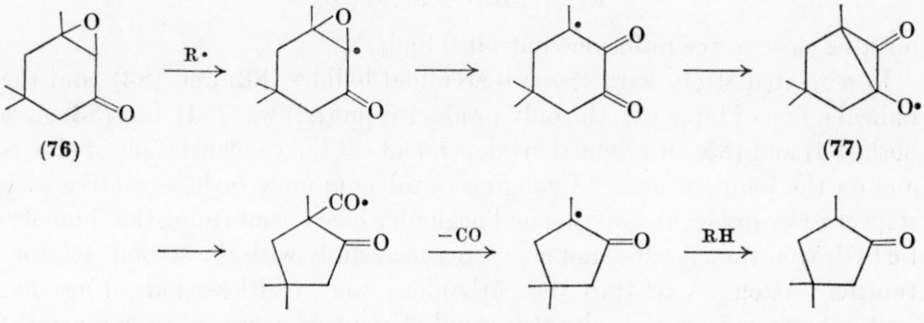

(76)   (77)

in the mechanism proposed for a 1,2-acyl shift in the homolytic ring-contraction of epoxy-ketone (76);[115] this may involve the intermediate (77).

Migration of hydrogen atoms in alkyl radicals has been reviewed,[116] and

$$CH_3CD_2COOD \xrightarrow[h\nu]{SO_2Cl_2} CH_2CHDCO + CH_3CDCOOD$$

(78)   (79)   (80)

(81)

[112] G. A. Razuvaev, V. S. Etlis, and E. P. Morozova, *Zh. Org. Khim.*, **2**, 256 (1966); *Chem. Abs.*, **65**, 2090 (1966).

[113] D. I. Davies, J. N. Done, and D. H. Hey, *Chem. Commun.*, **1966**, 725.

[114] C. R. Warner, R. J. Strunk, and H. G. Kuivila, *J. Org. Chem.*, **31**, 3381 (1966).

[115] W. Reusch, C. K. Johnson, and J. A. Manner, *J. Am. Chem. Soc.*, **88**, 2803 (1966).

[116] M. Lazar and O. Kysel, *Chem. Listy*, **60**, 192 (1966); *Chem. Abs.*, **64**, 11048 (1966).

evidence presented for a 1,2-hydrogen transfer.[117] The trideuterated propionic acid (78) reacts with sulphuryl chloride under the influence of ultraviolet light to give the monodeuterated cyclic anhydride (79), and the sulphonyl chloride (80) in roughly equal proportions. The results were interpreted in terms of hydrogen abstraction from the α-position, followed by formation of products from the bridged radical (81) which is supposedly stabilized by the adjacent carbonyl group.

The tendency of hex-5-enyl radicals to cyclize to cyclopentylmethyl radicals has been used to test for radical intervention in the Grignard synthesis of alcohols by reaction with oxygen.[118] Some 25% of cyclized alcohol was obtained from hex-5-enyl bromide compared with only traces of cyclization in carboxylation and other polar processes. The same criterion has been employed to investigate the reduction of alkyl halides by naphthalene anion radicals.[119] The predominant product was hex-1-ene, suggesting that radical intermediates were rapidly reduced to carbanions, and indeed it was concluded that the rate of the reaction

$$R\cdot + [C_{10}H_8]^{-}\cdot \rightarrow R^- + C_{10}H_8$$

must be close to the diffusion-controlled limit.

In a related study with the two steroidal halides (82) and (83), and the radical anion of biphenyl, the only product from (82) was (84), but (83) gave both (84) and (85) in proportions dependent on the concentration of $(Ph_2)^{-}\cdot$ and on the temperature.[120] Changing to solvents more or less reactive with respect to hydrogen abstraction had negligible effect, confirming that homolytic hydrogen-transfer does not compete successfully with the second electron-transfer. Attempts to trap the carbanions were fruitless, indicating that proton-transfer from the solvent is rapid. A reduced degree of rearrangement observed at low temperatures indicates positive activation energy for the rearrangement and thus further discredits the concept of non-classical intermediates in such radical rearrangements.

Returning to the reactions of hex-5-enyl radicals, it has now been shown that in the reaction of hex-5-enyl bromide with tributylstannane, cyclization competes favourably with hydrogen-transfer to the straight-chain radical.[121] However, the ratios of open-chain to cyclized products under different conditions seem to require that at least part of the cyclized product arises by a concerted process, implying association of the double bond with the incipient radical centre. A comparable analysis of the triphenylethyl radical rearrangement[103] would be of interest.

[117] T. Nagai, K. Nishitomi, and N. Tokura, *Tetrahedron Letters*, **1966**, 2419.
[118] R. C. Lamb, P. W. Ayers, M. K. Toney, and J. F. Garst, *J. Am. Chem. Soc.*, **88**, 4261 (1966).
[119] J. F. Garst, P. W. Ayers, and R. C. Lamb, *J. Am. Chem. Soc.*, **88**, 4260 (1966).
[120] S. J. Cristol and R. V. Barbour, *J. Am. Chem. Soc.*, **88**, 4262 (1966).
[121] C. Walling, J. H. Cooley, A. A. Ponaras, and E. J. Racah, *J. Am. Chem. Soc.*, **88**, 5361 (1966).

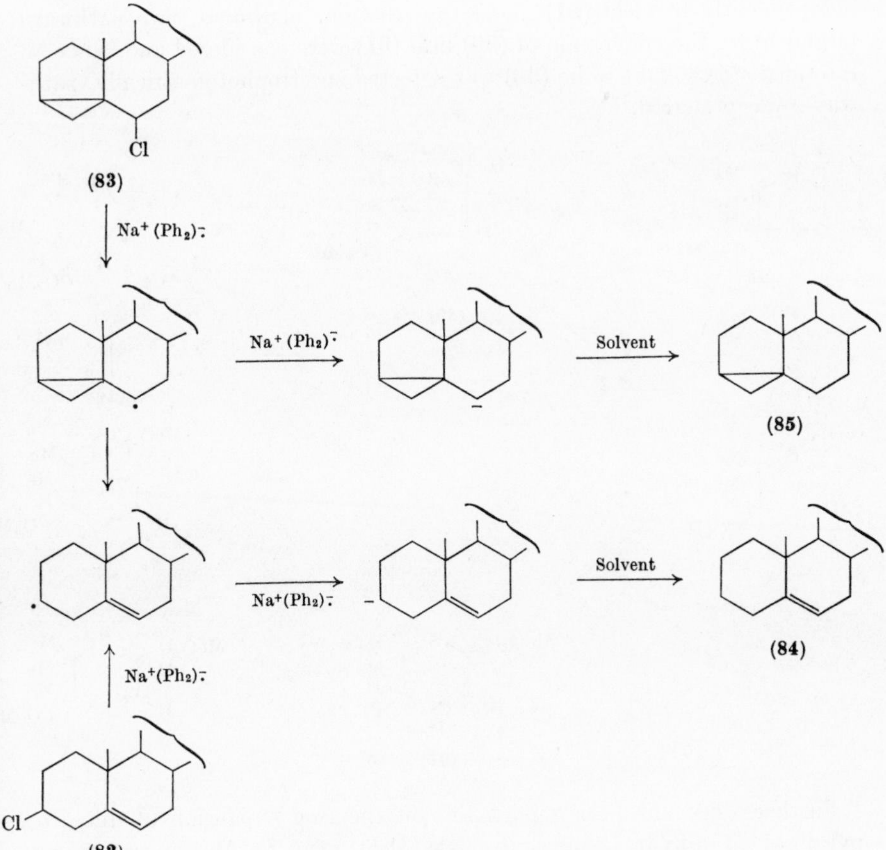

(83)

Na⁺ (Ph₂)⁻

Na⁺ (Ph₂)⁻ ⟶ Solvent ⟶

(85)

Na⁺(Ph₂)⁻

Solvent ⟶

Na⁺(Ph₂)⁻ ⟶

(84)

Na⁺(Ph₂)⁻

Cl

(82)

The photochemical homolytic rearrangement of *N*-halogenoacetanilides has been studied,[122] as well as the radical-initiated rearrangement (86) → (87).[123]

$$\text{Ph} - \underset{\underset{\text{Me}}{|}}{\overset{\overset{\text{Me}}{|}}{\text{C}}} - \text{SPh} \longrightarrow \text{MePhCHCH}_2\text{SPh}$$

(86)   (87)

Heterocyclic Rearrangements

6-Chloropenicillanic acid (88), on treatment with sodium methoxide, is converted into dimethyl 2,3-dihydro-2,2-dimethyl-1,4-thiazine-3(D),6-dicarboxylate (91). Ester (89) was postulated as an intermediate and shown

122 D. D. Tanner and E. Protz, *Can. J. Chem.*, **44**, 1555 (1966); K. M. Johnston, G. H. Williams, and H. J. Williams, *Chem. and Ind.*, **1966**, 991.
123 A. B. Terent'ev, *Izv. Nauk SSSR, Ser. Khim.*, **1965**, 1258; *Chem. Abs.*, **63**, 12990 (1965).

8*

independently to yield (**91**) under the reaction conditions. Two pathways (a and b) for the conversion of (**90**) into (**91**) were considered and, since an intermediate thought to be (**90**) was detected spectrophotometrically, pathway b was preferred.[124]

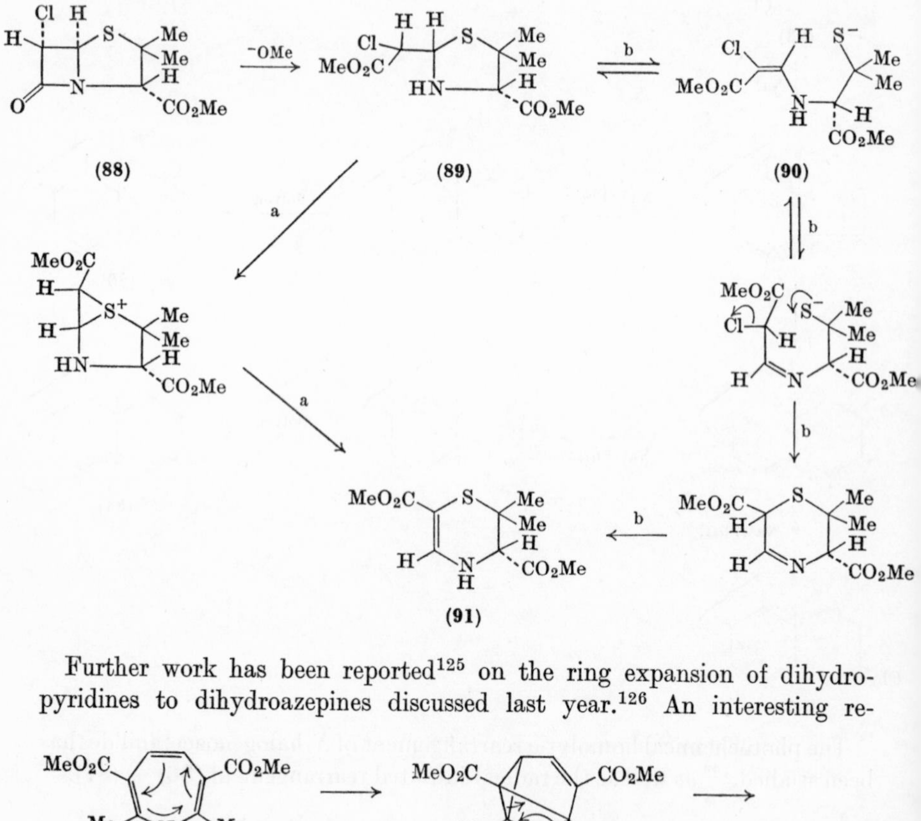

(**88**)   (**89**)   (**90**)

(**91**)

Further work has been reported[125] on the ring expansion of dihydropyridines to dihydroazepines discussed last year.[126] An interesting re-

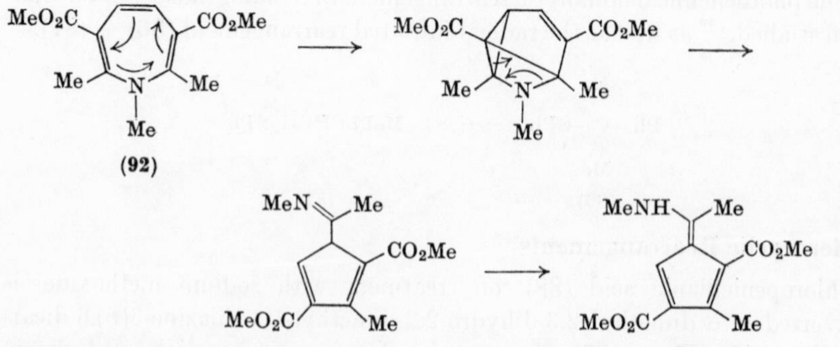

(**92**)

(13)

(**93**)

[124] I. McMillan and R. J. Stoodley, *Tetrahedron Letters*, **1966**, 1205.
[125] R. F. Childs and A. W. Johnson, *J. Chem. Soc., C*, **1966**, 1950.
[126] See *Organic Reaction Mechanisms*, **1965**, 187.

arrangement of the azepine (92) into the fulvene (93) has also been described and formulated as shown in equation (13).[127]

The ring expansion of the 2-(dichloromethyl)quinazoline 3-oxide (94) with alkali to the 1,4-benzodiazepin-2-one 4-oxide (95) has been shown to proceed with ring opening to the *anti*-oxime (96).[128]

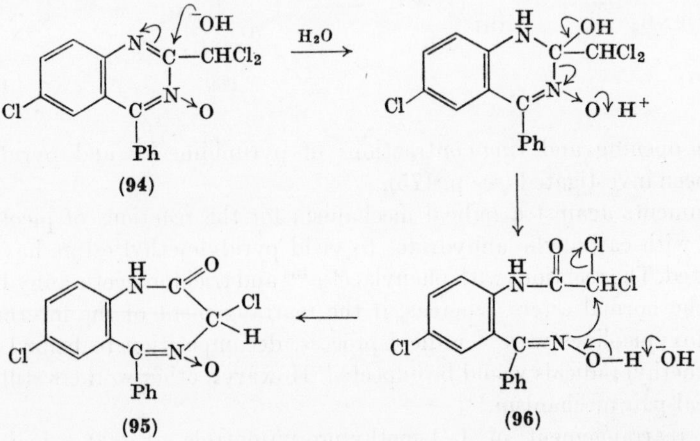

(94)

(95)   (96)

There have been extensive investigations of the rearrangements of benzo-furazan oxides and related compounds, mainly by NMR spectroscopy. Most of the evidence supports the view that the reactions of the benzofurazan proceeds through intermediate dinitroso-compounds, as shown in equation (14).[129]

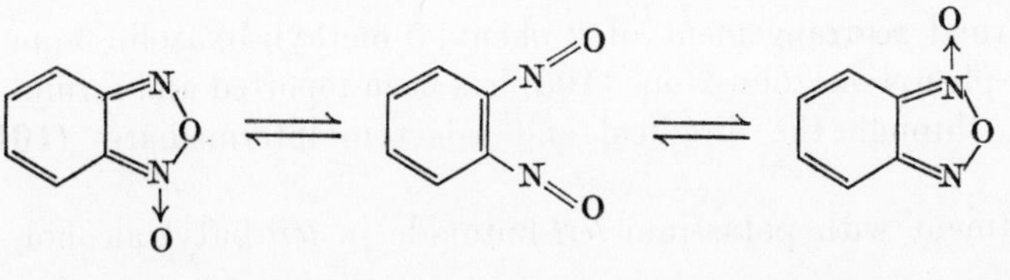

(14)

2-[^{15}N]Aminopyridine (97) undergoes a slow rearrangement when heated in aqueous HCl or ammonia (50—100 hours, 200°) into the compound (99) with the ring-nitrogen labelled. This reaction, which presumably proceeds by

[127] R. F. Childs, R. Grigg, and A. W. Johnson, *Chem. Commun.*, 1966, 442.
[128] A. Stempel, E. Reeder, and L. H. Sternbach, *J. Org. Chem.*, 30, 4267 (1965); G. F. Field, W. J. Zally, and L. H. Sternbach, *Tetrahedron Letters*, 1966, 2609.
[129] F. B. Mallory and A. Cammarata, *J. Am. Chem. Soc.*, 88, 61 (1966); A. J. Boulton, A. C. G. Gray, and A. R. Katritzky, *J. Chem. Soc.*, 1965, 5958; F. B. Mallory, S. L. Manatt, and C. S. Wood, *J. Am. Chem. Soc.*, 87, 5433 (1965); A. J. Boulton, P. B. Ghosh, and A. R. Katritzky, *J. Chem. Soc.*, *B*, 1966, 1004, 1011; A. J. Boulton, A. C. Gripper Gray, and A. R. Katritzky, *Chem. Commun.*, 1966, 741.

ring opening, is accompanied by hydrolysis to ammonia and 2-pyridone. The isotopic composition of the ammonia indicates, however, that the 2-pyridone is not formed from the symmetrical acyclic intermediate (98).[130] The Dimroth rearrangement has also been investigated.[131]

(97)   (98)   (99)

Ring-opening and ring-contractions of pyrimidines[132] and pyridines[133] have been investigated (see p. 175).

Arguments against a radical mechanism for the reactions of picoline N-oxides with carboxylic anhydrides to yield pyridylmethyl esters have been presented. The reactions with phenylacetic[134] and trichloroacetic anhydride[135] yield the normal esters, whereas, if the rearrangement of the intermediate N-acyloxypicolines were a radical process, decomposition to benzyl or trichloromethyl radicals would be expected. However, other workers still prefer a radical-pair mechanism.[136]

The rearrangement of 1-(1-methylpropyl)pyrrole at 600° yields 2-(1-methylpropyl)pyrrole with 77% retention of configuration and 3-(1-methylpropyl)pyrrole with 10% retention of configuration. 1-(α-Methylbenzyl)pyrrole similarly yields the 2-isomer with 77% retention and the 3-isomer with 10% retention. The transition state was considered to be a cyclic one in which homolytic bond-breaking has advanced to a greater extent than bond-formation.[137]

The thermal rearrangement of 2-phenyl-5-methylisoxazolin-3-one (100) into the N-phenyl oxazolin-2-one (103) has been reported and formulated as proceeding through the diradical and α-lactam intermediates (101) and (102).[138]

On treatment with potassium tert-butoxide in tert-butyl alcohol, 3(cis)-

[130] M. Wahren, Z. Chem., 6, 181 (1966).
[131] D. D. Perrin and I. H. Pitman, J. Chem. Soc., 1965, 7071; D. J. Brown and M. N. Paddon-Row, J. Chem. Soc., C, 1966, 164.
[132] H. W. van Meeteren and H. C. van der Plas, Tetrahedron Letters, 1966, 4517.
[133] H. J. den Hertog, R. J. Martens, H. C. van der Plas, and J. Bon, Tetrahedron Letters, 1966, 4325.
[134] T. Cohen and J. H. Fager, J. Am. Chem. Soc., 87, 5701 (1965).
[135] T. Koenig, J. Am. Chem. Soc., 88, 4045 (1966).
[136] V. J. Traynelis and A. I. Gallagher, J. Am. Chem. Soc., 87, 5710 (1965); S. Oae, S. Tamagaki, and S. Kozuka, Tetrahedron Letters, 1966, 1513; S. Oae, S. Kozuka, Y. Sakaguchi, and K. Hiramatsu, Tetrahedron, 22, 3143 (1966).
[137] J. M. Patterson and L. T. Burka, J. Am Chem. Soc., 88, 3671 (1966).
[138] A. R. Gagneux and R. Göschke, Tetrahedron Letters, 1966, 5451.

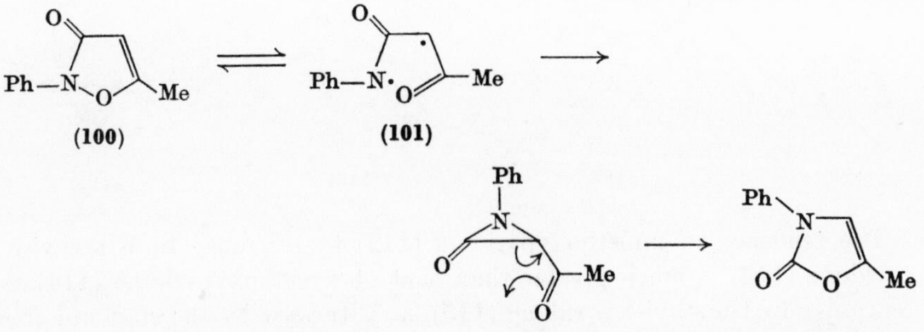

(100) (101)

(102) (103)

chloro-3-methyl-1,2-diphenylaziridine (**104**) yields the anilide (**105**); and its ethyl analogue (**106**) yields the analogous anilide (**107**). The methyl group of (**104**) thus becomes the α-methylene group of the anilide (**105**). With Me_3COK in Me_3COD, (**104**) yields an anilide in which there has been 95% and 90% incorporation of deuterium at the α- and the β-position, respectively. The mechanism of equation (15) was proposed.[139]

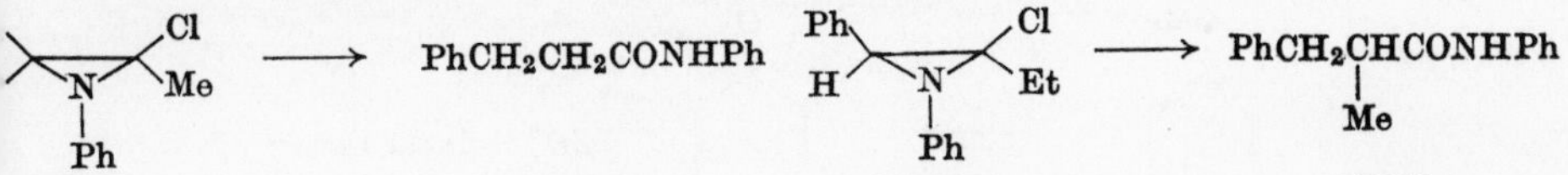

(104) (105) (106) (107)

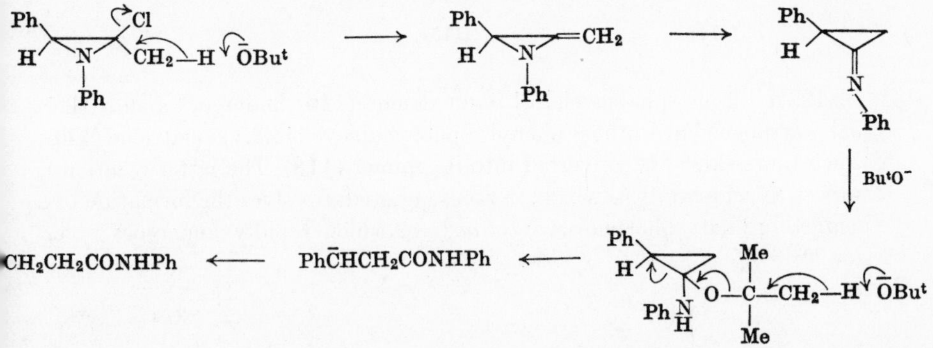

(15)

In refluxing methanolic silver nitrate, *N*-chloroisoquinuclidine (**108**) undergoes an interesting rearrangement to 2-methoxy-1-azabicyclo[3.2.1]-octane (**111**). At present it is not known whether the reaction involves an intermediate nitrenium ion (**109**) which rearranges to a carbonium ion (**110**) or whether the latter is formed in a concerted process.[140]

139 J. A. Deyrup and R. B. Greenwald, *Tetrahedron Letters*, **1966**, 5091.
140 P. G. Gassman and B. L. Fox, *Chem. Commun.*, **1966**, 153.

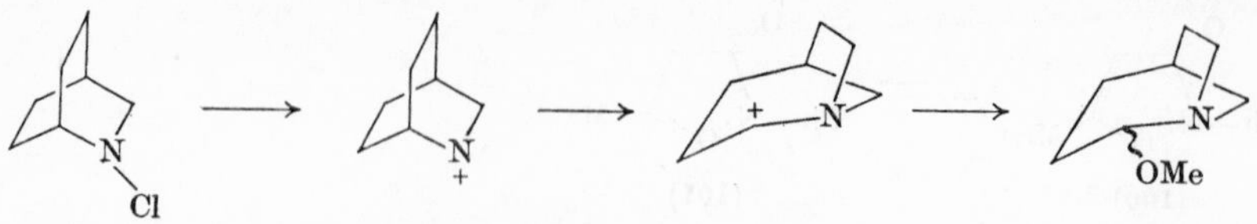

(108)   (109)   (110)   (111)

The tendency of 2-methoxypyridine (112) to rearrange to 1-methyl-2-pyridone (113) is much greater than that of 4-methoxypyridine (114) to rearrange to 1-methyl-4-pyridone (115), as witnessed by the standard free energies for these rearrangements in the gas-phase, which have the values shown.[141]

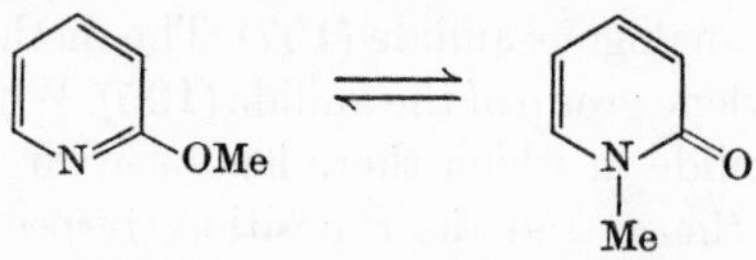

$\Delta G^\circ < -6$ kcal. mole^{-1}

(112)   (113)

$\Delta G^\circ < -2$ kcal. mole^{-1}

(114)   (115)

9-Phenyl-9-phosphabicyclo[6.1.0]nonatriene (116) undergoes a slow thermal rearrangement to the 9-phenyl-9-phosphabicyclo[4.2.1]nonatriene (117), which more slowly is converted into its epimer (118). The latter reaction is subject to acid-catalysis which, it was suggested, involves the formation of a pentaco-ordinate phosphorus intermediate which rapidly undergoes inversion.[142]

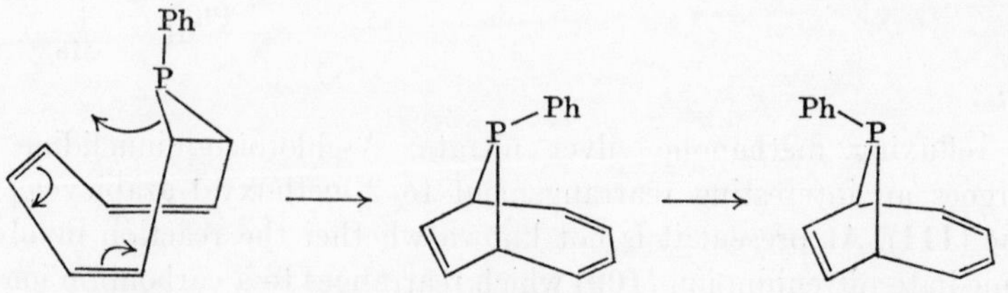

(116)   (117)   (118)

[141] P. Beak and J. Bonham, *Chem. Commun.*, **1966**, 631.
[142] T. J. Katz, C. R. Nicholson, and C. A. Reilly, *J. Am. Chem. Soc.*, **88**, 3832 (1966).

Other heterocyclic rearrangements which have been investigated include: rearrangement of tetrahydroquinolines to 4-aminoindanes,[143] 1,2-dihydro-2-phenylimino-4H-3,1-benzoxazin-4-one to 3-phenylquinazoline-2,4($1H$,$3H$)-dione,[144] anhydrodilactams into diazaspiranes,[145] N-acylaziridines into oxazolines[146] (see also, p. 56), and 1,2-dihydro-2-methylpapaverine to 3,4-dihydroisoquinolinium salts;[147] the tautomerism of 6-hydroxy-6-amino- and 6-acylamino-7-azaindolines,[148] and of side-chain derivatives of heterocyclic compounds;[149] the Fischer indole synthesis;[150] the Nenitzescu indole synthesis;[151] ring expansion of 2-substituted indanones to 2-hydroxyisocarbostyril derivatives;[152a] and reaction of dithiolium salts with ammonia to give isothiazoles.[152b]

Other Rearrangements

Two interesting investigations of Beckmann rearrangements that proceed by abnormal mechanisms have been reported.[153, 154] In the first, Hill, Conley, and Chortyk[153] showed that pinacolone oxime in polyphosphoric acid yields N-*tert*-butylacetamide and 2-methyl-2-phenylpropiophenone oxime yields N-benzoyl-α,α-dimethylbenzylamine, but that when the two oximes are allowed to react in the same solution crossed products, N-*tert*-butylbenzamide and N-acetyl-α,α-dimethylbenzylamine, are also obtained. Fragmentation of the oximes to carbonium ions and nitriles, followed by recombination in a

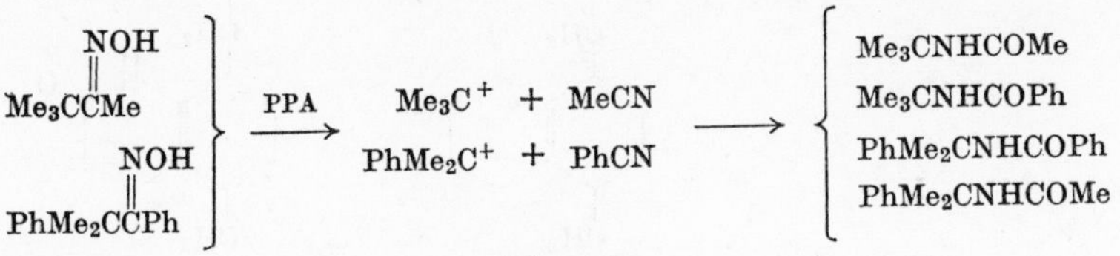

$$
\left.\begin{array}{c}
\text{NOH} \\
\| \\
\text{Me}_3\text{CCMe} \\
\text{NOH} \\
\| \\
\text{PhMe}_2\text{CCPh}
\end{array}\right\}
\xrightarrow{\text{PPA}}
\begin{array}{c}
\text{Me}_3\text{C}^+ + \text{MeCN} \\
\text{PhMe}_2\text{C}^+ + \text{PhCN}
\end{array}
\longrightarrow
\left\{\begin{array}{c}
\text{Me}_3\text{CNHCOMe} \\
\text{Me}_3\text{CNHCOPh} \\
\text{PhMe}_2\text{CNHCOPh} \\
\text{PhMe}_2\text{CNHCOMe}
\end{array}\right.
$$

Scheme 7

143 W. H. Cliffe, D. Dodman, and O. Meth-Cohn, *J. Chem. Soc.*, *C*, **1966**, 514.

144 M. Kurihara and N. Yoda, *Bull. Chem. Soc. Japan*, **39**, 1942 (1966).

145 K. H. Büchel, A. K. Bocz, and F. Korte, *Chem. Ber.*, **99**, 724 (1966).

146 P. E. Fanta, and E. N. Walsh, *J. Org. Chem.*, **31**, 59 (1966); H. W. Heine, D. C. King, and L. A. Portland, *ibid.*, p. 2662.

147 J. Knabe and K. Detering, *Chem. Ber.*, **99**, 2873 (1966).

148 L. N. Jakhontov, D. M. Krasnokutskaya, E. M. Peresleni, J. N. Sheinker, and M. V. Rubtsov, *Tetrahedron*, **22**, 3233 (1966).

149 R. Mondelli and L. Merlini, *Tetrahedron*, **22**, 3253 (1966).

150 R. E. Lyle and L. Skarlos, *Chem. Commun.*, **1966**, 644.

151 G. R. Allen and M. J. Weiss, *Chem. Ind.* (*London*), **1966**, 117.

152a E. J. Moriconi and F. J. Creegan, *J. Org. Chem.*, **31**, 2090 (1966).

152b R. A. Olofson, J. M. Landesberg, R. O. Berry, D. Leaver, W. A. H. Robertson, and D. M. McKinnon, *Tetrahedron*, **22**, 2119 (1966); J. M. Landesberg and R. A. Olofson, *ibid.*, p. 2135.

153 R. K. Hill, R. T. Conley, and C. T. Chortyk, *J. Am. Chem. Soc.*, **87**, 5646 (1965).

154 P. T. Lansbury and N. R. Mancuso, *J. Am. Chem. Soc.*, **88**, 1205 (1966).

Ritter reaction, to yield amides (Scheme 7) was therefore postulated. 9-Acetyl-*cis*-decalin oxime also rearranges by this mechanism in polyphosphoric acid since it yields *N*-(*trans*-9-decalyl)acetamide.[153]

Lansbury and Mancuso[154] have shown that 4,7-dimethyl- and diethyl-indan-1-one oxime [e.g., (119)] on treatment with polyphosphoric acid yields imines [e.g., (121)] by an insertion reaction on the benzylic carbon, and also lactams [e.g., (122) and (123)] from a Beckmann rearrangement with the former, the product of a *cis*-alkyl migration predominating. Both the products from the insertion reaction and those from the rearrangement were formulated as being formed via an iminium ion (120).[154]

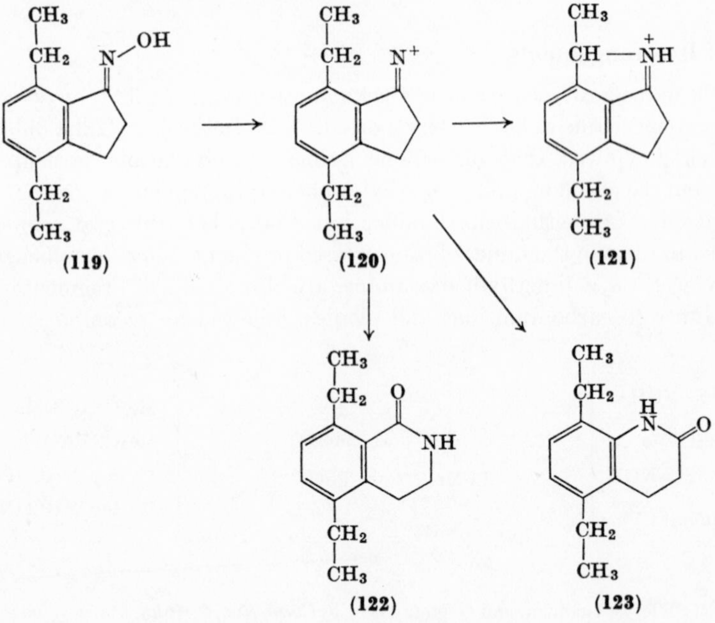

Previous reports[155] of carbon-14 isotope effects in the Beckmann rearrangement have been shown to be incorrect.[156]

The Beckmann rearrangement of cyclopentanone oxime in sulphuric acid[157] and of bicyclo[2.2.2]octan-2-one oxime[158] have also been studied.

(+)-Allylbenzylmethylphenylammonium iodide (124) with potassium *tert*-butoxide in dimethyl sulphoxide gave, *inter alia*, optically active α-allyl-

155 Y. Yukawa and M. Kawakani, *Chem. Ind.* (*London*), **1961**, 1401.
156 I. T. Glover and V. F. Raaen, *J. Org. Chem.*, **31**, 1987 (1966).
157 N. G. Zarakhani, V. V. Budylina and M. I. Vinnik, *Zh. Fiz. Khim.*, **39**, 1561 (1965): *Chem. Abs.*, **63**, 13012 (1965).
158 K. Morita and Z. Suzuki, *J. Org. Chem.*, **31**, 233 (1966).

N-methyl-N-phenylphenethylamine (**126**) in which the transfer of asymmetry from nitrogen to carbon has been demonstrated for the first time. The absolute configurations of (**124**) and (**126**) require that the transition-state geometry corresponds to (**125**) with the phenyl and vinyl groups *cisoid*. If this Stevens rearrangement is a two-step elimination–readdition process retention of optical activity demands a tight unsymmetrical ion pair, undissociated in dimethyl sulphoxide.[159]

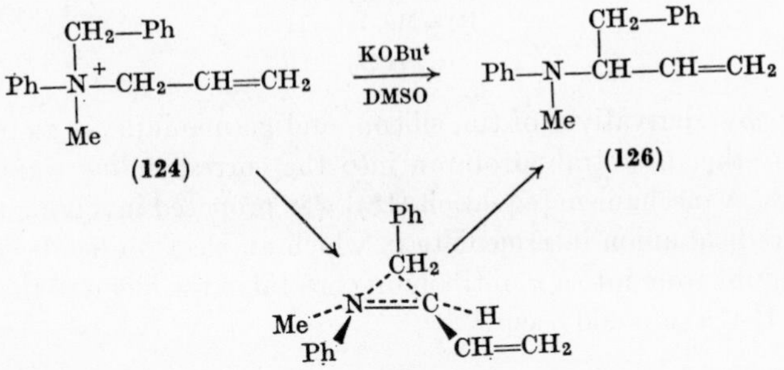

A 1,3-Stevens rearrangement has been described.[160]

The yields of phenylalkanols obtained in the Wittig rearrangement of tertiary-alkyl benzyl ethers do not parallel the stability of the corresponding alkyl carbanions. Thus, 1-norbornyl benzyl ether does not undergo the rearrangement although 1-norbornyl-lithium is very stable for a tertiary alkyl-lithium compound.[161] Also there is generally no accompanying elimination reaction with tertiary alkyl ethers, but this is often the predominating reaction of primary alkyl ethers. It was, therefore, suggested that the mechanism of the rearrangement, at least with tertiary alkyl benzyl ethers, involved not a tertiary alkyl carbanion [equation (16)] but a tertiary alkyl radical anion [equation (17)].[161]

The Wittig rearrangements of compounds (**127**) proceed with complete inversion of the allyl group, suggesting an $S_N i'$ mechanism.[162]

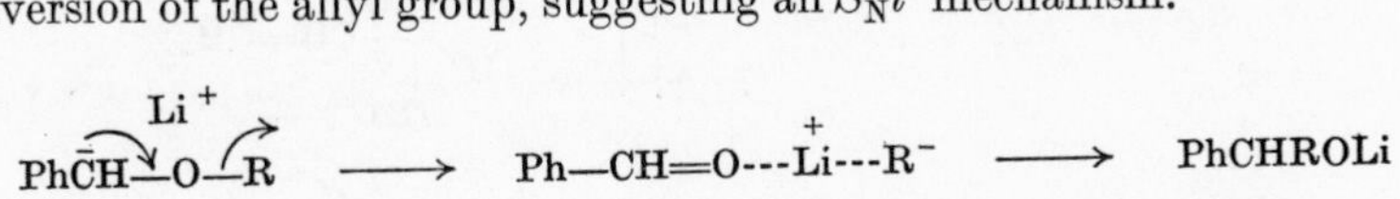

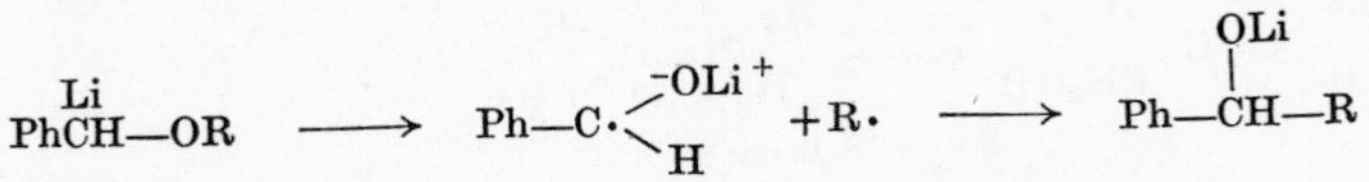

159 R. K. Hill and T.-H. Chan, *J. Am. Chem. Soc.*, **88**, 866 (1966).
160 E. F. Jenny, A. Melzer, and A. Lüttringhaus, *Tetrahedron Letters*, **1966**, 3507.
161 P. T. Lansbury, V. A. Pattison, J. D. Sidler, and J. B. Bieber, *J. Am. Chem. Soc.*, **88**, 78 (1966).
162 U. Schöllkopf and K. Fellenberger, *Ann. Chem.*, **698**, 80 (1966).

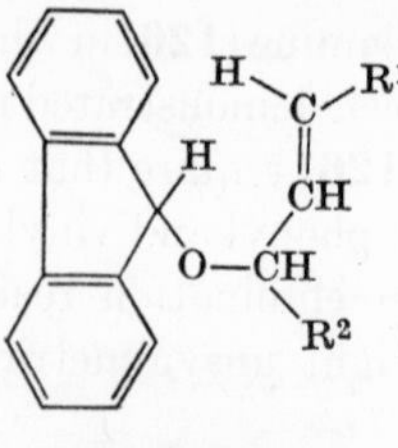

R^1 = H, R^2 = Me
R^1 = Me, R^2 = H

(127)

cis-Propenyl derivatives of tin, silicon, and germanium are isomerized by lithium in ether or tetrahydrofuran into the corresponding *trans*-propenyl derivatives. A mechanism [equation (18)] was proposed involving the formation of a radical anion intermediate in which an electron has been donated from a lithium atom into a π-antibonding orbital of the olefin so that rotation about the C–C axis could occur.[163]

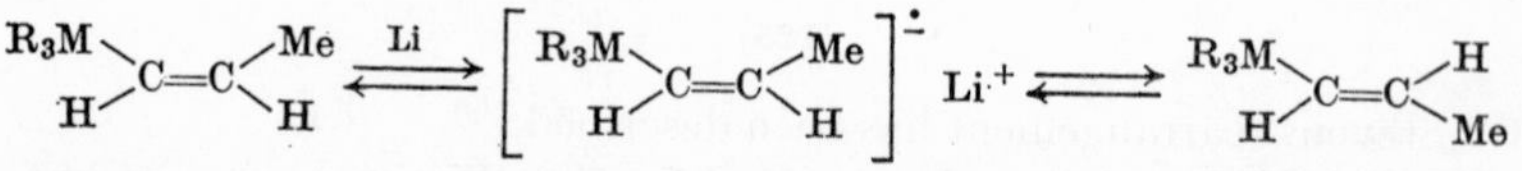

The thermal racemization of sulphoxides has been shown to proceed by several mechanisms depending on the structure of the attached alkyl or aryl groups.[164a]

Allylic rearrangements have been reviewed.[164b]

The acid-catalysed interconversion of *cis*- and *trans*-crotyl alcohol proceeds only via but-3-en-2-ol. This is consistent with the *cis*- and *trans*-crotyl

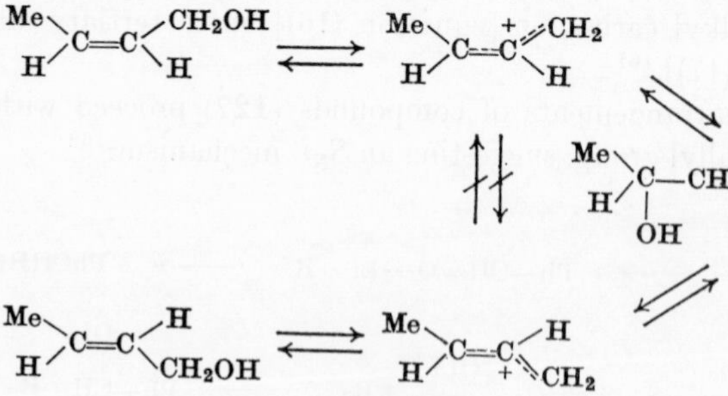

Scheme 8

[163] D. Seyferth, R. Susuki, and L. G. Vaughan, *J. Am. Chem. Soc.*, **88**, 286 (1966).
[164a] D. R. Rayner, E. G. Miller, P. Bickart, A. J. Gordon, and K. Mislow, *J. Am. Chem. Soc.*, **88**, 3138 (1966).
[164b] C. A. Vernon in "Studies on Chemical Structure and Reactivity," J. H. Ridd, ed., Methuen, London, 1966.

alcohols' ionizing, respectively, only to the *cis-* and *trans-*butenyl cations, which are not interconvertible. But-3-en-2-ol, on the other hand, can yield either cation depending on the conformation from which it ionizes. The whole process may then be depicted as shown in Scheme 8.[165]

Allylic rearrangements of 1-phenylallyl chlorides,[166] 1-phenylallyl acetate and chlorophenoxyacetate,[167] α-(cyclohex-1-enyl)benzyl methyl ether,[168] and allylic azides[169] have also been studied.

The rearrangement of $(-)$-*sec*-butyl isocyanide at 200° into the corresponding cyanide proceeds with retention of configuration. It seems unlikely that carbonium ions or ion pairs are intermediates since cyclobutyl isocyanide yielded cyclobutyl cyanide without a trace of cyclopropylmethyl or but-3-enyl cyanide. Substituent effects on the rate of rearrangement of aryl isocyanides are slight. It was therefore concluded that the mechanism was synchronous and involved little charge separation in the transition state.[170]

The rearrangement of *N*-bromo-α-halogenoamides [equation (19)] does not involve a cyclic transition state, as previously proposed since the kinetics are

$$RCO \cdot NHBr + NaOH \rightarrow RBr + NaNCO + H_2O \qquad (19)$$

complex; the reaction shows an induction period and is sensitive to the presence of oxygen; a radical-chain process seems more likely.[171]

The values of the rate constants k_1 to k_4 and k_6 and the corresponding Arrhenius parameters have been determined for the amino-ketone rearrangements (see Scheme 9).[172]

Other rearrangements which have been studied include: DL- into *meso*-1,2-dibromo-1,2-diphenylethane,[173] *N*,*N*-dialkylallylamines into *cis*-enamines,[174] *N*-nitroso-*N*-(diphenylcyclopropyl)urea into 1-diazo-2,2-diphenylcyclopropane,[175] 2,3-dihydro-2-methylpyran into 2,3-dihydro-6-methylpyran,[176] and aminodiacylhydrazines into acylamino-acid hydrazides;[177] rearrangement of

165 W. G. Young and J. S. Franklin, *J. Am. Chem. Soc.*, **88**, 785 (1966).
166 M. Y. Shandala, E. S. Waight, and M. Weinstock, *J. Chem. Soc.*, B, **1966**, 590.
167 G. Meyer, P. Viout, and P. Rumpf, *Compt. Rend.*, *Ser. C.*, **262**, 1099 (1966).
168 I. Elphinoff-Felkin and J. Huet, *Tetrahedron Letters*, **1966**, 1933.
169 C. A. Vander Werf and V. L. Heasley, *J. Org. Chem.*, **31**, 3534 (1966).
170 J. Casanova, N. D. Werner, and R. E. Schuster, *J. Org. Chem.*, **31**, 3473 (1966).
171 W. P. Judd and B. E. Swedlund, *Chem. Commun.*, **1966**, 43.
172 C. L. Stevens, H. T. Hanson, and K. G. Taylor, *J. Am. Chem. Soc.*, **88**, 2769 (1966); C. L. Stevens, A. B. Ash, A. Thuillier, J. H. Amin, A. Balys, W. E. Dennis, J. P. Dickerson, R. P. Glinski, H. T. Hanson, M. D. Pillai, and J. W. Stoddard, *J. Org. Chem.*, **31**, 2593 (1966); C. L. Stevens, A. Thuillier, K. G. Taylor, F. A. Daniher, J. P. Dickerson, H. T. Hanson, N. A. Nielsen, N. A. Tikotkar, and R. M. Weier, *ibid.*, p. 2601.
173 G. Heublein, *Z. Chem.*, **6**, 221 (1966).
174 J. Sauer and H. Prahl, *Tetrahedron Letters*, **1966**, 2863.
175 W. M. Jones, D. L. Muck and T. K. Tandy, *J. Am. Chem. Soc.*, **88**, 68 (1966); D. L. Muck, and W. M. Jones, *ibid.*, p. 74.
176 W. J. Gensler, I. Ruks, and S. Marburg, *Chem. Commun.*, **1966**, 782.
177 M. Brenner, *Acta Chim. Akad. Sci. Hung.*, **44**, 81 (1965).

benzyldimethylamine oxide,[178] thioncarbonates and thiocarbamates,[179] and *tert*-butyldifluoroamines;[180] the epimerization of N-alkyl-N-aryl-α-chloro-α-phenylacetamides;[181] the Favorskii rearrangement;[182] 1,3-elimina-

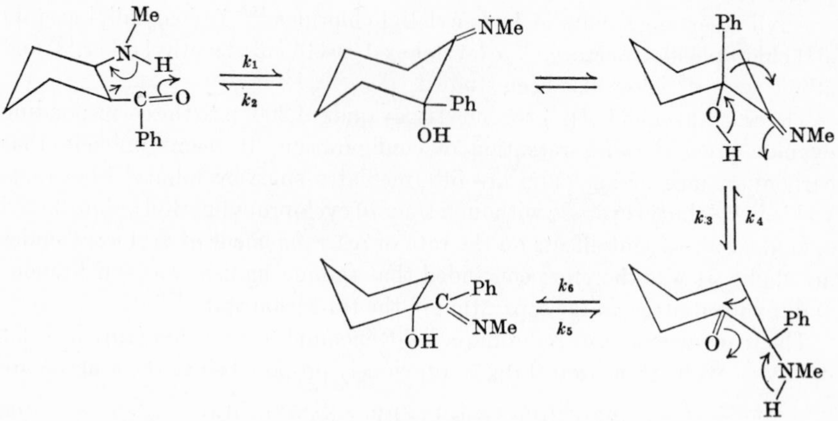

Scheme 9

tion rearrangement of 2-acetoxy-6-bromocyclohexanones;[183] the Wolff,[184] Lossen,[185] Michaelis–Arbuzov,[186] and uranediol[187] rearrangements; and rearrangements of epoxides,[188] sulphoxides,[189] and sulphenates.[190]

[178] G. P. Shulman, P. Ellgen, and M. Connor, *Can. J. Chem.*, **43**, 3459 (1965).

[179] H. Kwart and E. R. Evans, *J. Org. Chem.*, **31**, 410 (1966).

[180] K. Baum and H. M. Nelson, *J. Am. Chem. Soc.*, **88**, 4459 (1966).

[181] T. H. Siddall, *Tetrahedron Letters*, **1965**, 4515.

[182] E. V. Dehnow, *Z. Naturforsch.*, **20**, 1128 (1965); W. B. Smith and C. Gonzalez, *Tetrahedron Letters*, **1966**, 5751; C. Montpetit, L. Giral, and J. Rouzand, *Compt. Rend.*, **261**, 4142 (1965); A. Skrobek and B. Tchoubar, *Compt. Rend., Ser. C.*, **263**, 80 (1966); C. Rappe and K. Andersson, *Arkiv Kemi*, **24**, 303 (1965); C. Rappe, *ibid.*, p. 315; C. Rappe, T. Nilsson, G.-B. Carlsson, and K. Anderson, *ibid.*, p. 95; C. Rappe and G.-B. Carlsson, *ibid.*, p. 105; E. E. Smissman and J. L. Diebold, *J. Org. Chem.*, **30**, 4005 (1965); E. E. Smissman, T. L. Lemke, and O. Kristiansen, *J. Am. Chem. Soc.*, **88**, 334 (1966); C. Rappe, *Acta Chem. Scand.*, **20**, 862 (1963); H. T. Nagasawa and J. A. Elberling, *Tetrahedron Letters*, **1966**, 5393.

[183] F. G. Bordwell and K. M. Wellman, *J. Org. Chem.*, **31**, 351 (1966).

[184] P. Yates and R. J. Crawford, *J. Am. Chem. Soc.*, **88**, 1561, 1562 (1966); A. L. Wilds, N. F. Woolsey, J. Van Den Berghe, and C. H. Winestock, *Tetrahedron Letters*, **1965**, 4841.

[185] D. C. Berndt and W. J. Adams, *J. Org. Chem.*, **31**, 976 (1966).

[186] K. D. Berlin, D. M. Hellwege, M. Nagabhushanam, and E. T. Gaudy, *Tetrahedron*, **22**, 2191 (1966).

[187] H. Hirschmann, F. B. Hirschmann, and A. P. Zala, *J. Org. Chem.*, **31**, 375 (1966).

[188] J. W. Blunt, M. P. Hartshorn, and D. N. Kirk, *Tetrahedron*, **22**, 1421 (1960); *Chem. Commun.*, **1966**, 160; M. P. Hartshorn and D. N. Kirk, *Tetrahedron Letters*, **1966**, 3913; W. Reusch, C. K. Johnson and J. A. Manner, *J. Am. Chem. Soc.*, **88**, 2803 (1966); R. N. McDonald, and T. E. Tabor, *Chem. Commun.*, **1966**, 655.

[189] W. Carruthers, I. D. Entwistle, R. A. W. Johnstone, and B. J. Millard, *Chem. Ind. London*), **1966**, 342.

[190] E. G. Miller, D. R. Rayner, and K. Mislow, *J. Am. Chem. Soc.*, **88**, 3139 (1966).

There have been many investigations of the *cis–trans*[191] and positional isomerization[192] of compounds with carbon–carbon double bonds.

[191] L. D. Hawton and G. P. Semeluk, *Can. J. Chem.*, **44**, 2143 (1966); J. Binenboym, A. Burcat, A. Lifshitz, and J. Shamir, *J. Am. Chem. Soc.*, **88**, 5039 (1966); W. Langenbeck, V. Kaufmann, and A. Schellenberger, *Ann. Chem.*, **690**, 42 (1965); O. V. Bragin, L.-H. T'ao, and A. L. Liberman, *Dokl. Akad. Nauk. SSSR*, **168**, 99 (1966); *Chem. Abs.*, **65**, 7019 (1966); K. Herbig, R. Huisgen, and H. Huber, *Chem. Ber.*, **99**, 2546 (1966); D. Y. Curtin, E. J. Grubbs, and C. G. McCarty, *J. Am. Chem. Soc.*, **88**, 2775 (1966).

[192] D. R. Ross and E. S. Waight, *J. Chem. Soc.*, **1965**, 6710; R. C. Cambie and T. D. R. Manning, *Chem. Ind. (London)*, **1966**, 1884; C. Moussebois and J. Dale, *J. Chem. Soc.*, *C*, **1966**, 260, 264; L. Krabisch and B. Borgström, *Acta Chem. Scand.*, **19**, 2005 (1965); F. Asinger and B. Fell, *Erdoel Kohle*, **19**, 345, 406, 500 (1966); H. D. Harlan, H. W. Temple, and J. D. Wicks, *Texas J. Sci.*, **18**, 166 (1966); A. Cozzone, J. Grimaldi, and M. Bertrand, *Bull. Soc. Chim. France*, **1966**, 1656; K. W. Egger and S. W. Benson, *J. Am. Chem. Soc.*, **88**, 236, 241 (1966); R. Cramer, *ibid.*, p. 2272; Y. Barron, G. Maire, J. M. Muller, and F. G. Gault, *J. Catalysis*, **5**, 428 (1966); M. Orchin, *Adv. Catalysis*, **16**, 1 (1966); F. Plenat and G. Bergson, *Arkiv Kemi*, **25**, 109 (1966); F. Asinger, B. Fell, and P. Krings, *Chem. Ber.*, **99**, 1737 (1966); R. Cramer and R. V. Lindsey, *J. Am. Chem. Soc.*, **88**, 3534 (1966); J. F. Harrod and A. J. Chalk, *ibid.*, p. 3491; F. Asinger, B. Fell, and P. Krings, *Tetrahedron Letters*, **1966**, 633; B. Fell, P. Krings, and F. Asinger, *Chem. Ber.*, **99**, 3688 (1966).

CHAPTER 9

Radical Reactions

The year has seen a symposium[1] on free radicals to mark the hundredth anniversary of the birth of Moses Gomberg who, at the turn of the century, was the first to identify a stable organic free radical. Two recent texts on free-radical chemistry are now available,[2a, 2b] and numerous reviews have appeared, as well as the first volume of "Advances in Free Radical Chemistry."[2c]

Last year an attempt was made to mention some of the more interesting radical anions and cations whose electron spin resonance (ESR) spectra had been recorded. For reasons of space, coverage of this aspect of free-radical chemistry has largely been omitted this year, except where points of more general interest have been evident.

The reader is again directed to Chapters 5, 7, and 8 for aspects of free-radical chemistry not dealt with here.

Radical-forming Reactions

The photochemical and the thermal decomposition of azocumene have been the subject of detailed study by Nelson and Bartlett.[3] Normal activation parameters are found, but the cumyl radicals largely dimerize to bicumyl. Only ca. 5% of the disproportionation product, α-methylstyrene, is found. This contrasts with the behaviour of *tert*-butyl radicals from azoisobutane, which disproportionate to the extent of 80%. The difference may perhaps lie in the greater hyperconjugative C–H bond-weakening in the latter case; cumyl radicals presumably gain most of their stabilization by benzylic resonance. A new product was detected in low-temperature photolysis experiments: ca. 2% of the dimerization of cumyl radicals appears to give the

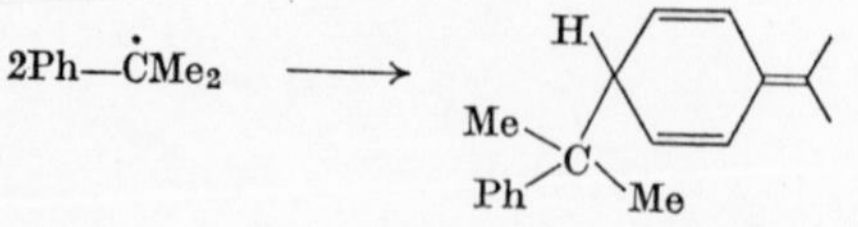

$$2Ph\!-\!\dot{C}Me_2 \longrightarrow$$

(1) 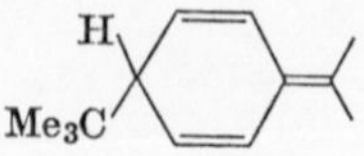   (2)

[1] *Chem. and Eng. News*, Oct. 3rd, 1966.
[2] (a) "Radicals in Organic Chemistry", C. J. M. Stirling, Oldbourne, London, 1965; (b) "Free Radicals," W. A. Pryor, McGraw-Hill, 1966; (c) "Advances in Free Radical Chemistry", G. H. Williams, ed., Vol. I, Logos Press and Academic Press, London and New York, 1965.
[3] S. F. Nelson and P. D. Bartlett, *J. Am. Chem. Soc.*, **88**, 137, 143 (1966).

isomer (1) which is unstable to both light and heat, redissociating readily to a pair of cumyl radicals. Spectroscopic observation of a more stable analogue (2) was reported from the photolysis of azoisobutane in cumene, but in neither case was isolation possible. Related examples of *para*-coupling of benzylic radicals were also observed, and the general subject discussed. No evidence for *ortho*-coupling was obtained. Scavenging experiments gave a value of 27% for the proportion of radical combination in a cage process at 40°. This was for the thermal reaction, but extrapolation of the results of photochemical decomposition to 40° gave a value some 6% higher. As there was no difference between the cage effect in direct and sensitized photolysis, the radical pair appears to undergo spin relaxation within the solvent cage much faster than it diffuses out of the cage. No explanation was offered for the discrepancy between thermal and photochemical cage effects. A conceivable one is that the molecules of solvent are less randomly oriented at the moment of a thermal fragmentation, and, for a portion of the molecules, escape from the cage could in a sense proceed in concert with the decomposition.

An interesting device for determining the cage component of a reaction is the cross-over experiment employed with α-azophenylethane (3) and its deuteriated analogue (4).[4] The cage component was found to be 29% at 105°, but unfortunately no results of scavenging experiments were available for comparison. The secondary isotope effect ($k_H/k_D = 1.018$ per D atom) on the decomposition of (4) was also determined.

$$\underset{\text{(3)}}{\overset{\displaystyle \underset{|}{\overset{\text{Ph}}{|}}\quad\overset{\text{Ph}}{|}}{\text{Me}-\text{C}-\text{N}=\text{N}-\text{C}-\text{Me}}} \qquad \underset{\text{(4)}}{\overset{\displaystyle \underset{|}{\overset{\text{Ph}}{|}}\quad\overset{\text{Ph}}{|}}{\text{CD}_3-\text{C}-\text{N}=\text{N}-\text{C}-\text{CD}_3}}$$

Cage effects in the photodecomposition of methylazoethane have also been measured, and the "activation energy for diffusion from the cage" discussed.[5]

Solvent effects on the rate of decomposition of triphenyl(phenylazo)methane have been re-examined, and the importance of both ground and transition state effects has been emphasized.[6]

Decomposition of cyclic azo-compounds has continued to receive attention, as a route to biradicals, in particular to trimethylenemethane (5) and its derivatives. A triplet ground state has been calculated for (5) and a triplet species has now been observed in the photolysis of (6) at −185°.[7] Pyrolysis of

[4] S. Seltzer and E. J. Hamilton, *J. Am. Chem. Soc.*, 88, 3775 (1966).
[5] S. Fujita, S. Kodama, and O. Toyama, *Bull. Chem. Soc. Japan*, 39, 1323 (1966).
[6] W. G. Bentrude and A. K. MacKnight, *Tetrahedron Letters*, 1966, 3147.
[7] P. Dowd, *J. Am. Chem. Soc.*, 88, 2587 (1966).

(6) gives methylenecyclopropane,[8] and of (7) gives a mixture of deuteriated isomers (8) and (9). Chemical labelling also reveals rearrangement in the decompositions of (10) (X = CO_2Et[9] or Cl[10]). When X = Cl the proportions

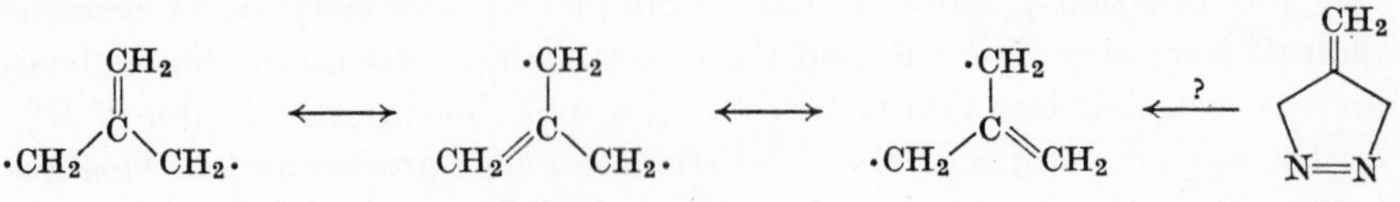

(5)   (6)

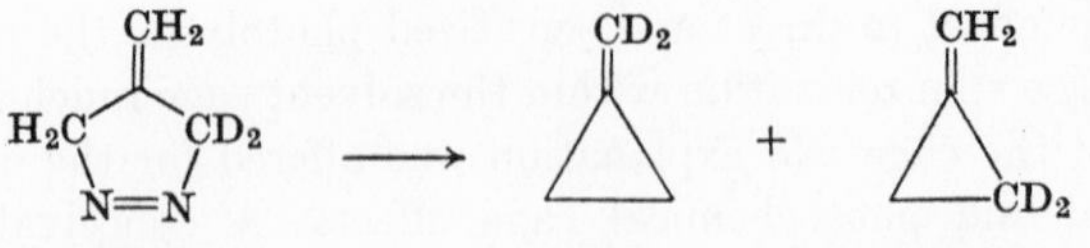

(7)   (8)   (9)

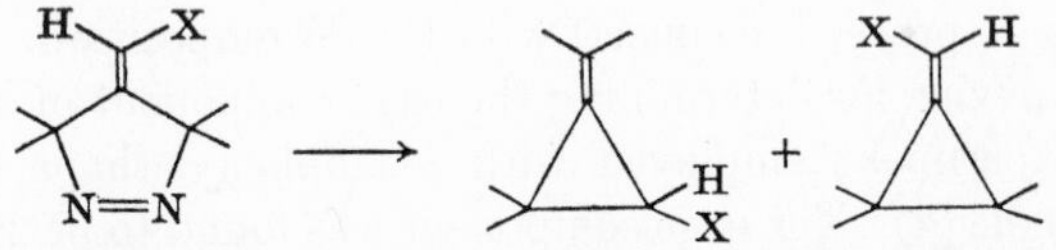

(10)   (11)   (12)

of rearranged (11) to unrearranged product (12) are 23:77 for direct irradiation, but 75:25 for the benzophenone-photosensitized reaction. Furthermore, the direct photolysis was not quenched by piperylene, nor was the product distribution altered, suggesting singlet intermediates in the unsensitized reactions. Trimethylenemethane has also been isolated as an iron carbonyl complex.[11]

Other pyrazoline decompositions have been reported,[12,13] as well as decompositions of triazolines leading to aziridines.[14,15] Interaction of electron spins in 1,3-biradicals seems to be sufficient for singlet and triplet states to be differentiated by their reactivity,[14] though this may not be so for 1,4-biradicals. An interesting definition[16] of a biradical states it to be "an atom or molecule that reacts as though it has two monoradical functions." This would clearly

[8] R. J. Crawford and D. M. Cameron, *J. Am. Chem. Soc.*, 88, 2589 (1966).

[9] A. C. Day and M. C. Whiting, *J. Chem. Soc.*, C, 1966, 464.

[10] S. D. Andrews, and A. C. Day, *Chem. Commun.*, 1966, 667.

[11] G. F. Emerson, K. Ehrlich, W. P. Giering, and P. C. Lauterbur, *J. Am. Chem. Soc.*, 88, 3172 (1966).

[12] R. J. Crawford and A. Mishra, *J. Am. Chem. Soc.*, 88, 3963 (1966); R. J. Crawford, A. Mishra, and R. J. Dummel, *ibid.*, p. 3959; see also, *Organic Reaction Mechanisms*, 1965, 194.

[13] T. F. Thomas and C. Steel, *J. Am. Chem. Soc.*, 87, 5290 (1965); C. G. Overberger, R. E. Zangaro, and J.-P. Anselme, *J. Org. Chem.*, 31, 2046 (1966).

[14] P. Scheiner, *J. Am. Chem. Soc.*, 88, 4759 (1966).

[15] G. Szeimies and R. Huisgen, *Chem. Ber.*, 99, 491 (1966).

[16] G. R. Freeman, *Can. J. Chem.*, 44, 245 (1966).

encompass both singlet and triplet 1,3-biradicals, though its stated inclusion of such species as singlet carbenes seems dubious and undesirable. In our opinion singlet carbenes and singlet states, other than those where two spin-paired electrons occupy different orbitals, are not encompassed by such a definition, nor should they be.

New evidence that the initial decomposition of acetyl peroxide is a single bond cleavage of the peroxide link is the discovery that cage recombination of acetoxy-radicals competes with their decarboxylation. This was shown[17] by the scrambling of an initial carbonyl ^{18}O label in undecomposed peroxide.

Several interesting perester decompositions have been investigated. Particularly important are the percinnamate decompositions,[18,19] which produce vinyl radicals. Both *cis*- and *trans*-isomers of *tert*-butyl $\alpha\beta$-dimethyl-percinnamate decompose in cumene at 110° to give *cis*- and *trans*-2-phenylbut-2-ene in the ratio *cis/trans* = 1.1—1.2. The peresters, acyloxy-radicals, and olefins are configurationally stable under the reaction conditions, and hence the vinyl radicals (13) and (14) equilibrate more rapidly than they react with

$$PhMeC{=}CMeCOOBu^t \longrightarrow$$

cis or *trans*

(13)   (14)

cumene.[18] Similar results have been obtained with the vinyl radicals from α-methyl- and α-phenyl-percinnamate,[19] though it was pointed out that the products are not formed in equilibrium proportions. This effect was attributed to a stereoselectivity in hydrogen-transfer to the isomeric vinyl radicals and was more pronounced for the α-phenyl than for the α-methyl radicals.

Comparable results are obtained for the reaction of β-styryl radicals from *cis*- and *trans*-cinnamoyl peroxide with carbon tetrachloride.[20] Each precursor gives *cis*- and *trans*-β-chlorostyrene in the proportions 19:81. However, with the more reactive bromotrichloromethane, the corresponding proportions of bromostyrene from the *trans*-peroxide are 14:86 and from the *cis*-peroxide 27:73. Here we appear to have the first evidence of a reaction competing with

(15)

[17] J. W. Taylor and J. C. Martin, *J. Am. Chem. Soc.*, **88**, 3650 (1966).
[18] J. A. Kampmeier and R. M. Fantazier, *J. Am. Chem. Soc.*, **88**, 1959, 5219 (1966).
[19] L. A. Singer and N. P. Kong, *Tetrahedron Letters*, **1966**, 2089; *J. Am. Chem. Soc.*, **88**, 5213 (1966).
[20] O. Simamura, K. Tokumaru, and H. Yui, *Tetrahedron Letters*, **1966**, 5141.

the vinyl radical isomerization. At the same time it appears to establish that vinyl radicals cannot have a linear structure such as (15). It would be interesting to substantiate these conclusions by means of a study of the variation of product ratio as a function of dilution (see also footnote 16 in ref. 55).

Propenyl radicals have been obtained by photolysis of 1-iodopropenes,[21] and vinyl radicals are formed in the gas-phase reaction of methyl radicals with acrolein.[22]

The mechanism of participation of the sulphur in the decomposition of perester (16) has been studied by examining the decomposition of related peresters.[23] For example, a similar degree of rate enhancement (ca. 10^4) is brought about by the introduction of an 8-phenylthio-substituent in *tert*-butyl per-1-naphthoate. This suggests participation at carboxylate-oxygen, because in the naphthalene system participation at the *tert*-butoxy-oxygen would involve a relatively unfavourable seven-membered ring structure (17). There was, however, no compelling evidence to distinguish between alternatives

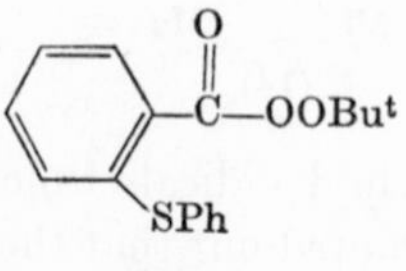

(16) 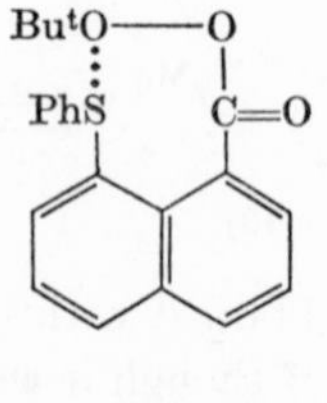   (17) 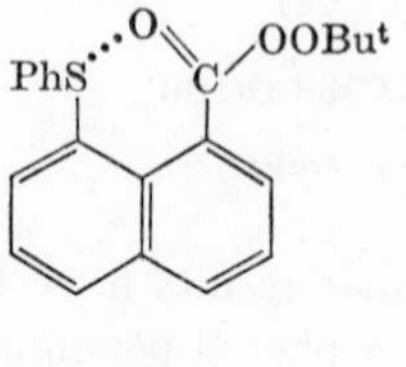   (18) 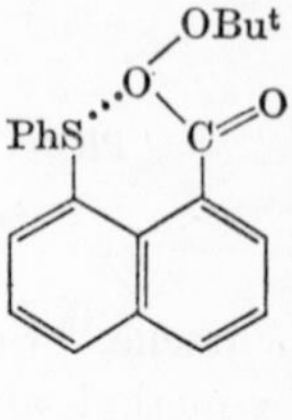   (19)

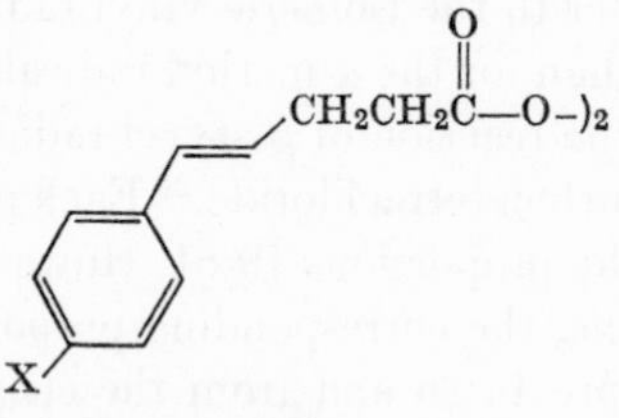

(20) 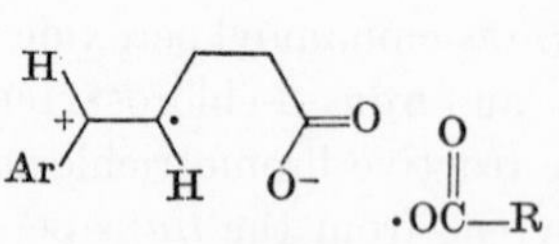   (21)

(18) and (19). Double-bond participation in the decomposition of peroxides (20), in the form of a contribution from structure (21) to the decomposition, is reflected in the correlation between decomposition rate and σ^+ values for the substituents X.[24] At 50°, $\rho = -1.16$. Contribution from a competing ionic decomposition does not alter this conclusion.

[21] R. C. Neuman, *J. Org. Chem.*, **31**, 1852 (1966).
[22] N. A. Weir, *J. Chem. Soc.*, **1965**, 6870.
[23] T. H. Fisher and J. C. Martin, *J. Am. Chem. Soc.*, **88**, 3382 (1966).
[24] R. C. Lamb, L. P. Spadafino, R. G. Webb, E. B. Smith, W. E. McNew, and J. G. Pacifici, *J. Org. Chem.*, **31**, 147 (1966).

tert-Butyl triphenylperacetate undergoes concerted two-bond homolysis at 25° to give triphenylmethyl and *tert*-butoxy-radicals.[25] The reaction is dominated by the high concentration of triphenylmethyl which builds up; significant products include the *para*-coupled ether (22). The instability of peresters (23) and (24) presumably reflects stability in the cyclopropenyl and cycloheptatrienyl radicals, respectively,[26a] but single-bond cleavage characterizes perester (25a). Presumably electron reorganization to phenalenyl radical cannot promote the decomposition of this compound. Two-bond cleavage is again observed in the decomposition of (25b) and indeed this occurs nearly 3000 times as rapidly as the decomposition of *tert*-butyl phenylperacetate.[26b] The result is in accordance with the greater stabilization predicted by molecular orbital calculation for a methyl radical substituted by tropenium rather than for one stabilized by phenyl.

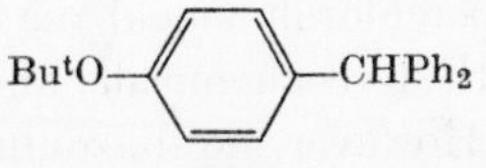

Bu^{t}O—⟨⟩—CHPh$_2$

(22)

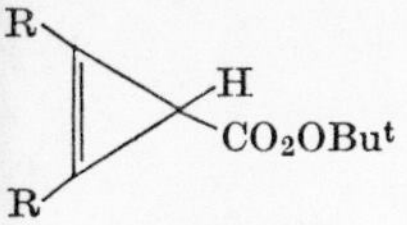

(23) 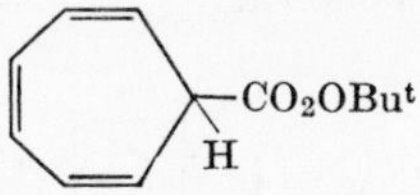   (24) 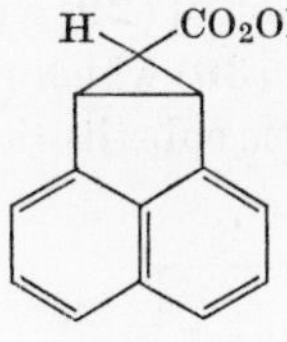   (25a) 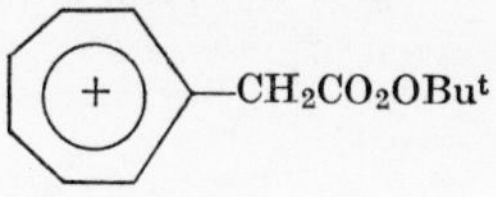   (25b)

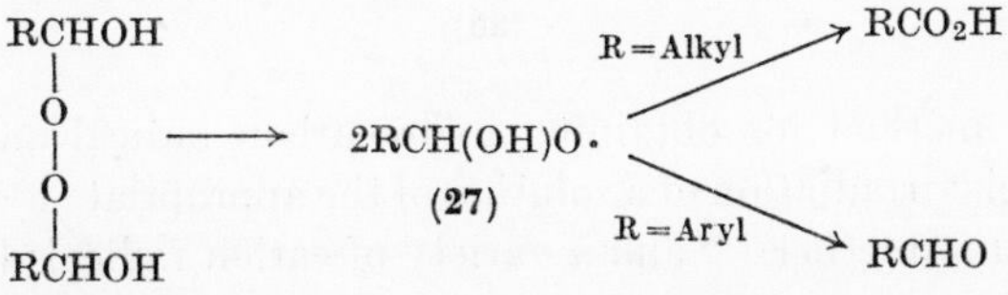

RCHOH
|
O
|
O
|
RCHOH

(26)

⟶ 2RCH(OH)O·

(27)

R = Alkyl ⟶ RCO$_2$H

R = Aryl ⟶ RCHO

PhCOOCOMe

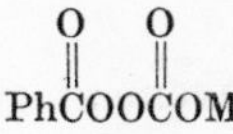

(28)

The decomposition of peroxides (26), and the behaviour of radicals (27) as a function of R, have been studied,[27] as has the decomposition of (28).[28] The kinetics of decomposition of *tert*-butyl hydroperoxide have been re-examined,[29]

[25] J. P. Lorand and P. D. Bartlett, *J. Am. Chem. Soc.*, **88**, 3294 (1966).
[26a] C. Rüchardt and H. Schwarzer, *Chem. Ber.*, **99**, 1861, 1871 (1966).
[26b] G. R. Jurch and T. G. Traylor, *J. Am. Chem. Soc.*, **88**, 5228 (1966).
[27] A. I. Kirillov, *Zh. Organ. Khim.*, **2**, 1048 (1966); *Chem. Abs.*, **65**, 15189 (1966).
[28] G. A. Razuvaev, V. A. Dodonov, and T. I. Starostina, *Zh. Organ. Khim.*, **2**, 857 (1966); *Chem. Abs.*, **65**, 12065 (1966).
[29] N. I. Larionova and N. N. Ugarova, *Vestn. Mosk. Univ. Ser. II: Khim.*, **21**, 21 (1966); *Chem. Abs.*, **65**, 2107 (1966).

and its reactions with triphenylhydrazine[30] and dialkyl diselenides[31] studied. Rather than inhibiting, diphenylpicrylhydrazyl accelerates the decomposition of hydroperoxides,[32] and two studies of amine-induced decomposition of benzoyl peroxide have also been reported.[33]

The solid-state decompositions of *m*- and *p*-nitroperoxybenzoic acids have been studied.[34a]

Aryliodine dibenzoates [ArI(OCOPh)$_2$] are considered to undergo initial decomposition to ArOCOPh and IOCOPh, and radicals are then produced in an induced decomposition by the hypoiodite.[34b]

Cyano-radicals are produced in the electrolysis of mercuric cyanide[35] as well as by its photolysis,[36] but the photolysis of alkyl(or aryl)mercuric cyanides gives initially R· (or Ar·) and HgCN.[37] Bis(triphenylsilyl)mercury constitutes a source of triphenylsilyl radicals,[38] and trimethylsilyl radicals are formed by pyrolysis of hexamethyldisilane at 600°.[39]

Deamination of the aminoperchlorohomocubane (**29**) to give a carbonium ion would be unfavourable both stereochemically and because of the inductive effect of the chlorine atoms. However, no diazonium intermediate could be isolated from the reaction of (**29**) with nitrosyl chloride. Instead, nitrogen was lost to give the radical (**30**) which reacted with, for example, nitrobenzene to give a typical homolytic substitution pattern.[40]

(**29**)   (**30**)

A convenient general method for obtaining hydrocarbon radical anions appears to be by ultraviolet irradiation of a solution of the appropriate hydrocarbon and phenyl-lithium in ether,[41a] and a variety of cation radicals have

[30] K. Maruyamía and T. Otsuki, *Tetrahedron Letters*, **1966**, 3705.
[31] D. T. Woodbridge, *J. Chem. Soc., B*, **1966**, 50.
[32] A. W. Schoenmakers and B. G. Tarladgis, *Nature (London)*, **210**, 1151 (1966).
[33] P. K. Nandi and U. S. Nandi, *J. Phys. Chem.*, **69**, 4071 (1965); N. M. Beileryan, F. O. Karapetyan, and O. A. Chaltykyan, *Armyansk. Khim. Zh.*, **19**, 128 (1966); *Chem. Abs.*, **65**, 3683 (1966).
[34a] D. F. Debenham, A. J. Owen, and E. F. Pembridge, *J. Chem. Soc., B*, **1966**, 213; D. F. Debenham and A. J. Owen, *ibid.*, p. 675.
[34b] J. E. Leffler, W. J. M. Mitchell, and B. C. Menon, *J. Org. Chem.*, **31**, 1153 (1966).
[35] K. Yoshida and S. Tsutsumi, *Tetrahedron Letters*, **1966**, 2501.
[36] K. Yoshida and S. Tsutsumi, *J. Org. Chem.*, **31**, 3635 (1966).
[37] K. Yoshida and S. Tsutsumi, *Tetrahedron Letters*, **1966**, 281.
[38] R. A. Jackson, *Chem. Commun.*, **1966**, 827.
[39] H. Sakurai, R. Koh, A. Hosomi, and M. Kumada, *Bull. Chem. Soc. Japan*, **39**, 2050 (1966).
[40] K. V. Scherer and R. S. Lunt, *J. Am. Chem. Soc.*, **88**, 2860 (1966).
[41a] H. J. S. Winkler, H. Winkler, and R. Bollinger, *Chem. Commun.*, **1966**, 70.

been advantageously obtained with $AlCl_3-MeNO_2$ [41b] or $PhNO_2-MeSO_3H$ [41c] replacing sulphuric acid.

Photolysis of nitromethane gives methyl radicals [42] as does pyrolysis of tetramethoxyethylene: [43]

$$
\underset{MeO}{\overset{MeO}{>}}\!\!=\!\!\underset{OMe}{\overset{OMe}{<}} \quad \xrightarrow[-Me\cdot]{Heat} \quad \underset{MeO}{\overset{MeO}{>}}\!\!-\!\!\overset{\cdot}{\underset{OMe}{C}}\!\!-\!\!O \quad \xrightarrow{-Me\cdot} \quad \underset{MeO}{\overset{O}{||}}\!\!-\!\!\overset{O}{\underset{OMe}{||}}
$$

The photolysis of $ClCOCO_2Et$ has been further investigated [44] and free radicals have been implicated in the photolytic decarbonylation of ethyl benzoylformate. [45a]

Triphenylmethyl radicals are formed in the reaction of triphenylaluminium with benzophenone, as shown by ESR spectroscopy. [45b] Phenyl radicals formed at the same time are said to attack these at the *para*-positions leading to such products as *p,p'*-diphenyltriphenylmethane. Radicals were considered to be formed by the sequence:

$$2AlPh_3 + 2Ph_2CO \xrightarrow[80°]{PhH} 2Ph_2\overset{+}{C}O\overset{-}{-}AlPh_3$$

$$2Ph_2\overset{+}{C}O\overset{-}{-}AlPh_3 \longrightarrow (Ph_3COAlPh_2)_2$$

$$(Ph_3COAlPh_2)_2 \longrightarrow 2Ph_3C\cdot + Ph-Al:O + 2Ph\cdot$$

Bamford and his colleagues [46] have studied the initiation of polymerization by metal carbonyl complexes and carbon tetrachloride and have compared manganic acetylacetonate with the tris-(α,α,α-trifluoroacetylacetonate) derivative. [47] The latter is effective only when the monomer has an electron-withdrawing group, as in acrylonitrile. The mechanism suggested is as indicated. The fluoro-derivative actually retards the polymerization of styrene. In the case of molybdenum acetylacetonates, the ESR spectrum of the initiating radical has been observed. [48]

Richardson has followed his detailed examination of the reaction of cobaltous salts with *tert*-butyl hydroperoxide by a comparably thorough study

[41b] W. F. Forbes and P. D. Sullivan, *J. Am. Chem. Soc.*, **88**, 2862 (1966).

[41c] P. A. Malachesky, L. S. Marcoux, and R. N. Adams, *J. Phys. Chem.*, **70**, 2064 (1966).

[42] S. Paszyc, *Bull. Soc. Amis. Sci. Lettres Poznan, Ser. B*, **18**, 5, 19 (1964/65).

[43] R. W. Hoffmann, J. Schneider, and H. Häuser, *Chem. Ber.*, **99**, 1892 (1966).

[44] C. Pac and S. Tsutsumi, *Bull. Chem. Soc. Japan*, **39**, 1926 (1966); *Organic Reaction Mechanisms*, **1965**, 121.

[45a] T. Tominaga, Y. Odaira, and S. Tsutsumi, *Bull. Chem. Soc. Japan*, **39**, 1824 (1966).

[45b] C. Harris, T. Mole, and F. D. Looney, *Tetrahedron Letters*, **1966**, 4195.

[46] C. H. Bamford, R. Denyer, and G. C. Eastmond, *Trans. Faraday Soc.*, **62**, 688 (1966); C. H. Bamford and R. Denyer, *ibid.*, p. 1567; C. H. Bamford, G. C. Eastmond and W. R. Maltman, *ibid.*, p. 2531; C. H. Bamford and W. R. Maltman, *ibid.*, p. 2823.

[47] C. H. Bamford and D. J. Lind, *Chem. Commun.*, **1966**, 792.

[48] I. Bernal, *Chem. Ind. (London)*, **1966**, 1343.

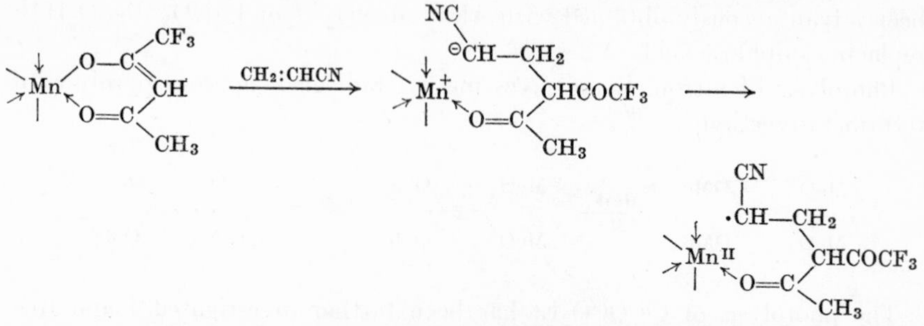

of the reaction with copper carboxylates.[49a] The kinetics show marked differences from the behaviour with cobalt salts, the rate being between half- and first-order in both copper ions and peroxide. The dimeric nature of the metal salts was again emphasized, and the importance of peroxy-radicals ($Bu^tOO\cdot$) in the proposed mechanistic scheme was demonstrated by trapping with 2,6-di-*tert*-butyl-*p*-cresol.

Bromomethylpyridinium salts react with chromous ion to give much more stable analogues[50] of the benzylchromium(III) derivatives reported last year.[49b] A similar radical mechanism is written for their formation. Tribenzylchromium reacts with D_2O to give largely deuterium-free toluene molecules, together with molecules containing as many as three or four deuterium atoms.[51] Free radicals could not be detected, and the suggestion was made that benzyl radicals react with co-ordinated solvent (tetrahydrofuran) before becoming completely free from the metal.

Reduction of benzyl halides by chromous salts to the corresponding radical is paralleled by the reduction of water-soluble organic halides (RX) by pentacyanocobaltate(II) (to give initially $R\cdot + [Co(CN)_5X]^{3-}$).[52] A further electron-

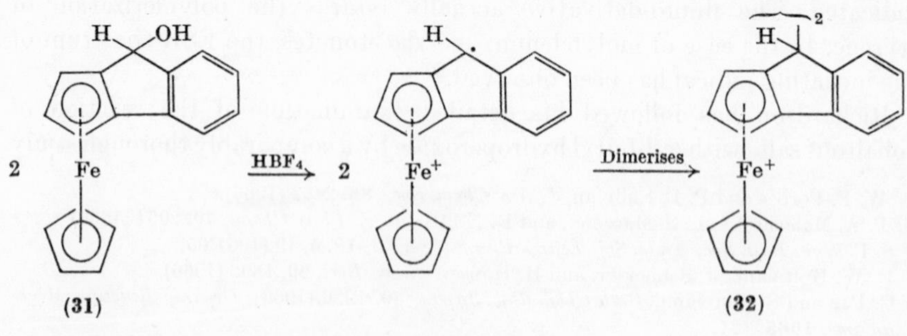

(31)   (32)

[49a] W. H. Richardson, *J. Am. Chem. Soc.*, **88**, 975 (1966).

[49b] See *Organic Reaction Mechanisms*, **1965**, 200.

[50] R. G. Coombes, M. D. Johnson, and N. Winterton, *J. Chem. Soc.*, **1965**, 7029; R. G. Coombes and M. D. Johnson, *J. Chem. Soc., A*, **1966**, 177.

[51] R. P. A. Sneeden, F. Glockling, and H. Zeiss, *J. Organometal. Chem.*, **6**, 149 (1966).

[52] J. Halpern and J. P. Maher, *J. Am. Chem. Soc.*, **87**, 5361 (1965).

transfer reduction which frustrated an ingenious approach to benzopentalene is shown in the sequence (31) → (32).[53]

Some interesting studies related to aryl coupling processes such as the Ullmann reaction have been reported. Suspensions of phenyl- or *p*-tolyl-silver or -copper(I) in ether decompose to form biphenyl or 4,4'-dimethylbiphenyl.[54] In spite of the negligible solubility of the suspensions, substantial yields of 4-methylbiphenyl are obtained from cross-over experiments. Benzene and toluene are also produced, presumably by hydrogen abstraction from ether, and aryl radical intermediates were considered to be involved. On the other hand, whilst aryl coupling was also observed in solution of the arylsilver compounds in pyridine, radical substitution (that would have been shown by formation of arylpyridines) was not evident. Whitesides and Casey[55] have obtained evidence against radical intermediates in the related instance of a vinyl coupling reaction. Thermal decomposition of solutions of *cis*-1-propenyl-(tri-*n*-butylphosphine)silver gives hexa-2,4-diene with essentially complete retention of stereochemical integrity at the olefinic sites. Similar results were obtained with the *trans*-isomer, and with the *cis*- and *trans*-isomers of but-2-enyl derivatives of both silver and copper(I). Estimates of the rate constants for inversion of configuration of a vinyl radical, lead to the conclusion that free vinyl radicals cannot be involved, and exclusive product formation from radical decomposition of organometallic aggregates within the solvent cage seems unlikely.

The reaction of aryl bromides or iodides with cuprous benzoate in anhydrous xylene gives the aryl benzoate (vinyl bromides give enol benzoates); however, in the presence of benzoic acid, reduction to the arene is observed.[56a] This result suggests an organocopper intermediate which may be intercepted by

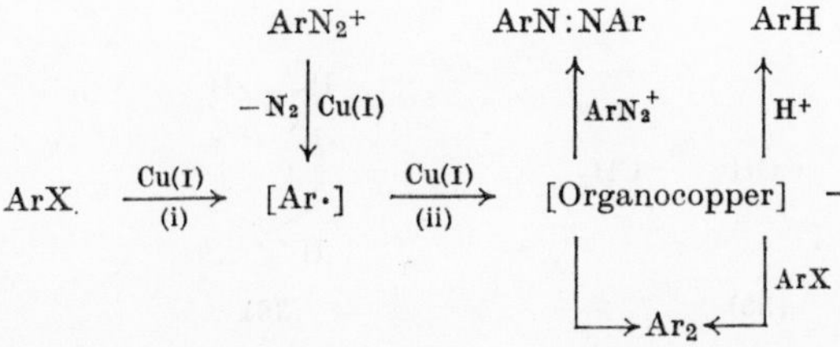

the proton source. The formation of the organocopper species is considered to involve the two steps (i) and (ii).

The intermediacy of aryl radicals was shown by intramolecular 1,5-hydrogen

[53] M. Cais, A. Modiano, and A. Raveh, *J. Am. Chem. Soc.*, **87**, 5607 (1965).
[54] H. Hashimoto and T. Nakano, *J. Org. Chem.*, **31**, 891 (1966).
[55] G. M. Whitesides and C. P. Casey, *J. Am. Chem. Soc.*, **88**, 4541 (1966).
[56a] T. Cohen and A. H. Lewin, *J. Am. Chem. Soc.*, **88**, 4521 (1966).

transfer[56b] in the reaction with (33) [to give (34)]. Organocopper species were also formed from diazonium ions and cuprous benzoate, aryl coupling products

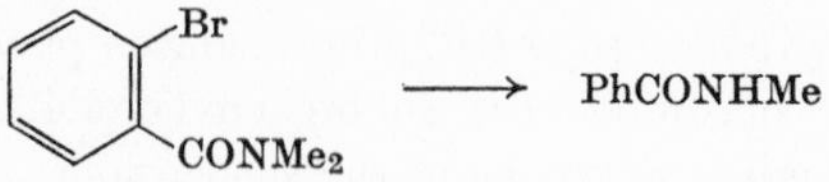

(33)   (34)

being isolated. Although detailed mechanisms have not been unravelled, the above scheme, encompassing a range of copper-promoted reactions, presents a starting point for further research;[56a] see also p. 179.

Reactions of Free Radicals

Radical abstraction and displacement processes. Iodine-catalysed isomerization of but-1-ene, reported last year, led to an estimate of 12.6 kcal mole^{-1} for the resonance energy of an allylic radical. It now appears[57] that ca. 2 kcal of this arises from stabilization by the methyl group, as from a study of the gas-phase reactions

$$CH_2=CHCH_3 + I_2 \rightleftarrows HI + CH_2=CHCH_2I$$

it has been possible to calculate a value of 10.2 kcal mole^{-1} for the resonance energy of the allyl radical itself. The degree of accuracy of the two results ($\pm$ ca. 1 kcal in each case) is sufficient to suggest that the difference between them is significant. Similar data on the reaction between iodine and toluene give 12.5 kcal mole^{-1} for the stabilization of a benzyl radical.[58] The gas-phase reaction between allyl radicals and toluene has also been studied.[59] Iodine-catalysed isomerization of penta-1,4-diene gives a resonance energy of 15.4 kcal mole^{-1} for the pentadienyl radical (35),[60] but the imposed geometry

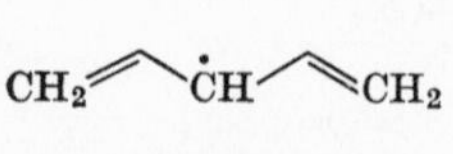

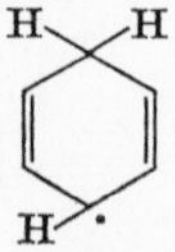

(35)   (36)

of the cyclohexadienyl radical (36) appears to impart a much greater stabilization of ca. 24 kcal mole^{-1}.[60, 61]

[56b] A. H. Lewin, A. H. Dinwoodie, and T. Cohen, *Tetrahedron*, **22**, 1527 (1966).
[57] D. M. Golden, A. S. Rodgers, and S. W. Benson, *J. Am. Chem. Soc.*, **88**, 3194, 3196 (1966).
[58] R. Walsh, D. M. Golden, and S. W. Benson, *J. Am. Chem. Soc.*, **88**, 650 (1966).
[59] R. J. Akers and J. J. Throssell, *Chem. Commun.*, **1966**, 432.
[60] K. W. Egger and S. W. Benson, *J. Am. Chem. Soc.*, **88**, 241 (1966).
[61] D. G. L. James and R. D. Suart, *Chem. Commun.*, **1966**, 484.

Various new observations on hydrogen abstraction to form substituted benzyl radicals have been reported. Aryl radicals from triaryl(arylazo)-methanes have been allowed to react with a range of hydrogen donors in competition with carbon tetrachloride.[62] For a given hydrogen abstraction, k_H/k_{Cl} increased in the order Ar = p-tolyl < phenyl < p-bromophenyl < p-nitrophenyl. The results were obtained from the ratio of ArH to ArCl produced, after extrapolation to infinite dilution and correction for the component of benzene formed in a cage process. They reflect the importance of contributions from structures $\overset{-}{Ar}...\overset{\cdot}{H}...\overset{+}{R}$ and $\overset{+}{Ar}...\overset{\cdot}{Cl}...\overset{-}{CCl_3}$ to the transition states of the competing reactions. ρ-Values for abstractions from a series of substituted toluenes were also determined, and the p-nitrophenyl radical was found to be significantly electrophilic ($\rho = -0.6$ against σ, and -0.44 against σ^+; both sets of parameters gave reasonable correlations).

Abstraction from toluenes by *tert*-butoxy-radicals was last year reported to correlate with Hammett σ-constants, though abstraction from 4-methyl-biphenyl was anomalous.[63] More extensive data by a second group of workers gives a superior correlation with σ^+, and the behaviour of 4-methylbiphenyl no longer appears exceptional.[64] For abstractions by bromine atoms, there

Table 1. Data on reactivity of substituted toluenes towards hydrogen-abstractions by bromine.

Compounds	Relative reactivity per hydrogen atom (Ar = Ph)	Hammett reaction constant ρ^a
ArCH$_3$	1.00	−1.38
ArCH$_2$Me	22.8	−0.69
ArCH$_2$OMe	52.6	−0.35
Ar$_2$CHOMe	109	0

^{a} Correlation with σ^+.

was no detectable substituent effect in a series of benzhydryl methyl ethers;[65] in a series of systems of varying reactivity the ρ-value is inversely related to ease of hydrogen abstraction, as shown in Table 1.

Hydrogen abstraction from substituted toluenes by a variety of other

[62] W. A. Pryor, J. T. Echols, and K. Smith, *J. Am. Chem. Soc.*, **88**, 1189 (1966).
[63] See *Organic Reaction Mechanisms*, **1965**, 203.
[64] B. R. Kennedy and K. U. Ingold, *Can. J. Chem.*, **44**, 2381 (1966).
[65] R. L. Huang and K. H. Lee, *J. Chem. Soc.*, C, **1966**, 932, 935.

9

radicals has been examined[66,67] and the effects of α-substitution of alkyl,[67] alkoxy-,[68] cyano-,[69,70] and carboxylate[69] groups have been studied.

α,α-Dicyanobenzyl radicals, obtained by reaction of dicyanotoluene and di-*tert*-butyl peroxide, combine to give a *para*-coupled dimer (37).[70] The stability imparted to these radicals by the cyano-groups is reflected by their

(37)

failure to react with oxygen or to initiate the polymerization of styrene.

Rates of successive brominations of 1,5-dimethylnaphthalene have been obtained.[71]

A report that benzyl radicals equilibrate with molecular hydrogen could not be substantiated.[72]

There is evidence from the substitution pattern that coiling of a long alkyl chain in a poor solvent interferes slightly with chlorination of internal methylene groups.[73] A more pronounced conformational effect limits the reactivity of the methine-hydrogen atoms in 2,4-dimethyl- and 2,2,4-tri-methyl-pentane.[74] The effect is enhanced in solvents capable of complexing with chlorine atoms and thus increasing the bulk of the attacking species. Tedder and his colleagues have reported further[75] on polar effects in the chlorination of terminally substituted *n*-alkanes.[76] The bearing on these results of the hydrogen-migration reported on p. 232 will have to be examined. An entropy factor is responsible for the greater selectivity in gas-phase chlorination of *n*-hexane than in the reaction in solution.[77]

The kinetics of chlorination by *tert*-butyl hypochlorite have been examined.[78,79] In chloroform, chain-termination is by dimerization of tri-

[66] K. Schwetlick, *Tetrahedron*, **22**, 785 (1966); K. Schwetlick and S. Helm, *ibid.*, p. 793.
[67] D. Mackay and W. A. Waters, *J. Chem. Soc.*, *C*, **1966**, 813; E. Kalatzis and G. H. Williams, *J. Chem. Soc.*, *B*, **1966**, 1112; K. M. Johnston, G. H. Williams, and H. J. Williams, *J. Chem. Soc.*, *B*, **1966**, 1114.
[68] R. E. Lovins, L. J. Andrews, and R. M. Keefer, *J. Org. Chem.*, **30**, 4150 (1965).
[69] G. A. Russell and Y. R. Vinson, *J. Org. Chem.*, **31**, 1994 (1966).
[70] H. D. Hartzler, *J. Org. Chem.*, **31**, 2654 (1966).
[71] P. W. Storms and G. B. Miller, *J. Org. Chem.*, **31**, 2705 (1966).
[72] J. C. J. Thynne, *J. Chem. Soc.*, *A*, **1966**, 806.
[73] D. J. Hurley, R. W. Rosenthal, and R. C. Williamson, *J. Org. Chem.*, **30**, 4314 (1965).
[74] G. A. Russell and P. G. Haffley, *J. Org. Chem.*, **31**, 1869 (1966).
[75] See *Organic Reaction Mechanisms*, **1965**, 205.
[76] H. Singh, and J. M. Tedder, *J. Chem. Soc.*, *B*, **1966**, 605, 608, 612.
[77] I. Galiba, J. M. Tedder, and (in part) J. C. Walton, *J. Chem. Soc.*, *B*, **1966**, 604.
[78] D. J. Carlsson, J. A. Howard. and K. U. Ingold, *J. Am. Chem. Soc.*, **88**, 4726 (1965).
[79] C. Walling and V. Kurkov, *J. Am. Chem. Soc.*, **88**, 4727 (1966).

chloromethyl radicals,[78] and the rate constant for this dimerization was estimated at 7×10^7 mole^{-1} sec^{-1} at 24°. A much higher value (3×10^{10} mole^{-1} sec^{-1}) has been obtained for the gas-phase.[80] "Hot" trichloromethyl radicals generated by photolysis of bromotrichloromethane at 229 or 265 mμ are capable of abstracting hydrogen from hydrocarbons: with light of 313 mμ this does not happen.[81] In the photodecomposition of bromodichloromethane, the sequence

$$\text{CHCl}_2\text{Br} \xrightarrow{h\nu} \text{Br}\cdot + \cdot\text{CHCl}_2\text{*} \rightarrow \text{CCl} + \text{HCl}$$

is thought to occur.

Exclusive *exo*-attack is found on the intermediate allylic radicals formed in bromination of (38).[82] At −50°, photochlorination of chloral competes with

(38)

X = Br or Ph

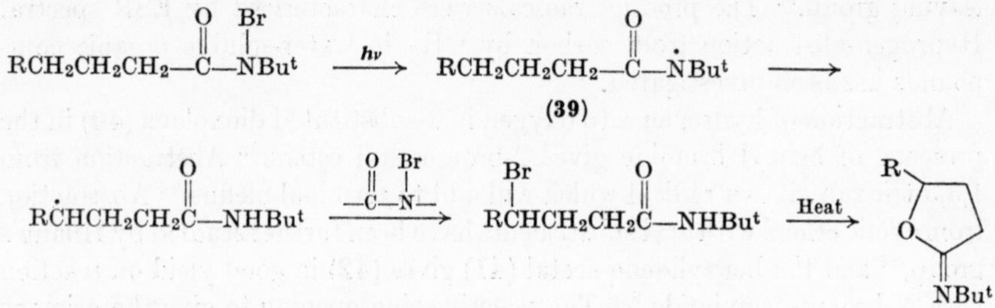

(39)

fragmentation of the intermediate Cl_3CCO radical.[83]

Intramolecular abstraction in the amido-radical (39) proceeds efficiently only with the *N-tert*-butyl group present; the amido-radicals fails to add to olefins.[84] Photolysis of hydrazine (to form $2\text{NH}_2\cdot$) in cyclohexane gives cyclohexylamine and ammonia,[85] and trifluoromethanesulphenyl chloride, in a similar reaction with cyclohexane, gives cyclohexyl chloride and cyclohexyl trifluoromethyl sulphide by two competing paths.[86]

[80] J. M. Tedder and J. C. Walton, *Chem. Commun.*, **1966**, 140.
[81] P. Cadman and J. P. Simons, *Trans. Faraday. Soc.*, **62**, 631 (1966).
[82] C. W. Jefford and E. H. Yen, *Tetrahedron Letters*, **1966**, 4477.
[83] B. G. Yasnitskii, E. B. Dol'berg, and Y. E. Aronov, *J. Org. Chem. USSR*, **1**, 439 (1965).
[84] R. S. Neale, N. L. Marcus, and R. G. Schepers, *J. Am. Chem. Soc.*, **88**, 3051 (1966).
[85] Y. Ogata, Y. Izawa, H. Tomioka, and T. Nishizawa, *Tetrahedron*, **22**, 1557 (1966).
[86] J. F. Harris, *J. Org. Chem.*, **31**, 931 (1966).

$$F_3CSCl \xrightarrow{h\nu} F_3CS\cdot + Cl\cdot$$

$$Cl\cdot + C_6H_{12} \longrightarrow C_6H_{11}\cdot + HCl$$

$$C_6H_{11}\cdot + F_3CSCl \longrightarrow C_6H_{11}SCF_3 + Cl\cdot$$

$$C_6H_{11}\cdot + F_3CSCl \longrightarrow C_6H_{11}Cl + F_3CS\cdot$$

$$2F_3CS\cdot \longrightarrow F_3CS—SCF_3$$

The effect of the silicon substituent on the radical reactivity of alkyl and other groups attached to silanes and siloxanes has been examined,[87] and it has been found that in the sulphuryl chloride chlorination of alkylhalogeno-silanes a $-SiCl_3$ group is effectively electron-withdrawing, whilst a $-SiMeCl_2$ group is electron-releasing.[88]

Methyl radicals abstract α-hydrogen with greater facility from cyclopentanone and acetophenone than from other n-alkyl ketones.[89] Radical centres α to a carbonyl group are also produced by the sequence:

$$\cdot OH + HO—\overset{H}{\underset{|}{\overset{|}{C}}}—\overset{|}{\underset{|}{C}}—X \longrightarrow H—O\overset{\curvearrowright}{\underset{\curvearrowleft}{}}\overset{|}{\underset{|}{C}}—\overset{|}{\underset{|}{C}}—X \xrightarrow{-HX} O=\overset{|}{C}—\overset{|}{\underset{|}{C}}\cdot$$

In the context of this reaction, X = OH (in a vicinal diol) constitutes a good leaving group.[90] The product radicals were characterized by ESR spectra. Hydrogen-abstraction from carbon by OH· in water-soluble organic compounds has been investigated.[91]

Abstraction of hydrogen α to oxygen in 2-substituted dioxolans (40) in the presence of benzyl bromide gives 2-bromoethyl esters.[92] Abstraction from 1,3,5-trioxan gives a radical which will add to terminal olefins.[93] Abstraction from cyclic ethers with aryl substituents have been further studied by Huang's group,[94] and the benzylidene acetal (41) gives (42) in good yield on reaction with N-bromosuccinimide.[95a] The selective ring-opening to give the primary bromide was attributed to a concerted process, as shown. Reaction with bromine after ring-opening would be expected to proceed via the more stable secondary radical (43). Hydroxyl radicals, formed by photolysis of hydrogen

[87] S. I. Beilin, N. A. Pokatilo, and B. A. Dolgoplosk, *Intern. Symp. Organosilicon Chem., Sci. Comm. Sci. Comm. Prague*, **1965**, 355; *Chem. Abs.*, **65**, 8711 (1966).

[88] Y. Nagai, N. Machida, and T. Migita, *Bull. Chem. Soc. Japan*, **39**, 412 (1966).

[89] I. V. Berezin, V. L. Ivanov, F. Kazanskaya, and N. N. Ugarova, *Zh. Fiz. Khim.*, **39**, 3011 (1965); *Chem. Abs.*, **64**, 11068 (1966).

[90] A. L. Buley, R. O. C. Norman, and R. J. Pritchett, *J. Chem. Soc.*, B, **1966**, 849.

[91] M. Anbar, D. Meyerstein, and P. Neta, *J. Chem. Soc.*, B, **1966**, 742.

[92] T. Ukai and H. Munakata, *Kogyo Kagaku Zasshi*, **68**, 1893 (1965); *Chem. Abs.*, **64**, 4915 (1966).

[93] D. Elad and I. Rosenthal, *Chem. Commun.*, **1966**, 684.

[94] R. L. Huang and S.-E. Loke, *J. Chem. Soc.*, **1965**, 6737; R. L. Huang and H. H. Lee, *J. Chem. Soc.*, C, **1966**, 929.

[95a] D. L. Failla, T. L. Hullar, and S. B. Siskin, *Chem. Commun.*, **1966**, 716.

peroxide, abstract hydrogen α to OH from aliphatic alcohols; however, in the presence of acid, the dominant abstraction product detected by ESR spectroscopy results from removal of a β-hydrogen atom.[95b] Abstraction of hydrogen

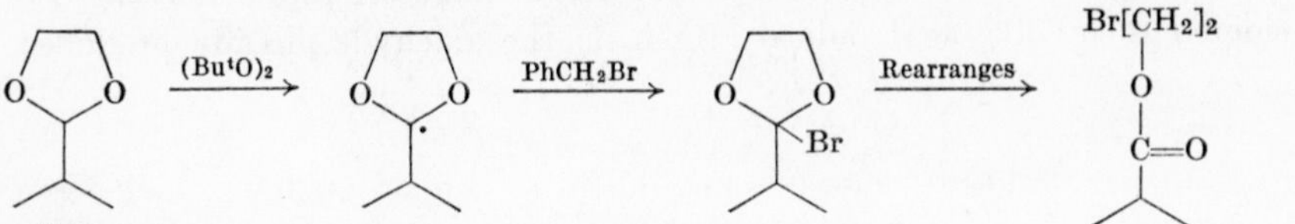

(40) $\xrightarrow{\text{(Bu}^t\text{O)}_2}$ $\xrightarrow{\text{PhCH}_2\text{Br}}$ (Br) $\xrightarrow{\text{Rearranges}}$ Br[CH$_2$]$_2$—O—C=O

(40)

$\xrightarrow{\text{R·}}$ $\xrightarrow{\text{R'CH:CH}_2}$ H—CH$_2$ĊHR' $\xrightarrow{\text{RH}}$ H—CH$_2$CH$_2$R'

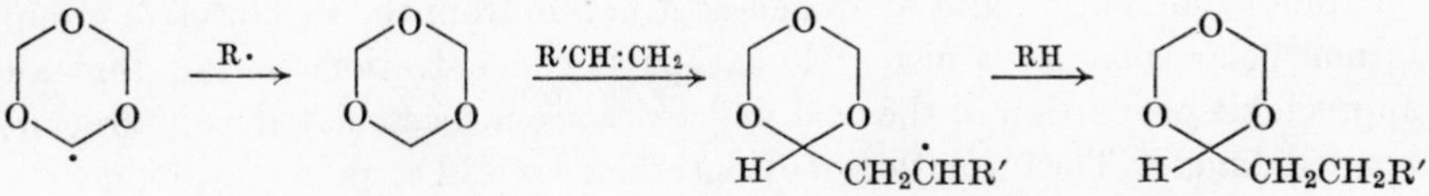

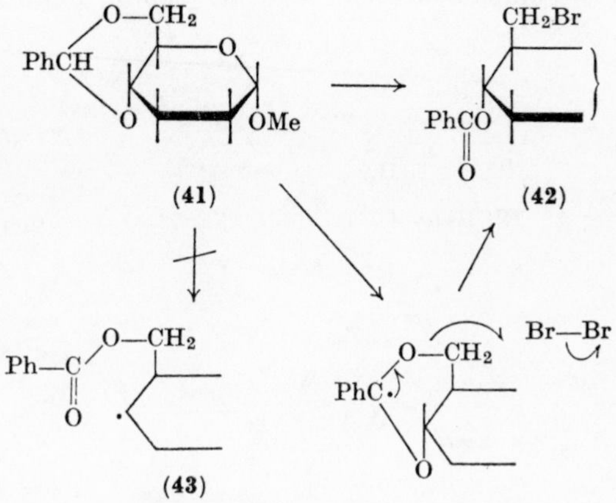

(41) PhCH, O—CH$_2$, O, OMe $\longrightarrow$ (42) PhCO, CH$_2$Br

(43) Ph—C(=O)—O—CH$_2$ · $\qquad$ PhC·—O—CH$_2$ $\qquad$ Br—Br

atom adjacent to oxygen in a variety of phosphorus compounds has also been detected by ESR spectroscopy.[95c]

The reduction of acyl halides to aldehydes by organotin hydrides has been examined,[96] as well as the accompanying formation of ester.[96, 97] Kuivila and Walsh[96] discussed the reactions in terms of free radicals and observed some fragmentation of the intermediate acyl radicals. However, even with triphenylacetyl chloride only slight fragmentation ($Ph_3CO· \rightarrow Ph_3C· + CO$) was observed, presumably because of the high reactivity of the metal hydride as a transfer agent. In the reactions of a series of aroyl chlorides, a good σ-correlation was found, but in ethyl acetate ρ had the large value of 4.0. This implies substantial contribution from (44) to the transition state for halogen

[95b] R. Livingston and H. Zeldes, *J. Am. Chem. Soc.*, **88**, 4333 (1966).
[95c] E. A. C. Lucken, *J. Chem. Soc.*, *A*, **1966**, 1354, 1357.
[96] H. G. Kuivila and E. J. Walsh, *J. Am. Chem. Soc.*, **88**, 571, 576 (1966).
[97] L. Kaplan, *J. Am. Chem. Soc.*, **88**, 1833, 4970 (1966).

$$\overset{\delta_-}{[ArCO}\cdots\overset{\cdot}{Cl}\cdots\overset{\delta_+}{Sn}]$$

(44)

abstraction. The most reasonable mechanism for ester formation was considered to involve acyl radical attack on the aldehyde already produced:

$$RCHO + R\overset{\cdot}{C}{=}O \rightarrow R\overset{O}{\overset{\|}{C}}{-}O\overset{\cdot}{C}HR \xrightarrow{R_3SnH} R\overset{O}{\overset{\|}{C}}{-}OCH_2R$$

Abstraction of hydrogen from phenolic oxygen[98] is retarded by hydrogen bonding to solvent,[98b] and hydrogen-abstraction from the carboxylate group in non-polar solvents is negligible except at concentrations so low that an appreciable proportion of the acid molecules are not associated as hydrogen-bonded dimer.[99] The formation of cyclic ethers by lead tetra-acetate oxidation of aliphatic alcohols is accompanied by an ionic reaction in pyridine which leads to ketone.[100]

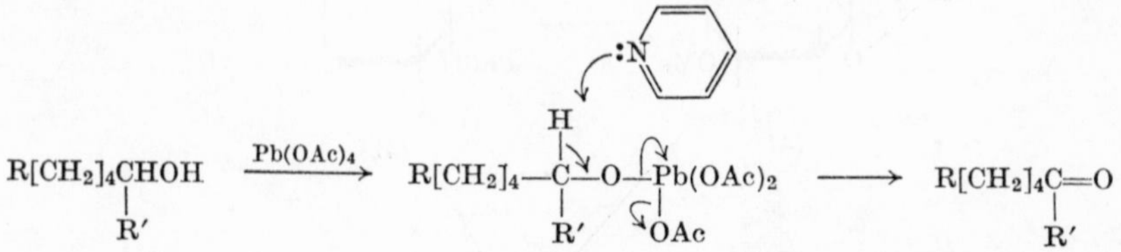

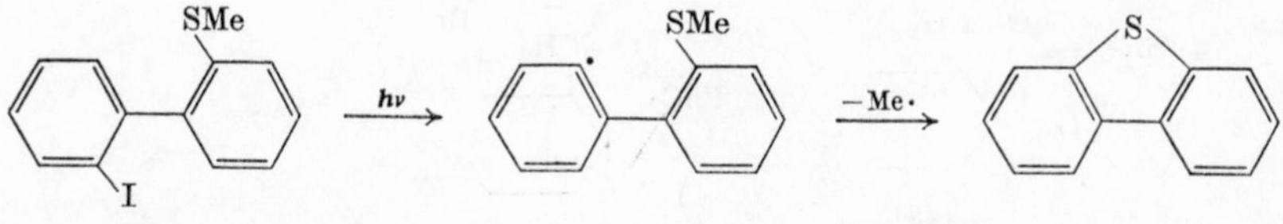

(45)

Phenyl radicals cleave the metal–metal bond in dimeric mercurous acetate:[101]

$$MeCO_2Hg{-}HgOCOMe + Ph\cdot \rightarrow PhHgOCOMe + MeCO_2Hg\cdot$$

Intramolecular displacement of methyl radicals from sulphur occurs after photolysis of the biaryl (45); the methyl radicals add to the solvent (benzene) to form toluene.[102]

Intramolecular displacement of a *tert*-butoxy-radical is observed in the

[98] (a) L. N. Shishkina and I. V. Berezin, *Zh. Fiz. Khim.*, **39**, 2547 (1965); (b) O. P. Sukhanova and A. L. Buchachenko, *ibid.*, p. 2413.

[99] I. Nemes, N. N. Ugarova, and O. Dobis, *Zh. Fiz. Khim.*, **40**, 466 (1966); *Chem. Abs.*, **64**, 17367.

[100] M. L. Mihailović and M. Miloradović, *Tetrahedron*, **22**, 723 (1966); M. L. Mihailović, J. Bošnjak, Z. Maksimović, Ž. Čeković, and L. Lorenc, *ibid.*, p. 955.

[101] Y. A. Ol'dekop, N. A. Maier, and V. N. Pshenichnyi, *J. Gen. Chem. USSR*, **35**, 906 (1965).

[102] J. A. Kampmeier and T. R. Evans, *J. Am. Chem. Soc.*, **88**, 4096 (1966).

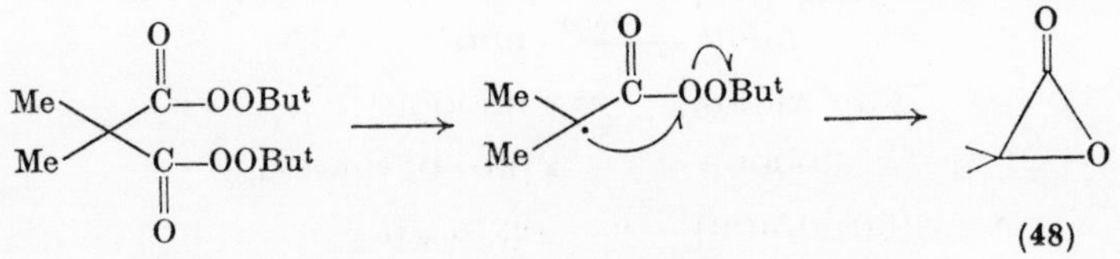

Me—C(Me)(C—OOBu^t)—C—OOBu^t (O, O) **(46)** → Me—C(Me)(·)—C—OOBu^t (O) → (O triangle O) **(48)**

Me—C(Me)(C—OEt)—C—OOBu^t (O, O)

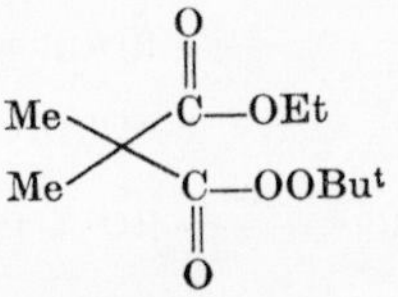

(47)

decomposition of the perester **(46)** in cumene.[103] The kinetics of decomposition give activation parameters comparable with those for perester **(47)** and consistent with an initial two-bond cleavage in both reactions. However, the major product from **(46)** is the polyester of 2-hydroxy-2-methylpropionic acid. In cumene, the only reasonable mechanism for formation of this is ionic polymerization of the α-lactone **(48)**.

Hydrogen-abstraction from cyclohexane, and subsequent reaction of the cyclohexyl radical with carbon monoxide (leading to aldehyde) and with nitric oxide [leading to N-nitrosohydroxylamine, $C_6H_{11}N(NO)OH$], have been reported.[104a]

Oxygen radicals. A short review detailing recent developments in the chemistry of unstable oxygen-centred radicals has now appeared in English translation.[104b]

The formation of peroxides by combination of two oxygen radicals appears to be of much greater importance than has been generally realized. The cage recombination of acetoxy-radicals[17] has already been mentioned, and the absolute rate constant for dimerization of free *tert*-butoxy-radicals has been determined[78] as 1.4×10^8 mole^{-1} sec^{-1} at 24°. This relatively high value emphasizes the importance of such reactions, and suggests that such processes may sometimes be important in the autoxidation of tertiary hydrocarbons.

Lead tetra-acetate oxidation of *tert*-butyl hydroperoxide at −70° in methylene chloride gives some oxygen, but further oxygen is evolved when the solution is allowed to warm to −30°. The latter process is considered to signify the decomposition of di-*tert*-butyl trioxide.[105] This product arises from the formation, outlined below, of *tert*-butoxy-radicals in the presence of a relatively high concentration of peroxy-radicals. Ready abstraction of the

103 L. B. Gortler and M. D. Saltzman, *J. Org. Chem.*, **31**, 3821 (1966).
104^a E. Perrotti, M. Lanzoni, G. Daniele, and M. DeMalde, *Ann. Chim.* (*Rome*), **55**, 485 (1965).
104^b L. M. Terman, *Russian Chem. Rev.*, **1965**, 185.
105 P. D. Bartlett and P. Günther, *J. Am. Chem. Soc.*, **88**, 3288 (1966).

$$ROOH \xrightarrow{Pb(OAc)_4} ROO\cdot$$

$$2ROO\cdot \rightleftharpoons ROOOOR$$

$$ROOOOR \longrightarrow [RO\cdot \ O_2 \ \cdot OR] \text{ "cage"}$$

$$[RO\cdot \ O_2 \ \cdot OR] \longrightarrow 2RO\cdot + O_2$$
$$ \longrightarrow ROOR + O_2$$

$$RO\cdot + ROO\cdot \longrightarrow ROOOR$$

$$ROOOR \xrightarrow{\ >-30°\ } RO\cdot + ROO\cdot$$

peroxy-hydrogen is also observed in the reaction of *tert*-butyl hydroperoxide with methyl radicals,[106] especially in hydrocarbon solvents unable to accept hydrogen bonds.

The *N*-nitroso-compound (49) rapidly rearranges in solution at room temperature, and the initial product then slowly evolves nitrogen. Significant quantities of *tert*-butyl perbenzoate are formed in a cage reaction, the extent of which increases with the viscosity of the medium.[107]

$$\overset{\displaystyle \overset{NO}{|}}{PhCO-N-OBu^t} \longrightarrow PhCO_2-N{=}N-OBu^t \longrightarrow PhCO_2\cdot + N_2 + \cdot OBu^t$$
(49)

Thermal dissociation of 2,2,3,3-tetraphenylbutane in the presence of oxygen gives peroxy radicals which may abstract hydrogen from 9,10-diphenyl-anthracene. The radicals thus formed also react with oxygen, and the two types of peroxide radicals show closely similar behaviour towards a wide range of phenolic oxidation inhibitors.[108]

Nitrogen radicals. Stable nitrogen-centred biradicals have been prepared based on the verdazyl[109] and on the diphenylpicrylhydrazyl[110] system; also on a new system (50).[111]

Combination of the verdazyl (51) with cyanopropyl radicals from azobis-isobutyronitrile gives compound (52), which redissociates above 150°.[109] A linear analogue (53) of the verdazyls has also been obtained.[112]

Among reports from Matevosyan's group on the chemistry of hydrazyl

[106] I. V. Berezin, N. F. Kazanskaya, and N. N. Ugarova, *Zh. Fiz. Khim.*, **40**, 766 (1966); *Chem. Abs.*, **65**, 3716 (1966).

[107] T. Koenig and M. Deinzer, *J. Am. Chem. Soc.*, **88**, 4518 (1966).

[108] L. R. Mahoney, *J. Am. Chem. Soc.*, **88**, 3035 (1966).

[109] R. Kuhn, F. A. Neugebauer, and H. Trischmann, *Monatsh. Chem.*, **97**, 525 (1966); F. A. Neugebauer, *ibid.*, p. 853.

[110] L. I. Stashkov and R. O. Matevosyan, *J. Org. Chem. USSR*, **1**, 624 (1965).

[111] U. Mayer, H. Baumgärtel, and H. Zimmermann, *Angew. Chem. Internat. Ed. Engl.*, **5**, 311 (1966).

[112] F. A. Neugebauer and H. Trischmann, *Monatsh. Chem.*, **97**, 554 (1966).

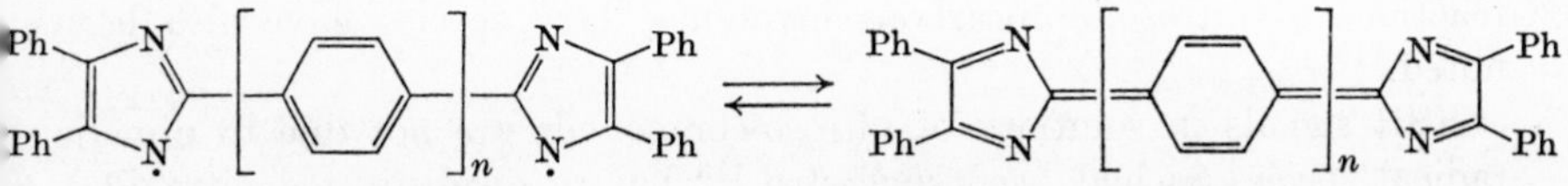

(50) $(n=1)$

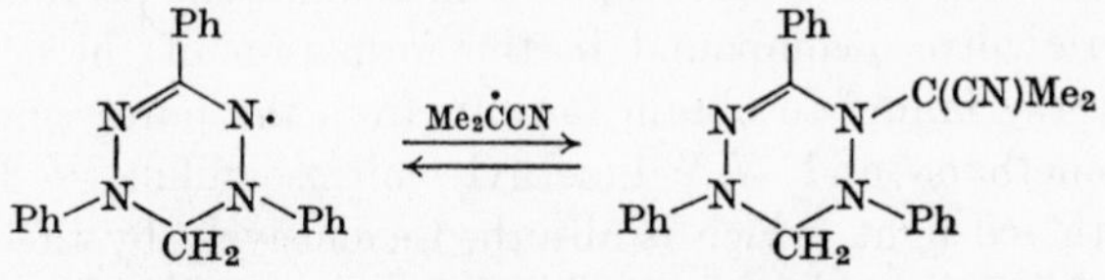

(51)   **(52)**

$$Ph_2N—N=CH—\overset{\cdot}{N}—NPh_2$$

(53)

radicals is a kinetic study of the reaction between diphenylpicrylhydrazyl and N-phenyl-2-naphthylamine.[113] This proves to be second-order in radical, and first-order in amine, suggesting that the apparently simple hydrogen-abstraction may involve a sequence such as that annexed.

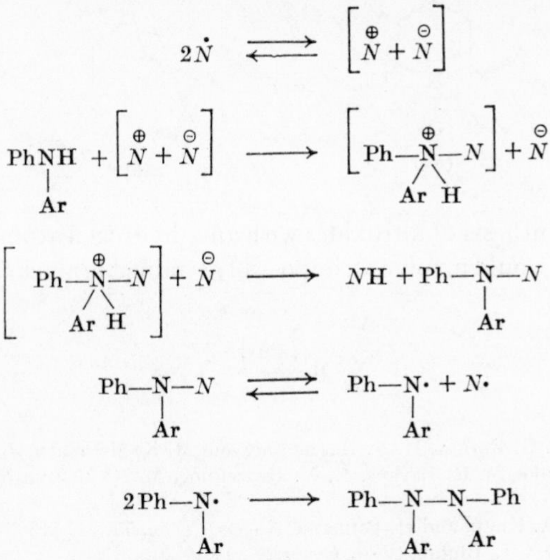

$(N =$ hydrazyl residue. $Ar = \beta\text{-}C_{10}H_7)$

Nitroxide radicals. Some new fluorocarbon nitroxides have been prepared and are regarded as members of a general class of stable nitroxides.[114] Radical

[113] L. I. Stashkov and R. O. Matevosyan, *J. Org. Chem., USSR*, **1**, 548 (1965).
[114] W. D. Blackley, *J. Am. Chem. Soc.*, **88**, 480 (1966).

9*

reactions of nitrosofluorocarbons involving these species have also been noted.[115]

ESR signals in solutions of nitroso-compounds are not due to dimeric radical species as had been suggested,[116] but to disubstituted nitroxides, formed by the effect of light.[117] For example, ultraviolet irradiation of solutions of nitrosobenzene gives diphenylnitroxide. The possible importance of the dimeric nitroso-compound in the formation of these radicals was suggested by the failure to obtain radicals from the purely monomeric trifluoronitrosomethane and *N,N*-dimethyl-*p*-nitrosoaniline.[117] However, irradiation with red light, which is absorbed exclusively by the monomer, is sufficient to form di-*tert*-butylnitroxide from 2-methyl-2-nitrosopropane.[118] Whether radicals are formed directly, or an excited molecule of nitroso-compound participates in a bimolecular process, has not yet been established.

Dipole moment measurements,[119a] as well as basicity,[119b] appear to be consistent with an sp^3-hybridized nitrogen in the piperidine *N*-oxyls (54). A pyramidal nitrogen configuration has also been assigned to the radical anions of certain aromatic nitro-compounds.[120]

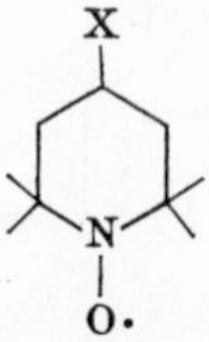

(54) 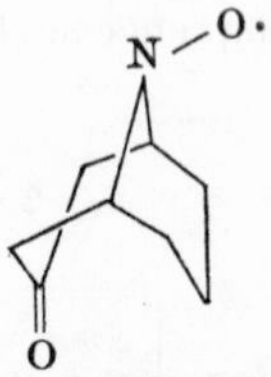   (55)

Attempted synthesis of nitroxides with an α-hydrogen atom normally leads to nitrones; this would involve an impossibly strained bridgehead double-bond

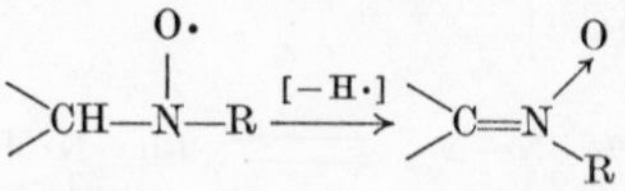

[115] R. E. Banks, M. G. Barlow, R. N. Haszeldine, and M. K. McCreath, *J. Chem. Soc.*, **1965**, 7203; R. E. Banks, M. G. Barlow, R. N. Haszeldine, M. K. McCreath, and H. Sutcliffe, *ibid.*, p. 7209.

[116] W. Theilacker, A. Knop, and H. Uffmann, *Angew. Chem.*, **77**, 717 (1965).

[117] E. T. Strom and A. L. Bluhm, *Chem. Commun.*, **1966**, 115.

[118] A. Mackor, T. A. J. W. Wajer, T. J. de Boer, and J. D. W. van Voorst, *Tetrahedron Letters*, **1966**, 2115.

[119a] E. G. Rozantsev and E. N. Gur'yanova, *Izv. Akad. Nauk SSSR, Ser. Khim.*, **1966**, 979; *Chem. Abs.*, **65**, 8728 (1966).

[119b] E. G. Rozantsev and E. G. Gintsberg, *Izv. Akad. Nauk SSSR, Ser. Khim.*, **1966**, 571; *Chem. Abs.*, **65**, 8735 (1966).

[120] W. M. Fox, J. M. Gross, and M. C. R. Symons, *J. Chem. Soc., A*, **1966**, 448; J. M. Gross and M. C. R. Symons, *ibid.*, p. 451.

in the case of norpseudopelletierine *N*-oxyl (**55**), which has now been prepared from the corresponding amine by Dupeyre and Rassat[121] and found to be stable.

The Cu(II)–(phenanthroline) oxidation of methanol is catalysed by di-*tert*-butylnitroxide.[122] The kinetics are consistent with a mechanism involving abstraction of hydrogen from methanol co-ordinated to the copper, and simultaneous electron-transfer to the copper. Loss of a proton gives formaldehyde. The nitroxide is regenerated by further reaction with cupric copper.

$$Cu(II)Ar(CH_3OH) \xrightarrow{R_2NO\cdot} Cu(I)Ar + CH_2O + H^+ + R_2NOH$$
$$Cu(II)Ar + R_2NOH \longrightarrow Cu(I)Ar + R_2NO\cdot + H^+$$

Oxidation of phenols to quinones by the stable nitroxide, Fremy's salt, was unfortunately classified last year with electrophilic substitution.[123] Similar reactions with organic nitroxides, of which di-(*p*-nitrophenyl)nitroxide is particularly effective, have now been studied.[124]

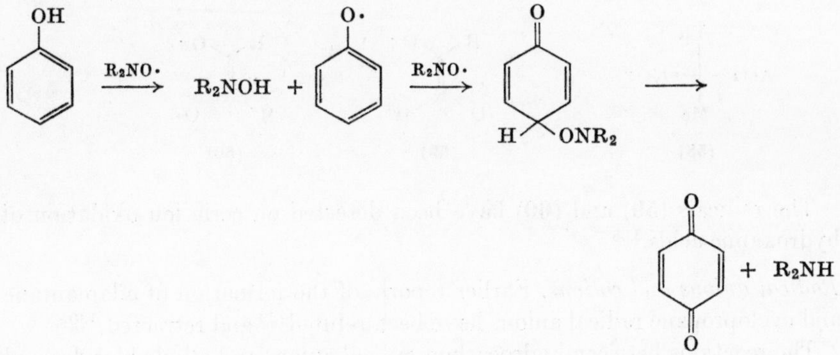

Nitrosobenzene radical anion and, in less basic media, its conjugate acid, are now established intermediates in both the oxidation of phenylhydroxylamine and the reduction of nitrosobenzene.[125]

Gilbert and Norman[126] have recorded the ESR spectra of a series of iminoxy radicals obtained by lead tetra-acetate oxidation of various ketoximes and benzaldoximes; a_N is generally ca. 30 gauss. However, Lown[127] has observed the additional formation of other radicals in these systems. Lead tetra-acetate oxidation of cyclohexanone oxime leads to a nitroxide (**56**) (a_N ca. 16 gauss), which is stable in the presence of an excess of oxidant, and hence is formed in

121 R.-M. Dupeyre and A. Rassat, *J. Am. Chem. Soc.*, **88**, 3180 (1966).
122 W. Brackman and C. J. Gaasbeek, *Rec. Trav. Chim.*, **85**, 221 (1966).
123 *Organic Reaction Mechanisms*, **1965**, 170.
124 A. R. Forrester and R. H. Thomson, *J. Chem. Soc.*, *C*, **1966**, 1844.
125 P. B. Ayscough, F. P. Sargent, and R. Wilson, *J. Chem. Soc.*, *B*, **1966**, 903.
126 B. C. Gilbert and R. O. C. Norman, *J. Chem. Soc.*, *B*, **1966**, 86, 722.
127 J. W. Lown, *J. Chem. Soc.*, *B*, **1966**, 441, 644.

competition with the isolated nitrosoacetate (57), and acetophenone oxime
gives the radical anion (58) in addition to the iminoxy-radical.

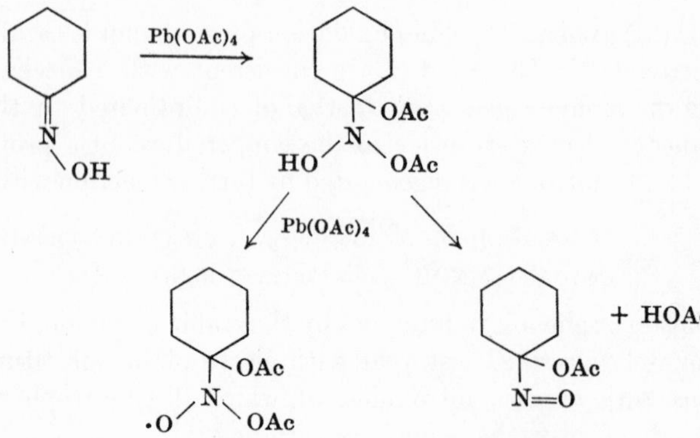

The radicals (59) and (60) have been detected on ceric ion oxidation of
hydroxamic acids.[128]

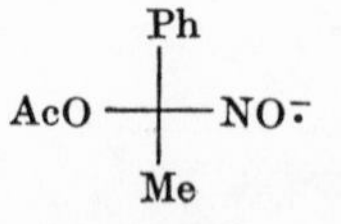

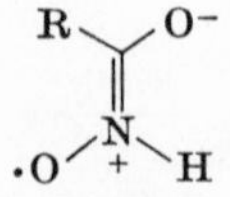

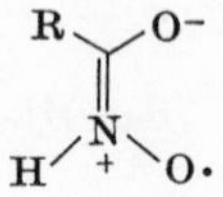

Radical anions and cations. Earlier reports of the formation of adamantane
and cyclopropane radical anions have been refuted[129] and retracted.[130]

The reactions between hydrocarbon radical anions and alkyl chlorides and
bromides are mentioned in Chapter 8. With alkyl iodides, higher radical
concentrations are possible, and dimerization and disproportionation appear
to compete effectively with further reduction to the anion.[131] The alternative
process $R^- + RI \rightarrow RR + I^-$ is discounted, as in a competition between *n*-
and iso-propyl iodides there is a statistical distribution of *n*-hexane (1 part),
isohexane (2 parts), and 2,3-dimethylbutane (1 part), as expected only of the
radical mechanism. Electron-transfer decomposition of alkyl toluene-*p*-
sulphonates has also been reported,[132] as well as the interaction of naphthalene radical anion with carbon monoxide.[133]

[128] J. V. Ramsbottom and W. A. Waters, *J. Chem. Soc., B,* **1966**, 132.
[129] M. T. Jones, *J. Am. Chem. Soc.,* **88**, 174 (1966); F. Gerson, E. Heilbronner, and J. Heinzer, *Tetrahedron Letters,* **1966**, 2095.
[130] K. W. Bowers, G. J. Nolfi, T. H. Lowry, and F. D. Greene, *Tetrahedron Letters,* **1966**, 4063.
[131] G. D. Sargent, J. N. Cron, and S. Bank, *J. Am. Chem. Soc.,* **88**, 5363 (1966).
[132] W. D. Closson, P. Wriede, and S. Bank, *J. Am. Chem. Soc.,* **88**, 1581 (1966).
[133] W. Büchner, *Chem. Ber.,* **99**, 1485 (1966).

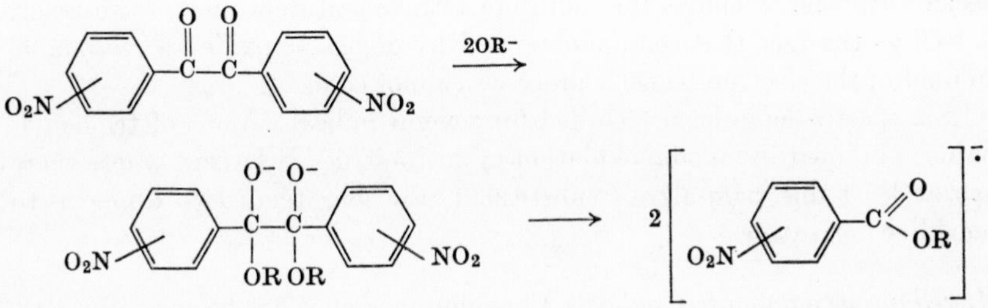

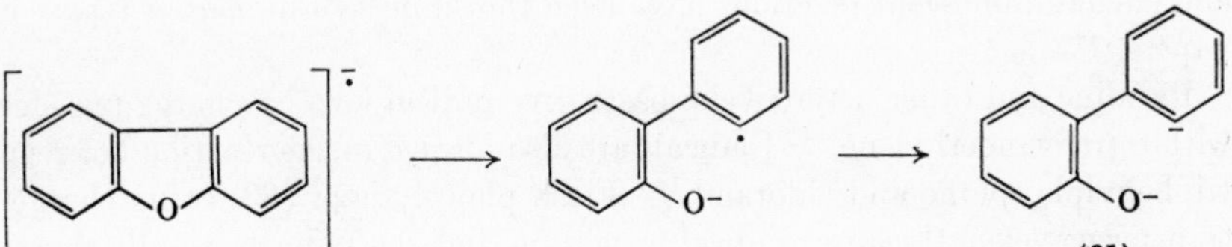

(61)

$$[Ph_2C:NPh]^{\cdot-} \rightleftharpoons Ph_2C:NPh + [Ph_2C:NPh]^{2-}$$
(62)

The 3,3'- and 4,4'-dinitro-derivatives of benzil react with alkoxide to give the radical anions shown.[134]

Evans' group have followed the decomposition of dibenzofuran radical anion to the dianion (61)[135] and have studied the disproportionation of (62).[136] Stable *ortho*-semiquinone salts have been isolated,[137] and the formation of *para*-benzoquinone radical anion from benzoquinone and hydroxide is thought to proceed as indicated.[138] Evidence for this, rather than direct

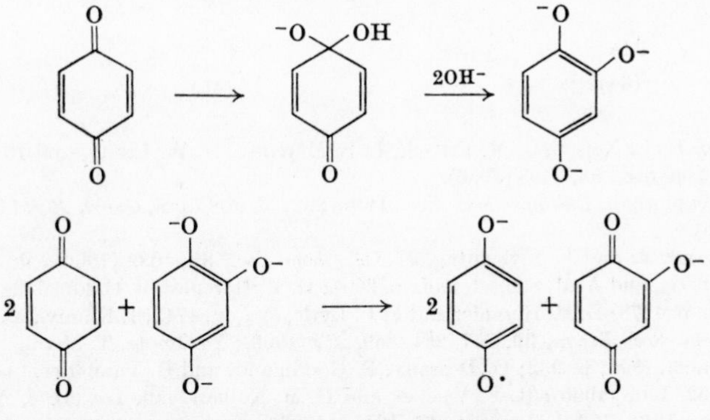

[134] H. Kurreck and W. Broser, *Z. Naturforsch.*, **20b**, 943 (1965).
[135] A. G. Evans, P. B. Roberts, and B. J. Tabner, *J. Chem. Soc.*, *B*, **1966**, 269.
[136] A. G. Evans and J. C. Evans, *J. Chem. Soc.*, *B*, **1966**, 271.
[137] E. Müller, F. Günter, K. Scheffler, P. Ziemek, and A. Rieker, *Ann. Chem.*, **688**, 134 (1965).
[138] V. B. Goluber, L. S. Yaguzhinskii, and A. V. Volkov, *Biofizika*, **11**, 572 (1966); *Chem. Abs.*, **65**, 12077 (1966).

electron-transfer, includes the failure of tetrasubstituted quinones to react, as well as the fact that semiquinone and hydrogen peroxide—a reasonable product of the electron-transfer process—cannot co-exist.

ESR spectra have been recorded for several radical cations of triphenylamines obtained by anodic oxidation in acetonitrile.[139] Except where there was at least one *para*-alkoxy-substituent, the ions tended to dimerize to benzidine derivatives.

Miscellaneous data on free radicals. Chemiluminescence has been reviewed,[140] and chemiluminescent reactions have been the subject of numerous research papers.[141]

Pyridine and other heterocyclic bases give radical ions by charge transfer with tetracyanoethylene.[142] Radicals are also formed in the reaction between triphenylphosphine and chloranil.[143] Flash photolysis of (63) at its charge-transfer wavelength causes radical formation, but the radicals rapidly revert

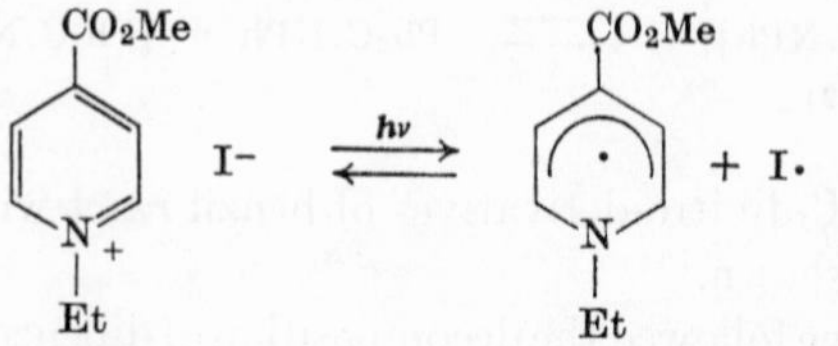

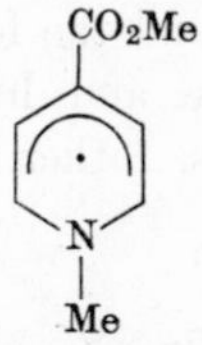

[139] E. T. Seo, R. F. Nelson, J. M. Fritsch, L. S. Marcoux, D. W. Leedy, and R. N. Adams, *J. Am. Chem. Soc.*, 88, 3498 (1966).

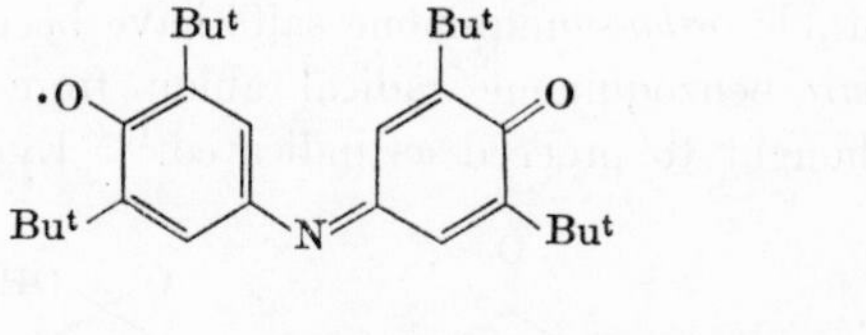

[140] V. Y. Shlyapintokh, *Russian Chem. Rev.*, 1966, 292; F. McCapra, *Quart. Rev. (London)*, 20, 485 (1966).

[141] E. A. Chandross and F. I. Sonntag, *J. Am. Chem. Soc.*, 88, 1089 (1966); M. M. Rauhut, B. G. Roberts, and A. M. Semsel, *ibid.*, p. 3604; D. M. Hercules, R. C. Lansbury, and D. K. Roe, *ibid.*, p. 4578; D. M. Hercules and F. E. Lytle, *ibid.*, p. 4745; I. Kamiya and R. Iwaki, *Bull. Chem. Soc. Japan*, 39, 257, 264, 269, 277 (1966); Y. Omote, T. Miyake, S. Ohmori, N. Sugiyama, *ibid.*, p. 932; O. Dessaux, P. Goudmand, and G. Pannetier, *Compt. Rend.*, *Ser. C*, 262, 1508 (1966); R. F. Vasil'ev and D. M. Nalbandyan, *Izv. Akad. Nauk SSSR*, *Ser. Khim.*, 1966, 773; *Chem. Abs.*, 65, 10458 (1966).

[142] V. V. Pen'kovs'kii, *Teor. i Eksperim. Khim. Akad. Nauk Ukr. SSR*, 2, 282 (1966); *Chem. Abs.*, 65, 15198 (1966); C. Nicolau and C. Cailly, *Bull. Classe Sci. Acad. Roy. Belg.*, 51, 181 (1965); *Chem. Abs.*, 64, 7981.

[1 3] E. A. C. Lucken, F. Ramirez, V. P. Catto, D. Rhum, and S. Dershowitz, *Tetrahedron*, 22, 637 (1966).

to starting material.[144] When solutions of radical **(64)** are cooled to $-100°$, only 10% of the compound exists as free radical;[145] this has been attributed to charge-transfer pairing of two radicals.

A short review of methods of trapping and studying free radicals has appeared.[146] The kinetics of radical scavenging by mixtures of HI and I_2 have been analysed,[147] and the stable 2,3',5',6-tetra-*tert*-butylindophenoxyl **(65)** (a nitrogen analogue of galvinoxyl) has been assessed as a radical scavenger.[148] The favourable conclusions were accompanied by the observation that towards *tert*-butoxy-radicals it is only ca. six times more reactive than the parent indophenol, which reacts by hydrogen transfer.

The products of photolysis of triphenylmethyl chloride have been interpreted in terms of reactions of an excited triphenylmethyl radical.[149] The heat of reaction of triphenylmethyl with oxygen has been estimated by an ESR technique to be 9 kcal mole^{-1}.[150] This involved the observation of an equilibrium between triphenylmethyl and triphenylmethylperoxy-radicals in the presence of oxygen.

Stable radicals have been divided into two classes:[151] (i) those (such as $Ar_3C\cdot$) in which *para*-substituents of electron-withdrawing or -donating character may stabilize the radical; and (ii) those (such as $Ar_2N\text{–}\dot{N}COPh \leftrightarrow$ $\cdot\overset{+}{N}Ar_2\text{–}\overset{-}{N}COPh$) where electron-donating substituents may stabilize the radical but electron-withdrawing substituents cause destabilization by preferentially delocalizing the lone pair of the uncharged structure, with resultant localization of the radical centre.

(66)

Further observations on hindered diarylmethyl radicals have been reported.[152, 153] Under conditions where di-(o-*tert*-butylphenyl)methyl is

[144] E. M. Kosower and L. Lindqvist, *Tetrahedron Letters*, **1965**, 4481.
[145] M. Itoh and S. Nagakura, *Tetrahedron Letters*, **1966**, 227.
[146] M. C. R. Symons, *Adv. Sci.*, **23**, 163 (1966).
[147] D. Perner and R. H. Schuler, *J. Phys. Chem.*, **70**, 2224 (1966); I. Mani and R. J. Hanrahan, *ibid.*, p. 2233.
[148] P. D. Bartlett and S. T. Purrington, *J. Am. Chem. Soc.*, **88**, 3303 (1966).
[149] H. G. Lewis and E. D. Owen, *Chem. Commun.*, **1966**, 216.
[150] C. L. Ayers, E. G. Janzen, and F. J. Johnston, *J. Am. Chem. Soc.*, **88**, 2610 (1966).
[151] R. I. Walter, *J. Am. Chem. Soc.*, **88**, 1923, 1930 (1966).
[152] K. H. Fleurke and W. T. Nauta, *Rec. Trav. Chim.*, **85**, 86 (1966).
[153] W. Theilacker and F. Koch, *Angew. Chem. Internat. Ed. Engl.*, **5**, 246 (1966).

more than 90% dimerized, di-(2,5-di-*tert*-butylphenyl)methyl **(66)** is completely monomeric.[153] The surprisingly large effect of the remote *tert*-butyl groups serves to emphasize the importance of steric factors in the dissociation of polyarylethanes.

Any given *para*-substituent has a more pronounced stabilizing effect on a benzyl radical than on an α-methylbenzyl radical, which in turn experiences greater stabilization from the substituent than does a cumyl radical.[154]

The thermal equilibration of symmetrical trisulphides with the unsymmetrical product proceeds by a free-radical chain reaction[155] with propagation by:

$$RS \cdot + R'SSSR' \rightarrow R'SSSR + R'S \cdot$$

Chain termination is said to involve formation of di- and tetra-sulphides. The activation energy (36 kcal mole^{-1}) for dissociation of tetrasulphides is much less than that for disulphides, but is close to the value for ring-opening of S_8.[156]

The reaction of thiols with propylene oxide is catalysed by tetraphenylhydrazine, but not by light or azobisisobutyronitrile.[157] This behaviour is attributed to proton transfer to the nitrogen radical, followed by heterolytic opening of the epoxide:

$$Ph_2NNPh_2 \rightleftharpoons 2Ph_2N \cdot$$
$$Ph_2N \cdot + RSH \rightarrow Ph_2\overset{\cdot +}{N}H + RS^-$$

$$RS^- + MeCH\overset{O}{\diagup\diagdown}CH_2 \rightarrow MeCH\overset{^-O}{\underset{|}{}}CH_2SR$$

Silyl radicals are assumed[158] to participate in the aryl exchange reaction (at 500°):

$$Cl_3SiH + PhSiMe_3 \rightleftharpoons Me_3SiH + PhSiCl_3$$

Radical reactions of organophosphorus compounds have been reviewed.[159] The radical chain reaction between pentanethiol and triethyl phosphite, photoinitiated with azobisisobutyronitrile, has interaction of two pentyl radicals as the sole chain-ending step; this has been suggested as a suitable system for studying the life-time of alkyl radicals in solution.[160] A heterolytic component to the reaction between triethyl phosphite and carbon tetrachloride has been confirmed by inhibition studies.[161]

[154] J. E. Hodgkins and E. D. Megarity, *J. Am. Chem. Soc.*, **87**, 5322 (1965).
[155] C. D. Trivette and A. Y. Coran, *J. Org. Chem.*, **31**, 100 (1966).
[156] I. Kende, T. L. Pickering, and A. V. Tobolsky, *J. Am. Chem. Soc.*, **87**, 5582 (1966).
[157] M. Takebayashi, T. Shingaki, and T. Mihara, *Bull. Chem. Soc. Japan*, **39**, 376 (1966).
[158] C. Eaborn, I. M. T. Davidson, and C. J. Wood, *J. Organometal. Chem.*, **4**, 489 (1965).
[159] C. Walling and M. S. Pearson in "Topics in Phosphorus Chemistry", Griffith and Grayson, ed., Interscience, New York, London, Sidney, Vol. III, 1966.
[160] R. D. Burkhart, *J. Phys. Chem.*, **70**, 605 (1966).
[161] J. I. G. Cadogan and J. T. Sharp, *Tetrahedron Letters*, **1966**, 2733.

Photolysis of $Ph_2P–PPh_2$ in (–)-octan-2-ol gives 1-methylheptyl diphenylphosphinite ($RR'CHOPPh_2$) with a high degree of retention of configuration.[162] This accords with the mechanism:

$$Ph_2P\cdot + RR'CHOH \rightarrow RR'CH\overset{+}{O}\!\!-\!\!\underset{\underset{H}{|}}{\overset{-}{P}}Ph_2 \xrightarrow{[-H\cdot]} RR'CHOPPh_2$$

which is favoured by the strength of the P–O bond, and the ability of phosphorus to accommodate an extra electron in a d-orbital. The $Ph_2P\cdot$ radical couples *para* with diphenylnitrogen to give (**67**).[163]

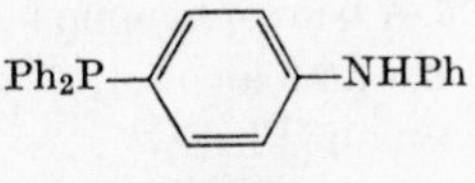

(**67**)

Photoinitiated phenylation of triphenylphosphine by Ph_2IBF_4 is a radical-chain process;[164, 165] the reaction is inhibited by hydroquinone,[164] and the main steps in the mechanism are as annexed.[165]

$$Ph_3P + Ph_2IBF_4 \longrightarrow [Ph_2I\!\!-\!\!PPh_3]^+BF_4^-$$

$$[Ph_2I\!\!-\!\!PPh_3]^+BF_4^- \xrightarrow{h\nu} Ph_2I\cdot + Ph_3P^+ + BF_4^-$$

$$Ph_2I\cdot + Ph_3P \longrightarrow Ph_4P\cdot + PhI$$

$$Ph_4P\cdot + Ph_2IBF_4 \longrightarrow Ph_4P^+BF_4^- + Ph_2I\cdot$$

Aryl radicals formed by reaction of aryl halides with a Grignard reagent and cobaltous halide have also been employed to arylate triphenylphosphine.[166a] The arylation of tervalent phosphorus by aryl radicals obtained by photolysis of aryl iodides or bromides has been found to occur with chlorine and fluorine compounds if the latter are activated by a *para*-phosphorus grouping,[166b] as shown.

Activation of bromine to photolysis is also effected by a *para*-acyl group

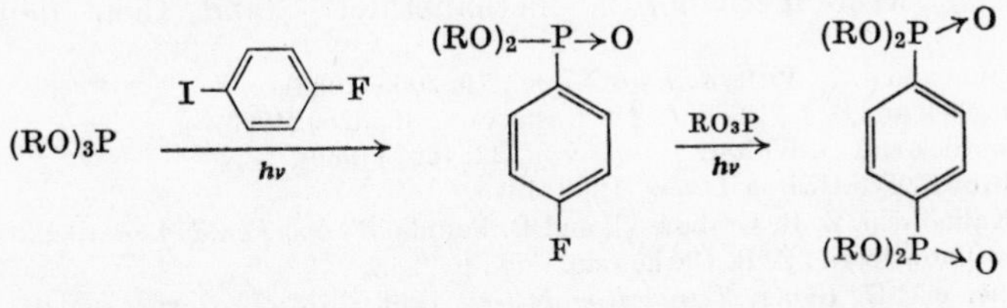

[162] R. S. Davidson, R. A. Sheldon, and S. Trippett, *Chem. Commun.*, **1966**, 99.
[163] H. Low and P. Tavs, *Tetrahedron Letters*, **1966**, 1357.
[164] O. A. Ptitsyna, M. E. Pudeeva, and O. A. Reutov, *Dokl. Akad. Nauk SSSR*, **168**, 595 (1966); *Chem. Abs.*, **65**, 8712.
[165] O. A. Ptitsyna, M. E. Pudeeva, and O. A. Reutov, *Dokl. Akad. Nauk SSSR*, **165**, 838 (1965); *Chem. Abs.*, **64**, 5129 (1966).
[166a] L. Horner and H. Moser, *Chem. Ber.*, **99**, 2789 (1966).
[166b] R. Obrycki and C. E. Griffin, *Tetrahedron Letters*, **1966**, 5049.

absorbing light which excites the carbonyl $n\pi^*$ state.[167] The suggestion was made that the $n\pi^*$ triplet crosses to a vibrationally excited ground state from which the bromine atom is ejected. Radicals are also formed by photolysis of C–O bonds and C–Br bonds of phenoxyphenols and bromophenols, respectively.[168]

Cross-coupling of radicals formed by hydrogen abstraction from several pairs selected from acetone, ether, toluene, methylene chloride, and chloroform has been reported.[169] α-Hydroxybenzyl radicals give roughly equal amounts of both *meso-* and racemic hydrobenzoin,[170] contradicting some earlier reports. The pK value of benzophenone ketyl, $Ph_2\dot{C}OH$, is comparable with that of a phenol rather than an alcohol;[171] this is consistent with charge delocalization in the radical anion $[Ph_2CO]^{\bar{\cdot}}$.

The radical-chain reaction of acyl azides and diazoketones with propan-2-ol gives amides and ketones, respectively.[172]

Half-esters of *tert*-alkylmalonic acids (68) have been subjected to the Kolbe reaction in methanol, in order to investigate the competition between

$$
\begin{array}{c}
RMe_2CCHCO_2R' \\
| \\
CO_2H \\
\textbf{(68)}
\end{array}
\xrightarrow{+e^-}
\begin{array}{c}
RMe_2C{-}CHCO_2R' \\
| \\
RMe_2C{-}CHCO_2R' \\
\textbf{(69)}
\end{array}
$$

radical and cationic intermediates. Good yields of the radical-coupling products (69) were obtained, together with much smaller amounts of complex mixtures of monomeric products, presumably produced from ionic intermediates which may have undergone rearrangement.[173] (Other anodic processes are discussed on p. 192.)

Miscellaneous gas-phase studies not already mentioned relate to: pyrolysis of ethane[174] and 4-methylpent-1-ene;[175] reactions of methyl radicals with *n*-butane,[176] with methanol,[177] methanethiol[178] and their deuteriated

[167] E. J. Baum and J. N. Pitts, *J. Phys. Chem.*, **70**, 2066 (1966).
[168] H.-I. Joschek and S. I. Miller, *J. Am. Chem. Soc.*, **88**, 3269 (1966).
[169] K. Schwetlick and D. Wolter, *Tetrahedron*, **22**, 1297 (1966).
[170] W. G. Brown, *Tetrahedron Letters*, **1966**, 1845.
[171] M. K. Kalinowski, Z. R. Grabowski, and B. Pakula, *Trans. Faraday Soc.*, **62**, 918 (1966); M. K. Kalinowski and Z. R. Grabowski, *ibid.*, p. 926.
[172] L. Horner and G. Bauer, *Tetrahedron Letters*, **1966**, 3573; L. Horner and H. Schwarz, *ibid.*, p. 3579.
[173] L. Eberson and B. Sandberg, *Acta Chem. Scand.*, **20**, 739 (1966).
[174] M. C. Lin and M. H. Back, *Canad. J. Chem.*, **344**, 2357, 2369 (1966); A. B. Trenwith, *Trans. Faraday Soc.*, **62**, 1538 (1966).
[175] M. Taniewski, *J. Chem. Soc.*, **1965**, 7436.
[176] J. M. Tedder and R. A. Watson, *J. Chem. Soc., B*, **1966**, 1069.
[177] R. Shaw and J. C. J. Thynne, *Trans. Faraday Soc.*, **62**, 104 (1966).
[178] G. Greig and J. C. J. Thynne, *Trans. Faraday Soc.*, **62**, 379 (1966).

analogues, with ethylamine,[179] hydrazines,[180] and other nitrogen-containing compounds,[181] as well as halogeno- and alkylhalogeno-silanes;[182] reaction between methyl and ethyl radicals;[183] attack of ethyl radicals on amines and hydrazine[184] and on allyl propionate.[185] In the last reaction, the initial adduct (70) fragments to give pentene.

$$EtCH_2CHCH_2OCOEt \rightarrow EtCH_2CH: CH_2 + CO_2 + Et\cdot$$
$$(70)$$

The dissociation energies $D(CF_3-Hal)$ are some 4 kcal mole^{-1} greater than the corresponding $D(CH_3-Hal)$.[186] $D(CF_3-H)$ has been redetermined and reported to have the values 106.3[187] and 106.0[188] kcal mole^{-1}. Other studies with trifluoromethyl and pentafluoroethyl radicals[189] include a report of direct iodine atom abstraction (by $CF_3\cdot$) from iodobenzene.[190] Difluoromethyl radicals, obtained by photolysis of tetrafluoroacetone, dimerize and disproportionate as shown.

$$2CF_2H\cdot \longrightarrow \begin{cases} HF_2CCF_2H \\ :CF_2 + CF_2H_2 \\ CF_2:CF_2 + HF \end{cases}$$

The third pathway, important for $CH_2F\cdot$ radicals, is insignificant here, presumably because the vibrational modes of tetrafluoroethane are better

179 P. Gray and A. Jones, *Trans. Faraday Soc.*, **62**, 112 (1966).
180 P. Gray and A. Jones, *Chem. Commun.*, **1965**, 606; P. Gray, A. A. Herod, A. Jones, and J. C. J. Thynne, *Trans. Faraday Soc.*, **62**, 2774 (1966).
181 D. A. Edwards, J. A. Kerr, A. C. Lloyd, and A. F. Trotman-Dickenson, *J. Chem. Soc.*, *A*, **1966**, 621.
182 J. A. Kerr, D. H. Slater, and J. C. Young, *J. Chem. Soc.*, *A*, **1966**, 104.
183 J. Grotewold, E. A. Lissi, and M. G. Neumann, *Chem. Commun.*, **1966**, 1.
184 D. A. Edwards, J. A. Kerr, A. C. Lloyd, and A. F. Trotman-Dickenson, *J. Chem. Soc.*, *A*, **1966**, 1500.
185 D. G. L. James and G. E. Troughton, *Trans. Faraday Soc.*, **62**, 120 (1966).
186 D. M. Tomkinson and G. O. Pritchard, *J. Phys. Chem.*, **70**, 1579 (1966).
187 J. C. Amphlett, J. W. Coomber, and E. Whittle, *J. Phys. Chem.*, **70**, 593 (1966).
188 J. W. Coomber and E. Whittle, *Trans. Faraday Soc.*, **62**, 1553 (1966).
189 J. R. Dacey, R. F. Mann, and G. O. Pritchard, *Can. J. Chem.*, **43**, 3215 (1965); P. G. Bowers and G. B. Porter, *J. Phys. Chem.*, **70**, 1622 (1966); L. A. Oksent'evich and R. N. Pravednikov, *Dokl. Akad. Nauk SSSR*, **169**, 1130 (1966); *Chem. Abs.*, **65**, 15188 (1966); A. S. Gordon, *Can. J. Chem.*, **44**, 529 (1966); G. O. Pritchard, J. R. Dacey, W. C. Kent, and C. R. Simonds, *ibid.*, p. 171; R. L. Thommarson and G. O. Pritchard, *J. Phys. Chem.*, **70**, 2307 (1966).
190 R. D. Giles and E. Whittle, *Trans. Faraday Soc.*, **62**, 128 (1966); W. G. Alcock and E. Whittle, *ibid.*, pp. 134, 664; J. C. Amphlett and E. Whittle, *ibid.*, p. 1662.

able to accommodate the heat of combination than is the case with difluoro-ethane.

Reactions of alkoxy-radicals from diethyl peroxide[191] and isopropyl nitrite[192] have been examined, and competing addition and allylic abstraction in the reaction of ethynyl radicals with olefins has been noted.[193] Addition of hydrogen atoms to toluene[194] which leads to methylcyclohexane, hydrogen-abstraction from butane by trichloromethyl radicals,[195] and sulphur hexa-fluoride-promoted decomposition of di-*tert*-butyl peroxide[196] have also been reported.

Electron-spin resonance data. A review of magnetic methods in free-radical chemistry,[197a] as well as two texts[197b] on ESR spectroscopy and its applica-tions, have appeared recently. The value of nuclear magnetic resonance spectra of free radicals has also been reviewed.[198]

The use of g-values in determining radical structure has been emphasized.[199] The conclusions drawn from ESR spectra concerning the conformations of semidiones[200] have been reviewed[201] and extended,[202] and the CH_3 proton couplings in the ESR spectra of semidiones (71) have been found to show a good correlation with the σ-values for the substituents X.[203] Conformational

(71)   (72)   (73)

[191] G. O. Pritchard and J. T. Bryant, *J. Phys. Chem.*, **70**, 1441 (1966); R. A. Livermore and L. Phillips, *J. Chem. Soc.*, B, **1966**, 640.

[192] D. L. Cox, R. A. Livermore, and L. Phillips, *J. Chem. Soc.*, B, **1966**, 245.

[193] A. M. Tarr, O. P. Strausz, and H. E. Gunning, *Trans. Faraday Soc.*, **62**, 1221 (1966).

[194] M. F. R. Mulcahy, R. J. Harrisson, and J. R. Wilmshurst, *Australian J. Chem.*, **19**, 1431 (1966).

[195] J. M. Tedder and R. A. Watson, *Trans. Faraday Soc.*, **62**, 1215 (1966).

[196] L. Batt and F. R. Cruickshank, *J. Phys. Chem.*, **70**, 723 (1966).

[197a] E. Müller, A. Rieker, K. Scheffler, and A. Moosmayer, *Angew. Chem. Intern. Ed. Engl.*, **5**, 6 (1966).

[197b] M. Bersohn and J. C. Baird, "An Introduction to Electron Paramagnetic Resonance", Benjamin, New York, 1966; H. M. Assenheim, "Introduction to Electron Spin Resonance", Hilger and Watts, London, 1966.

[198] K. H. Hausser, H. Brunner, and J. C. Jochims, *Mol. Phys.*, **10**, 253 (1966).

[199] B. G. Segal, M. Kaplan, and G. K. Fraenkel, *J. Chem. Phys.*, **43**, 4191 (1965); R. O. C. Norman and R. J. Pritchett, *Chem. Ind.* (*London*), **1965**, 2040; E. G. Janzen and J. G. Pacifici, *J. Am. Chem. Soc.*, **87**, 5504 (1965).

[200] See *Organic Reaction Mechanisms, 1965*, 214.

[201] G. A. Russell, E. T. Strom, E. R. Tilaty, K. Y. Change, R. D. Stephens, and M. C. Young, *Record Chem. Progr.*, **27**, 3 (1966).

[202] E. R. Talaty and G. A. Russell, *J. Org. Chem.*, **31**, 3455 (1966).

[203] E. T. Strom, *J Am. Chem. Soc.*, **88**, 2065 (1966).

equilibria in cycloalkanone ketyls (**72**) have been studied by the variation of α-proton coupling constants with temperature,[204] and examples of long-range couplings in the spectra of semiquinones have been reported.[205] The recent technique of electron nuclear double resonance (ENDOR) permitted the estimation of 5.5 kcal mole^{-1} for the energy barrier between the two propeller conformations of radical (**73**),[206] though no evidence could be adduced for the expected participation of sulphur at the radical centre.

Studies of electron-exchange reactions by ESR techniques[207—209] include the simultaneous observation of transfer between naphthalene and both its radical ion and the [Naphthalene]$\cdot^-$ M$^+$ ion pair.[208] The rates of electron-transfer from one enantiomer of 1-(α-methylbenzyl)naphthalene to the separate enantiomers of the hydrocarbon in dimethoxyethane differ by a factor of 2, contrary to theoretical prediction.[209]

Line-broadening studies have also been used to follow the hydrogen exchange between ROH and RO·, where RO· represents a nitroxide or phenoxy-radical.[210] There was evidence in the latter case for an intermediate, possibly RO...Ḣ...OR.

Analysis of the line broadening of superimposed spectra of durosemiquinone and its ion pair [Q]$\cdot^-$ M$^+$, permits calculation of equilibrium and rate constants for the ion-pair association.[211] Similar equilibria for hydrocarbon radical anions have been examined by Szwarc's group, using a conductance technique.[212] These studies[211, 212] amplify the effects of solvation in such systems.

Small interactions with the phosphorus and mercury nuclei were revealed in the spectra of (**74**)[213] and (**75**),[214] and strong conjugation through a sulphone grouping appears to be indicated by the similarity between the spectrum of diphenyl sulphone radical anion[215] and that reported for biphenyl radical anion. The complete absence of biphenyl from the system was carefully checked.

204 J. W. Lown, *Can. J. Chem.*, **43**, 3294 (1965); *J. Phys. Chem.*, **70**, 591 (1966).
205 D. Kosman and L. M. Stock, *J. Am. Chem. Soc.*, **88**, 843 (1966); S. F. Nelsen and B. M. Trost, *Tetrahedron Letters*, **1966**, 5737.
206 J. S. Hyde, R. Breslow, and C. DeBoer, *J. Am. Chem. Soc.*, **88**, 4763 (1966).
207 P. A. Malachesky, T. A. Miller, T. Layloff, and R. N. Adams, *Exchange Reactions Proc. Symp.*, Upton, N.Y., **1965**, 157; *Chem. Abs.*, **65**, 8714 (1966).
208 R. Chang and C. S. Johnson, *J. Am. Chem. Soc.*, **88**, 2338 (1966).
209 W. Bruning and S. I. Weissman, *J. Am. Chem. Soc.*, **88**, 373 (1966).
210 R. W. Kreilick and S. I. Weissman, *J. Am. Chem. Soc.*, **88**, 2645 (1966).
211 T. E. Gough and M. C. R. Symons, *Trans. Faraday Soc.*, **62**, 269 (1966).
212 R. C. Roberts and M. Szwarc, *J. Am. Chem. Soc.*, **87**, 5542 (1965); R. V. Slates and M. Szwarc, *J. Phys. Chem.*, **69**, 4124 (1965); P. Chang, R. V. Slates, and M. Szwarc, *ibid.*, **70**, 3180 (1966).
213 W. M. Gulick and D. H. Geske, *J. Am. Chem. Soc.*, **88**, 2928 (1966).
214 A. B. Shapiro, A. L. Buchachenko, A. A. Medzhidov, and E. G. Rozantsev, *Zh. Strukt. Khim.*, **7**, 187 (1966); *Chem. Abs.*, **65**, 2096 (1966).
215 E. T. Kaiser, M. M. Urberg, and D. H. Eargle, *J. Am. Chem. Soc.*, **88**, 1037 (1966).

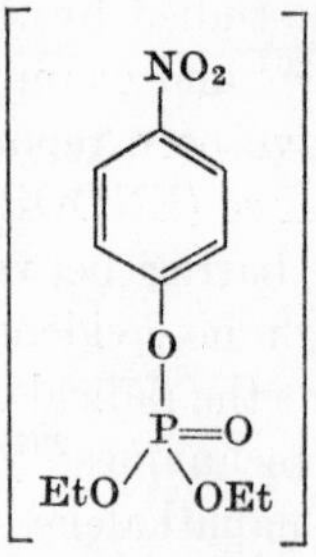

(74)

Dinitrobenzene radical anions often show two nitrogen coupling constants owing to partial electron localization in the ion pair. This has now been noted with the organic counter-ion $^+CH_2OH$, the spectrum exhibiting a small coupling with CH_2.[216] Ionic methylation of hydrocarbons by dimethylsulphinyl carbanion[217] offers an explanation for the anomalous formation of nitrobenzene radical anion with a strong base in dimethyl sulphoxide. The reaction is envisaged as follows:

$$PhNO_2 \xrightarrow{\text{Methylation}} MeC_6H_4NO_2$$

$$MeC_6H_4NO_2 \xrightarrow{\text{Base}} {}^-CH_2C_6H_4NO_2$$

$$PhNO_2 + {}^-CH_2C_6H_4NO_2 \longrightarrow [PhNO_2]^{\bar{\cdot}} + \cdot CH_2C_6H_4NO_2$$

Spectra of arylsulphonyl radicals ($ArSO_2\cdot$) have been reported,[218] as well as that of the unsubstituted methyl radical stabilized by absorption in a porous Vycor glass at room temperature.[219] The decay of the spectrum was used to follow the reactions of the methyl radical with absorbable gases admitted to the system.

[216] W. E. Griffiths, G. F. Longster, J. Myatt, and P. F. Todd, *J. Chem. Soc.*, B, **1966**, 1130.
[217] G. A. Russell and S. A. Weiner, *J. Org. Chem.*, **31**, 248 (1966); see also p. 166.
[218] M. McMillan, and W. A. Waters, *J. Chem. Soc.*, B, **1966**, 422.
[219] J. Turkevich and Y. Fujita, *Science*, **152**, 1619 (1966).

CHAPTER 10

Carbenes and Nitrenes

An English translation of a recent review of carbene chemistry is now available,[1] and aspects of nitrene chemistry are discussed in a review of the chemistry of organic azides.[2] It has been suggested that carbenes should be formulated as in (1) to emphasize the concept of full and vacant orbitals,[3] and in the same

$$\begin{matrix} R \\ R' \end{matrix} C^{\pm}$$

(1)

article it was pointed out that, according to I.U.P.A.C. nomenclature, carbonium ions, as protonated carbenes, should preferably be referred to as carbenium ions.[3]

Generation of methylene (CH_2) from diazomethane, diazirine, or ketene, continues to be a fruitful area of study for physical chemists. Aspects of the chemistry of hot methylene,[4] hot methane[5] (from $CH_2 + H_2$), and other hot hydrocarbons[6] (from CH_2 + alkanes) have received attention, and new information on the differentiation of singlet and triplet methylene has appeared. Thus a careful examination of the stoichiometry of the reaction of triplet methylene with alkanes shows that equation (1) cannot account for

$$RH + \cdot CH_2 \cdot \rightarrow R \cdot + CH_3 \cdot \rightarrow RCH_3 \qquad (1)$$

all the RCH_3 formed, and that some direct insertion (accompanied by spin inversion) seems likely.[7] Furthermore, two groups have noted aspects of the reaction of methylene with alkyl chlorides which are only satisfactorily explained by monoradical formation involving abstraction of hydrogen[8, 9] or chlorine[9] by singlet methylene.* Thus chemical distinctions between singlet

---

* The following quotation is taken from the summary of ref. 9: "It is suggested that . . . the difference between 'abstraction' and 'insertion' mechanisms may be one of nomenclature only, and that the physical processes are equivalent."

[1] G. G. Rozantsev, A. A. Fainzil'berg, and S. S. Novikov, *Russian Chem. Rev.*, **1965**, 69.
[2] E. Liebber, J. S. Curtice, and C. N. R. Rao, *Chem. Ind. (London)*, **1966**, 586.
[3] J. J. Jennen, *Chimia (Aarau)*, **20**, 309 (1966).
[4] A. M. Mansoor and I. D. R. Stevens, *Tetrahedron Letters*, **1966**, 1733.
[5] W. J. Dunning and C. C. McCain, *J. Chem. Soc., B*, **1966**, 68.
[6] G. Z. Whitten and B. S. Rabinovitch, *J. Phys. Chem.*, **69**, 4348 (1965).
[7] D. F. Ring and B. S. Rabinovitch, *J. Am. Chem. Soc.*, **88**, 4285 (1966).
[8] R. S. B. Johnstone and R. P. Wayne, *Nature*, **211**, 1396 (1966).
[9] C. H. Bamford, J. E. Casson, and R. P. Wayne, *Proc. Roy. Soc., A*, **289**, 287 (1965).

and triplet methylene may be much smaller than has been generally supposed.

An alkyl migration in the formation of 3-methylbut-1-ene from *trans*-butene is indicated by tritium-labelling experiments,[10] location of the tritium in the product being accommodated by the sequence:

$$\cdot CHT \cdot + MeCH{=}CHMe \rightarrow \underset{\underset{\cdot CHT}{|}}{Me{-}CH{-}\overset{\cdot}{C}HMe} \rightarrow \underset{\underset{CHT}{\|}}{\overset{\overset{Me}{|}}{CH{-}CHMe}}$$

Further evidence that triplet methylene is a product of direct photolysis of ketene, particularly on long-wavelength irradiation (366 mμ), has appeared: 40% of the methylene is formed in the triplet state.[11] The triplet methylene is considered to be formed by decomposition of triplet ketene, itself produced by intersystem crossing from the excited singlet. In the presence of olefin, the proportion of triplet reaction may be suppressed by quenching of the triplet state of the ketene.[12] Gas-phase reactions of methylene with tetrahydrofuran[13] and ethylidene chloride[14] have been reported. In the former, a ring-insertion reaction of singlet methylene gives tetrahydropyran; this reaction is not observed in solution.

Hoffmann[15] has carried out molecular-orbital calculations for the excited states involved in the photochemistry of diazomethane and diazirine, and an experimental study by Kibby and Kistiakowsky[16] has revealed some of the complexities of diazoethane photolyses.

Skell's group has elaborated some of their work on reactions of atomic carbon,[17] and MacKay and Wolfgang and their colleagues have reported extensively[18] on the reactions of monatomic ^{11}C generated radiochemically.

Further work on the photolysis of carbon suboxide has also appeared.[19, 20] In the presence of trimethylene oxide, the carbonylcarbene (:C:C:O) abstracts oxygen, and cyclopropane and propene are produced in proportions suggesting the intermediacy of the trimethylene biradical:[20]

[10] C. McKnight and F. S. Rowland, *J. Am. Chem. Soc.*, **88**, 3179 (1966).
[11] R. W. Carr and G. B. Kistiakowsky, *J. Phys. Chem.*, **70**, 118 (1966); see also, A. N. Strachan and D. E. Thornton, *J. Phys. Chem.*, **70**, 952 (1966).
[12] R. B. Cundall and A. S. Davies, *J. Am. Chem. Soc.*, **88**, 1329 (1966).
[13] H. M. Frey and M. A. Voisey, *Chem. Commun.*, **1966**, 454.
[14] J. A. Kerr, B. V. O'Grady, and A. F. Trotman-Dickenson, *J. Chem. Soc.*, A, **1966**, 1621.
[15] R. Hoffmann, *Tetrahedron*, **22**, 539 (1966).
[16] C. L. Kibby and G. B. Kistiakowsky, *J. Phys. Chem.*, **70**, 126 (1966).
[17] P. S. Skell and R. F. Harris, *J. Am. Chem. Soc.*, **87**, 5807 (1965); P. S. Skell and R. R. Engel, *ibid.*, **88**, 3749, 4883 (1966).
[18] T. Rose, C. MacKay, and R. Wolfgang, *J. Am. Chem. Soc.*, **88**, 1064 (1966); J. Nicholas, C. MacKay, and R. Wolfgang, *ibid.*, **88**, 1065, 1610 (1966); *Tetrahedron*, **22**, 2967 (1966).
[19] C. Willis and K. D. Bayes, *J. Am. Chem. Soc.*, **88**, 3203 (1966); R. N. Smith, R. A. Smith, and D. A. Young, *Inorg. Chem.*, **5**, 145 (1966).
[20] R. T. K. Baker, J. A. Kerr, and A. F. Trotman-Dickenson, *Chem. Commun.*, **1966**, 821.

$$C_3O_2 \xrightarrow{h\nu} CO + :C:C:O$$

$$:C:C:O + \overline{CH_2CH_2CH_2O} \rightarrow 2CO + \cdot(CH_2)_3\cdot$$

The ground-state triplet species, diphenylmethylene, has now been observed by optical spectroscopy.[21, 22] It was generated by photolysis of diphenyl-diazomethane in a rigid organic glass at 77°K. Further radiation is absorbed by diphenylmethylene, which then undergoes photochemical reaction with the solvent. Benzhydryl radicals, as well as radicals originating from the solvent, were detectable by ESR spectroscopy.[22]

Diphenylmethylene is also produced by photolysis of diphenylketene.[23] Typical free-radical products obtained when this photolysis is effected in toluene include bibenzyl, 1,1,2-triphenylethane, and 1,1,2,2-tetraphenyl-ethane. With diphenylethylene, 1,1,2,2-tetraphenylcyclopropane is produced. Diphenylmethylene (and other triplet carbenes) has been found to catalyse the homolytic oxygenation of alkanes.[24] Diphenylcarbene gives a cyclopropane with the olefin (2) very much more readily than with hept-1-ene.[25] In our

$$\underset{\textbf{(2)}}{Me_3SiCH\!=\!CH_2} \qquad \underset{\textbf{(3)}}{Ph_2\overset{\cdot}{C}\!-\!CH_2\overset{\cdot}{C}HCH_2C_4H_9}$$

opinion this may largely be due to the fact that in the initial 1,3-biradical adduct (3) from hept-1-ene, intramolecular hydrogen-transfer, to give

$$Ph_2CHCH_2CH\!=\!CHC_4H_9$$

may compete favourably with ring-closure to cyclopropane; the polar effect suggested in the paper[25] seems less relevant. The high yields of cyclopropane from the addition of diphenylmethylene to diphenylethylene (cf. ref. 23) may be similarly explained.

Some interesting results have been obtained from studies of the base-promoted decomposition of tosylhydrazones. It was mentioned last year that for the decomposition of (4)[26] the incursion of carbene or carbonium ion intermediates depended respectively on whether a proton source (ethylene glycol) was absent or present. Deuterium-labelling experiments have now led to the claim that in the presence of a proton source, and with deficient base, the bicyclobutane does not incorporate the external protons, but that with an excess of base it does. The latter behaviour was attributed to base-catalysed exchange [reaction (2)] of the diazo-intermediate (5). Bicyclobutane

21 I. Moritani, S.-I. Murahashi, and M. Nishino, *Tetrahedron Letters*, **1966**, 373.
22 W. A. Gibbons and A. M. Trozzolo, *J. Am. Chem. Soc.*, **88**, 172 (1966).
23 H. Nozaki, M. Nakano, and K. Kondô, *Tetrahedron*, **22**, 477 (1966).
24 G. A. Hamilton and J. R. Giacin, *J. Am. Chem. Soc.*, **88**, 1584 (1966).
25 I. A. D'yakonov, I. B. Repinskaya, and G. V. Golodnikov, *Zh. Obshch. Khim.*, **36**, 949 (1965); *Chem. Abs.*, **65**, 8704 (1966).
26 See *Organic Reaction Mechanisms*, **1965**, 232.

formation was suggested to involve N-protonation as shown.[27] If these conclusions were correct, then the extent of incorporation of the external hydrogen in the bicyclobutane should compare with the incorporation into the carbenic

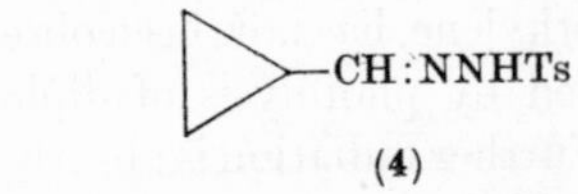

(4)

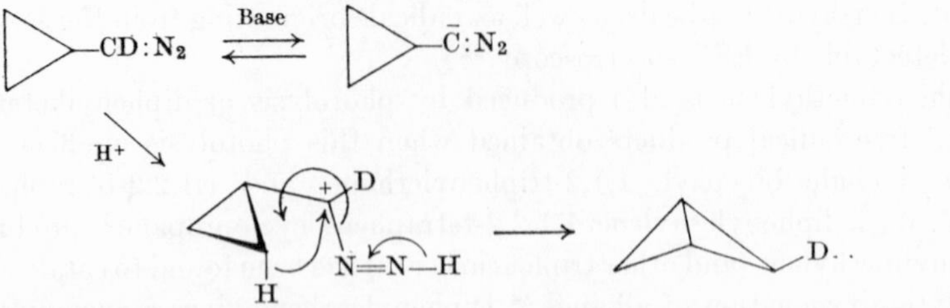

... (2)

decomposition product, cyclobutene. Further work indicates that this is not the case, and indeed contradicts the claim that, with deficient base, external protons are not incorporated to any great extent in the bicyclobutane.[28] The former study[27] shows that with an excess of base the external hydrogen adopts the *exo*-configuration in the bicyclobutane; the latter[28] is not in conflict with this in stating that with deficient base the external hydogen

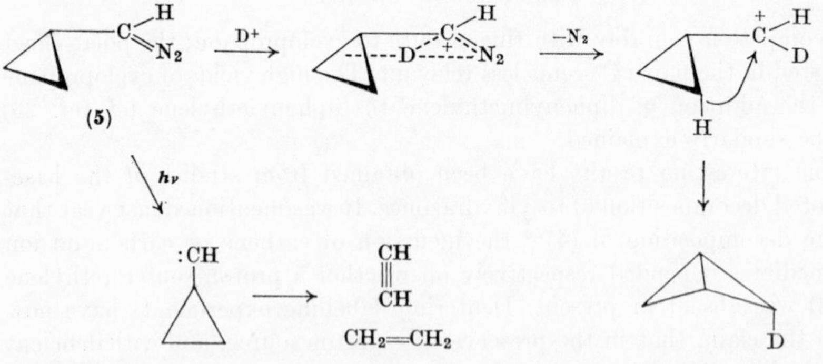

(5)

... (3)

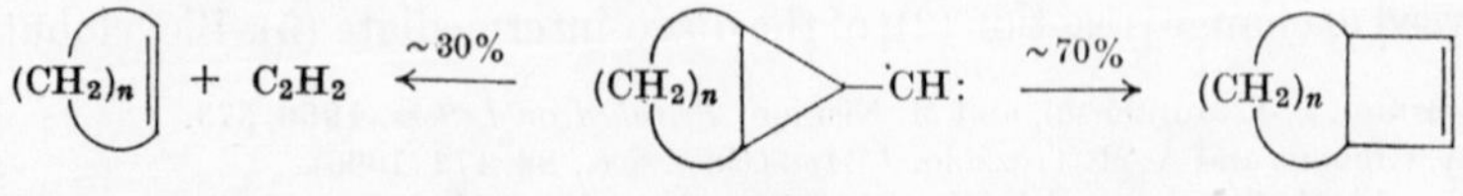

(6)

[27] K. B. Wiberg and J. M. Lavanish, *J. Am. Chem. Soc.*, **88**, 365 (1966).
[28] F. Cook, H. Schechter, J. Bayless, L. Friedman, R. L. Foltz, and R. Randall, *J. Am. Chem. Soc.*, **88**, 3870 (1966).

adopts the *endo*-configuration in the product. Neither result, however, allows a free cyclopropylcarbonium ion intermediate, for which no stereoselectivity would be observed. One possible explanation[28] involves virtually simultaneous *C*-protonation of the intermediate (5) and collapse to bicyclobutane. The stereochemical result may be a consequence of incorporation of external hydrogen co-ordinated to the cyclopropane ring, as implied in (3). Further light should be shed on these reactions now that the unstable intermediate (5) has been isolated;[29, 30] on photolysis of (5) in the gas phase[30] there is much fragmentation to ethylene and acetylene, presumably via the carbene, but only a trace to cyclobutene. Similar fragmentation is an important pathway observed in the reaction of carbenes (6) obtained from the corresponding tosylhydrazones under aprotic conditions.[31]

The carbenic reaction of norcamphor tosylhydrazone labelled with 6-*exo*- or 6-*endo*-deuterium gives nortricyclene with complete retention of label.[32] Under protic conditions, some label is lost, and this is much more pronounced for the *endo*- than for the *exo*-deuterium.[32] Non-classical (or equilibrating classical) carbonium ions cannot be involved, as the two labelled positions would then become equivalent, and label should be lost to an equivalent extent from each precursor. The explanation advanced involved *C*-protonation of the diazo-intermediate (from the *exo*-direction) and competing bimolecular and unimolecular decomposition of the resulting diazonium ion. The greater loss of *endo*-hydrogen suggested that this was the proton which was lost in the concerted process.

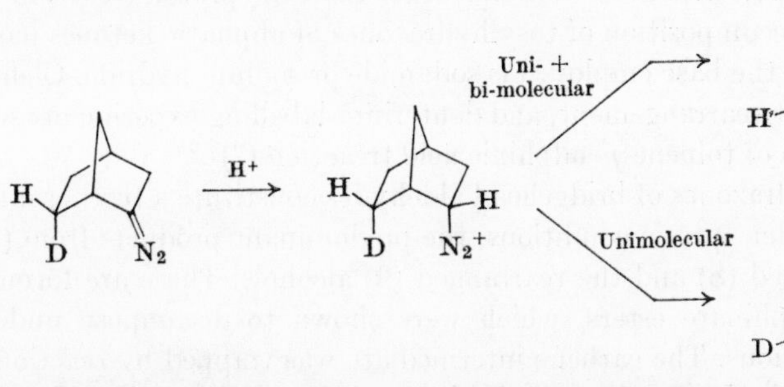

Acid-catalysed decomposition of phenyldiazomethane in an olefin at $-70°$ leads to phenylcyclopropanes, together with benzylated olefins and addition products. The latter predominate if the olefin contains tertiary carbon.[33] Two competing mechanisms were advanced. Only slight incorporation of deuterium

[29] R. A. Moss and F. C. Shulman, *Chem. Commun.*, **1966**, 372.
[30] P. B. Shevlin and A. P. Wolf, *J. Am. Chem. Soc.*, **88**, 4735 (1966).
[31] W. Kirmse and K.-H. Pook, *Chem. Ber.*, **98**, 4022 (1965).
[32] A. Nickon and N. H. Werstiuk, *J. Am. Chem. Soc.*, **88**, 4543 (1966).
[33] G. L. Closs, R. A. Moss, and S. H. Goh, *J. Am. Chem. Soc.*, **88**, 364 (1966).

from deuteriated acid into the cyclopropanes suggests a carbenoid addition [reaction (4)], whilst olefin formation involves incipient benzyl cation [reaction (5)] and is favoured when the olefin contains tertiary carbon. Decomposition

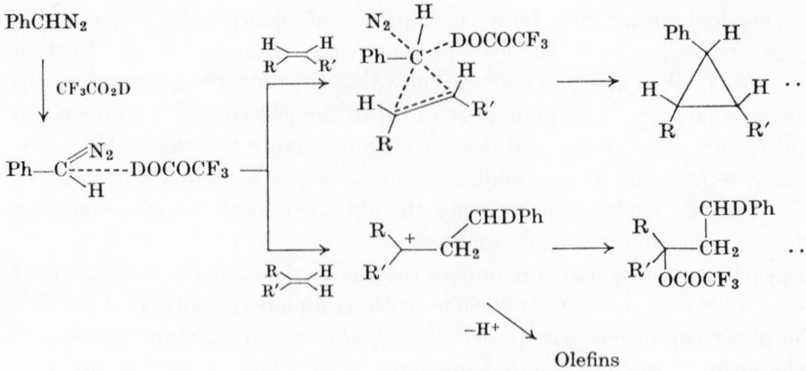

of diazo-compounds from tosylhydrazones may follow the carbonium ion pattern in the presence of Lewis acids other than the proton [reaction (6)].[34] Non-carbene decomposition of tosylhydrazones of aliphatic ketones has been observed when the base employed is sodamide or sodium hydride. Olefins are formed without rearrangement, and deuterium-labelling experiments suggest 1:4 elimination of toluene-p-sulphinic acid [reaction (7)].[35]

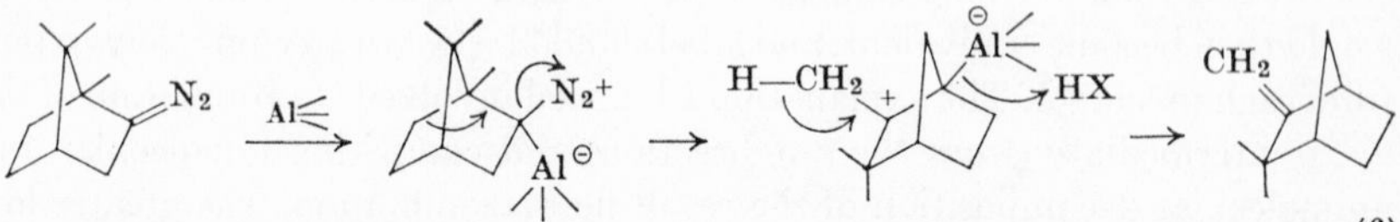

The tosylhydrazones of bridgehead aldehydes constitute a further interesting case.[36] Under aprotic conditions, the predominant products from (7) are the unrearranged (8) and the rearranged (9) alcohols. These are formed via the toluenesulphinate esters, which were shown to decompose under the reaction conditions. The carbene intermediate was trapped by reaction with pyridine N-oxide. In the absence of this trap it is sufficiently long-lived to be protonated (by undecomposed starting material). Carbenes (7a), (10), and (11) were regarded as "constrained" carbenes, relatively stable with respect to isomerization.

Protonation of phenylcarbene is important in the thermal decomposition of

[34] R. H. Shapiro, *Tetrahedron Letters*, **1966**, 3401.
[35] W. Kirmse, B.-G. von Bülow, and H. Schepp, *Ann. Chem.*, **691**, 41 (1966).
[36] J. W. Wilt, C. A. Schneider, H. F. Dabek, J. F. Kraemer, and W. J. Wagner, *J. Org. Chem.*, **31**, 1543 (1966).

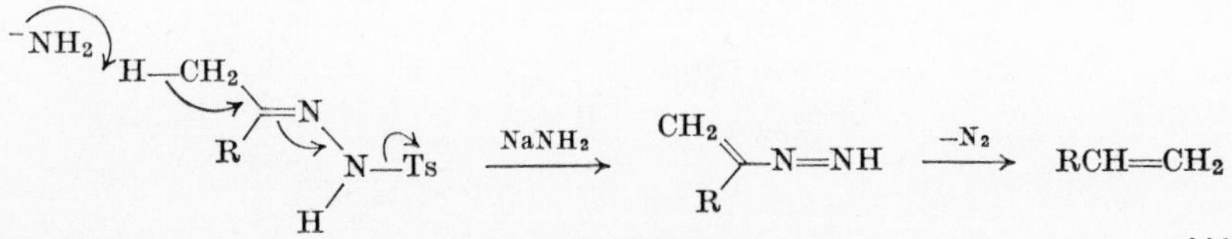

. . . (7)

(7) (7a) (8) (9)

(10) (11)

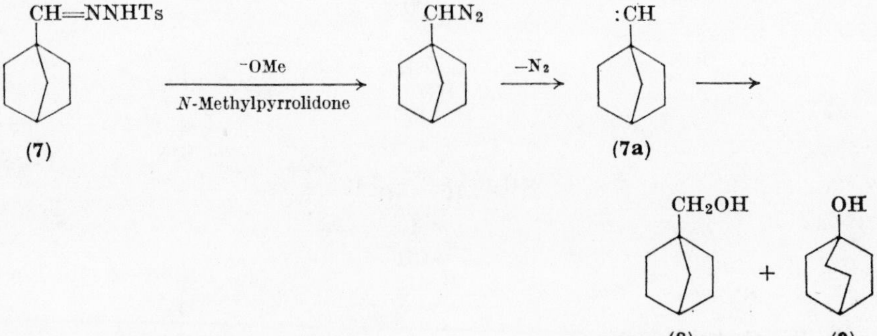

phenyldiazomethane in aqueous acetonitrile:[37] increasing the water concentration to 2M has little effect on decomposition rate, but greatly enhances the proportion of products arising from a benzyl cation; with water concentrations greater than 2M, the decomposition rate increases and this, coupled with product analysis, suggests that benzyl cation is now being formed additionally via protonation of the diazo-compound.

(12) (n=5 or 6) (13) (14) (15)

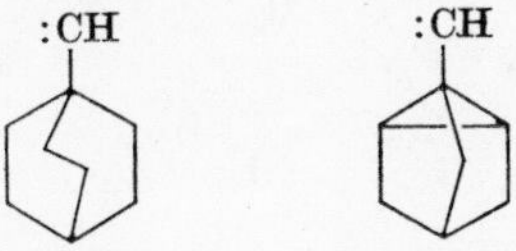

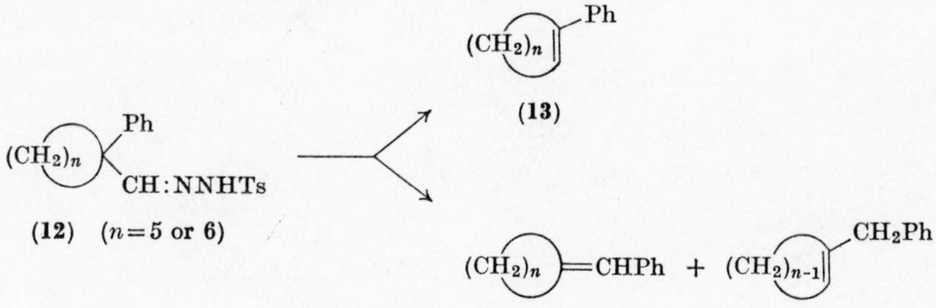

[37] D. Bethell and D. Whittaker, *J. Chem. Soc., B*, **1966**, 778.

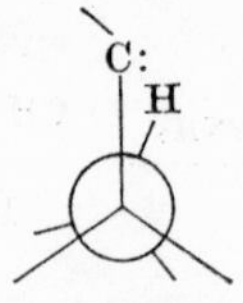

(16)

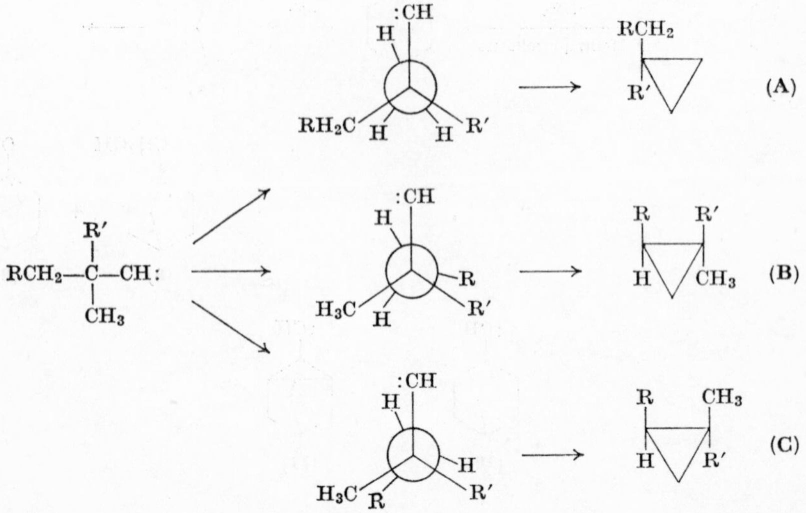

(A)

(B)

(C)

Relative yields:

	A	**B**	**C**
$R = R' = CH_3$	79.5	20.5	
$R = CH_3;\ R' = H$	21.5	11.5	3.5

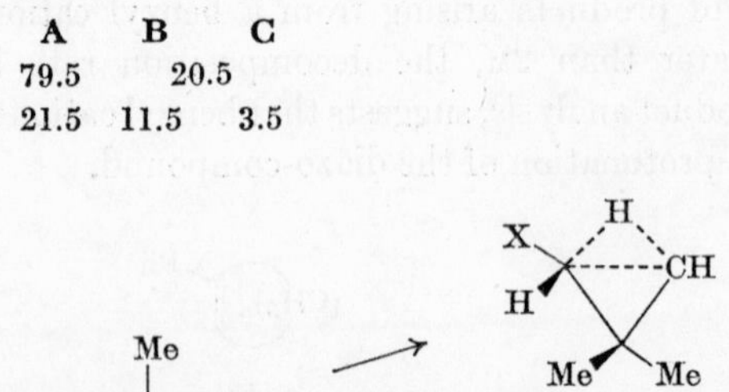

(17)   (18)

Base-promoted decomposition of (**12**) under aprotic conditions gave more ring expansion (**13**) than phenyl migration (**14** + **15**).[38]

Kirmse's group have reported several aspects of intramolecular carbenic processes. Intramolecular insertion in a series of branched-chain alkylcarbenes formed by aprotic decomposition of tosylhydrazones appears to involve an eclipsed conformation (**16**);[39] two examples, the results of which may be accommodated in these terms, are given opposite. Cyclopropane formation by α-elimination from a related 1-chloroalkane is also shown. Under these conditions, the carbenoid intermediate shows a greater selectivity towards insertion into secondary and tertiary, rather than primary, C–H bonds.[40] A C–H bond α to an electron-donating substituent in (**17**) (X = Ph, OMe, or NMe$_2$) was strongly deactivated with respect to carbene insertion.[41] This was discussed in terms of synchronous insertion. A two-step process involving (**18**) is clearly excluded.

Alk-ω-enylcarbenes, obtained by photolysis of the appropriate diazo-compounds, showed no evidence of intramolecular addition; the major

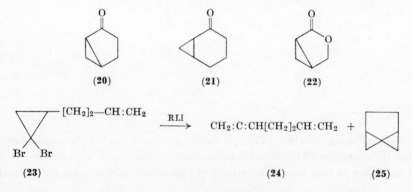

$$CH_2{=}CH{-}[CH_2]_3{-}CHN_2 \xrightarrow{\ Cu\ }$$

(**19**)

products were α,ω-dienes resulting from hydrogen migration.[42] However, copper-complexing did allow cyclization to occur, and a maximum 36% of cyclic product was achieved with the 6-carbon chain (**19**). Ring-size is also the major controlling factor in copper-catalysed cyclization of unsaturated

(**20**)   (**21**)   (**22**)

$$\overset{[CH_2]_2{-}CH{:}CH_2}{\underset{Br\quad Br}{\diagdown}} \xrightarrow{\ RLi\ } CH_2{:}C{:}CH[CH_2]_2CH{:}CH_2 \ +$$

(**23**)   (**24**)   (**25**)

[38] J. W. Wilt, J. F. Zawadzki, and D. G. Schultenover, *J. Org. Chem.*, **31**, 876 (1966).
[39] W. Kirmse and G. Waechtershäuser, *Tetrahedron*, **22**, 63 (1966).
[40] W. Kirmse and G. Waechtershäuser, *Tetrahedron*, **22**, 73 (1966).
[41] W. Kirmse, H. J. Schladetsch, and H. W. Bücking, *Chem. Ber.*, **99**, 2579 (1966).
[42] W. Kirmse and D. Grassmann, *Chem. Ber.*, **99**, 1746 (1966).

diazo-ketones.[43] Bicyclic ketones (20) and (21) are both readily accessible by this route. Allyl diazoacetate gives the bicyclic lactone (22) under similar conditions,[44] and formation of the allene (24) from (23) is accompanied by cyclization to the tricyclic compound (25).[45]

The decomposition of methyl diazoacetate in styrene has been promoted by an optically active copper chelate, and some 6% of asymmetry was induced in the *cis-* and *trans*-2-phenylcyclopropanecarboxylates.[46] The carbene is assumed to form a complex with the copper, as in (26), reaction with styrene then occurring in an asymmetric environment.

Kaplan and Meloy[47] have demonstrated (by NMR) the existence of an appreciable energy barrier between *cis-* and *trans*-conformations of diazo-

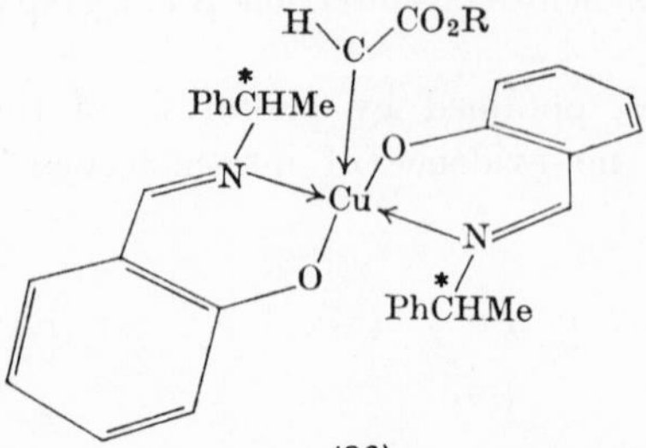

$$(26)$$

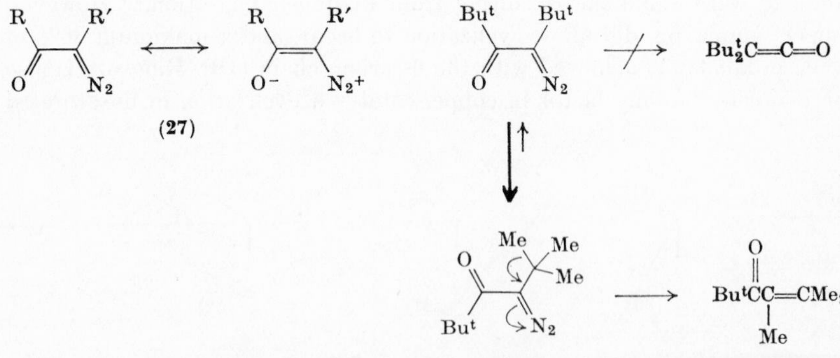

$$(27)$$

$$(28) \qquad (29)$$

ketones. The *cis*-structure (27) is normally preferred, and it was pointed out that the chemistry of the diazo-ketones must normally be interpreted in terms of reactions of this form. The failure of compound (28) to undergo normal

[43] M. M. Fawzi and C. D. Gutsche, *J. Org. Chem.*, **31**, 1390 (1966).
[44] W. Kirmse and H. Dietrich, *Chem. Ber.*, **98**, 4027 (1965).
[45] L. Skattebøl, *J. Org. Chem.*, **31**, 2789 (1966).
[46] H. Nozaki, S. Moriuti, H. Takaya, and R. Noyori, *Tetrahedron Letters*, **1966**, 5239.
[47] F. Kaplan and G. K. Meloy, *J. Am. Chem. Soc.*, **88**, 950 (1966).

Wolff rearrangement may be explained in this way. Only a *trans*-conformation is possible, and decomposition of this leads to (**29**) by methyl migration.

Intramolecular insertion has been employed to synthesize "2,4-dehydro-adamantane" (**30**).[48]

Isomeric tricyclic dienes (**32**) are obtained by the decomposition of the carbenoid (**31**). The intermediacy of a cyclobutadiene was assumed,[49] and the possibility of the formation of the latter via a tetrahedrane intermediate was considered.[49] Until the reactivity patterns of such species have been delineated, the possibility that (**32**) might be formed directly from two molecules of tetrahedrane seems a valid alternative.

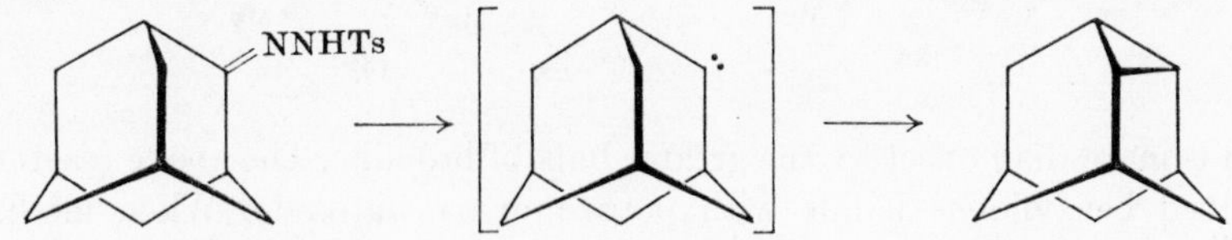

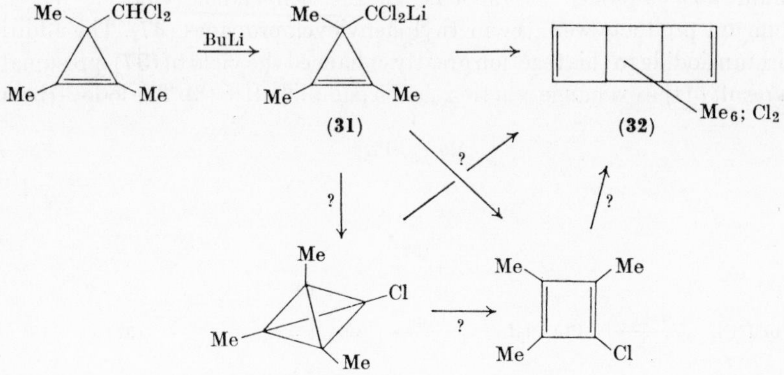

Further work on carbene versus carbenoid intermediates in α-eliminations is discussed in Chapter 4. It now seems generally accepted that α-eliminations promoted by alkyl-lithium involve organometallic carbenoid species. This general problem is discussed by Köbrich and Drischel,[50] who report on the formation of butatrienes from (**33**)[50] and the more stable (**34**).[51]

[48] A. C. Udding, J. Strating, H. Wynberg, and J. L. M. A. Schlatmann, *Chem. Commun.*, **1966**, 657.
[49] G. L. Closs and V. N. M. Rao, *J. Am. Chem. Soc.*, **88**, 4116 (1966).
[50] G. Köbrich and W. Drischel, *Tetrahedron*, **22**, 2621 (1966).
[51] G. Köbrich, H. Fröhlich, and W. Drischel, *J. Organometal. Chem.*, **6**, 194 (1966).

10

When a substituted carbene can add to an olefin to give more than one cyclopropane, the thermodynamically less stable isomer often predominates, steric effects apparently being offset by electrostatic and other associative interactions in the transition state.[52] Additions of bromo(phenyl)carbene[53] and chloro(phenyl)carbene[54] to a series of olefins have now been studied. With *cis*-butene, chloro(phenyl)carbene gives product ratio (35)/(36) (X = Cl) of 3.0 whilst (35)/(36) (X = Br) is 1.35. The greater polarizability of the C–Br

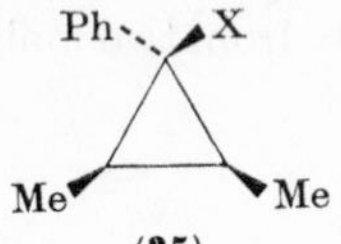

(35) 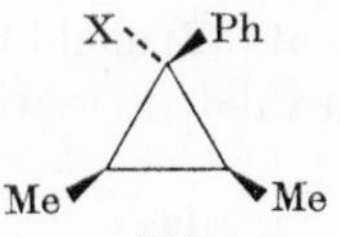   (36)

bond is more than offset by the greater bulk of bromine. The above reactions involved benzylidene halide with potassium *tert*-butoxide. When methyl-lithium was employed as the base in the benzylidene chloride reaction, significant products were the methylphenylcyclopropanes (37). The addition of lithium iodide to this reaction greatly enhanced the yield of (37), presumably as a result of the exchange reaction shown (simplified) in (8). The iodocarbenoid

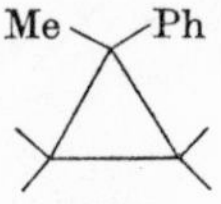

(37)

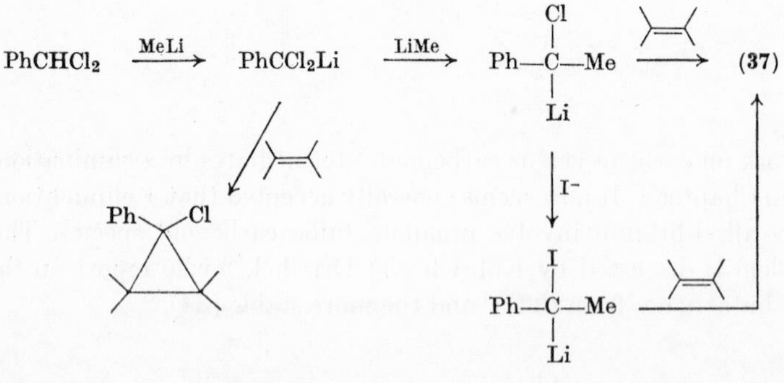

$$PhCHCl_2 \xrightarrow{MeLi} PhCCl_2Li \xrightarrow{LiMe} Ph-\overset{\overset{\displaystyle Cl}{|}}{\underset{\underset{\displaystyle Li}{|}}{C}}-Me \longrightarrow (37)$$

... (8)

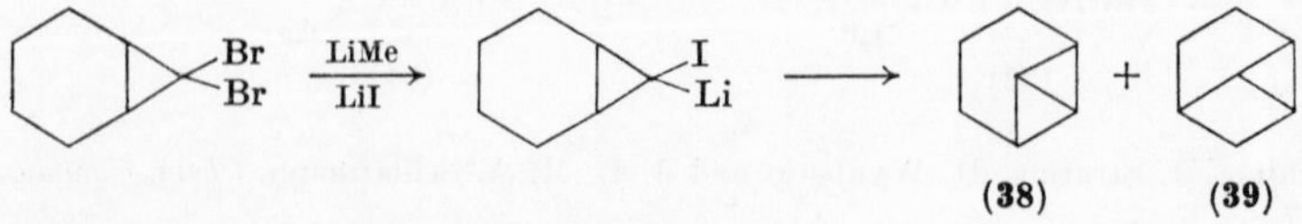

(38)   (39)

[52] See *Organic Reaction Mechanisms*, **1965**, 227.
[53] R. A. Moss and R. Gerstl, *Tetrahedron*, **22**, 2637 (1966).
[54] G. L. Closs and J. J. Coyle, *J. Org. Chem.*, **31**, 2759 (1966).

is considered to be much more reactive towards olefin than its chloro-analogue. Similar behaviour has been observed in the formation of the insertion products (38) and (39). The yields of these are much reduced if iodide is absent.[55]

The reaction of allyl chloride with sodamide provides a low-yield, though very convenient, route to cyclopropene via vinylcarbene.[56] Cyclopentadienylidene (40) cannot undergo the normal vinylcarbene → cyclopropene rearrangement, and with olefins it is found to give products of both insertion

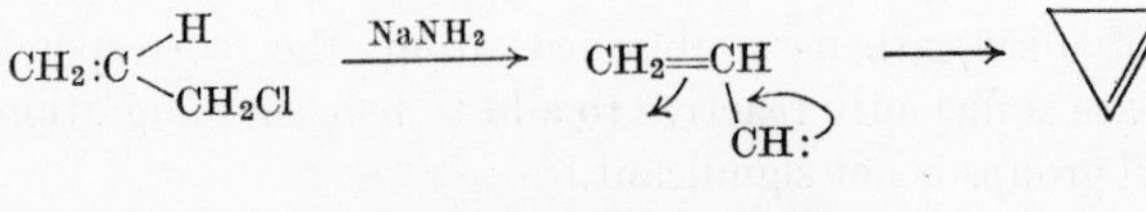

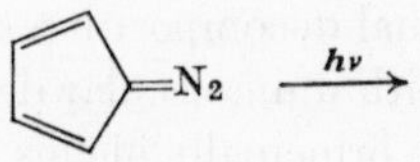

$$CH_2:C \underset{CH_2Cl}{\overset{H}{\diagdown}} \xrightarrow{NaNH_2} CH_2{=}CH \underset{CH:}{\diagdown} \longrightarrow \triangledown$$

(40)

and addition.[57] The additions are not completely stereospecific, but it was argued that reaction proceeds largely by way of a singlet state.

Stereospecific *cis*-addition of di-iodocarbene generated by the reaction of iodoform with *tert*-butoxide has been observed.[58] The unstable di-iodocyclopropanes were reduced (by R_3SnH) to the more tractable monoiodo-derivatives to facilitate the analysis. 7-Chloronorcarane has been obtained by the reaction of *tert*-butoxide with dichloroacetophenone in cyclohexene.[59]

$$PhCOCHCl_2 \xrightarrow{Bu^tO^-} PhCO_2Bu^t + :CHCl + Cl^-$$

Bromonorcaranes are obtained from the reaction of CH_2Br_2, $CHBr_3$, and CBr_4 with cyclohexene and metallic lithium in tetrahydrofuran;[60] also isolated was the tetrahydrofuranyl derivative (41).

The relatively stable sulphur ylide (42) gives 7-benzoylnorcarane on photolysis or copper-catalysed decomposition in cyclohexene.[61]

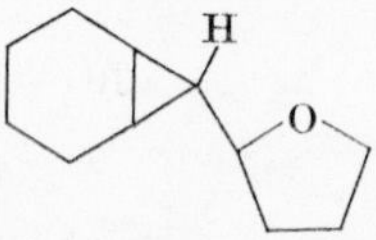

$$PhCO\bar{C}H\overset{+}{S}Me_2$$

(41)   (42)

[55] E. T. Marquis and P. D. Gardner, *Chem. Commun.*, **1966**, 726.
[56] G. L. Closs and K. D. Krantz, *J. Org. Chem.*, **31**, 638 (1966).
[57] R. A. Moss, *Chem. Commun.*, **1965**, 622; *J. Org. Chem.*, **31**, 3296 (1966).
[58] J. P. Oliver and U. V. Rao, *J. Org. Chem.*, **31**, 2696 (1966).
[59] M. K. Saxena and M. M. Bokadia, *Chem. Ind. (London)*, **1966**, 666.
[60] O. M. Nefedov and A. A. Ivashenko, *Izv. Akad. Nauk SSSR, Ser. Khim.*, **1965**, 2209; *Chem. Abs.*, **64**, 11100 (1966).
[61] B. M. Trost, *J. Am. Chem. Soc.*, **88**, 1587 (1966).

Products attributable to reactions of carbenes **(44)** are observed on photolyses of **(43)** in various solvents.[62]

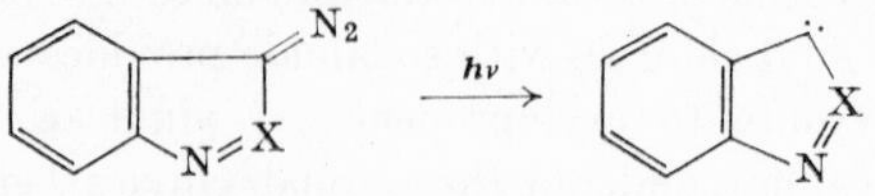

(43)   **(44)**

(X = N or CH)

Bis(perfluoroalkyl)carbenes, obtained from the corresponding diazo-compounds, are sufficiently reactive to add to benzene; migration of fluorine or fluoroalkyl groups is not significant.[63]

Kinetics and products of thermal decomposition of some dialkyldiazirines in the gas-phase are consistent with unimolecular decomposition to carbenes and nitrogen.[64] The carbenes give principally olefins, by hydrogen-migration.

Difluorocarbene is obtained by pyrolysis of chlorodifluoromethane at 700°[65] and of hexafluorocyclopropane at 270°.[66]

Photolysis of stilbene oxide appears to constitute the most convenient source of phenylcarbene.[67] Interestingly, this reacts with *cis*-butene to give

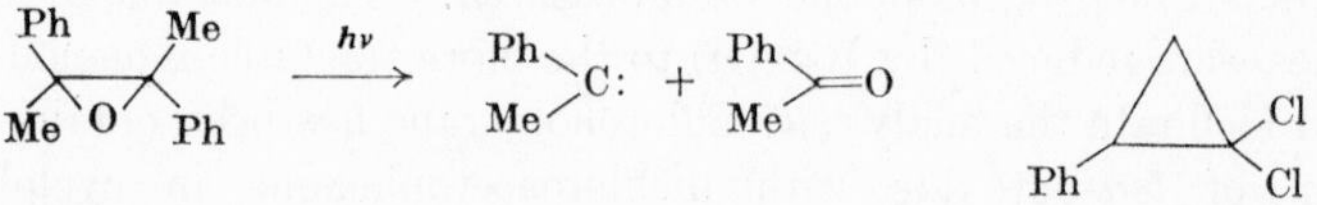

(45)   **(46)**

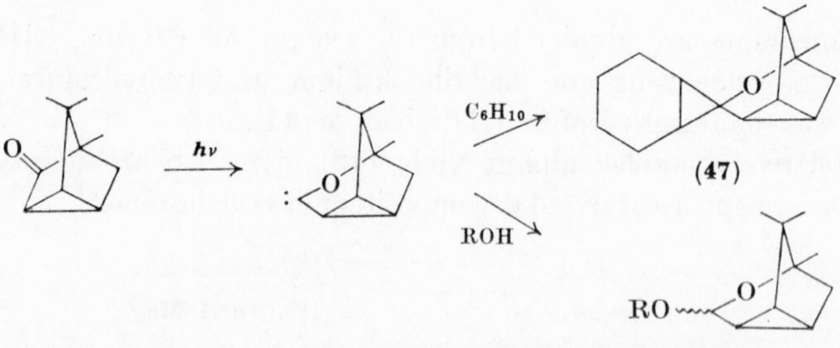

(47)

(48)

predominantly the *least* hindered cyclopropane. Methylphenylcarbene is obtained by photolysis of the epoxide **(45)**,[68] and dichlorocarbene from the

[62] U. Simon, O. Süs, and L. Hörner, *Ann. Chem.*, **697**, 17 (1966).
[63] D. M. Gale, W. J. Middleton, and C. G. Krespan, *J. Am. Chem. Soc.*, **88**, 3617 (1966).
[64] H. M. Frey and A. W. Scaplehorn, *J. Chem. Soc., A*, **1966**, 968.
[65] F. Gozzo and C. R. Patrick, *Tetrahedron*, **22**, 3329 (1966).
[66] B. Atkinson and D. McKeagan, *Chem. Commun.*, **1966**, 189.
[67] H. Kristinsson and G. W. Griffin, *J. Am. Chem. Soc.*, **88**, 1579 (1966).
[68] H. Kristinsson, *Tetrahedron Letters*, **1966**, 2343.

cyclopropane (**46**);[69] arylcarbenes appear to be produced on photolysis of other arylcyclopropanes.[70]

Photolysis of cyclocamphanone in cyclohexene gives (**47**), presumably via the ring-expanded carbene.[71] The same intermediate is probably involved in the formation of (**48**) when the photolysis is carried out in alcoholic solution. Similar behaviour has been observed on photolysis of benzocyclobutenedione (see p. 377).

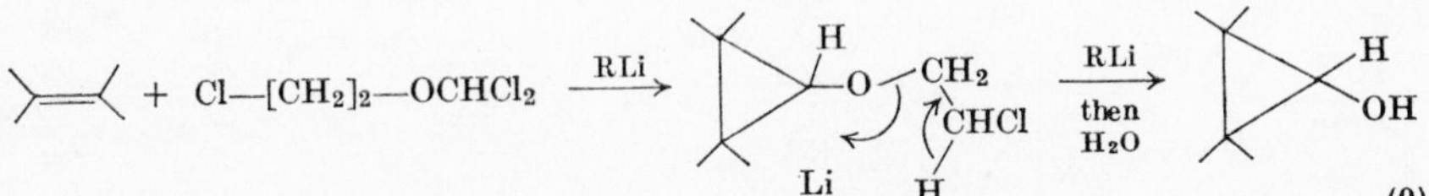

...(9)

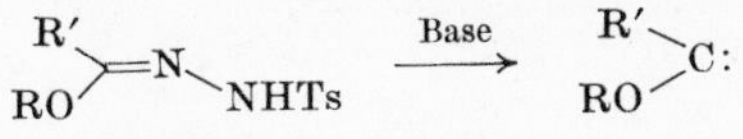

(**49**)

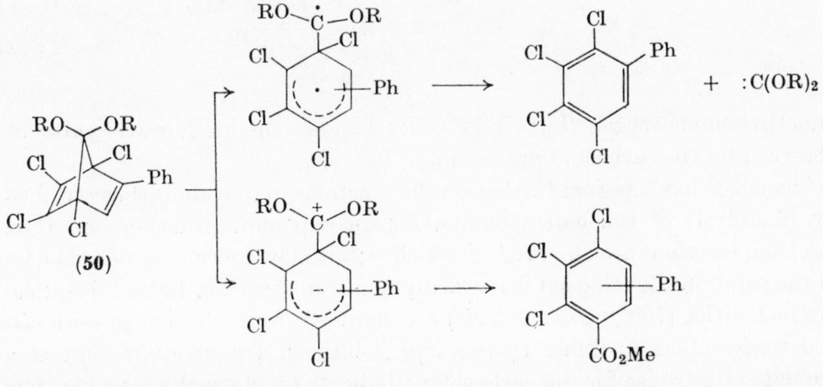

(**50**)

The sequence (9) provides a convenient route to cyclopropanols.[72] Alkoxy-carbenes are also involved in the base-promoted decomposition of ester tosylhydrazones (**49**),[73] and dialkoxycarbenes appear to be established as intermediates in the thermal decomposition of substituted norbornadienone ketals (**50**).[74] The latter decomposition is interpreted as proceeding by both homolytic and heterolytic cleavage, the relative importance of each depending on solvent.

[69] M. Jones, W. H. Sachs, A. Kulczycki, and F. J. Waller, *J. Am. Chem. Soc.*, **88**, 3167 (1966).
[70] P. A. Leermakers and M. E. Ross, *J. Org. Chem.*, **31**, 301 (1966); H. Kristinsson, K. N. Mehrotra, G. W. Griffin, R. C. Petterson, and C. S. Irving, *Chem. Ind.* (*London*), **1966**, 1562.
[71] P. Yates and L. Kilmurry, *J. Am. Chem. Soc.*, **88**, 1563 (1966).
[72] U. Schöllkopf, J. Paust, A. Al-Azrak, and H. Schumacher, *Chem. Ber.*, **99**, 3391 (1966).
[73] R. M. McDonald and R. A. Krueger, *J. Org. Chem.*, **31**, 488 (1966).
[74] D. M. Lemal, E. P. Gosselink, and S. D. McGregor, *J. Am. Chem. Soc.*, **88**, 582 (1966).

A reaction which is probably related to the Simmons–Smith reaction is the rapid formation of cyclopropanes when a dialkyl zinc is mixed with a solution of methylene iodide in olefin.[75]

The first-order decomposition of the cycloheptatriene (51) occurs by competing proton shift (a) ($\rightarrow$ 52) and what appears to be extrusion of

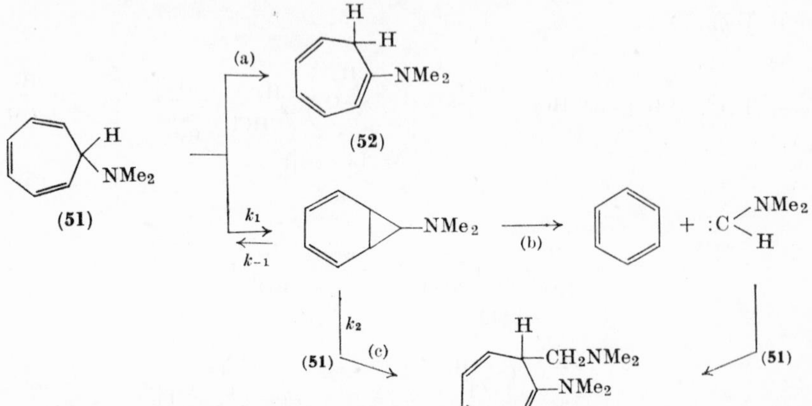

dimethylaminocarbene (b).[76] First-order kinetics might, however, also be observed for the carbenoid process (c), if $k_2 \gg k_{-1}$.

Ciganek[77] has reported further on the reactions of dicyanocarbene formed by photolysis of the corresponding diazo-compound. Addition and C–H insertion reactions are observed with olefins; with low concentrations of olefin in the solution the addition is markedly non-stereospecific. Indeed, identical product ratios (70% *trans*:30% *cis*) are obtained from addition to both *cis*- and *trans*-butene in dilute cyclohexane solutions. These results suggest a ground-state triplet for the carbene and indicate an unusually long life-time for the initial 1,3-biradical adduct.

Dicyanocarbene was probably not involved in the base-catalysed reaction of bromomalononitrile with olefins reported last year.[78] The intermediate adduct

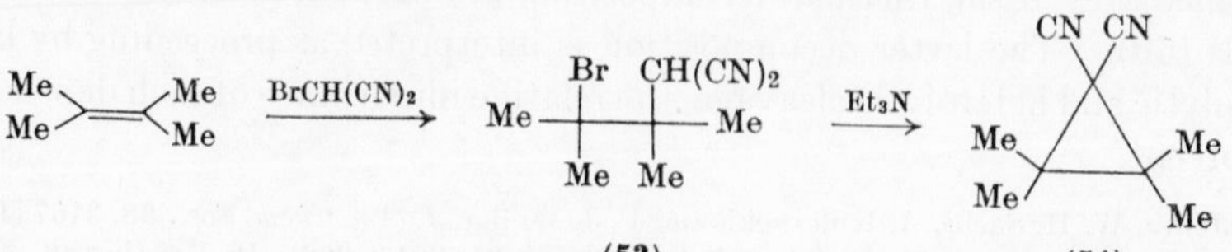

[75] J. Furukawa, N. Kawabata, and J. Nishimura, *Tetrahedron Letters*, **1966**, 3353.
[76] A. P. Ter Borg, E. Razenberg, and H. Kloosterziel, *Rec. Trav. Chim.*, **85**, 774 (1966).
[77] E. Ciganek, *J. Am. Chem. Soc.*, **88**, 1979 (1966).
[78] See *Organic Reaction Mechanisms*, **1965**, 229.

(53) has now been isolated, and this eliminates hydrogen bromide on treatment with triethylamine to give the reported cyclopropane (54).[79]

Subjecting propargylic alcohols to the conditions of the Simmons–Smith reaction gives the cyclopropylmethyl ketones (55);[80] anomalous reaction products are also obtained from hex-3-yne (56),[81] and the reported[82] synthesis of sterculic acid has been seriously questioned.[81]

$$RCHOHC{\equiv}CR' \xrightarrow[\text{Zu/Cu}]{\text{CH}_2\text{I}_2} \triangleright\!\!\!<\!\!{\overset{R'}{\underset{CH_2COR}{}}} \; + \; {\overset{R'}{\underset{Me}{}}}\!\!\!>\!\!{=}CHCOR$$

(55)

$$EtC{\equiv}CEt \xrightarrow[\text{Zu/Cu}]{\text{CH}_2\text{I}_2} MeCH{=}CH\!\!-\!\!\triangle\!\!-\!\!Et \; + \; MeCH{=}CHC\!\!-\!\!Et$$
$$\underset{CH_2}{\overset{\|}{}}$$

(56)

The internal competition of double and triple bonds for dichlorocarbene has been reinvestigated.[83–85] The double bond, particularly with alkyl substitution, appears more reactive, though Dehmlow[85] has obtained low yields of cyclopropenones by reaction at the triple bond of unbranched enynes. In similar studies with the copper-catalysed reaction of diazoacetic ester, reaction again occurs preferentially at an alkylated double bond.[86]

Stereochemical aspects of the reaction of the enol ether of testosterone with dibromocarbene have received attention.[87] More interesting, however, is the reaction of the corresponding enolate anion (57) with dichlorocarbene,[88] as this constitutes a model for the Reimer–Tiemann reaction of phenols. The product (58) is similar to a postulated, but never isolated, intermediate in the phenol reaction. 6-Methyltestosterone enolate gives the "abnormal" product (59). Dichlorocarbene has been added successfully to 4H-pyran and 4H-thiapyran,[89] but, under the conditions shown, the adducts of other enol ethers appear to rearrange [reaction (10)].[90] Treatment of the dichlorocarbene

79 P. Boldt and L. Schulz, *Tetrahedron Letters*, **1966**, 1415.
80 M. Vidal, C. Dumont, and P. Arnaud, *Tetrahedron Letters*, **1966**, 5081.
81 S. D. Andrews and J. C. Smith, *Chem. Ind. (London)*, **1966**, 1636.
82 N. T. Castellucci and C. E. Griffin, *J. Am. Chem. Soc.*, **82**, 4107 (1960).
83 L. P. Danilkina, I. A. D'yakonov, and G. I. Roslovtseva, *J. Org. Chem. USSR*, **1**, 456 (1965).
84 M. G. Avetyan, L. L. Nikogosyan, and S. G. Matsoyan, *Izv. Akad. Nauk Arm. SSR, Khim. Nauk*, **18**, 427 (1965); *Chem. Abs.*, **63**, 17917 (1965).
85 E. V. Dehmlow, *Tetrahedron Letters*, **1966**, 3763.
86 L. P. Danilkina and I. A. D'yakonov, *Zh. Org. Khim.*, **2**, 3 (1966); *Chem. Abs.*, **64**, 14101 (1966).
87 A. B. Font, *Bull. Soc. Chim. France*, **1965**, 3516.
88 T. D. J. D'Silva and H. J. Ringold, *Tetrahedron Letters*, **1965**, 4487.
89 K. Dimroth, W. Kinzebach, and M. Soyka, *Chem. Ber.*, **99**, 2351 (1966).
90 J. Buddrus, F. Nerdel, P. Hentschel, and D. Klamann, *Tetrahedron Letters*, **1966**, 5379; F. Nerdel, J. Buddrus, W. Brodowski, and P. Weyerstahl, *ibid.*, **1966**, 5385.

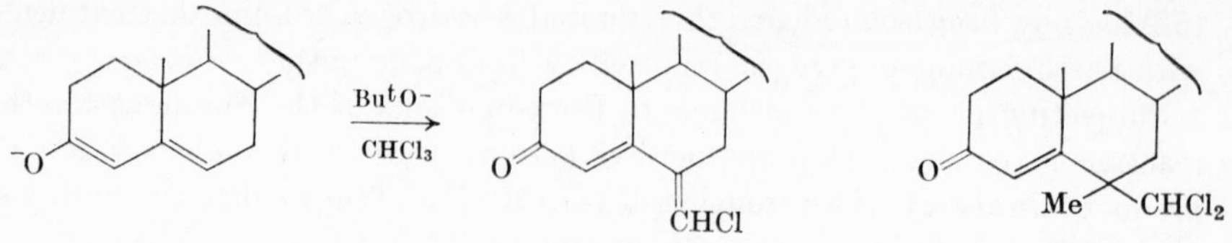

(57)   (58)   (59)

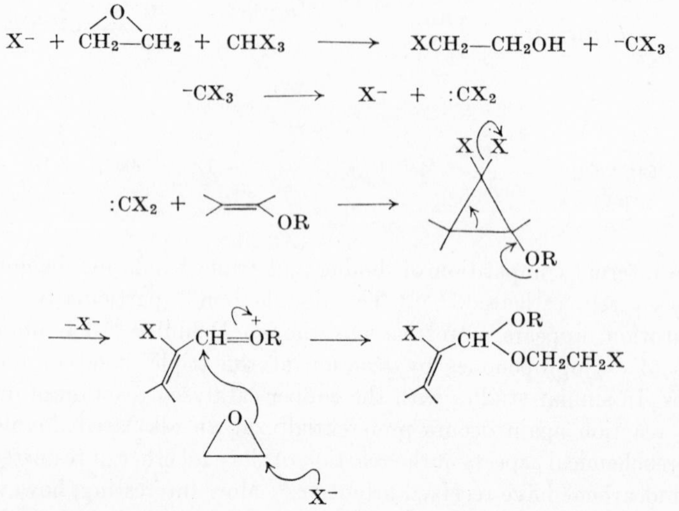

$$X^- + CH_2\!-\!CH_2 + CHX_3 \longrightarrow XCH_2\!-\!CH_2OH + {}^-CX_3$$

$${}^-CX_3 \longrightarrow X^- + :CX_2$$

... (10)

adducts (60) of cycloalkanone enol acetates with lithium aluminium hydride
provides the basis for a novel ring-expansion sequence.[91]

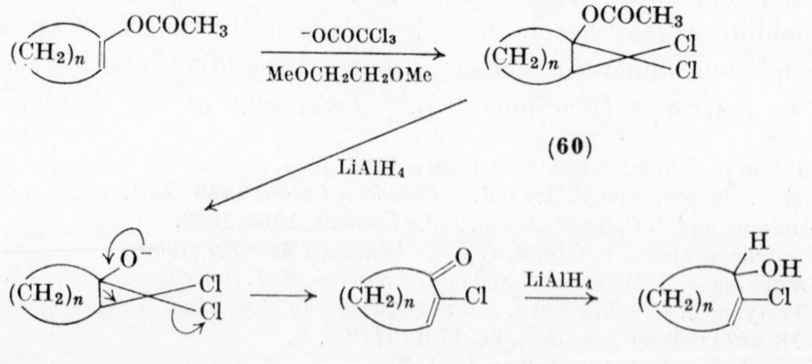

(60)

Additions of dichlorocarbene to ferrocenylethylenes,[92] and of ethoxycarbonylcarbene to cyclopentadiene,[93] have been noted, and the selective
attack of dihalogenocarbenes at one of the *trans*-double bonds of cyclododeca-

[91] R. C. De Selms, *Tetrahedron Letters*, **1966**, 1965.
[92] W. M. Horspool and R. G. Sutherland, *Chem. Commun.*, **1966**, 456.
[93] J. Warmentin, E. Singleton, and J. F. Edgar, *Can. J. Chem.*, **43**, 3456 (1965).

1,5,9-triene has been confirmed;[94] addition of a second carbene molecule occurs at the *cis*-double bond. Although benzothiophen is unreactive towards dichlorocarbene, the 3-methoxy-derivative gives the thiochromone (**61**).[95]

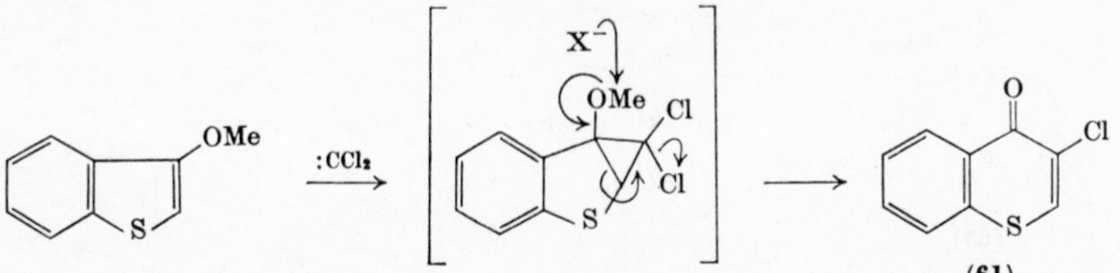

(61)

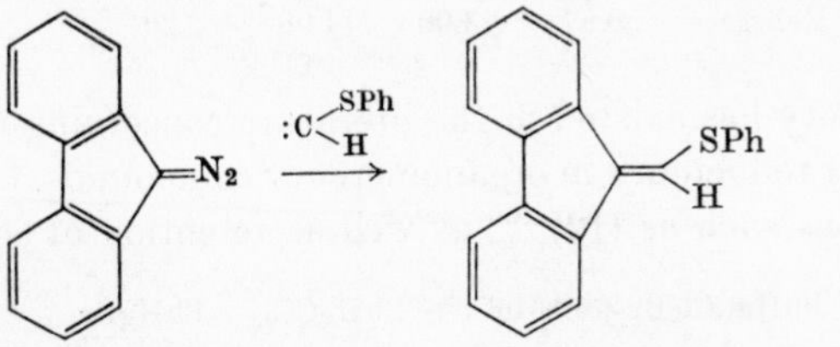

...(11)

The formation of substituted ethylenes by interaction between carbenes and diazoalkanes has been extended [e.g., reaction (11)].[96]

Ethoxycarbonylcarbene reacts with styrene oxide to give a complex mixture arising from initial attack on oxygen.[97] The ylide first formed in the corresponding reaction with 2-phenyloxetan, on the other hand, gives geometrical isomers of (**62**) in high yield.[97] Parham and Groen[98] have extended

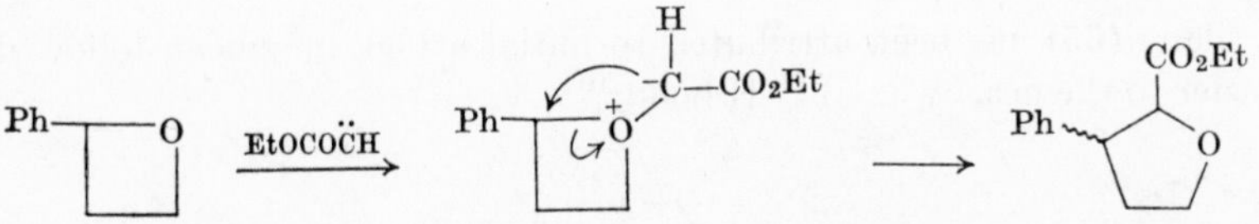

(62)

their examination of the mechanistic paths open to the sulphur ylides formed initially in the reaction of dichlorocarbene with allyl sulphides. The rates of reaction of dichlorocarbene with the phosphorus ylides (**63**) are consistent

[94] H. Nozaki, S. Katô, and R. Noyori, *Can. J. Chem.*, **44**, 1021 (1966); M. Mühlstädt and J. Graefe, *Chem. Ber.*, **99**, 1192 (1966).
[95] D. G. Hawthorne and Q. N. Porter, *Australian J. Chem.*, **19**, 1751 (1966).
[96] H. Reimlinger, *Chem. Ind.* (*London*), **1966**, 1682.
[97] H. Nozaki, H. Takaya, and R. Noyori, *Tetrahedron*, **22**, 3393 (1966).
[98] W. E. Parham and S. H. Groen, *J. Org. Chem.*, **31**, 1694 (1966).

10*

with the mechanism shown, the electrophilic attack on the ylide being rate-determining.[99]

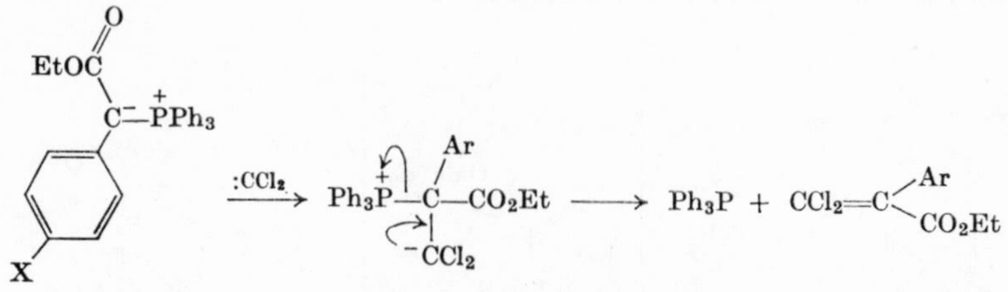

(63)

X:	Cl	H	Me	OMe
Rel. rate:	0.87	1.00	1.06	1.20

Some uncertainty has existed in the literature concerning the insertion of carbenes adjacent to mercury in organomercury compounds. Observations on exchange reactions such as (12),[100] as well as retention of configuration on

$$PhHgCCl_2Br + PhHgCl \rightarrow PhHgCCl_3 + PhHgBr \tag{12}$$

insertion into dialkylmercury compounds [reaction (13)],[101] leave little doubt as to the possibility of such processes. Dichlorocarbene is also inserted into a β-CH bond of di-n-propylmercury.[101] Similar insertion into a β-CH bond of

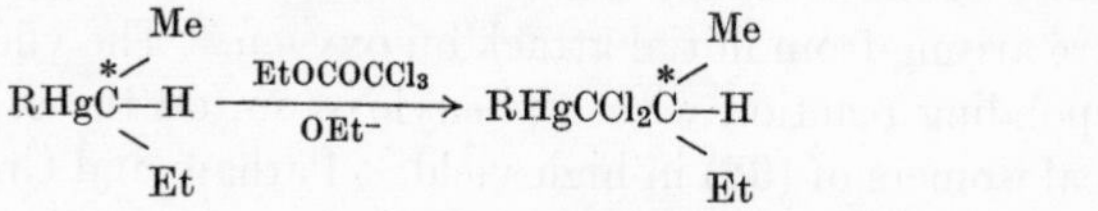

(64)

the silane (65) has been attributed to initial attack on silicon followed by transfer to the nearby axial C–H bond.[102]

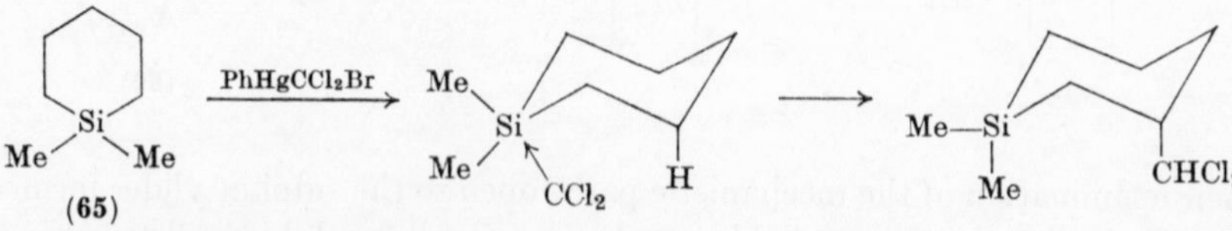

(65)

Thermal decomposition of mercury derivatives (64) gives olefin, formally by hydrogen migration in the initial alkylchlorocarbene.[103] The reaction of

[99] Y. Ito, M. Okano, and R. Oda, *Tetrahedron*, **22**, 2615 (1966).
[100] M. E. Gordon, K. V. Darragh, and D. Seyferth, *J. Am. Chem. Soc.*, **88**, 1831 (1966).
[101] J. A. Landgrebe and R. D. Mathis, *J. Am. Chem. Soc.*, **88**, 3545 (1966).
[102] D. Seyferth and S. S. Washburne, *J. Organometal. Chem.*, **5**, 389 (1965).
[103] J. A. Landgrebe and R. D. Mathis, *J. Am. Chem. Soc.*, **88**, 3552 (1966).

dichlorocarbene from (trichloromethyl)phenylmercury with secondary amines gives products incorporating two carbene carbon atoms:[104]

$$R_2NH + :CCl_2 \rightarrow R_2NCCl:CCl_2 + (R_2N)_2C:CCl_2$$

Mechanistic explanations were discussed.[104] In the reaction with a trialkylboron, the products can be interpreted as arising by initial nucleophilic attack on the boron, as shown.[105a]

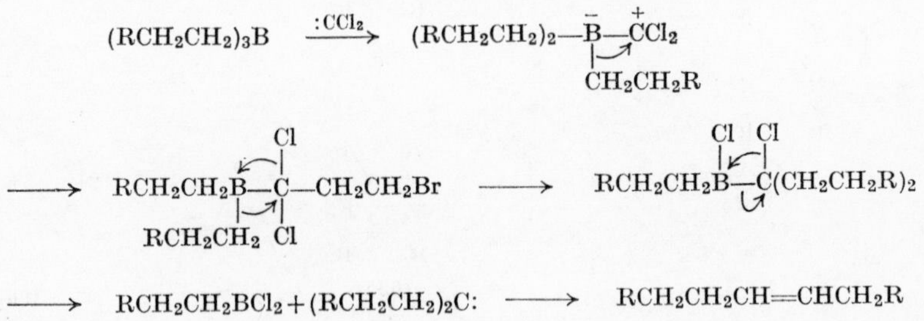

Carbene complexes of chromium,[105b] iron,[106] and iridium[107] have now been examined chemically or by X-ray crystallography, and two of these[106, 107] have been found to act as carbenoid intermediates. *gem*-Dihalides react with chromous ions in the presence of olefins[108] to give cyclopropanes; 2,2-dibromopropane adds the dimethylcarbene moiety in this reaction without undergoing rearrangement.

It was mentioned last year[109] that the reactions of Wanzlick's nucleophilic carbenes could satisfactorily be explained in terms of reactions of the carbene dimers. Further comment on this has now appeared,[110] as well as a new reaction of the dimer.[111] New evidence that (65a) exists in equilibrium with the monomer (66) comes from observation of "crossing" between two differently substituted dimers.[112] The monomer (66) and the dimer (65a) also react differently towards organic azides, formation of monomer having been established in this way also.[113]

Wanzlick and Ahrens[114] have attributed the coupling reactions of benz-

104 W. E. Parham and J. R. Potoski, *Tetrahedron Letters*, **1966**, 2311.
105a D. Seyferth and B. Prokai, *J. Am. Chem. Soc.*, **88**, 1834 (1966).
105b O. S. Mills and A. D. Redhouse, *Chem. Commun.*, **1966**, 814.
106 P. W. Jolly and R. Petit, *J. Am. Chem. Soc.*, **88**, 5044 (1966).
107 F. D. Mango and I. Dvoretzky, *J. Am. Chem. Soc.*, **88**, 1654 (1966).
108 C. E. Castro and W. C. Kray, *J. Am. Chem. Soc.*, **88**, 4447 (1966).
109 See *Organic Reaction Mechanisms*, **1965**, 233.
110 C.-C. Ma, C.-Y. Ch'en, H. K. Chiang and M.-Y. Ma, *K'o Hsueh, T'ung Pao*, **17**, 299 (1966); *Chem. Abs.*, **65**, 13463 (1966).
111 H.-W. Wanzlick and H. Ahrens, *Chem. Ber.*, **99**, 1580 (1966).
112 J. J. Vorsanger, *Bull. Soc. Chim. France*, **1966**, 1772.
113 H. Quast and S. Hünig, *Chem. Ber.*, **99**, 2017 (1966).
114 H.-W. Wanzlick and H. Ahrens, *Ann. Chem.*, **693**, 176 (1966).

anthrone **(67)** in basic media to reactions of the conjugate base to which the carbene structure **(68)** contributes.

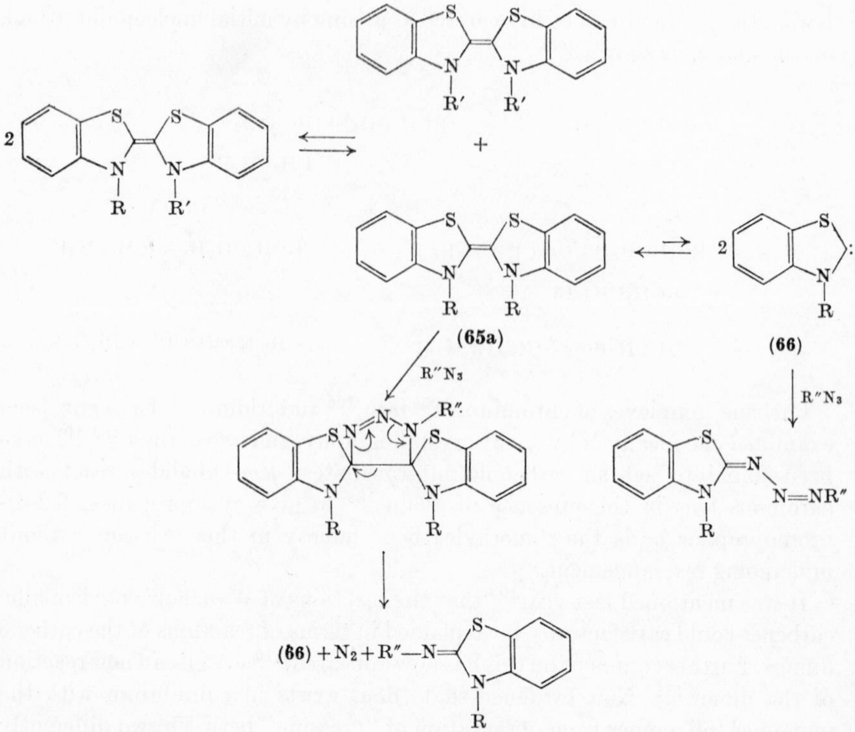

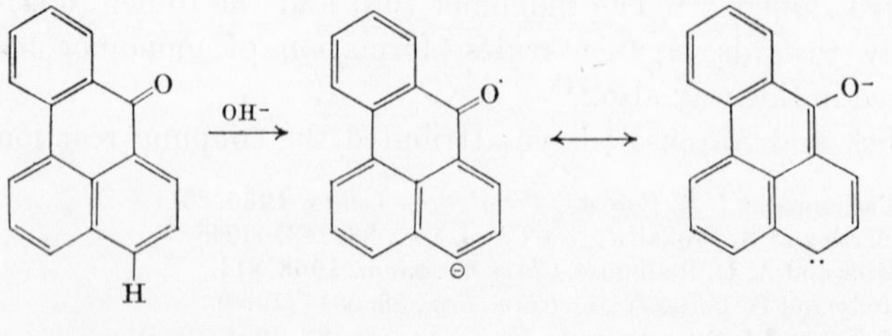

New ESR observations have been made on nitrenes generated by photolysis of azides.[115] Electronic spectra of nitrenes thus generated have also

115 R. M. Moriarty, M. Rahman, and G. J. King, *J. Am. Chem. Soc.*, **88**, 842 (1966).

reported.[116,117] E.g. photolysis of 2-azidobiphenyl in a rigid glass at 77°K permitted measurement of the spectrum of the corresponding nitrene, the presumed intermediate in the formation of carbazole in this system.[117] Light absorbed by the nitrene promoted carbazole formation at 77°K. At higher temperatures cyclization is spontaneous. The question of spin-

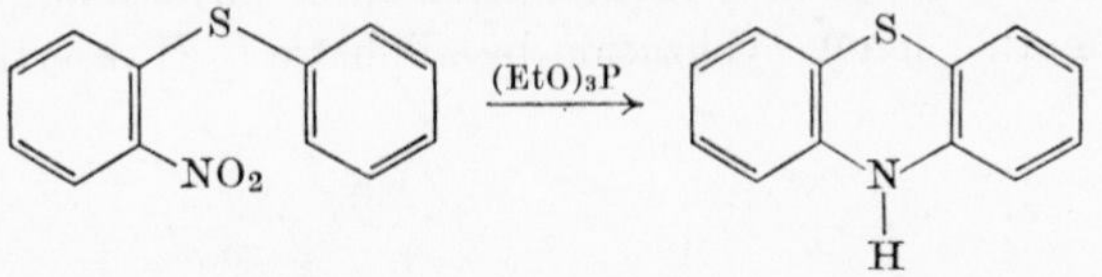

(14)

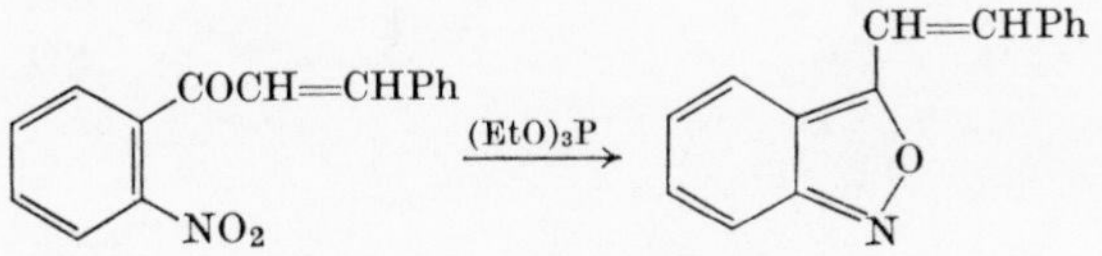

(15)

(69)   (70)

multiplicity of the species undergoing cyclization remains unanswered. Related nitrenes have now been established as intermediates in the cyclizations brought about by deoxygenation of nitro- and nitroso-compounds by

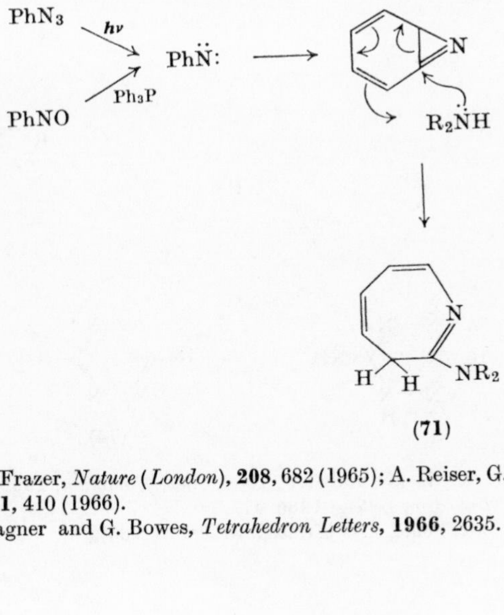

(71)

116 A. Reiser and V. Frazer, *Nature* (*London*), **208**, 682 (1965); A. Reiser, G. C. Terry, and F. W. Willets, *ibid.*, **211**, 410 (1966).
117 A. Reiser, H. Wagner and G. Bowes, *Tetrahedron Letters*, **1966**, 2635.

tervalent phosphorus [such as the novel syntheses of the phenothiazine and anthranil ring systems,[118] reactions (14) and (15)]. Evidence for this comes from the observation of products of intramolecular insertion reactions when o-alkylnitrobenzenes react with triethyl phosphite.[119,120] In particular, the dihydroindole (70) retains ca. 50% of the asymmetry of the precursor (69). This is very similar to the retention of configuration in the corresponding azide pyrolysis.[120] On the other hand, cyclization by aliphatic C–H insertion was

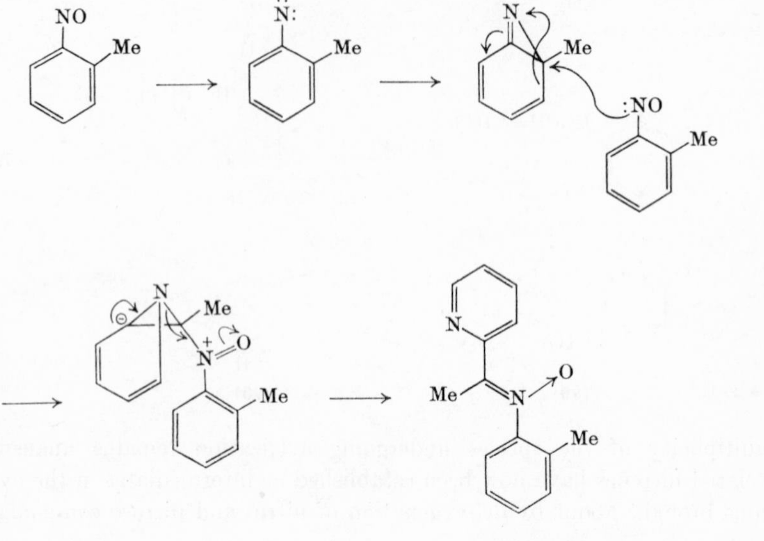

(72)

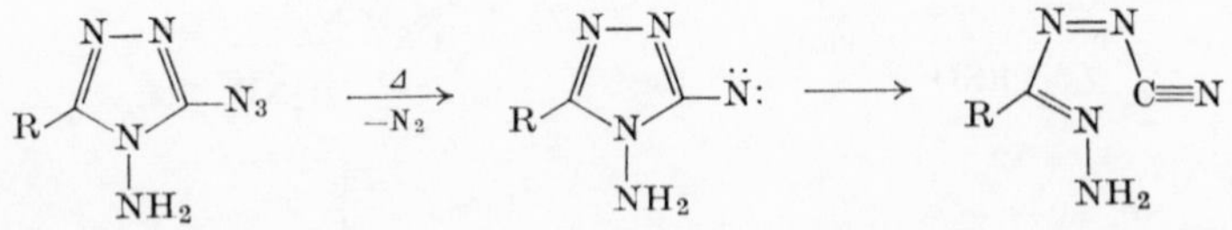

(73)   (R = Me or Ph)

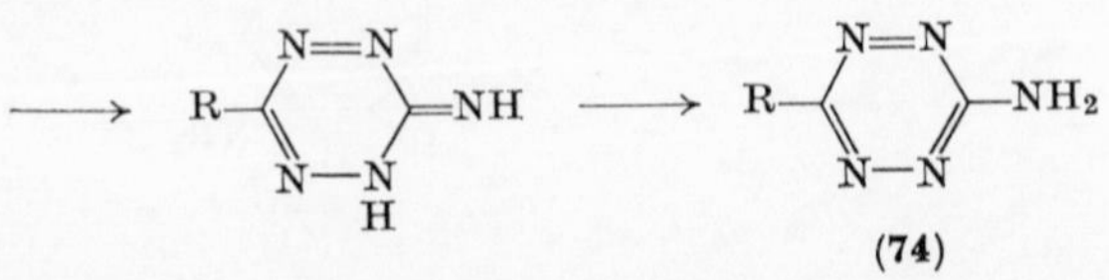

(74)

[118] J. I. G. Cadogan, R. K. Mackie, and M. J. Todd, *Chem. Commun.*, **1966**, 491.
[119] R. J. Sundberg, *Tetrahedron Letters*, **1966**, 477.
[120] G. Smolinsky and B. I. Feuer, *J. Org. Chem.*, **31**, 3882 (1966).

not observed when the nitro-compounds were reduced by ferrous oxalate, and it was argued that other cyclizations which have been effected by this reagent proceed by a different mechanism.

Photolysis of phenyl azide in the presence of secondary amine gives the 3H-azepine derivative (**71**)[121] (not 7H, as reported earlier), and similar products are obtained when nitrosobenzene is treated with triphenylphosphine and secondary amine. A common reaction path via the nitrene intermediate was assumed.[122] Formation of the pyridine derivative (**72**), found among the products of deoxygenation of *o*-nitroso(but not *o*-nitro)-toluene, was rationalized as indicated.[123]

The ring-expansion of triazole (**73**) to tetrazine (**74**) may proceed as shown.[124] The possibility of a concerted process requiring nucleophilic participation by –$\dot{N}H_2$ seems to be excluded by the fact that both the amino-compound (**73**) and its acetamido-analogue decompose at approximately the same rate.

Kinetics of decomposition of the *o*-nitro-azides (**75**) reveal a negative entropy of activation suggesting participation of the nitro-group in the transition state.[125] The substituent effects of X reveal a significant contribution from the polar structure (**76**) to the transition state of these azide decompositions.

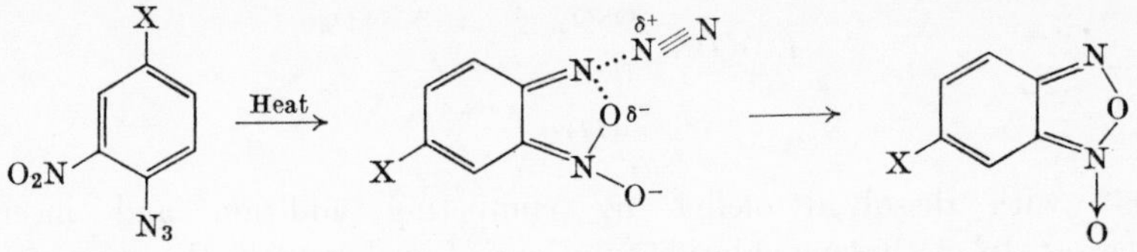

(75)

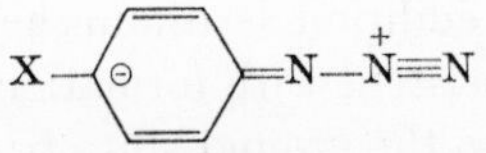

(76)

The thermal decomposition of ethyl azidoformate in the presence of anthracene, phenanthrene, or pyrene gives mixtures of arylurethanes (not azepines) in proportions suggesting that they are formed by a combination of electrophilic or radical substitution together with azepin formation with subsequent rearrangement.[126] No correlation between reaction pathway and

[121] W. von E. Doering and R. A. Odum, *Tetrahedron*, **22**, 81 (1966).
[122] R. A. Odum and M. Brenner, *J. Am. Chem. Soc.*, **88**, 2074 (1966).
[123] R. J. Sundberg, *J. Am. Chem. Soc.*, **88**, 3781 (1966).
[124] H. H. Takimoto and G. C. Denault, *Tetrahedron Letters*, **1966**, 5369.
[125] S. Patai and Y. Gotshal, *J. Chem. Soc.*, *B*, **1966**, 489.
[126] A. L. J. Beckwith and J. W. Redmond, *Australian J. Chem.*, **19**, 1859 (1966).

spin-multiplicity has yet been possible. Pyrolysis of methanesulphonyl azide in aromatic solvents gives substitution products considered to arise exclusively

$$MeSO_2N_3 \xrightarrow[-N_2]{Heat} MeSO_2\ddot{N}: \xrightarrow[(a)]{PhH} \quad \xrightarrow{(b)} \quad \cdots (16)$$

by rearrangement of intermediate aziridines.[127] This substitution [reaction (16)] reveals low substrate selectivity in competitive experiments, but positional selectivity is high, consistent with the proposed mechanism. Typically, anisole reacts faster than benzene by a factor of only 2.5 [competition in step (a)] but the isomer distribution for substitution in anisole is *o* 56, *m* 1, *p* 43% [competition in step (b)].

Lwowski and his colleagues,[128] continuing their work with ethoxycarbonyl-nitrene, have shown that methylene chloride is essentially an inert solvent for this intermediate. The nitrene was formed both by photolysis of ethyl azido-formate and by α-elimination from (77). It has been found that the nitrene

$$EtOCON\begin{smallmatrix}OSO_2-\\H\end{smallmatrix}\!\!-\!\!\bigcirc\!\!-\!\!NO_2$$

(77)

reacts with dissolved olefins by competing addition and insertion processes. In methylene chloride solutions of cyclohexene, the proportion of addition to insertion is highest with low olefin concentrations. Similarly, with the butenes stereospecificity of addition is diminished at low olefin concentrations. These results are consistent with formation of the nitrene in the singlet state, followed by decay to the ground-state triplet. The fact that in concentrated olefin solutions greater stereospecificity is observed in the α-elimination reactions suggests that decomposition of photoexcited azide molecules may, in part, be preceded by intersystem crossing to an excited triplet state, which would give triplet nitrene directly.

Photolysis of methyl azidoformate in but-2-yne gives the oxazole (78) and cyclopropene (79).[129] The latter rearranges on warming to (80). The possibility that the azirine (81) might be an intermediate in the formation of (78) becomes more attractive in the light of the report that furan (83) is produced

[127] R. A. Abramovitch, J. Roy, and V. Uma, *Can. J. Chem.*, **43**, 3407 (1965).
[128] W. Lwowski and J. S. McConaghy, *J. Am. Chem. Soc.*, **87**, 5490 (1965); W. Lwowski and F. P. Woerner, *ibid.*, **87**, 5491 (1965)
[129] J Meinwald and D. H. Aue, *J. Am. Chem. Soc.*, **88**, 2849 (1966).

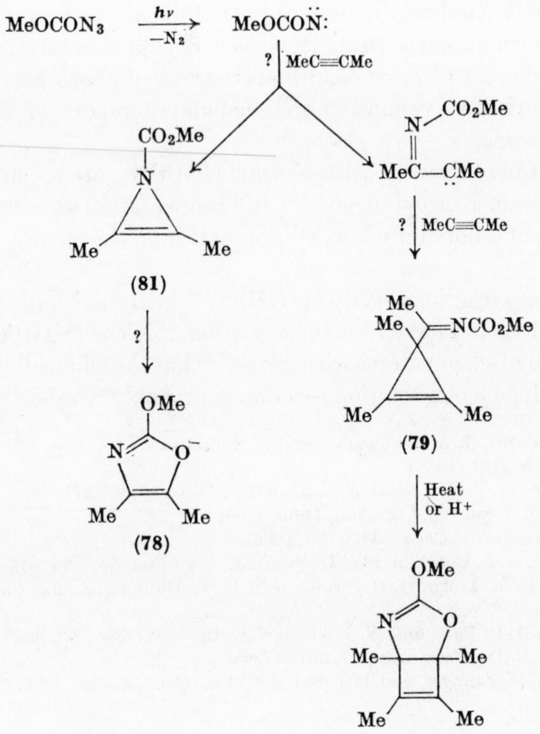

$$MeOCON_3 \xrightarrow[-N_2]{h\nu} MeOCON:$$

(81)

(78)

(79)

(80)

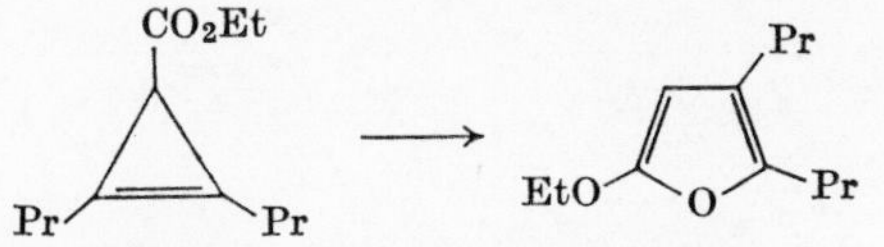

(82) → (83)

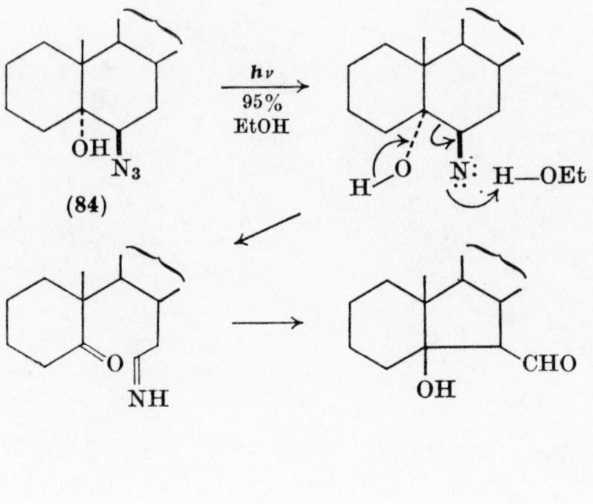

(84)

from the copper-catalysed reaction of ethyl diazoacetate and oct-4-yne via the isolable cyclopropene (**82**).[130] However, copper-catalysis does provide profoundly different reaction conditions to those of photolysis.

Further work on cyanonitrene[131] includes a report of 1,4-addition to cyclo-octatetraene.

Products of photolysis of benzoyl azide (PhCON$_3$) are accommodated by a scheme involving benzoylnitrene.[132] A fragmentation process accounts for the formation of B-nor-steroids as by-products from the photolysis of hydroxy-azides (**84**).[133]

The gas-phase reactions of triplet (NH),[134] and of singlet and triplet sulphur atoms,[135] with olefins have received attention. Silylene (SiH$_2$) may be formed in the reaction of silicon atoms with silane,[136] but the claimed[137] intermediacy of dimethylsilylene in a solution reaction is probably invalid.[138]

[130] M. I. Komendatov, I. A. D'yakonov, and T. S. Smirnova, *Zh. Org. Khim.*, **2**, 559 (1966); *Chem. Abs.*, **65**, 7124 (1966).

[131] A. G. Anastassiou, *J. Am. Chem. Soc.*, **87**, 5512 (1965); **88**, 2322 (1966).

[132] J.-P. Anselme, *Chem. Ind.* (*London*), **1966**, 1794.

[133] W. J. Wechter, *J. Org. Chem.*, **31**, 2136 (1966).

[134] D. W. Cornell, R. S. Berry, and W. Lwowski, *J. Am. Chem. Soc.*, **88**, 544 (1966).

[135] K. S. Sidhu, E M Lown, O. P. Strausz, and H. E. Gunning, *J. Am. Chem. Soc.*, **88**, 254 (1966).

[136] P. P. Gaspar, B. D. Pate, and W. Eckleman, *J. Am. Chem Soc*, **88**, 3878 (1966).

[137] R. A. Braun, *J. Am. Chem. Soc.*, **87**, 5516 (1965).

[138] C. L. Frye, R. M. Salinger, and T. J. Patin, *J. Am. Chem. Soc.*, **88**, 2343 (1966).

CHAPTER 11

Reactions of Aldehydes and Ketones and their Derivatives[1]

Formation and Reactions of Acetals and Ketals

Replacement of the hydrogen at $C_{(2)}$ of 2-phenyl-1,3-dioxolan by a methyl or ethyl group results in a 5- or 25-fold decrease in the rate of the acid-catalysed hydrolysis in 50% dioxan–water at 30°.[2] Similar replacements in benzaldehyde

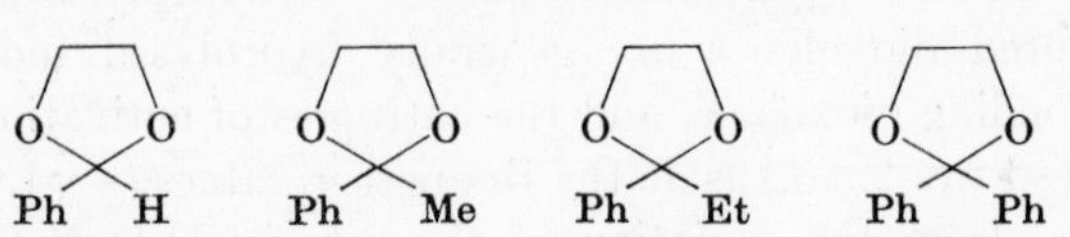

k_2	Ph H	Ph Me	Ph Et	Ph Ph
l. mole^{-1} min^{-1}	25.4	5.00	1.04	0.216

diethyl acetal result in 33- and 9-fold rate increases. The entropies of activation for the hydrolyses of the dioxolans are negative (*ca.*–9 e.u.) and the slower rates of the 2-methyl-2-phenyl- and 2-ethyl-2-phenyl than of the 2-phenyl compound are the result of higher energies of activation. It was also found that 2,2-diphenyldioxolan is hydrolysed about 120 times more slowly than 2-phenyldioxolan which is to be compared with the 20-fold slower rate of hydrolysis of benzophenone diethyl ketal than of benzaldehyde diethyl acetal.[3] A possible explanation is that the transition state resembles the protonated substrate so that conjugation by substituents is relatively unimportant. Alternatively, a steric effect may be important. This could be either steric inhibition of resonance between the phenyl group and the carbonium ion centre[3] or an effect arising from the transition state's having oxonium ion character which requires $C_{(2)}$, $O_{(3)}$, $C_{(4)}$, and the bonds to $C_{(2)}$ to be coplanar.[4a] In our opinion the latter explanation is the more likely.

It has been suggested that the rate-dependence on glycerol content of water–glycerol mixtures may be used as a criterion for distinguishing between *A*-1 and *A*-2 mechanisms in acid-catalysed reactions.[4b] One of the *A*-1

---

[1] An extensive monograph on reactions of aldehydes and ketones has been published: "Chemistry of the Carbonyl Group", S. Patai, ed., John Wiley, London, New York, Sydney, 1966.
[2] T. H. Fife and L. Hagopian, *J. Org. Chem.*, **31**, 1772 (1966).
[3] M. M. Kreevoy and R. W. Taft, *J. Am. Chem. Soc.*, **79**, 4016 (1957).
[4a] P. Salomaa and A. Kankaanperä, *Acta Chem. Scand.*, **15**, 871 (1961).
[4b] L. L. Schaleger, C. N. Richards, and N. Watamori, *Chem. Commun.*, **1966**, 381.

reactions studied was the hydrolysis of 2,2-dimethyldioxolan which give a plot of log k_ψ/C_{H^+} against log a_{H_2O} with the expected slope.

The effects of substituents on the rates of hydrolysis of 1,3-dioxolans and 1,3-dioxans have been discussed.[5] The rates of hydrolysis and the equilibrium constant for the hydrolysis of 2-methyl-1,3-dioxan have been determined; there is an appreciable concentration of hemiacetal present at equilibrium.[6]

1,3-Dioxol-4-ones unsubstituted at $C_{(2)}$ are hydrolysed faster than the corresponding dioxolans. Since the entropies of activation are strongly negative (−20 to −25 e.u.) and the Bunnett w value is +4 to +5, it was considered that hydrolysis proceeds by an A_{Ac}-2 mechanism.[7] This contrasts with the behaviour of acyclic acylals which are hydrolysed by a unimolecular mechanism. Presumably the factor responsible for rapid hydrolysis of γ-lactones, namely, dipole repulsion in the *cis*-ester group, is also important in facilitating the A_{Ac}-2 mechanism for the hydrolysis of the dioxolones. 2-Substituted dioxolones are generally hydrolysed more slowly than the corresponding dioxolans, and the entropies of activation have intermediate values (−4 to −9 e.u.) as do the Bunnett w-values (~ +1.0). It was concluded, however, from the variation of the rate in D_2O–H_2O mixtures that the transition state has at least three exchangeable protons and that the mechanism is A-2. It was suggested that the A-1 transition state (1) in which $C_{(5)}$, $O_{(1)}$, $C_{(2)}$, and $O_{(3)}$ are moving into coplanarity is achieved only with difficulty by the dioxolones owing to the unfavourable steric situation created by sp^2-hydridization of $C_{(4)}$.

(1)

By following the change in NMR spectrum it has been shown that the reaction of glycerol and benzaldehyde in dimethylformamide in the presence of toluene-*p*-sulphonic acid yields first the *cis*- and *trans*-dioxolans [(2) and (3)], with the former in slight excess, and that these are slowly converted into the equilibrium mixture in which the dioxans [(4) and (5)] predominate.[8,9]

5 F. Aftalion, *Rev. Inst. Franc. Petrole Ann. Combust. Liquides*, **20**, 1032 (1965); *Chem. Abs.*, **63**, 17822 (1965).
6 K. Pihlaja, *Acta Chem. Scand.*, **19**, 2250 (1965); K. Pihlaja, *Suomen Kemistilehti, A*, **39**, 114 (1966).
7 P. Salomaa, *Acta Chem. Scand.*, **20**, 1263 (1966).
8 N. Baggett, J. M. Duxbury, A. B. Foster, and J. M. Webber, *Carbohydrate Res.*, **2**, 216 (1966).
9 Cf. *Organic Reaction Mechanism*, **1965**, 240.

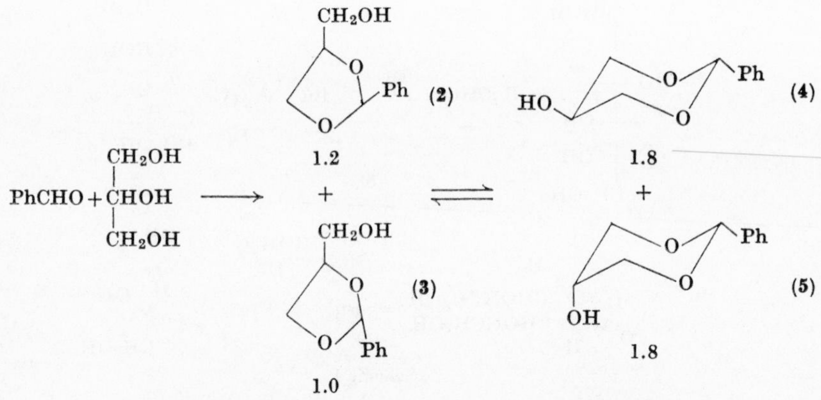

CH₂OH

(2)   Ph   HO   (4)

CH₂OH   1.2   1.8

PhCHO + CHOH ⟶ + ⇌ +

CH₂OH   CH₂OH

(3)   Ph   (5)

OH   1.8

1.0

The figures are the proportions present at equilibrium

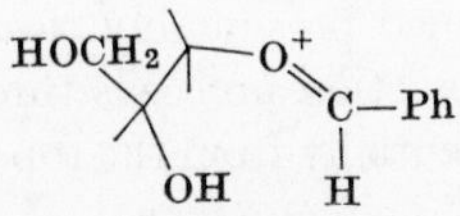

HOCH₂ — O⁺
       ‖
       C—Ph
OH   H

(6)

Thus, on the assumption that it is the primary alcohol group of glycerol which is used in hemiacetal formation and that the reaction involves an ion (6), the ionic centre is captured by the internal hydroxyl group preferentially, to form a five- rather than a six-membered ring although the latter would yield the thermodynamically more stable products.[10] The effects of solvent and temperature on the equilibrium proportions of the acetals were also determined.

It has also been shown by following the reaction by gas chromatography that glucitol (0.25M) and *n*-butyraldehyde (0.25M) in M aqueous sulphuric or hydrochloric acid yield first the five-membered cyclic 2,3-acetal and only later the more stable 2,4- and 3,4-acetals.[11] Hydrolysis of the 2,3-acetal under the same conditions was shown to yield D-glucitol rapidly, before any other acetal could be detected. It was claimed that this was evidence for formation of the other acetals by direct combination of butyraldehyde and glucitol rather than by ring migration. In our opinion, however, this experiment does not permit this distinction since the results indicate rapid equilibration between aldehyde and glucitol, forming a 2,3-acetal (Scheme 1), and this makes it impossible to decide from which side of the equilibrium the other acetals are being formed.

[10] For a discussion of the factors which govern the dependence of the rates of ring-closure reactions on ring size, see B. Capon, *Quart. Rev.* (*London*), **18**, 45 (1964).

[11] T. G. Bonner, E. J. Bourne, P. J. V. Cleare, and D. Lewis, *Chem. Ind.* (*London*), **1966**, 1268.

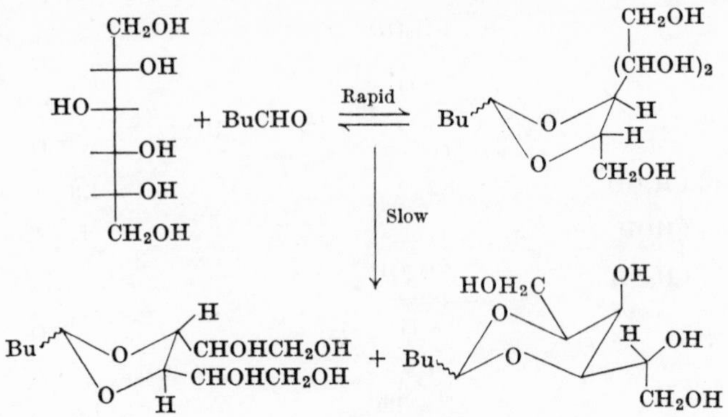

Scheme 1

2,4-O-Benzylidene-D-erythrose, on treatment with toluene-p-sulphonic acid in dimethylformamide, yields 2,3-O-benzylidene-D-erythrofuranose (**7**) with the phenyl group *endo*, formed presumably through the *cis*-aldehyde (**8**).[12] It was suggested that the reaction proceeds through the *trans*-oxonium ion (**9**) which is attacked preferentially from the top by $O_{(2)}$.

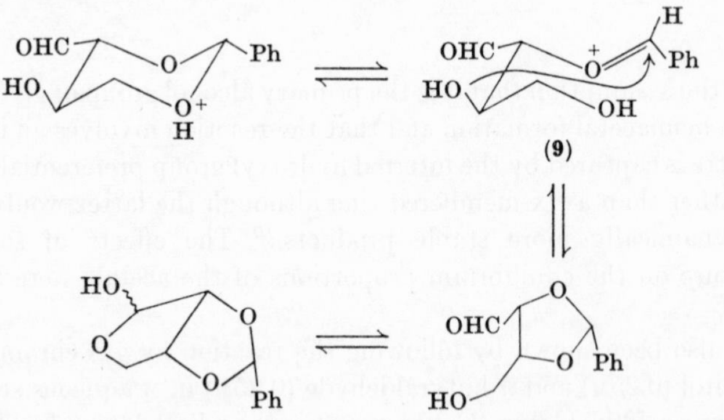

The rates of hydrolysis of large number of acetals of aliphatic aldehydes at pH 3.7 and 20° have been measured.[13] Treatment of maleic dialdehyde with an equimolar amount of water in the presence of phosphoric acid yields 2,5-diethoxydihydrofuran; glutaraldehyde diethyl acetal likewise yields some 2,6-diethoxytetrahydropyran.[14]

[12] N. Baggett, K. W. Buck, A. B. Foster, B. H. Rees, and J. M. Webber, *J. Chem. Soc., C*, **1966**, 212.
[13] L. A. Yanovskaya and R. N. Stepanova, *Izv. Akad. Nauk SSSR, Ser. Khim.*, **1965**, 1416; *Chem. Abs.*, **63**, 16150.
[14] L. A. Yanovskaya and V. M. Belikov, *Izv. Akad. Nauk SSSR, Ser. Khim.*, **1965**, 1363; *Chem. Abs.*, **65**, 10445 (1966).

The acid-catalysed methanol exchange reactions of norbornan-2-one and of camphor dimethyl ketal in deuteriomethanol have been investigated (see p. 11).[15]

Other reactions of acetals which have been investigated include *trans*-acetalation,[16,17] and the hydrolysis of acrolein dimer.[18] Equilibrium constants for acetal formation between aromatic aldehydes[19] and cyclic ketones[20] and methanol have been determined.

Other interesting, but not strictly mechanistic, investigations with acetals include studies of hydrogen bonding in the acetals of glycerol and acetaldehyde,[21] of the equilibration of the isomeric 2,4,5-trimethyl-1,3-dioxolones,[22] and of the conformations of 1,3-dioxans.[23]

The acid-catalysed hydrolysis[24] and the alkaline fission[25] of glycosides have been reviewed.

The rate of the acid-catalysed hydrolysis of 2-pyridyl glycosides is rapid owing, it is claimed, to intramolecular catalysis as symbolized by (10).[26] This involves a four-membered hydrogen-bonded ring and, in our opinion,

(10)

it is more likely that the driving force is derived from *N*-protonated 2-hydroxy-pyridine's being a very good leaving group, since it separates as the stable 2-pyridone. It is significant that the standard free-energy change for the conversion of 2-methoxypyridine into 1-methyl-2-pyridone in the gas phase has recently been evaluated as < -6 kcal mole^{-1}, while that for the conversion of 4-methoxypyridine into 1-methyl-4-pyridone was given as only < -2 kcal

[15] T. G. Traylor and C. L. Perrin, *J. Am. Chem. Soc.*, **88**, 4934 (1966).
[16] I. Jansson, *Suomen Kemistilehti, B*, **38**, 184 (1965); I. Jansson and J. Soimajärvi, *Suomen Kemistilehti, A*, **39**, 114 (1966).
[17] C. Piantadosi, C. E. Anderson, C. L. Yarbro, E. A. Brecht, and C. A. Di Fazio, *J. Elisha Mitchell Sci. Soc. Suppl. No. 1*, **81**, 31 (1965); *Chem. Abs.*, **64**, 6424 (1966).
[18] A. Misono, T. Osa, and S. Koda, *Yukagaku*, **15**, 199 (1966); *Chem. Abs.*, **65**, 2087 (1966).
[19] J. M. Bell, D. G. Kubler, P. Sartwell, and R. G. Zepp, *J. Org. Chem.*, **30**, 4284 (1965).
[20] R. Garrett and D. G. Kubler, *J. Org. Chem.*, **31**, 2665 (1966).
[21] G. Aksnes and P. Albriktsen, *Acta Chem. Scand.*, **20**, 1330 (1966).
[22] A. Kankaanperä, *Suomen Kemistilehti, A*, **39**, 116 (1966).
[23] J. Delmau and J. Duplan, *Tetrahedron Letters*, **1966**, 2693.
[24] P. Nuhn and G. Wagner, *Pharmazie*, **21**, 261 (1966).
[25] G. Wagner and P. Nuhn, *Pharmazie*, **21**, 205 (1966).
[26] G. Wagner and H. Frenzel, *Z. Chem.*, **5**, 454 (1965).

mole^{-1}.[27] Whatever the cause, though, 2-pyridyl glycosides are hydrolysed rapidly and 2-pyridazinyl glycosides faster still. The hydrolyses of 5-cyano- and 5 chloro-2-(1-β-D-glucopyranosyloxy)pyridazine are so fast that the aromeric configuration of the glucose first formed can be determined and is α, the reaction proceeding with predominant inversion.[26]

It has been suggested that the hydrolysis of poly- and oligo-saccharides containing uronic acid residues that proceed at enhanced rates at pH's above 2 involve intramolecular catalysis as shown in (11).[28]

(11)

The determination by X-ray diffraction of the three-dimensional structure of lysozyme and of its complex with the inhibitor chitotriose has lead to speculations on its mechanism of action.[29] The carboxylic acid residues of glutamic acid 35 and aspartic acid 52 are in suitable positions to act as catalytic groups, and it has been suggested that the former provides general acid-catalysis and that the latter in its ionized form stabilizes the intermediate carbonium ion. It is also possible that the binding forces of the enzyme distort the pyranose ring towards the half-chair conformation in which stabilization of the ion by the mesomeric electron-release of the ring-oxygen atom will be maximized. The mechanism can therefore be represented schematically as shown in Scheme 2.

p-Nitrophenyl chitotrioside and chitobioside have been shown to be substrates, though poor ones, for lysozyme.[30] There have been several other investigations of mechanistic interest concerning lysozyme[31] and other glycosidases.[32]

The rates of the alkaline cleavage of phenyl glycosides, thioglycosides, and

[27] P. Beak and J. Bonham, *Chem. Commun.*, **1966**, 631; see p. 238.
[28] O. Smidsrød, A. Haug, and B. Larsen, *Acta Chem. Scand.*, **20**, 1026 (1966).
[29] C. C. F. Blake, *New Scientist*, **29**, 333 (1966); D. C. Phillips, *Scientific American*, **215**, 78 (1966); L. N. Johnson, *Sci. Progr.*, **54**, 367 (1966).
[30] T. Osawa, *Carbohydrate Res* , **1**, 435 (1966); T. Osawa and Y. Nakazawa, *Biochem. Biophys. Acta*, **130**, 56 (1966)
[31] S. S. Lehrer and G. D. Fasman, *Biochem. Biophys. Res. Comm.*, **23**, 133 (1966); E. W. Thomas, *ibid.*, p. 611; A. N. Glazer and N. S. Simmons, *J. Am. Chem. Soc.*, **88**, 2335 (1966); F. W. Dahlquist, L. Jao, and M. Raftery, *Proc. Natl. Acad. Sci.*, **56**, 26 (1966); I. Covelli and J. Wolff, *Biochemistry*, **5**, 860, 867 (1966).
[32] K. Hiromi, Z. Hamauzu, K. Takahashi and S. Ono, *J. Biochem.* (*Tokyo*), **59**, 411 (1966); M. G. Harrington and U. M. Kehoe, *Irish. J. Agr. Res.*, **2**, 61 (1963); B. B. Jørgensen and O. B. Jørgensen, *Acta Chem. Scand.*, **20**, 1437 (1966); J. L. Brown, S. Koorajian, J. Katze, and I. Zabin, *J. Biol. Chem.*, **241**, 2826 (1966); K. Myrback, *Arkiv Kemi*, **25**, 315 (1965).

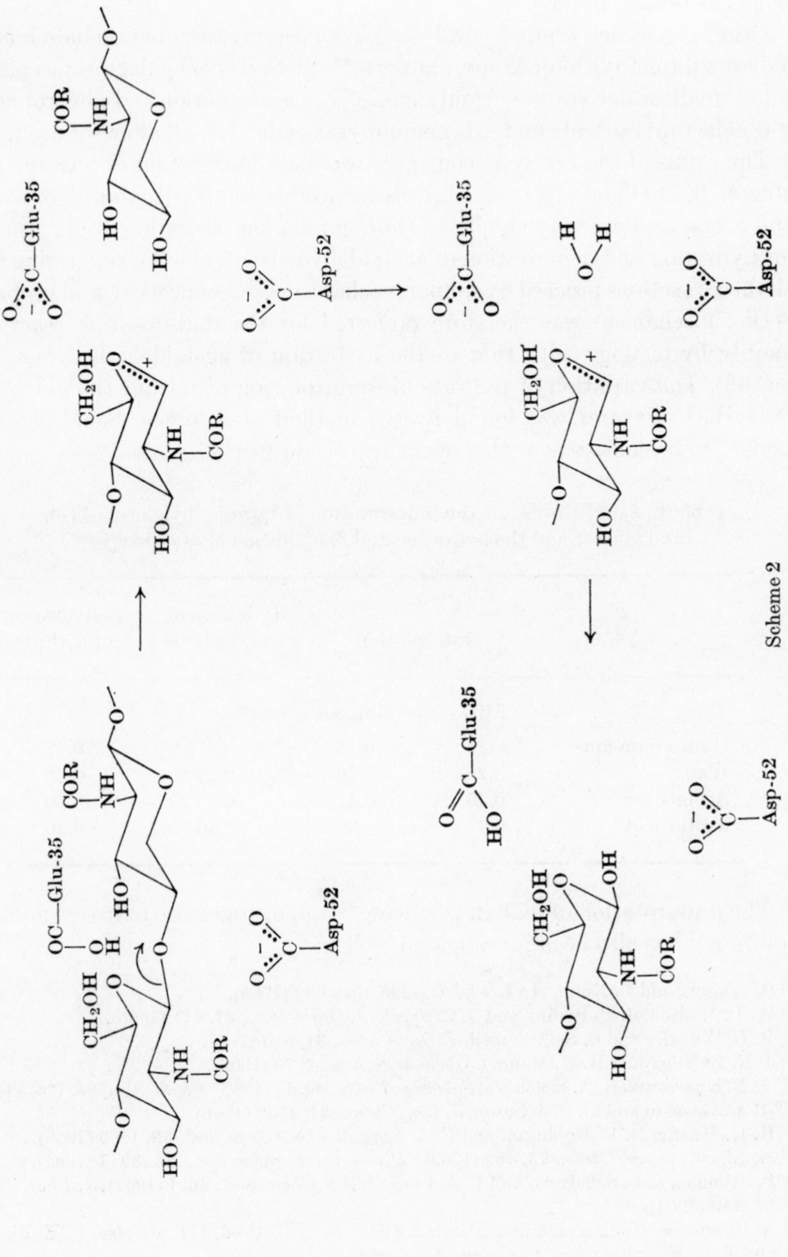

Scheme 2

selenoglycosides fall in the order Se $\gg$ S > O and of the acid-catalysed hydrolysis in the reverse order.[33]

Other glycosides whose hydrolyses have been investigated include methyl 6-deoxy-6-(methylthio)hexopyranosides,[34] methyl β-D-galactothioseptanoside,[35] maltose derivatives,[36] and sucrose[37a] in acid solution and p-nitrophenyl β-D-galactopyranoside and α-D-mannopyranoside[37b] in alkaline solution.

The ratios of the catalytic constants for the mutarotation of tetramethylglucose in D_2O and H_2O for catalysis by acetate ion, hydroxium ion, water, and acetic acid are very similar to those for the mutarotation of glucose and for hydration and dehydration of acetaldehyde (see Table 1), suggesting that all these reactions proceed by similar mechanisms.[38] A concerted, and probably cyclic, mechanism was therefore preferred for the mutarotation reactions, mainly by analogy with that of the hydration of acetaldehyde[39] (see also ref. 46). The variation of the rate of mutarotation of tetramethylglucose in D_2O–H_2O mixtures was found by the method of Salomaa, Schaleger, and Long[40] to be consistent with a cyclic transition state.[38]

Table 1. k_D/k_H Ratios for the mutarotation of tetramethylglucose (TMG) and glucose and the hydration and dehydration of acetaldehyde.

	Mutarotation		Hydration of acetaldehyde	Dehydration of hydrate
	TMG	Glucose		
Hydronium ion	0.75	0.73	0.77	0.71
Water	0.28	0.26	0.28	0.26
Acetate ion	0.45	0.42	0.43	0.40
Acetic acid	0.41	0.39	0.40	0.36

The mutarotation of molten D-glucose[41] and of D-glucose in frozen aqueous solution[42] has also been investigated.

[33] G. Wagner and P. Nuhn, *Arch. Pharm.*, **298**, 686, 692 (1965).
[34] W. L. Madson, J. P. Riehm, and J. C. Speck, *J. Org. Chem.*, **31**, 611 (1966).
[35] R. L. Whistler and C. S. Campbell, *J. Org. Chem.*, **31**, 816 (1966).
[36] J. N. BeMiller and R. K. Mann, *Carbohydrate Res.*, **2**, 70 (1966).
[37a] S. E. Kharin and R. A. Kolcheva, *Sakharn. Prom.*, **40**, 17 (1966); *Chem. Abs.*, **65**, 7257 (1966).
[37b] R. C. Gasman and D. C. Johnson, *J. Org. Chem.*, **31**, 1830 (1966).
[38] H. H. Huang, R. R. Robinson, and F. A. Long, *J. Am. Chem. Soc.*, **88**, 1866 (1966).
[39] M. Eigen, *Angew. Chem.*, **75**, 489 (1963); *Discussion Faraday Soc.*, No. **39**, 7 (1965).
[40] P. Salomaa, L. L. Schaleger, and F. A. Long, *J. Am. Chem. Soc.*, **86**, 1 (1964); *J. Phys. Chem.*, **68**, 410 (1964).
[41] A. Broido, Y. Houminer, and S. Patai, *J. Chem. Soc.*, B, **1966**, 411; see also, R. E. Pincock and T. E. Kiovsky, *Chem. Commun.*, **1966**, 864.
[42] T. E. Kiovsky and R. E. Pincock, *J. Am. Chem. Soc.*, **88**, 4704 (1966).

(–)-α-Methylbenzylamine is reported to be a more effective catalyst than its enantiomer for the mutarotation of α-L-rhammose.[43]

It has been suggested that the protonated amino-groups of 2-amino-2-deoxy-D-mannose and of 2-amino-3,6-anhydro-2-deoxy-D-mannose provided intramolecular catalysis for the mutarotation of these sugars.[44]

There have been several other investigations of mutarotation.[45a]

As mentioned above, a reaction closely related mechanistically to mutarotation is the hydration of aldehydes,[45b] and the acid-catalysed hydration of acetaldehyde has been studied by NMR line-broadening techniques.[46] On changing from water to 60 mole % acetaldehyde–water the value of H_0 increases 1 unit but the rate decreases by about 40%. It was concluded, therefore, that the reaction did not involve a rapid pre-equilibrium proton-transfer but rather a slow concerted one, possibly involving a cyclic transition state.

The kinetics of dehydration of methanediol have been studied by scavenging anhydrous formaldehyde with nitrogen bases and with sulphite. The reaction is general acid–base-catalysed with Brønsted α- and β-coefficients of 0.24 and 0.40, respectively.[47]

Rates of oxygen-exchange which presumably proceeds by hydration and dehydration have been measured for a range of ketones in acidified tetrahydrofuran[48] and acidified acetonitrile.[49]

The kinetics of the reactions between a series of aldehydes and ketones and a series of thiols to form hemithioacetals and hemithioketals have been measured. The reaction is general acid- and specific base-catalysed, with no pH-independent reaction detectable. The reaction of acetaldehyde with mercaptoethanol (0.1—0.2M) at pH 5.08 was shown to be a reaction of the unhydrated aldehyde and not of the hydrate. Under these conditions dehydration of the hydrate is rate-determining and on addition of an equilibrated mixture of acetaldehyde and its hydrate to the thiol there is a rapid decrease in absorbance at 280 mμ on reaction of unhydrated aldehyde with the thiol, followed by a slow increase as the hydrate is dehydrated to restore the equilibrium. The Brønsted α-coefficient for the general acid-catalysed reaction

[43] V. A. Pavlov, E. I. Klabunovskii, and A. A. Balandin, *Kinetika i Kataliz*, **7**, 551 (1966); *Chem. Abs.*, **65**, 10645 (1966).

[44] D. Horton, J. S. Jewell, and K. D. Philips, *J. Org. Chem.*, **31**, 3843 (1966); M. L. Wolfrom, P. Chakravarty, and D. Horton, *ibid.*, p. 2502.

[45a] H. Schmid and G. Bauer, *Monatsh. Chem.*, **96**, 583, 2010 (1965); *ibid.*, **97**, 168 (1966); A. de Grandchamp-Chaudin, *Compt. Rend., Ser. C.*, **262**, 1141 (1966); H. Kawahara, M. Hojo, and T. Tsuruta, *Kogyo Kagaku Zasshi*, **69**, 309 (1966); *Chem. Abs.*, **65**, 9003 (1966).

[45b] For a review see R. P. Bell, *Adv. Phys. Org. Chem.*, **4**, 1 (1966).

[46] M. L. Ahrens and H. Strehlow, *Discussion Faraday Soc.*, No. **39**, 112 (1965).

[47] R. P. Bell and P. G. Evans, *Proc. Roy. Soc.*, A, **291**, 297 (1966).

[48] M. Byrn and M. Calvin, *J. Am. Chem. Soc.*, **88**, 1916 (1966).

[49] G. Aksnes, D. Aksnes, and P. Albriktsen, *Acta Chem. Scand.*, **20**, 1325 (1966).

of 2-methoxyethanethiol and acetaldehyde is about 0.7 and the solvent deuterium isotope effect for the H_3O^+-catalysed reaction is $k_{H_3O^+}/k_{D_3O^+} = 0.59$ which was considered to be consistent with general-acid-catalysis. Transition state (12) was suggested. The base-catalysed reaction was thought to involve an attack of the thiolate anion on the carbonyl group.[50]

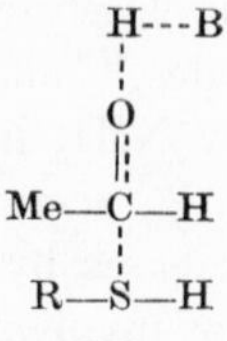

$$
\begin{array}{c}
\text{H---B} \\
\vdots \\
\text{O} \\
\| \\
\text{Me—C—H} \\
\vdots \\
\text{R—S—H}
\end{array}
$$

(12)

Other reactions investigated include isomerization of the methyl(methyl galactosid)uronates,[51] acetolysis of 2,3,4,5,6-penta-*O*-acetyl-D-glucose diethyl dithioacetal and 1,2,3,4,5,6-hexa-*O*-acetyl-D-glucose,[52] the reaction of phenol and formaldehyde,[53] polymerization of trioxan catalysed by boron trifluoride etherate,[54] and polymerization of formaldehyde in D_2O.[55]

Reactions with Nitrogen Bases

A detailed kinetic study of the reaction of *p*-chlorobenzaldehyde with hydroxyl-amine to give an oxime [reaction (1)] and with *N*-methylhydroxylamine to give the nitrone [reaction (2)] has been reported.[56] The reactions are kinetically

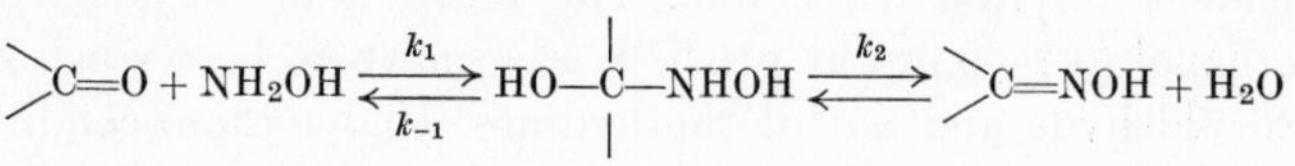

$$
\text{C=O} + \text{NH}_2\text{OH} \underset{k_{-1}}{\overset{k_1}{\rightleftharpoons}} \text{HO—C—NHOH} \underset{}{\overset{k_2}{\rightleftharpoons}} \text{C=NOH} + \text{H}_2\text{O} \tag{1}
$$

$$
K_1
$$

$$
\text{C=O} + \text{MeNHOH} \underset{k_{-1}}{\overset{k_1}{\rightleftharpoons}} \text{HO—CNMeOH} \underset{}{\overset{k_2}{\rightleftharpoons}} \text{C=}\overset{+}{\text{N}}\text{—O}^- \tag{2}
$$

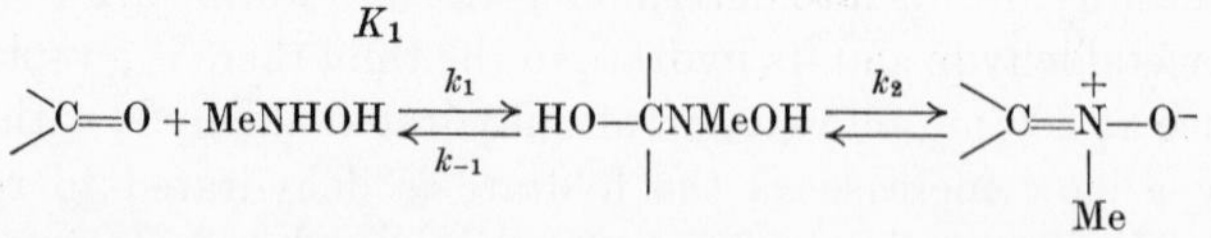

very similar and show similar bell-shaped pH–rate profiles. In the pH range 5—8 there is a rapid and reversible formation of a carbinolamine followed by a slow dehydration, but in more acidic solutions the formation of the carbinol-

[50] G. E. Lienhard and W. P. Jencks, *J. Am. Chem. Soc.*, **88**, 3982 (1966).
[51] H. W. H. Schmidt and H. Neukom, *Helv. Chim. Acta*, **49**, 510 (1966).
[52] N. H. Kurihara and E. P. Painter, *Can. J. Chem.*, **44**, 1773 (1966).
[53] S. Murayama, *Bull. Chem. Soc. Japan*, **39**, 1019, 1027, 1032 (1966).
[54] T. Higashimura, T. Miki, and S. Okamura, *Bull. Chem. Soc. Japan*, **38**, 2067 (1965); **39**, 25, 31, 36, 41 (1966).
[55] K. Moedritzer and J. R. Van Wazer, *J. Phys. Chem.*, **70**, 2025 (1966).
[56] J. E. Reimann and W. P. Jencks, *J. Am. Chem. Soc.*, **88**, 3973 (1966).

amine becomes the slow step. The equilibrium both for the overall reaction and for carbinolamine formation is less favourable with reaction (2) than reaction (1) (Table 2).

Table 2. Rate and equilibrium constants for the reaction of hydroxylamine and N-methylhydroxyl-amine with p-chlorobenzaldehyde at 25°.

	NH_2OH	MeNHOH
K (Overall l. mole^{-1})	6.1×10^7	9.4×10^5
K_1 (l. mole^{-1})	23.5	6.60
k_1 (l. mole^{-1} min^{-1})	2.31×10^6	2.5×10^6
k_{-1} (min^{-1})	9.8×10^4	3.8×10^5
k_2 (l. mole^{-1} min^{-1})	3.33×10^6	9.2×10^5

Under conditions where dehydration is the slow step, both reactions show general acid-catalysis with cationic and anionic acids, to yield the same α-value of 0.77. The similarity of the catalysis in the two reactions suggests that in the oxime formation this does not involve the proton on the nitrogen atom of the carbinolamine [as (14)] and that most probably the transition state is as shown in (13).[56] The kinetics of nitrone formation from N-cyclohexylhydroxylamine and several aliphatic aldehydes have also been investigated.[57]

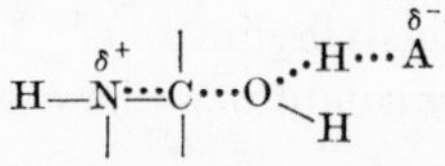

(13) 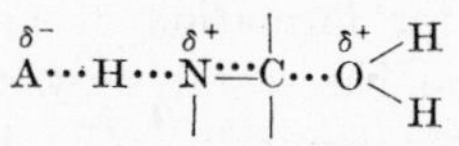   (14)

The kinetics of the formation of benzaldehyde oxime have been investigated in the pH range 1.0—6.54[58] and 6.0—11.08.[59] In the latter region, where dehydration of the intermediate carbinolamine is the slow step, the plot of log k against pH shows a sharp minimum at pH 8.3 with the rate proportional to $[H^+]$ at lower pH's and to $[^-OH]$ at higher pH's. A similar plot for the formation of acetone oxime, however, shows a broad minimum in the pH region 8.4—10 where the rate is independent of pH. The solvent isotope effect on the ^-OH-catalysed formation of benzaldehyde oxime was found to be

[57] M. Masui and C. Yijima, *J. Chem. Soc., B*, **1966**, 56.
[58] L. do Amaral, W. A. Sandstrom, and E. H. Cordes, *J. Am. Chem. Soc.*, **88**, 2225 (1966).
[59] A. Williams and M. L. Bender, *J. Am. Chem. Soc.*, **88**, 2508 (1966).

$k_{-OD}/k_{-OH} = 1.4$ and this was considered to support specific hydroxide ion catalysis as shown in equation (3). The pH-independent reaction found with acetone oxime probably involves general acid-catalysis by water.

$$\begin{array}{c}
\diagdown\text{C}\diagup^{\text{OH}}_{\diagdown\text{NHOH}} \rightleftharpoons \diagdown\text{C}\diagup^{\text{OH}}_{\diagdown\text{NOH}} \longrightarrow \diagdown\text{C}{=}\text{NOH} \qquad (3)
\end{array}$$

The kinetics of the hydrolysis of cyclopentanone oxime[60] in acid solutions, and of the formation of the $C_{(10)}$-oximes of some cardiac glycosides,[61] of the oximes of *cis-* and *trans-*1-acetyl 2-methylcyclohexane,[62] and of *p*-benzoquinone dioxime,[63] have also been investigated.

The pH–rate profile for the formation of benzaldehyde phenylhydrazone is similar to that for formation of benzaldehyde semicarbazone and benzylideneaniline.[58] The slow step in the pH range 5—7.5 is dehydration of the carbinolamine, but in more acidic solutions it is attack by phenylhydrazine on the aldehyde. Under the latter conditions the reaction shows general acid-catalysis with a Brønsted α-value of 0.20. This catalysis was considered to be genuine general acid-catalysis [transition state (15)] rather than the kinetically equivalent general base–specific-acid catalysis [transition state (16)]. In

$$\begin{array}{cc}
\overset{\text{H}}{\underset{\text{H}}{\overset{|}{\underset{|}{\text{R}{-}\overset{\delta^+}{\text{N}}{\cdots}\text{C}{\overset{{\cdots}}{\underset{{\cdots}}{\,}}\text{O}{\cdots}\text{H}{\cdots}\overset{\delta^-}{\text{B}}}}}} & \qquad \overset{\text{R}}{\underset{\text{H}}{\overset{|}{\underset{|}{\overset{\delta^-}{\text{B}}{\cdots}\text{H}{\cdots}\text{N}{\cdots}\text{C}{\overset{{\cdots}}{\underset{{\cdots}}{\,}}\text{O}{-}\overset{\delta^+}{\text{H}}}}}} \\
(15) & (16)
\end{array}$$

contrast, for formation of benzophenone phenylhydrazone[64] little or no general acid–base-catalysis was observed under conditions where dehydration of the carbinolamine was the slow step.

A detailed investigation of the mechanism of hydrolysis of *N*-isopropyl-2-, -3-, and -4-hydroxy- and -methoxybenzylideneimine have been reported.[65] At neutral pH's the *o-* and *p*-hydroxy-compounds react, respectively, 40 and 10 times slower than the corresponding methoxy-compounds and the values of pK_1 for the equilibrium $SH^+ \rightleftarrows S + H^+$ are 2.55 and 1.3 units less for the hydroxy- than for the corresponding methoxy-compounds. It was concluded

[60] N. G. Zarakhani, V. V. Budylina, and M. I. Vinnik, *Zh. Fiz. Khim.*, **39**, 1863 (1965); *Chem. Abs.*, **63**, 16150 (1965).
[61] M. O. Kazarinov and N. P. Dzyuba, *Farmatsevt. Zh. (Kiev)*, **20**, 28 (1965); *Chem. Abs.*, **64**, 11283 (1966).
[62] A. Heymes and M. Dvolaitzky, *Bull. Soc. Chim. France*, **1966**, 2819.
[63] A. Dargelos, C. Leibovici and M. Chaillet, *Bull. Soc. Chim. France*, **1966**, 2023.
[64] J. C. Powers and F. H. Westheimer, *J. Am. Chem. Soc.*, **82**, 5431 (1960).
[65] W. Bruyneel, J. J. Charette, and E. De Hoffmann, *J. Am. Chem. Soc.*, **88**, 3808 (1966).

that this arose because the hydroxy-compounds existed in the quinonoid forms (17) and (18), and strong support for this was provided by the ultraviolet spectra of the *o*- and *p*-hydroxy-compounds, which show strong shifts of the bands at ca. 250 and 300 mμ to longer wavelengths. At high pH's the

(17)   (18)

rates for all six hydroxy- and methoxy-compounds are of the same order of magnitude and it was concluded that there was no evidence to support the suggestions[66] that the 2-hydroxybenzylidene derivatives are hydrolysed with intramolecular catalysis.

Shifts were also observed in the ultraviolet spectra of 2- and 4-hydroxybenzylidene derivatives of aromatic amines in alcoholic solution and it was concluded that these also exist in quinonoid forms.[67]

The kinetics of the hydrolysis of the Schiff bases of salicylaldehyde and several other amines have been investigated,[68] and the equilibrium constant for formation of the Schiff base from salicylaldehyde and methylamine has been found to be 3.72×10^4 l. mole^{-1} at 25° in water.[69]

The rate of hydrolysis of *N*-benzylideneaniline is strongly decreased in the presence of cetyltrimethylammonium bromide, presumably owing to its incorporation into the micelles.[70]

The pH-independent hydrolyses, at pH ~ 10, of a series of Schiff bases, PhCH=NAr, have a ρ-value of -0.80.[58] This was considered to support earlier evidence that the reaction is an attack of $^-$OH on the protonated Schiff base. The reactions of these bases with *O*-methylhydroxylamine were also investigated in the hope that there would be a change in rate-determining step from nucleophilic attack when electron-withdrawing substituents are present in Ar, to decomposition of the tetrahedral intermediate when electron-releasing substituents are present;[58] this was, however, not found.

The rate of the reaction of acetone and methylamine to yield acetone ketimine has been measured in the pH range 10—12 both directly and as the rate of oxime formation in the presence of an excess of hydroxylamine which traps the ketimine as fast as it is formed. The results were considered

[66] See *Organic Reaction Mechanisms*, **1965**, 243–244.
[67] J. W. Ledbetter, *J. Phys. Chem.*, **70**, 2245 (1966); G. O. Dudek and E. P. Dudek, *J. Am. Chem. Soc.*, **88**, 2407 (1966).
[68] J. Charette, C. Decoene, G. Falthansl, and P. Teyssié, *Bull. Soc. Chim. Belges*, **74**, 518 (1965).
[69] R. W. Green and E. L. Le Mesurier, *Australian J. Chem.* **19**, 229, 1966.
[70] K. G. van Senden and C. Koningsberger, *Tetrahedron*, **22**, 1301 (1966).

to be consistent with the mechanism of equation (4), the slow step (dehydration of the carbinolamine) proceeding with the direct expulsion of $^-$OH.

$$Me_2CO + MeNH_2 \;\underset{}{\overset{Fast}{\rightleftharpoons}}\; Me_2C\overset{\curvearrowright OH}{\underset{\curvearrowleft NHMe}{\big\langle}} \;\overset{Slow}{\longrightarrow}\; Me_2C\overset{+}{=}NHMe + HO^-$$

$$\downarrow \text{Fast}$$

$$Me_2C{=}NMe + H_2O \tag{4}$$

It has been suggested that hydrolysis of compound (19) proceeds by the mechanism shown [equation (5)], with the direct expulsion of EtS$^-$.[71]

$$PhCH\overset{SEt}{\underset{NMe_2}{\big\langle}} \;\longrightarrow\; \underset{\underset{EtS^-}{+}}{PhCH{=}\overset{+}{N}Me_2} \;\overset{H_2O}{\underset{-H^+}{\longrightarrow}}\; PhCHO + Me_2NH \tag{5}$$

$$(19)$$

The reaction of aliphatic aldehydes with hydrazine in ethanol to yield compounds of structure (20) has been investigated.[72] Their ease of formation decreases in the order $R = Me > Et > Pr^i > $ Neopentyl.

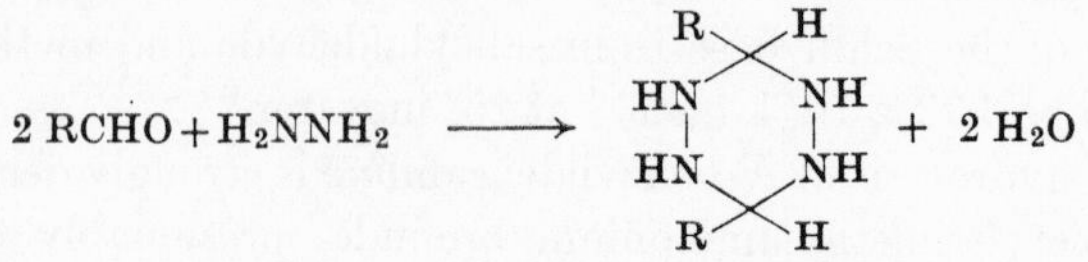

$$2\,RCHO + H_2NNH_2 \;\longrightarrow\; \begin{matrix} R & H \\ HN & NH \\ | & | \\ HN & NH \\ R & H \end{matrix} \;+\; 2\,H_2O$$

$$(20)$$

The hydrolysis of acetone 2-phenylsemicarbazone to acetone and 1-phenyl-semicarbazide proceeds by the sequence of reactions given in equations (6) and (7).[73]

$$Me_2C{=}NNPhCONH_2 \;\overset{Slow}{\longrightarrow}\; Me_2C{=}NNHPh + HNCO \;\overset{Fast}{\longrightarrow}\; CO_2 + NH_3 \tag{6}$$

$$\text{Fast}\downarrow H_2O$$

$$MeCOMe + H_2NNHPh$$

$$PhNHNH_2 + HNCO \;\overset{Fast}{\longrightarrow}\; PhNHNHCONH_2 \tag{7}$$

The following reactions have also been investigated: hydrolysis of pyrimidine nucleosides,[74] N-glucosides,[75] (p-N-dimethylaminophenyl)iminobenzoyl-

[71] W. M. Schubert and Y. Motoyama, *J. Am. Chem. Soc.*, **87**, 5507 (1965).
[72] W. Skorianetz and E. sz. Kováts, *Tetrahedron Letters*, **1966**, 5067.
[73] A. Fischer, D. A. R. Happer, and J. Vaughan, *J. Chem. Soc.*, **1965**, 7444.
[74] E. R. Garrett, J. K. Seydel, and A. J. Sharpen, *J. Org. Chem.*, **31**, 2219 (1966).
[75] T. Jasiński and K. Smiataczowa, *Roczniki Chem.*, **40**, 1279 (1966).

acetanilides,[76] and Schiff bases of ethylenediamine;[77] reactions of aldehydes with urea[58,78] and of D-gluconohydrazide with alicyclic ketones;[79] formazan formation;[80] and transamination.[81]

Enolization and Related Reactions

A preliminary report of an important investigation by Rappe of the halogenation of butan-2-one has appeared.[82,83] The results obtained indicate that, contrary to previous belief, under certain conditions the reactions do not proceed through enols or enolate ions. Two different mechanisms seem to be followed in the pH regions 5—7 and 12—14. For the former pH region the most important evidence is: (*a*) the ratios of 3-halogenation: 1-halogenation (K_{Hal}) are different from the ratio of 3-deuteriation to 1-deuteriation (K_D); (*b*) bromine and iodine react at different rates; (*c*) in D_2O the rate of deuteriation is not influenced by the addition of bromine; and (*d*) the reaction is catalysed by sodium acetate. It was suggested that under these conditions the reaction involved either base-catalysed attack of hypohalous acid on the unenolized ketone or attack on the ketone by a species formed from "hypohalous acid and another halogenated component formed in a base catalysed reaction of hypohalous acid."

In the pH region 12—14 another mechanism must be followed since here the proportion of 1-halogenation is very high ($K_{Hal} = 0$) but still different from the proportion of 1-deuteriation; also no deuteration occurs while bromination goes to completion. It was suggested that the reaction is one between hypohalite ions and unenolized ketone.

It has also been suggested that chlorination of optically active ketones (**21**) and (**23**) in $CHCl_3$, CCl_4, and HOAc, which yield optically active chloroketones (**22**) and (**24**), may proceed by direct electrophilic substitution competitive with enolization.[84]

The rates of exchange at positions 1 and 3 of butan-2-one in D_2O have been reported.[85] These are nearly equal for catalysis by ^-OD, but the methylene

[76] E. de Haffmann and A. Bruylants, *Bull. Soc., Chim. Belg.*, **75**, 91 (1966).
[77] E. Hoyer, *Z. Chem.*, **5**, 231 (1965).
[78] R. Kveton, *Coll. Czech. Chem. Commun.*, **31**, 2701 (1966); Y. Ogata, A. Kawasaki, and N. Okumura, *Tetrahedron*, **22**, 1731 (1966).
[79] D. Todd and C. Brozek, *J. Chem. Soc., C*, **1966**, 312.
[80] A. F. Hegarty and F. L. Scott, *Chem. Commun.*, **1966**, 622.
[81] J. W. Thanassi, A. R. Butler, and T. C. Bruice, *Biochemistry*, 1965, **4**, 1463; D. L. Leussing and E. M. Hanna, *J. Am. Chem. Soc.*, **88**, 693, 696 (1966); M. Y. Karpeisky and V. I. Ivanov, *Nature*, **210**, 493 (1966).
[82] C. Rappe, *Acta Chem. Scand.*, **20**, 376 (1966).
[83] C. Rappe, *Acta Chem. Scand.*, **20**, 1721 (1966).
[84] M. J. Ronteix and A. Marquet, *Tetrahedron Letters*, **1966**, 5801.
[85] J. Warkentin and O. S. Tee, *Chem. Commun.*, **1966**, 190; see, however, C. Rappe, *Acta Chem. Scand.*, **20**, 2305 (1966).

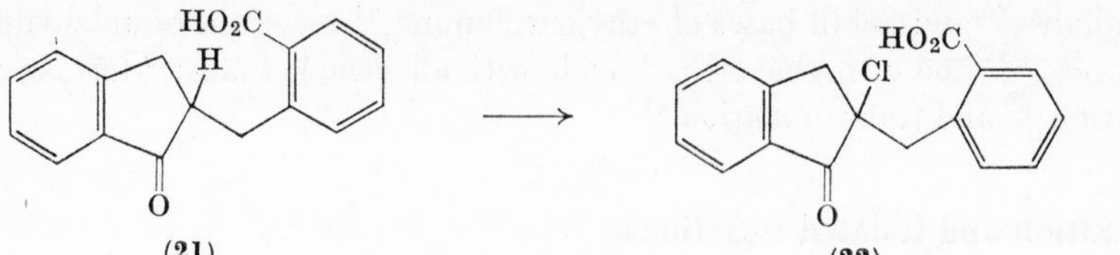

(21)   (22)

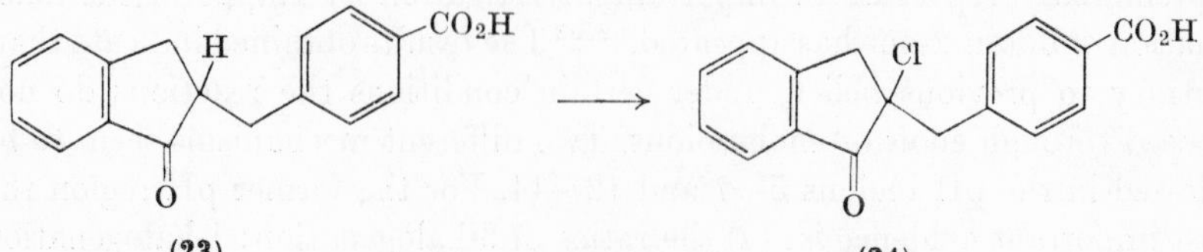

(23)   (24)

group exchanges more rapidly when the catalyst is p-nitrobenzoate or acetate ion. The lower overall rate of enolization of butan-2-one than of acetone cannot, therefore, be explained simply in terms of inductive destabilization of an enolate-like transition state by the 4-methyl group, and it was suggested that the transition state is enol-like, the reaction being termolecular, with water acting as an acid.

As mentioned briefly last year,[86] Harper and Bender[87] have reported a detailed investigation of the enolization of o-isobutyrylbenzoic acid.[87] The rate of enolization was determined as the rate of iodination to give the iodo-

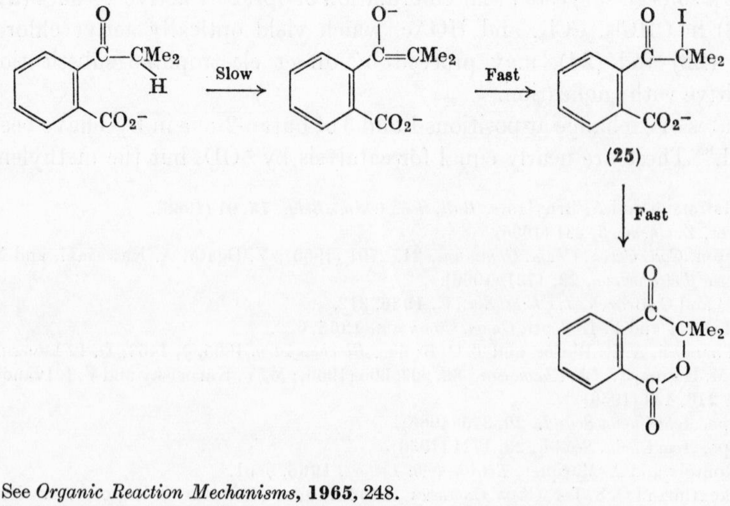

(8)

[86] See *Organic Reaction Mechanisms*, **1965**, 248.
[87] E. T. Harper and M. L. Bender, *J. Am. Chem. Soc.*, **87**, 5625 (1965).

compound (25) which rapidly underwent ring closure, the complete reaction sequence being as shown in equation (8). The pH–rate profile in the range 2.5—8.75 was sigmoid, the observed rate constant depending on the concentration of *o*-isobutyrylbenzoate ion; general acid–base-catalysis by external acids and bases could not be detected. To account for these results and the high rate observed, intramolecular general base-catalysis [equation (9)] was suggested and it was estimated that the efficiency of this catalysis was equivalent to that of a hypothetical concentration of 56M-benzoate ions on the enolization of isobutyrophenone.

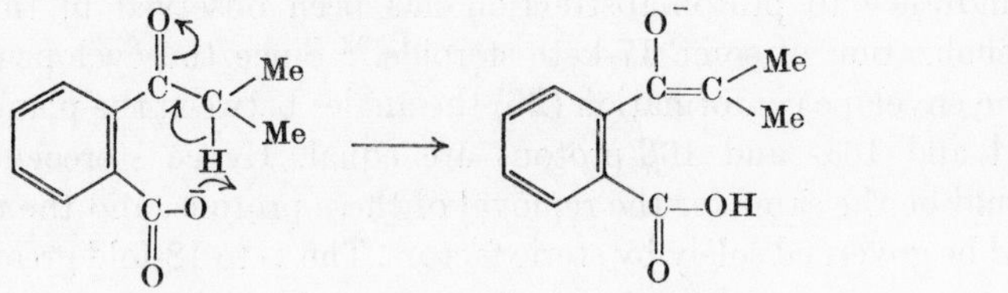

$$(9)$$

   The enolization of acetone is a general acid–base-catalysed reaction, the observed rate constant in buffers depending on the concentrations of the acidic (A) and basic (B) forms of the buffer according to an equation:

$$k_{obs} = k_0 + k_a[A] + k_b[B] + k_{ab}[A][B]$$

The values of k_a (measured by iodination and deuterium exchange) for ammonium ions are several powers of ten greater than those calculated from the Brønsted slopes with other acids and it was suggested that the reactions pass through Schiff base intermediates as shown in equation (10):

In support of this it was found that at low [B]/[A] ratios (< 0.05) the rate fell below the values extrapolated from higher ratios, suggesting that there is a change in rate-determining step from enolization to dehydration of the intermediate carbinolamine.[88] A similar mechanism has been suggested for deuterium exchange by 2-deuterioisobutyraldehyde in methylamine buffers, and by NMR spectroscopy the ketimine was shown to be present at high concentrations of the aldehyde (0.1—0.5M) in the presence of an excess of methylamine.[89]
   Catalysis of the iodination of acetol phosphate and acetone by lysine has also been investigated.[90]

[88] M. L. Bender and A. Williams, *J. Am. Chem. Soc.*, 88, 2502 (1966).
[89] J. Hine, B. C. Menon, J. H. Jensen, and J. Mulders, *J. Am. Chem. Soc.*, 88, 3367 (1966).
[90] N. V. Volkova, I. V. Mel'nichenko, and A. A. Yasnikov, *Ukr. Khim. Zh.* 31, 936 (1965); *Chem. Abs.*, 64, 9534 (1966).

Further work on deuterium-exchange of norbornyl derivatives has confirmed that norbornan-2-one exchanges one hydrogen, presumably 3-*exo*-,
preferentially.[91] However, 5,6-dehydronorbornan-2-one exchanges two
hydrogen atoms rapidly. It was suggested that the driving force for exchange
of the *exo*-3-hydrogen in norbornan-2-one was the movement of the 3-*endo*-
hydrogen up and away from the 5-*endo*-hydrogen. Since this interaction
between the 3- and 5-hydrogen atoms is absent from the dehydro-compound
this special driving force is also absent, and thus *exo*- and *endo*-hydrogen
atoms exchange at comparable speeds.

Steric hindrance to proton-abstraction has been observed in the acid-
catalysed enolization of some 17-keto-steroids.[92] Since the cyclopentanone
ring is in the envelope conformation (26) the angles between the plane of the
17-carbonyl and 16α- and 16β-protons are equal. Hence stereoelectronic
factors should be the same for the removal of these protons, and the relative
rates should be governed solely by steric factors. The 4- to 18-fold greater rate

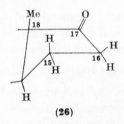

(26)

of removal of the 16α-proton, as determined by deuterium- and tritium-
labelling experiments, was therefore attributed to steric hindrance to the
removal of the 16β-proton by the 18-methyl group and the pseudo-axial
15β-proton.

Rate constants have been calculated for the enolization of acetone and
pentan-3-one and compared with experimental values; good agreement is
claimed.[93a]

It has been reported that the rate constants for reaction of the enolate
anions of 2-phenyl- and 2-*p*-methoxyphenyl-indane-1,3-dione with H_3O^+ are
10^9 and 10^{10} l. mole^{-1} sec^{-1}, respectively.[93b]

Bromination of acetone in 0.2—94% sulphuric acid,[94] halogenation of

[91] J. M. Jerkunica, S. Borčić, and D. E. Sunko, *Tetrahedron Letters*, **1965**, 4465; K. Humski, S. Borčić, and D. E. Sunko, *Croat. Chem. Acta*, **38**, 55 (1966).
[92] J. Fishman, *J. Org. Chem.*, **31**, 520 (1966).
[93a] E. A. Pshenichnov and N. D. Sokolov, *Kinetika i. Kataliz*, **6**, 802 (1965).
[93b] V. Kadis and J. Stradins, *Latvijas PSR Zinatnu Akad. Vestis, Kim. Ser.*, **1966**, 382; *Chem. Abs.*, **65**, 15176 (1966).
[94] U. Haldna, H. Kuura, L. Erreline, and V. Palm, *Reaktsionnaya Sposobnost Organ. Soedin.*, *Tartusk. Gos. Univ.*, **2**, 194 (1965); *Chem. Abs.*, **64**, 3304 (1966).

halogenoacetones,[95] and photoenolization 3-benzoyl-2-benzyl-chromones and 3-benzoyl-2-benzyl-4-quinolones[96] have also been investigated.

The enol proportions of cyclopentanone and cyclohexanone in aqueous solution at 25° are, respectively, 1.3×10^{-5} and 4.1×10^{-6} as determined by the extent of the initial rapid reaction with bromine.[97]

Equilibrium constants for the enolization of many dicarbonyl compounds have been measured.[98]

Homoenolization is receiving an increasing amount of attention. Its discoverers, Nickon and Lambert, have now described in detail their work on camphenilone.[99] Optically active camphenilone (**27**) racemizes when heated with potassium *tert*-butoxide in *tert*-butyl alcohol, and undergoes deuterium exchange when Bu^{t}OD is used as solvent. The rates of deuterium exchange (for the first deuterium) and racemization are approximately equal and it was suggested that proton-abstraction from carbon-6 occurs to yield an homo-

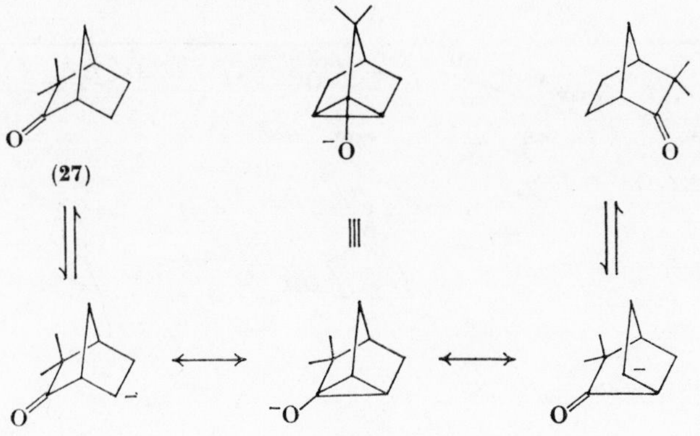

enolate anion (**28**). Several alternative mechanisms were excluded and, consistently with the intervention of (**28**), mono-, di-, and tri-deuterated species were present, after 48 hours at 185°. Under more forcing conditions,

[95] C. Rappe, *Arkiv Kemi*, **24**, 321 (1965).
[96] K. R. Huffman, M. Loy, and E. F. Ullman, *J. Am. Chem. Soc.*, **87**, 5417 (1965).
[97] R. P. Bell and P. W. Smith, *J. Chem. Soc.*, B, **1966**, 241.
[98] J. L. Burdett and M. T. Rogers, *J. Phys. Chem.*, **70**, 939 (1966); L. A. Paquette and R. W. Begland, *J. Am. Chem. Soc.*, **88**, 4685 (1966); S. J. Rhoads, *J. Org. Chem.*, **31**, 171 (1966); G. Allen and R. A. Dwek, *J. Chem. Soc.*, B, **1966**, 161; Z. Bánkowska, *Roczniki Chem.*, **40**, 587, 1177 (1966); T. Kameo, T. Hirashima, O. Manabe, and H. Hiyama, *Kagaku To Kogyo (Osaka)*, **40**, 135 (1966); *Chem. Abs.*, **65**, 10466 (1966); S. T. Yoffe, E. I. Fedin, P. V. Petrovskii, and M. I. Kabachnik, *Tetrahedron Letters*, **1966**, 2661; I. Deutsch and K. Deutsch, *ibid.*, p. 1849; A. Marinangeli, *Ann. Chem. (Rome)*, **56**, 673 (1966); K. Bredereck and E. F. Sommermann, *Tetrahedron Letters*, **1966**, 5009.
[99] A. Nickon and J. L. Lambert, *J. Am. Chem. Soc.*, **88**, 1905 (1966).

however, nine hydrogen atoms were exchanged and these were shown to be those at positions 1 and 6 and those on the methyl groups.[100] It was suggested that the latter were exchanged via the homoenolate anion (29).

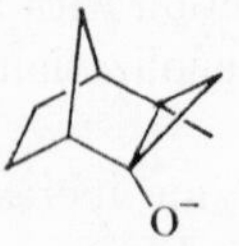

(29)

The steric course of homoenolization was investigated by studying the reverse reaction, the homoketonization of ion (30).[101] This was generated by mild alkaline fission of 1-acetoxynortricyclene in Bu^tOD, $MeOD$, and $MeOD$—$DMSO$, yielding norbornanone with an *exo*-C–D bond formed with

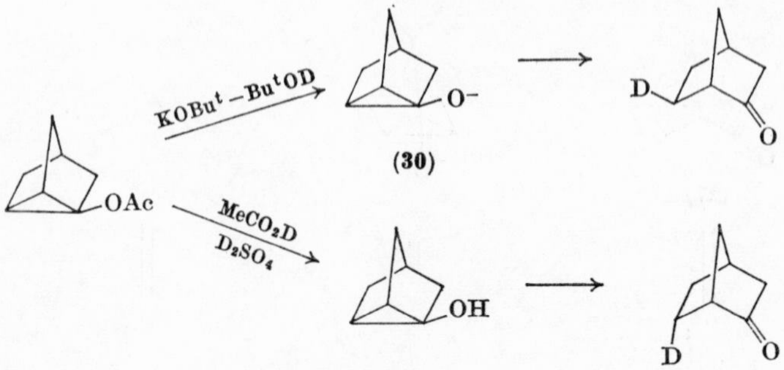

(30)

(31)   (32)

94.5—98% stereospecificity. It was, therefore, concluded that the reverse reaction, the base-catalysed homoenolization of norbornan-2-one, would proceed stereospecifically with abstraction of the 6-*exo*-proton, there being overlap between the π-orbital of the carbonyl group and the posterior of the lobe of the $C_{(6)}$-orbital, as shown in (31). In deuteriated acetic acid and deuteriated methanol in the presence of D_2SO_4, 1-acetoxynortricyclene yields norbornan-2-one with *endo*-deuterium formed with 40—45% stereospecificity.

[100] A. Nickon, J. L. Lambert, and J. E. Oliver, *J. Am. Chem. Soc.*, **88**, 2787 (1966).
[101] A. Nickon, J. L. Lambert, R. O. Williams, and N. H. Werstiuk, *J. Am. Chem. Soc.*, **88**, 3354 (1966).

It appears then that the hypothetical acid-catalysed homoenolization of norbornan-2-one would proceed with abstraction of the 6-*endo*-proton with overlap of the anterior lobe of the $C_{(6)}$-orbital as shown in **(32)**.

If the homoketonization reactions are regarded as electrophilic substitutions on $C_{(6)}$ it is seen that the base-catalysed reaction proceeds with inversion, and the acid-catalysed reaction with retention, of configuration. The result for the base-catalysed reaction contrasts with Cram's observation[102] that $S_{E}1$ reactions in KOBu^t–Bu^{t}OH normally proceed with retention of configuration. This is thought to be a special property of the nortricyclenol system rather than one of cyclopropanols in general, since 1,6-dimethylbicycloheptan-*endo*- and -*exo*-7-ol **(33)** undergo ring opening with retention of configuration on treatment with KOBu^t and Bu^{t}OH; also in accord with the Cram's observations is the substantial amount of inversion found when ethylene glycol is used as solvent and its sodium salt as base.[103]

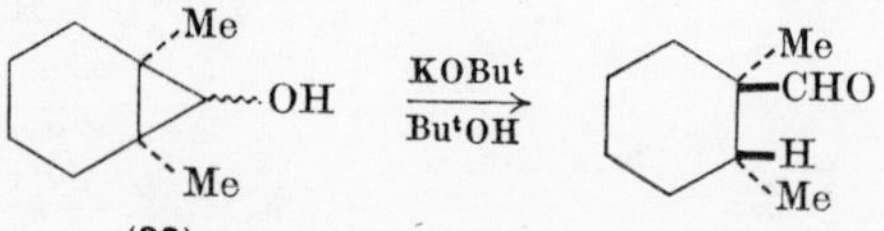

(33)

These results should be compared with those of DePuy, Dreitbeil, and DeBruin[104] on the stereochemistry of the ring opening of *cis*-2-phenyl-1-methylcyclopropanol.[104] With NaOD in D_2O–dioxan, 4-deuterio-4-phenyl-butan-2-one is formed with inversion of configuration [equation (11)] in

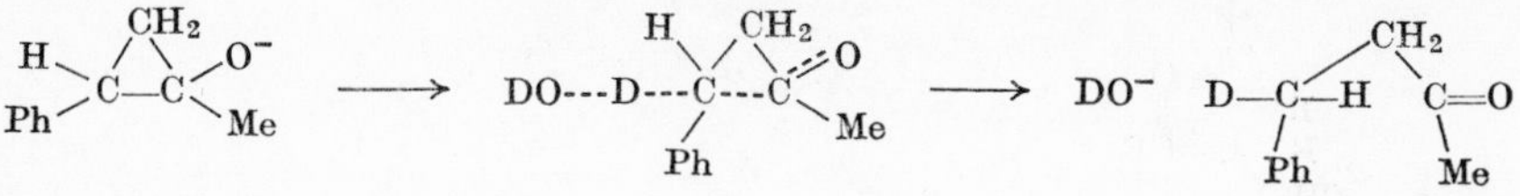

(11)

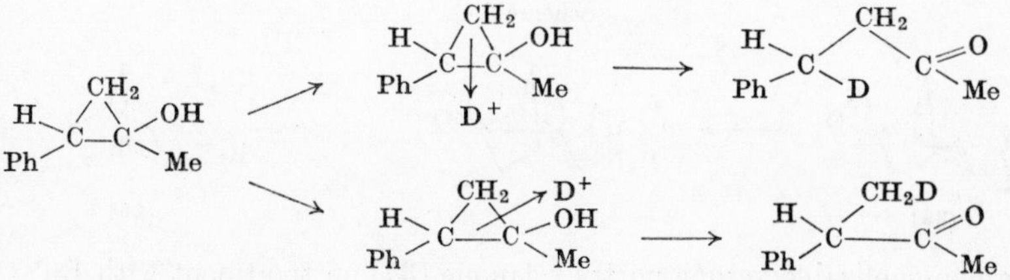

(12)

[102] D. J. Cram, "Fundamentals of Carbanion Chemistry", Academic Press Inc., New York, N.Y., 1965, pp. 144—153.

[103] P. S. Wharton, and T. I. Blair, *J. Org. Chem.*, **31**, 2480 (1966).

[104] C. H. DePuy, F. W. Dreitbeil, and K. R. DeBruin, *J. Am. Chem. Soc.*, **88**, 3347 (1966); C. H. DePuy, *Trans. N.Y. Acad. Sci.*, **28**, 561 (1966).

agreement with Cram's finding[102] that S_E1 processes proceed with inversion of configuration in solvents of high dissociating power capable of donating protons. With DCl in D_2O–dioxan a 60:40 mixture of 4-deuterio-4-phenyl- and 4-deuterio-3-phenyl-butan-2-one is obtained (equation 12), the former with retention of configuration. These reactions were considered to be S_E2 processes, in which configuration is commonly retained.

Other reactions for which homoenolate anions have been suggested as intermediates include the formation of the ketones (**34**) on treatment of 3-acetoxy-1-pyrazolines with alkali (see Scheme 3),[105] and the formation in 1% yield of 5-morpholinobicyclo[2.2.1]heptan-2-one (**36**) from norbornenone (**35**) and morpholine.[106]

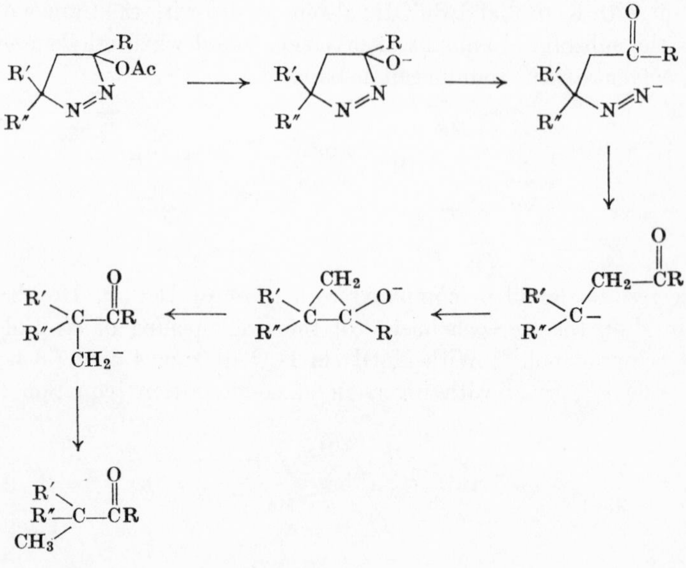

(**34**)

Scheme 3

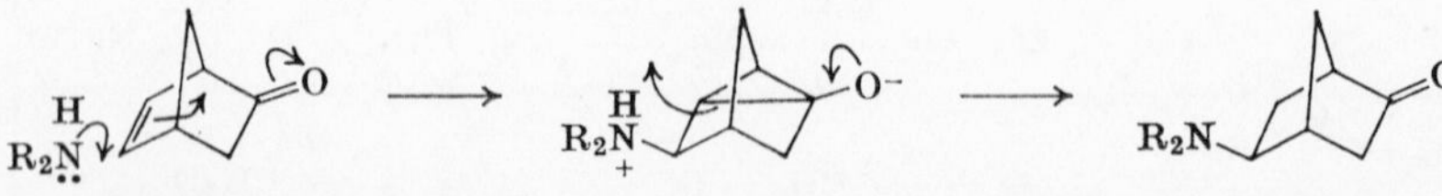

(**35**)   (**36**)

The non-enolizable ketone nortricyclanone (**37**) on treatment with Bu^tO^- in Bu^tOD at 200° exchanges $H_{(1)}$, $H_{(2)}$ and $H_{(4)}$, but not $H_{(3)}$ (see Table 2).[107] Nortricyclane (**39**) and 7,7-dimethoxynortricyclane (**38**) undergo exchange

[105] J. P. Freeman and J. H. Plonka, *J. Am. Chem. Soc.*, **88**, 3662 (1966).
[106] A. G. Cook and W. M. Kosman, *Tetrahedron Letters*, **1966**, 5847.
[107] P. G. Gassman and F. V. Zalar, *J. Am. Chem. Soc.*, **88**, 3070 (1966).

only under more vigorous conditions, and only $H_{(1)}$ and $H_{(2)}$ are exchanged. Norbornan-7-one (40) exchanges only $H_{(2)}$ (see Table 2). It was concluded from these results that the inductive effect of the carbonyl group was im-

Table 2. Deuterium exchange observed on treatment with KOBu. in Bu^tOD^t

Compound	Time (hr)	Temp. (°C)	%D incorporated per hydrogen			
			$H_{(1)}$	$H_{(2)}$	$H_{(3)}$	$H_{(4)}$
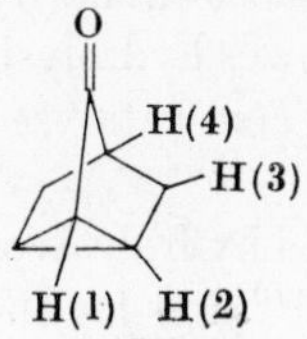 (37)	29	195—200	83	73	0	76
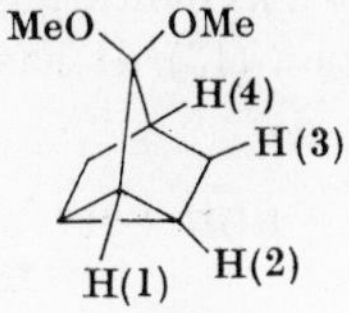 (38)	48	215—220	60	40.4	0	0
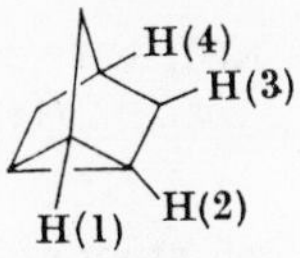 (39)	64	260—265	22	22	0	0
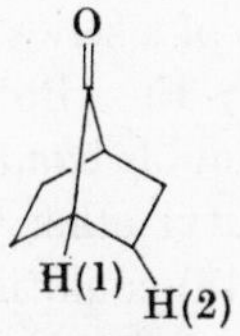 (40)	48	195—200	25	0	—	—

portant in stabilizing the carbanions at $C_{(1)}$ and $C_{(4)}$ of nortricyclanone [cf. results for (38) and (39)] and that also the cyclopropane ring helped stabilize the carbanion (41) at $C_{(4)}$ [cf. results for (40)]. The failure of $H_{(2)}$ of norbornan-7-one and $H_{(3)}$ of nortricyclanone to undergo exchange indicates that the homoenolate anions of type (42) are not formed.

11*

$$(41) \qquad\qquad (42)$$

Contrary to earlier proposals it has been suggested that the acid-catalysed hydrolysis of vinyl acetate proceeds by the A_{Ac}-2 mechanism.[108] The evidence for this is the close similarity of the entropy of activation ($\Delta S^{\ddagger} = -26.7$ cal $\deg^{-1}$ at 25°), solvent isotope effect ($k_{H_2O}/k_{D_2O} = 0.73$ at 25°), and Bunnett w value (+3.55) to those for the hydrolysis of ethyl acetate, the close similarity of the rates to those for phenyl and alkyl acetates, and the slower hydrolysis of isopropenyl acetate. The hydrolysis of vinyl ethers is general acid-catalysed with a Brønsted α-coefficient of ca. 0.5.[109]

The solvent isotope effect for the hydrochloric acid-catalysed hydrolysis of diethylene glycol monovinyl ether is $k_{H_2O}/k_{D_2O} = 3.64$ at 20°[110] and for the perchloric acid-catalysed hydrolysis of n-butyl vinyl ether is $k_{H_2O}/k_{D_2O} = 2.63$ at 25° in dioxan–water (80:20).[111] These results were interpreted as indicating a slow rate-determining proton-transfer, as shown in equation (13). It has

$$H_3O^+ + CH_2\text{=}CHOR \xrightarrow{\text{Slow}} \underset{\substack{+\\ H_2O}}{CH_3\text{—}CH\overset{+}{\text{---}}OR} \xrightarrow{\text{Fast}} CH_3CHO + ROH + H^+ \tag{13}$$

$$H_3O^+ + CH_2\text{=}CHOR \xrightarrow{\text{Slow}} H_2C\overset{\substack{-CH-\\ +}}{\underset{H}{}}OR \xrightarrow{\text{Fast}} CH_3CHO + ROH + H^+ \atop + H_2O \tag{14}$$

also been suggested that the transition state involves the oxygen atom and that the rate-determining proton transfer is as shown in equation (14).[112] The basis for the latter suggestion is that the rates of hydrolysis of a series of vinyl ethers, $ROCH\text{=}CH_2$, fall in the sequence $R = Bu^t > Pr^i > Et > Bu^i > $ Me, whereas the NMR spectra show that electron-release to the double bond is greatest with the methyl ether and smallest with the *tert*-butyl ether.[112] It was, therefore, concluded that the mechanism of equation (13) could not be correct and that of equation (14) was preferred. In our view, however, arguments of this type, based solely on ground-state physical properties,

108 T. Yrjänä, *Suomen Kemistilehti*, B, **39**, 81, 86 (1966); *ibid.*, A, **39**, 109.
109 P. Salomaa, *Suomen Kemistilehti*, A, **39**, 109 (1966).
110 M. F. Shostakovskii, A. S. Atavin, B. V. Prokop'ev, B. A. Trofinov, V. I. Lavrov, and N. M. Deriglazov, *Dokl. Akad. Nauk SSSR*, **163**, 1412 (1965).
111 D. M. Jones and N. F. Wood, *J. Chem. Soc.*, **1964**, 5400.
112 A. Ledwith and H. J. Woods, *J. Chem. Soc.*, B, **1966**, 753.

are of dubious validity, especially for reactions such as this where the transition state is probably "carbonium-ion-like" rather than "initial-state-like" (note that isopropenyl ethyl ether reacts 2×10^4 times faster than ethyl vinyl ether).[111]

Vinyl interchange between benzoic acid and vinyl acetate catalysed by mercuric acetate has been investigated.[113]

Removal of the 6β-axial proton of androst-4-en-3,17-dione (43) by Bu^tO^- in Bu^tOH to form the enolate ion (44) occurs 53 times faster than removal of the 6α-equatorial proton.[114] The 19-nor compound reacts five times faster than

$$+ \; K^+ \; {}^-OBu^t \; \rightleftharpoons \; K^+ \qquad\qquad + \; HOBu^t$$

(43)   (44)

androst-4-ene-3,17-dione itself, so in the absence of an axial methyl group removal of the axial proton is faster by a factor of 250—300 owing, presumably, to the transition state in which σ–π overlap is possible being highly favoured. The effects of fluoro- and methyl substituents on the rate of enolization and position of equilibrium were also determined. Of particular interest was the observation that a 2α-methyl group destabilized the enolate ion by about 1.4 kcal mole^{-1} compared with 0.7 kcal found for a 2β-methyl substituent. It was suggested this was the result of steric interaction between the 2α-methyl group and the solvated ion pair and that "the ion pair may be unsymmetrical about $C_{(2)}$ and $C_{(4)}$ with the greatest bulk directed away from the double bond and the $C_{(4)}$ position and toward $C_{(2)}$." A similar conclusion has been reached by Malhotra and Johnson[115] who found that the enolate ion of 2,6-dimethyl-cyclohexanone exists appreciably in a conformation with the methyl group that is not attached to the double bond quasiaxial and it was concluded that "the ion pair interacts quite strongly with the adjacent methyl group when the latter is equatorially oriented."

Treatment of 2-methylcyclohexanone with trityl-lithium in 1,2-dimethoxy-ethane yields a kinetically controlled mixture of the lithium enolates containing 86% of (45) and 14% of (46), but the equilibrium mixture contains 10% of (45) and 90% of (46). Competition experiments showed that enolate ion (46) is alkylated by methyl toluene-p-sulphonate and by ethyl iodide 1.62—2.33 times faster than ion (45). These reactivities were discussed[116] in

113 G. Slinckx and G. Smets, *Tetrahedron*, **22**, 3163 (1966).
114 G. Subrahmanyam, S. K. Malhotra, and H. J. Ringold, *J. Am. Chem. Soc.*, **88**, 1332 (1966).
115 S. K. Malhotra and F. Johnson, *J. Am. Chem. Soc.*, **87**, 5513 (1965).
116 D. Caine and B. J. L. Huff, *Tetrahedron Letters*, **1966**, 4695.

terms of the inductive effect of the methyl group of (**46**) enhancing, and the steric effect reducing, its nucleophilicity. It was also thought that with (**45**)

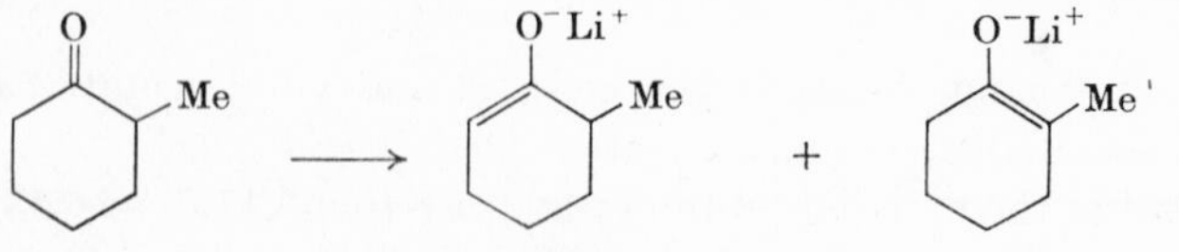

(**45**)   (**46**)

there might be an unfavourable interaction between the solvated lithium counter-ion and the methyl group when the latter is quasiequatorial, leading to a relatively high concentration of the conformation where it is quasiaxial. Since alkylation shows a stereoelectronic preference for axial attack, there is an unfavourable 1,3-diaxial interaction in the transition state for alkylation of this conformation; hence the overall rate of alkylation of (**45**) may be reduced.

Other reactions which have been investigated include the protonation of α,β-unsaturated β-amino-carbonyl compounds[117] and 1-benzoyl-2-phenylcyclohexane,[118] and the interconversion of 4-alkylcyclohex-3- and -4-enones[119] and of cycloalk-2- and -3-enones.[120]

The site of protonation of enamines has been further investigated.[121, 122] The NMR spectrum of the morpholino-enamine of isobutyraldehyde in 6M-HCl shows signals corresponding to the methyl groups of both the *C*-protonated (**47**) and *N*-protonated (**48**) conjugate acids, with the latter predominating. In more dilute acid solutions the *C*-protonated form could not be observed. These results are thus in accord with those of Stamhuis and Maas reported last year.[122]

(**47**)   (**48**)

The relative stabilities of the enamines of 2-methylcyclohexanone have been measured and discussed.[123]

Several interesting examples of reaction courses controlled by magnesium

[117] H. E. A. Kramer, *Ann. Chem.*, **696**, 15, 28 (1966).
[118] P. Angibeaud, H. Riviere, and B. Tchoubar, *Compt. Rend., Ser. C*, **263**, 160 (1966).
[119] K. G. Lewis and G. J. Williams, *Tetrahedron Letters*, **1965**, 4573.
[120] N. Heap and G. H. Whitham, *J. Chem. Soc., B*, **1966**, 164.
[121] J. Elguero, R. Jacquier, and G. Tarrago, *Tetrahedron Letters*, **1965**, 4719.
[122] See *Organic Reaction Mechanisms*, **1965**, 253.
[123] W. D. Gurowitz and M. A. Joseph, *Tetrahedron Letters*, **1965**, 4433.

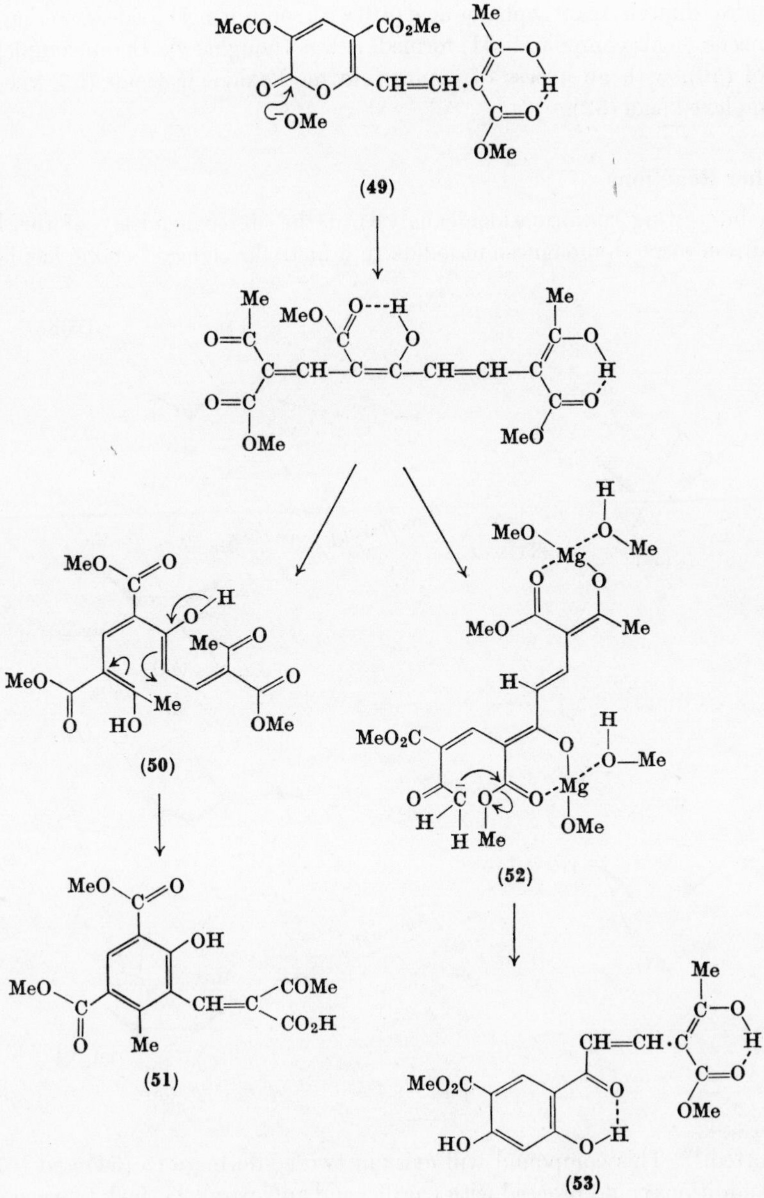

(49)

(50)

(52)

(51)

(53)

chelation of an enol form have been reported.[124] For example, it was shown that whereas dimethylxanthophanic acid (49) with sodium methoxide in methanol–benzene yields compound (51) formed, it was thought, via the uncomplexed enol (50), with an excess of magnesium methoxide, it yields (53) via the complexed enol (52).

Other Reactions

An interesting conformational analysis of the stereochemistry of the 1,4-addition of methylmagnesium iodide to 5-methylcyclohex-2-enone has been

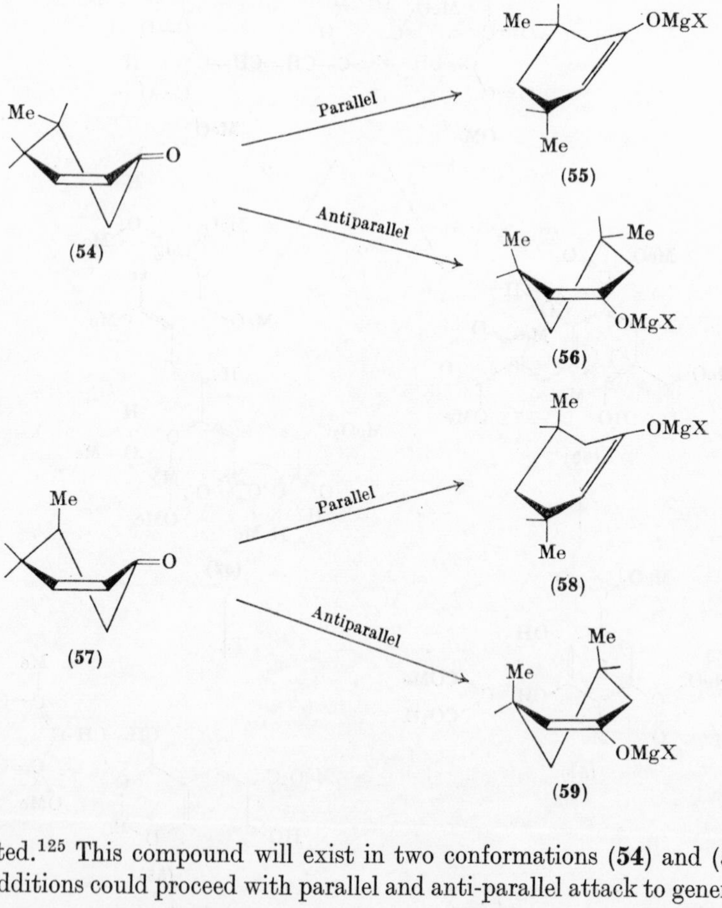

reported.[125] This compound will exist in two conformations (54) and (57), and additions could proceed with parallel and anti-parallel attack to generate

---

[124] L. Crombie, D. E. Games, and M. H. Knight, *Chem. Commun.*, **1966**, 355; L. Crombie and A. W. G. James, *ibid.*, p. 357.

[125] N. L. Allinger and C. K. Riew, *Tetrahedron Letters*, **1966**, 1269.

the enolate ions in half-boat (55) and (58) or half-chair (56) and (59) conformations. It was considered that the transition states leading to the half-boat conformations would be disfavoured and of the two leading to half-chair conformations, that leading to (56) should clearly be of lower energy. It was, therefore, predicted that the major product should be *trans*-3,5-dimethylcyclohexanone and this was confirmed experimentally.

A similar effect was observed in the 1,6-addition of a series of alkylmagnesium bromides to 10-methyl-$\Delta^{1(9),7}$-2-hexalone (60) in the presence of cupric acetate. Here, axial addition proceeded predominantly by way of the chairlike transition state (61) rather than by way of the boat-like transition state (62).[126]

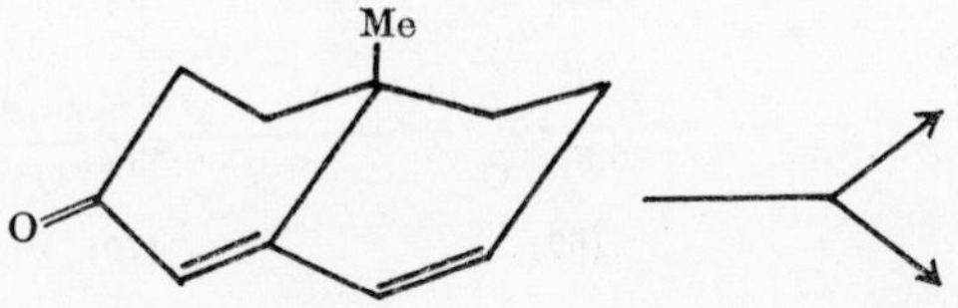

(60)

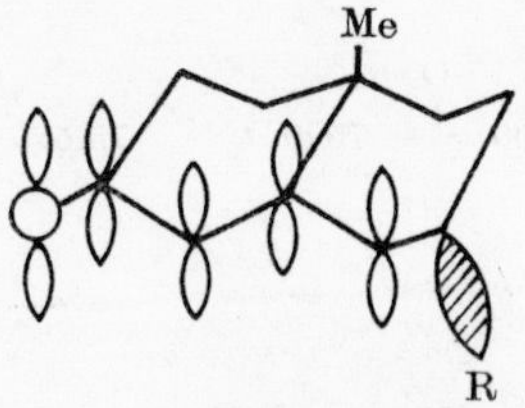

(61)

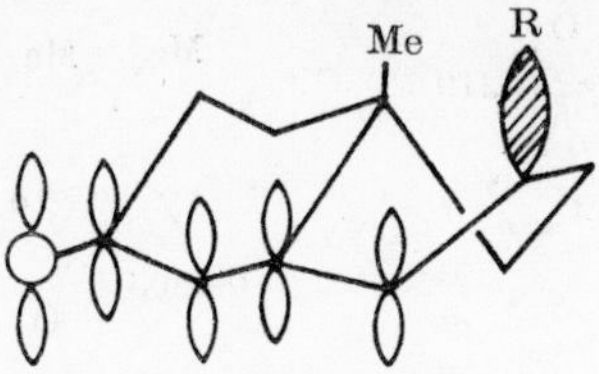

(62)

There have also been other discussions of 1,4-additions to α,β-unsaturated ketones and their derivatives.[127]

An important investigation of the kinetics of reduction of a large number of bicyclic ketones by sodium borohydride in propan-2-ol has been reported.[128] Some of the compounds studied, with the partial rate constants ($10^4 k_2$ l. mole^{-1} sec^{-1}) for attack in the indicated direction, are given in formulae (63)—(74). Points of interest include the high rate for norbornan-7-one (67) which should be compared with its carbonyl stretching frequency (1773 cm^{-1}) and the low rate of solvolysis of 7-norbornyl *p*-bromobenzenesulphonate, the

126 J. A. Marshall and H. Roebke, *J. Org. Chem.*, 1966, **31**, 3109 (1966).
127 E. Toromanoff, *Bull. Soc., Chim. France*, 1966, 1445, 3357; C. Mantescu and A. Genunche, *Tetrahedron Letters*, 1966, 5675; H. O. House, W. L. Respess, and G. M. Whitesides, *J. Org. Chem.*, 1966, **31**, 3128 (1966).
128 H. C. Brown and J. Muzzio, *J. Am. Chem. Soc.*, 1966, **88**, 2811 (1966).

greater rate of *exo-* than of *endo-*attack on norbornan-2-one **(65)**, the greater rate of *endo-* than of *exo-*attack on 7,7-dimethylnorbornan-2-one **(72)**, the greater rate of *endo-*attack on norbornan-2-one **(65)** than on norbornen-2-one **(69)**, and the smaller rate of attack in both *endo-* and *exo-*directions on 1-methylnorbornan-2-one **(73)** than on norbornanone **(65)**. The relative rates

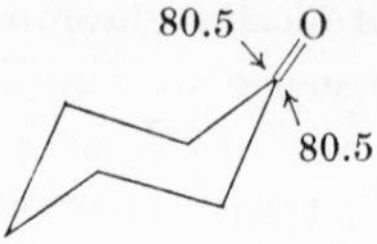

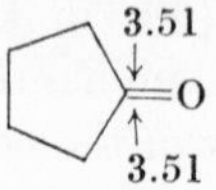

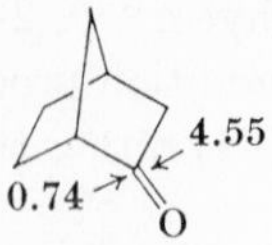

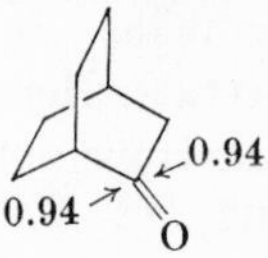

of these reactions were compared with those for the solvolysis of the corresponding *p*-bromobenzenesulphonates (see p. 2).

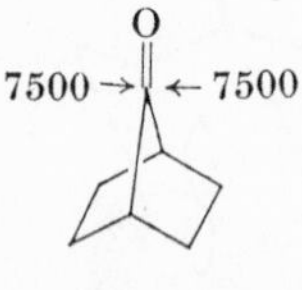

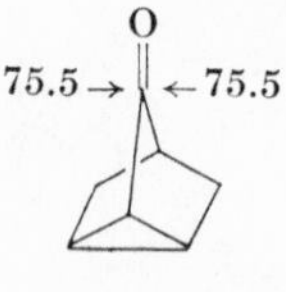

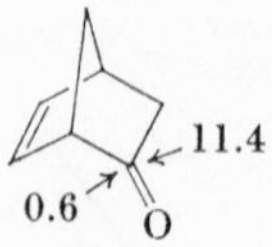

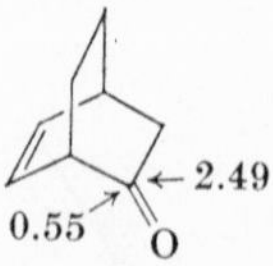

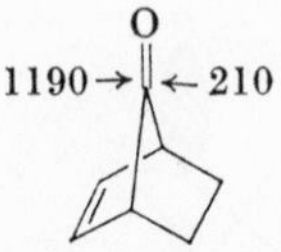

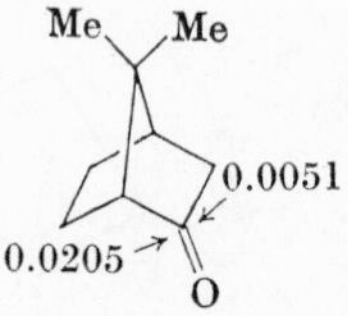

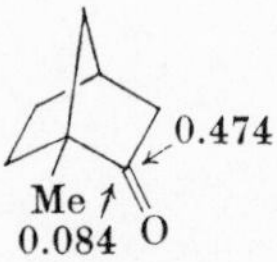

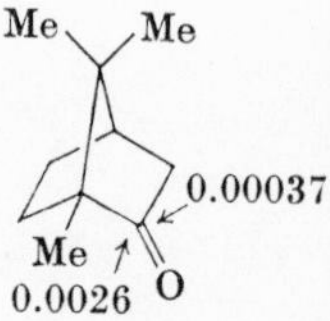

The heats of reduction of acetone, isopropyl methyl ketone, cyclopentanone, and cyclohexanone with $NaBH_4$ have been measured.[129] The reactions are faster than in propan-2-ol, but the differences in the relative rates are less.

The ρ-constant for the reduction of *meta-* and *para-*substituted acetophenones with sodium borohydride in propan-2-ol at 30° is consistent with nucleophilic attack on carbonyl-carbon.[130]

The effect of α-deuteriation on the rates of reduction of several ketones by borohydride has been determined.[131]

The steric course of the reduction of a large number of ketones by metal

[129] R. E. Davis and J. Carter, *Tetrahedron*, **22**, 495 (1966).
[130] K. Bowden and M. Hardy, *Tetrahedron*, **22**, 1169 (1966).
[131] P. Geneste and G. Lamaty, *Tetrahedron Letters*, **1965**, 4633.

hydrides has been determined. Among those studied are 3-aminoalkylnorbornan-2-ones,[132] 2-phenyl-1-tetralone,[133] 4-*tert*-butylcycloheptanone,[134] 3-*tert*-butylcyclopentanone,[135] 3β-hydroxy-13α-androst-5-en-17-one,[136] piperidones,[137] 6,9-*endo*-methylenehomopseudopelletierine,[138] *cis*- and *trans*-3-*tert*-butyl-4-methoxycyclohexanones and 3-*tert*-butylcyclohexanone.[139] The steric course of the reduction of camphor by Grignard reagents has also been investigated.[140] Other reductions of aldehydes and ketones are discussed on p. 414.

The amine-catalysed dealdonization of diacetone alcohol has been investigated and the catalytic constants have been determined for several amines.[141] The mechanism given in equation (15) was suggested.

$$\text{Me}\!\!>\!\!C\!\!=\!\!O + RNH_2 + CH_2\!\!=\!\!C\!-\!Me \quad (15)$$

Other reactions which have been investigated include: addition of Grignard reagents to carbonyl groups,[142] hydration and cyclization of semiphorone,[143] sodamide cleavage of norbornan-2-one to yield *cis*- and *trans*-cyclopentanecarboxyamide,[144] opening of conjugated cyclopropyl ketones with lithium in liquid ammonia,[145] disproportionation of benzoin in the molten state,[146]

[132] H. Krieger, and K. Manninen, *Suomen Kemistilehti, B*, **38**, 175 (1965).
[133] S K. Hanaya, *Nippon Kagaku Zasshi*, **87**, 745 (1966); *Chem. Abs.*, **65**, 15203 (1966).
[134] M. Mühlstädt, R. Borsdorf, and F.-J. Strüber, *Tetrahedron Letters*, **1966**, 1879.
[135] J.-C. Richer and C. Gilardeau, *Can. J. Chem.*, **43**, 3419 (1965).
[136] L. J. Chinn, *J. Org. Chem.*, **30**, 4165 (1965).
[137] E. A. Mistryukov, *Izv. Akad. Nauk SSSR, Ser. Khim.*, **1965**, 1826.
[138] L. A. Paquette and J. W. Heimaster, *J. Am. Chem. Soc.*, **88**, 763 (1966).
[139] A. M. Prokhoda, A. A. Akhrem, and A. V. Kamernitskii, *Izv. Akad. Nauk SSSR, Ser. Khim.*, **1965**, 1713.
[140] P. J. Malkonen, *Suomen Kemistilehti, B*, **38**, 89 (1965).
[141] R. W. Hay and K. R. Tate, *Australian J. Chem.*, **19**, 1651 (1966).
[142] S. G. Smith and G. Su, *J. Am. Chem. Soc.*, **88**, 3995 (1966); *Tetrahedron Letters*, **1966**, 4417; J.-C. Richer and P. Bélanger, *Can. J. Chem.*, **44**, 2067 (1966); R. A. Benkeser and T. E. Johnston, *J. Am. Chem. Soc.*, **88**, 2220 (1966); L. Mandell and J. M. Brodmann, *J. Org. Chem.*, **31**, 591 (1966).
[143] S. Cabani and N. Ceccanti, *J. Chem. Soc.*, *B*, **1966**, 77.
[144] H. Krieger and K. Manninen, *Suomen Kemistilehti, B*, **39**, 33 (1966).
[145] W. G. Dauben, and E. J. Deviny, *J. Org. Chem.*, **31**, 3794 (1966).
[146] Y. Halpern, M. Michman, and S. Patai, *J. Chem. Soc.*, *B*, **1966**, 149.

reaction of pinacolone with formaldehyde,[147] aldehyde polymerization,[148] Robinson–Schöpf synthesis,[138] cyanohydrin formation from glyceraldehyde and some monosaccharides[149] and from benzaldehyde in the presence of optically active polymers,[150] the benzoin condensation in the presence of an optically active catalyst,[151] the Cannizzaro,[152] Houben–Hoesch,[153] Knoevenagel,[154] and Wittig reactions,[155] cyclization of 4-acetyl-1-methoxycyclohex-1-ene to 4-alkoxybicyclo[2.2.2]octan-2-one,[156] ninhydrin reaction,[157] o-phenylenediamine cleavage of ketones,[158] and bromination of hydrazones.[159]

[147] D. R. Moore and A. Oroslan, *J. Org. Chem.*, **31**, 2620 (1966).
[148] C. Walling and T. A. Augurt, *J. Am. Chem. Soc.*, **88**, 4163 (1966); Y. Ohtsuka and C. Walling, *ibid.*, p. 4167 (1966).
[149] K. Lohs, W. Theil, and M. Muehlstadt, *Z. Chem.*, **6**, 222 (1966).
[150] S. Tsuboyama, *Bull. Chem. Soc. Japan*, **39**, 698 (1966).
[151] J. C. Sheehan and D. H. Hunneman, *J. Am. Chem. Soc.*, **88**, 3666 (1966).
[152] D. Luther and H. Koch, *Chem. Ber.*, **99**, 2227 (1966).
[153] E. A. Jeffery and D. P. N. Satchell, *J. Chem. Soc.*, B, **1966**, 579.
[154] L. Rand, D. Haidukewych, and R. J. Dolinski, *J. Org. Chem.*, **31**, 1272 (1966).
[155] A. W. Johnson and V. L. Kyllingstad, *J. Org. Chem.*, **31**, 334 (1966).
[156] K. Morita and T. Kobayashi, *J. Org. Chem.*, **31**, 229 (1966).
[157] M. Friedman and C. W. Sigel, *Biochemistry*, **5**, 478 (1965).
[158] G. E. Risinger, *Nature*, **209**, 1022 (1966).
[159] A. F. Hegarty and F. L. Scott, *J. Chem. Soc.*, B, **1966**, 672, 1031.

CHAPTER 12

Reactions of Acids and their Derivatives[1]

Carboxylic Acids

The relative importance of nucleophilic and general base-catalysis by acetate ion in the hydrolysis of a series of aryl acetates has been determined by trapping with aniline the acetic anhydride which is an intermediate in the nucleophilically catalysed reaction.[2] Nucleophilic catalysis predominates with acetates of phenols having a $pK_a < 5$ but could not be detected with those of phenols with $pK_a > 8$. This is reasonable if the nucleophilic catalysis involves a tetrahedral intermediate which can partition by returning to reactants or by going on to yield acetic anhydride [equation (1)].

$$\text{ArOCO} \cdot \text{Me} + {}^-\text{OAc} \underset{k_{-1}}{\overset{k_1}{\rightleftharpoons}} \text{ArO} - \underset{\underset{\text{OAc}}{|}}{\overset{\overset{\text{O}^-}{|}}{\text{C}}} - \text{Me} \underset{}{\overset{k_2}{\rightleftharpoons}} \text{ArO}^- + \text{Ac}_2\text{O} \qquad (1)$$

With phenols of low acidity the stability of the leaving phenoxide ion is also low and it will be a poor leaving group; hence the intermediate partitions exclusively to yield reactants i.e., $k_{-1} \gg k_2$. The rate of the general base-catalysed reaction also increases with decreasing pK_a of the phenol but not so much as the rate of the nucleophilically catalysed reaction. The difference in solvent isotope effect for the two mechanisms is quite small. Thus with 2,4-dinitrophenyl acetate which reacts exclusively with nucleophilic catalysis $k_{\text{OAc}}(\text{H}_2\text{O})/k_{\text{OAc}}(\text{D}_2\text{O}) = 1.8$, and with p-tolyl acetate which reacts with exclusive general base-catalysis it is 2.4. The entropies of activation for the general base-catalysed reactions (ca. -32 e.u.) appear, however, to be significantly more negative than those for the nucleophilically catalysed reactions (ca. -10 e.u.) and the difference is approximately that to be expected for the inclusion of one extra water molecule in the transition state for the former.

The rate of hydrolysis of benzoyl cyanide decreases with increasing acidity and in the pH range 0—4.5 follows an expression [equation (2)] which is similar

$$k_{\text{obs}} = 1.53/(1 + 177[\text{H}_3\text{O}^+]) \qquad (2)$$

[1] For an excellent review of many aspects of the mechanisms of reactions of carboxylic acids and phosphoric acid and their derivatives see: T. C. Bruice and S. J. Benkovic, "Bioorganic Mechanisms," Vols. I and II, W. A. Benjamin, New York, 1966.

[2] D. G. Oakenfull, T. Riley, and V. Gold, *Chem. Commun.*, **1966**, 385.

to that reported last year[3] for the hydrolysis of S-ethyl trifluorothioacetate and a similar mechanism was proposed.[4] This involves a tetrahedral intermediate which decomposes to reactants with, and to products without, acid-catalysis [equations (3) and (4)]. The reaction also shows general base-catalysis which was thought to be associated with a general base-catalysed addition to the carbonyl group.

$$\text{PhCOCN} + 2\text{H}_2\text{O} \;\rightleftharpoons\; \text{Ph}-\overset{\overset{\displaystyle O^-}{|}}{\underset{\underset{\displaystyle OH}{|}}{C}}-\text{CN} + \text{H}_3\text{O}^+ \qquad (3)$$

$$\text{Ph}-\overset{\overset{\displaystyle O^-}{|}}{\underset{\underset{\displaystyle OH}{|}}{C}}-\text{CN} \;\longrightarrow\; \text{PhCO}_2\text{H} + \text{CN}^- \qquad (4)$$

Kinetic evidence for the intervention of a tetrahedral intermediate in the hydrolysis of 2,2,2-trifluoro-N-methylacetanilide in alkaline solutions has been presented by Schowen and his co-workers.[5] In glycine–glycinate buffers in the pH range 9.5—10 the reaction shows general base-catalysis superimposed on an initial specific hydroxide ion-catalysis. This could arise from either a general base-catalysed elimination of N-methylaniline from an intermediate or a base-catalysed attack by hydroxide ion in a concerted displacement reaction. The dependence of the rate constant on hydroxide ion concentration in the pH range 11.2—12.6 is only consistent, however, with the former interpretation.[6] The reaction may thus be formulated as illustrated.

$$\text{CF}_3\text{CONMePh} \;\underset{k_{-a}}{\overset{k_a}{\rightleftharpoons}}\; \text{CF}_3-\overset{\overset{\displaystyle O^-}{|}}{\underset{\underset{\displaystyle OH}{|}}{C}}-\text{NMePh} \;\xrightarrow[k_2]{^-\text{OH}}\; \text{CF}_3\text{CO}_2^- + \text{PhNHMe}$$

$$\xrightarrow[k_1]{\text{H}_2\text{O}}\; \text{CF}_3\text{CO}_2^- + \text{PhNHMe}$$

Solvent isotope effects on k_a, k_2, and k_1 have been determined to be $(k_{\text{H}_2\text{O}}/k_{\text{D}_2\text{O}})$ 1.0, 2.2, and 3.3, respectively.[7] The preferred explanation of the last two values

---

[3] See *Organic Reaction Mechanisms*, **1965**, 260.

[4] F. Hibbert and D. P. N. Satchell, *Chem. Commun.*, **1966**, 516.

[5] R. L. Schowen and G. W. Zuorick, *J. Am. Chem. Soc.*, **88**, 1223 (1966).

[6] R. L. Schowen, H. Jayaraman, and L. Kershner, *J. Am. Chem. Soc.*, **88**, 3373 (1966); *Tetrahedron Letters*, **1966**, 497.

[7] R. L. Schowen, H. Jayaraman, L. Kershner, and G. W. Zuorick, *J. Am. Chem. Soc.*, **88**, 4008 (1966).

was that the rate-determining step in the decomposition of the tetrahedral intermediate was a proton-transfer not concerted with bond-breaking but giving either (1) or (2), which decomposed rapidly. The main reason for this

$$
\begin{array}{cc}
\underset{\text{(1)}}{\overset{\displaystyle O^-}{\underset{\displaystyle O^-}{\overset{\displaystyle |}{\underset{\displaystyle |}{CF_3-C-N{\overset{\displaystyle Me}{\underset{\displaystyle Ph}{\diagdown}}}}}}}}
&
\underset{\text{(2)}}{\overset{\displaystyle O^- \; Me}{\underset{\displaystyle O^- \; Ph}{\overset{\displaystyle | \;\; |}{\underset{\displaystyle | \;\; |}{CF_3-C\overset{+}{-}N-H}}}}}
\end{array}
$$

conclusion was an analogy with the mutarotation of glucose which was considered to proceed by a non-concerted mechanism (see, however, ref. 38, p. 314).

Following the report last year[8] that the aminolysis of phenyl acetate by *n*-butylamine does not show a term which is second-order in amine, Jencks and Gilchrist[9] have re-examined the aminolysis of phenyl acetate by a series of primary amines. A second-order term with methylamine, ethylamine, *n*-propylamine, and *n*-butylamine was readily detectable at 5°, but at 25° (the temperature used previously by Jencks and Carriuolo and by Bruice and Willis) a second-order term in *n*-butylamine was only detected with difficulty.

The validity of the claim[10] that the hydrazinolysis of phenyl acetate by 3-dimethylaminopropylhydrazine proceeds with intramolecular catalysis by the amino-group has been questioned.[9] The reported 10^3-fold rate enhancement was based on a pK_a value of 6.83 for the dissociation of protonated hydrazine according to equation (5). However, the dissociation constant which

$$
\overset{+}{Me_2NH}[CH_2]_3\overset{+}{NHNH_3} \rightleftharpoons \overset{+}{Me_2NH}[CH_2]_3NHNH_2 + H^+ \tag{5}
$$

should have been used is that for the equilibrium of equation (6) and this could be quite different.

$$
Me_2N[CH_2]_3\overset{+}{NHNH_3} \rightleftharpoons Me_2N[CH_2]_3NHNH_2 + H^+ \tag{6}
$$

The rates of exchange of a series of methyl-labelled, substituted methyl benzoates with methanolic sodium methoxide [equation (7)] have been measured. Since the tetrahedral intermediate is symmetrical $k_2 = k_3$, and the

$$
Ar-C{\overset{\displaystyle O}{\underset{\displaystyle OMe^*}{\diagup}}} + MeO^- \underset{k_2}{\overset{k_1}{\rightleftharpoons}} \; Ar-\underset{\underset{\displaystyle OMe^*}{\displaystyle |}}{\overset{\overset{\displaystyle O^-}{\displaystyle |}}{C}}-OMe \; \overset{k_3}{\longrightarrow} \; ArCO_2Me + {}^-OMe^* \tag{7}
$$

[8] See *Organic Reaction Mechanisms*, **1965**, 262.
[9] W. P. Jencks and M. Gilchrist, *J. Am. Chem. Soc.*, **88**, 104 (1966).
[10] See *Organic Reaction Mechanisms*, **1965**, 262.

rate of exchange $k_1(k_2/k_3 + 1) = 2k_1$. The values of k_1 so obtained can be correlated by the Hammett equation with a ρ-value of 2.41 (30.1°). The entropies of activation, however, vary from -20.1 e.u. for the p-methoxy- to -29.5 for the p-nitro-compound (i.e., increase with increasing σ-value).[11a]

A full investigation of the kinetics of hydrolysis of the monoesters of phthalic acid have been reported by Thanassi and Bruice.[11b] In the pH range 5—1.5 the rate for esters with poor leaving groups, e.g., methyl hydrogen phthalate, is proportional to the concentration of ester with an un-ionized carboxyl group: rate $= k[C_6H_4(CO_2Me)CO_2H]$ (carboxyl participation), but with esters with a good leaving group, e.g., phenyl hydrogen phthalate, it is proportional to concentration with the carboxyl group ionized: rate $= k[C_6H_4(CO_2Ph)CO_2^-]$ (carboxylate participation). With propargyl hydrogen phthalate, where the leaving group has an intermediate tendency, both rate laws are followed to the same extent and the rate is virtually independent of pH in the range 5—2. It was suggested that the esters which were hydrolysed with carboxylate participation followed the mechanism of reaction (8).

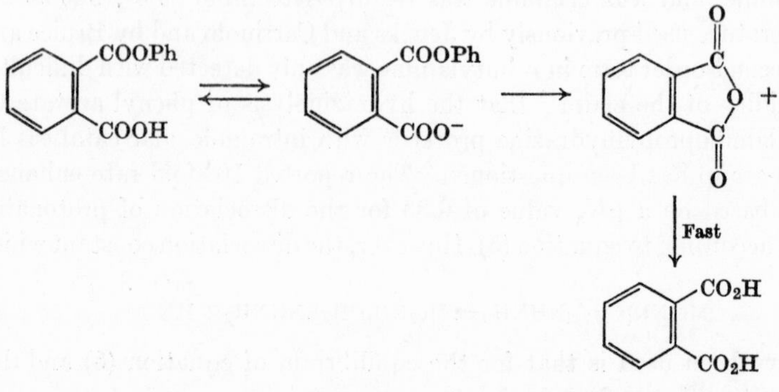

(8)

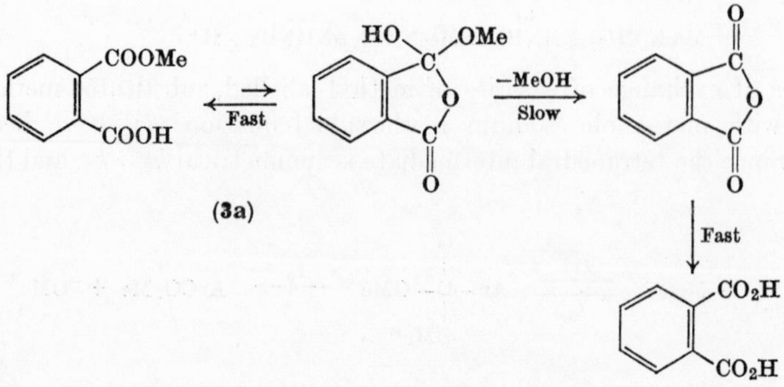

(3a)

(9)

[11a] L. B. Jones and T. M. Sloane, *Tetrahedron Letters*, **1966**, 831.
[11b] J. W. Thanassi and T. C. Bruice, *J. Am. Chem. Soc.*, **88**, 747 (1966).

Various mechanisms were considered for those which are hydrolysed with carboxyl participation, but no definite conclusion was reached as to the correct one. In our opinion the mechanism of reaction (9) provides an attractive alternative to those proposed by Thanassi and Bruice. Here intermediate (**3a**) is formed in a rapid and reversible step, and breaks down only slowly, with loss of the poor leaving group, to yield phthalic anhydride.

Other examples of carboxyl-group participation are found in the hydrolyses of *N*-benzoylaspartic and *N*-benzoylglutamic acid. The former reaction was thought to proceed through the mixed anhydride (**3b**), since the corresponding methanolysis yielded free aspartic acid and its β-ester. *N*-Benzoylglutamic acid yields 5-oxopyrrolidine-2-carboxylic acid, which is stable in water but is converted in dilute acid into glutamic acid and was thought to be formed by intramolecular nucleophilic attack by an amine group on the mixed glutamic benzoic anhydride.[12a]

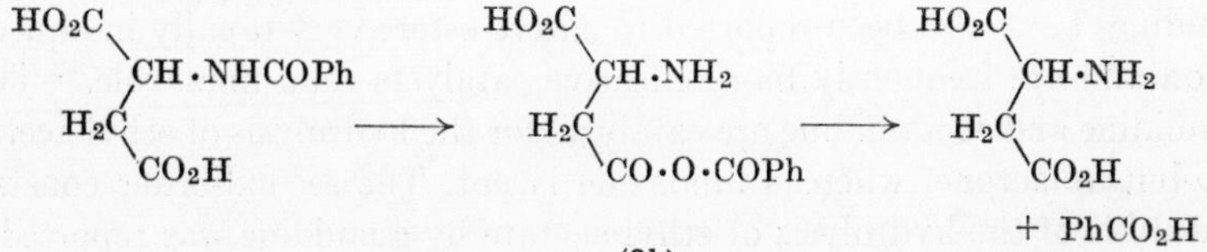

(3b)

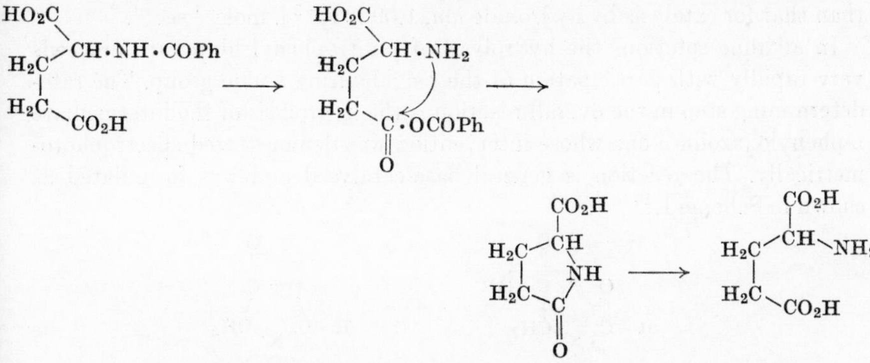

A striking example of bifunctional catalysis was reported by Menger[12b] who showed that the reaction of *p*-nitrophenyl acetate with benzamidine in chlorobenzene is only four times slower than that with hydroxide ion in water. The reaction is first-order in benzamidine, in contrast to the reaction with *n*-butylamine which is second-order in amine. It was estimated that the reaction of *p*-nitrophenyl acetate with benzamidine is at least 15,000 times

[12a] J. B. Capindale and H. S. Fan, *Chem. Commun.*, **1966**, 227.
[12b] F. M. Menger. *J. Am. Chem. Soc.*, **88**, 3081 (1966).

faster than that with *n*-butylamine monomer. Probably nucleophilic attack by benzamidine proceeds by a cyclic process (4) in which charge formation is avoided. The second-order dependence of the reaction with *n*-butylamine suggests that this proceeds by similar but much less favourable pathway (5). The alternative pathway (6) seems unlikely since it involves creation of charge and also since it was shown that the tertiary amine, 1-methylpiperidine, has only a small effect on the rate.

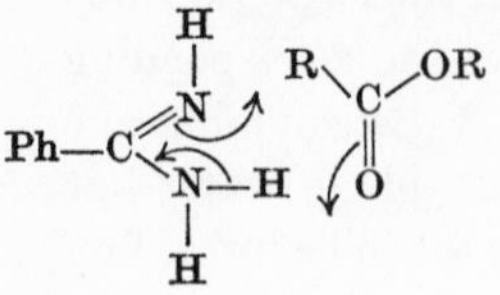

(4) 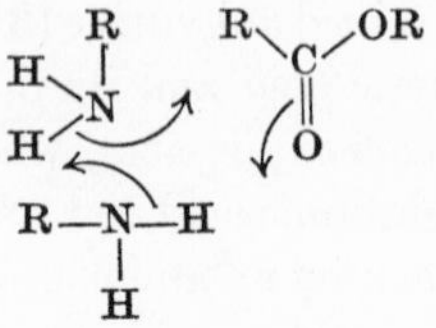   **(5)** 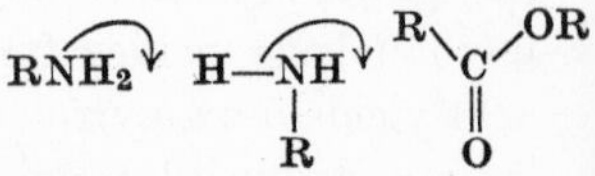   **(6)**

Amidines have also been reported to cleave esters very rapidly in aqueous solution and are frequently more effective catalysts than imidazole.[13] Thus benzamidine and acetamidine are catalysts for the hydrolysis of ethyl acetate and γ-butyrolactone, whereas imidazole is not. The second-order constant for catalysis of the hydrolysis of ethyl acetate by guanidine was reported as 3.75×10^{-3} l. mole^{-1} sec^{-1} at 30° in 85% ethanol–water, only slightly slower than that for catalysis by hydroxide ion, 1.09×10^{-2} l. mole^{-1} sec^{-1}.

In alkaline solutions the hydrolysis of *p*-nitrophenyl hippurate proceeds very rapidly with participation of the neighbouring amide group. The rate-determining step in the overall reaction is the hydrolysis of the intermediate L-phenyloxazolin-5-one whose intervention was demonstrated spectrophotometrically. The reaction is general base-catalysed and was formulated as shown in Scheme 1.[14]

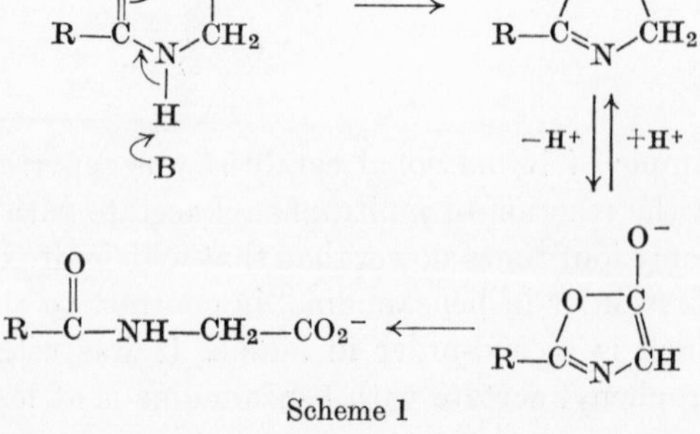

Scheme 1

[13] E. Haruki, T. Fujii and E. Imoto, *Bull. Chem. Soc. Japan*, **39**, 852 (1966).
[14] J. de Jersey, A. A. Kortt, and B. Zerner, *Biochem. Biophys. Res. Commun.*, **23**, 745 (1966).

In acid solution, cyclization of N-methylphthalamic acid to N-methyl-phthalimide is only about five times slower than its hydrolysis.[15] Imide formation from phthalamic acid is, however, about 300 times slower than hydrolysis. The hydrolysis of N-acetylphthalamic acid was also investigated; it proceeds by three pathways, to yield phthalimide and acetic acid, phthalamic acid and acetic acid, and phthalic acid and acetamide; the last of these involves intramolecular catalysis by the carboxyl group similar to that found in the hydrolysis of phthalamic acid itself, but the rate constant here is about 300 times smaller.

An investigation of the kinetics of hydrolysis of succinanilic acid and its methyl-substituted derivatives has been reported.[16] In the pH range 6—2 the rates are much greater than the rate of hydrolysis of acetanilide and are proportional to the concentration of the species with the carboxyl group un-ionized; i.e., rate $= k[\mathrm{HO_2CCR_2CR_2CONHPh}]$, where $\mathrm{R} = \mathrm{H}$ or Me. The reactions presumably involve intramolecular catalysis by the carboxyl group and proceed through the succinic anhydrides. The tetramethyl compound reacts about 1000 times faster than succinanilic acid itself, presumably as a result of being constrained to a conformation suitable for ring closure.[17]

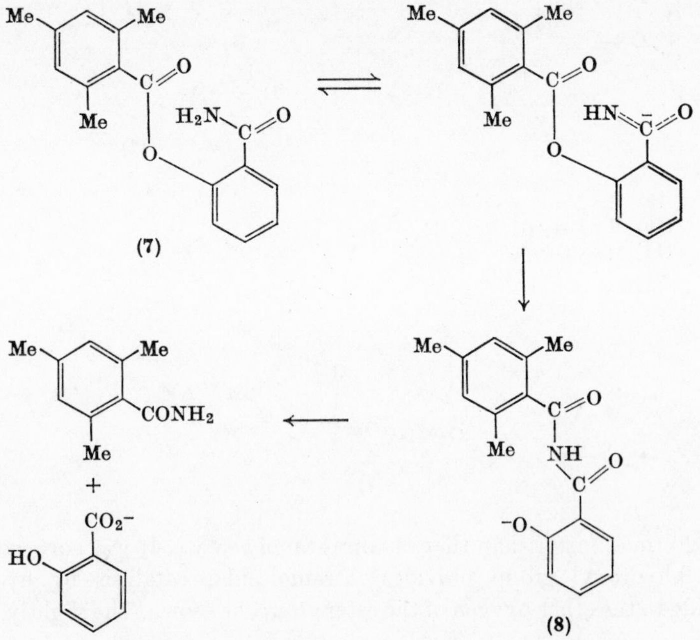

(7)

(8)

[15] J. Brown, S. C. K. Su, and J. A. Shafer, *J. Am. Chem. Soc.*, **88**, 4468 (1966).
[16] T. Higuchi, L. Eberson, and A. K. Herd, *J. Am. Chem. Soc.*, **88**, 3805 (1966).
[17] For other examples of this effect see *Organic Reaction Mechanisms*, **1965**, 269.

The hydrolyses of maleamic, phthalamic, N-ethyl- and N,N-diethyl-maleamic, and phthalamic acid have also been investigated.[18]

An interesting example of hydroxyl ion-catalysed participation by an amide group with exclusive N-attack is found with compound (7).[19] This is converted at pH 10 in 9.5% ethanol–water into an imide (8) and thence into mesitamide and salicyclic acid, about 80,000 times faster than its isomer with the amide group in the *para*-position is hydrolysed under the same conditions (see also, p. 55).

Kupchan and his co-workers[20] have published details of their work on intramolecular catalysis in the methanolysis of 1,3-diaxial hydroxy-acetates. The rates of methanolysis of coprostane-$3\beta,5\beta$-diol 3-monoacetate (9), strophanthidol 3-acetate (10), and methyl strophanthidinate 3-acetate (11) in triethylamine buffers in methanol–chloroform occur, respectively, 300, 470,

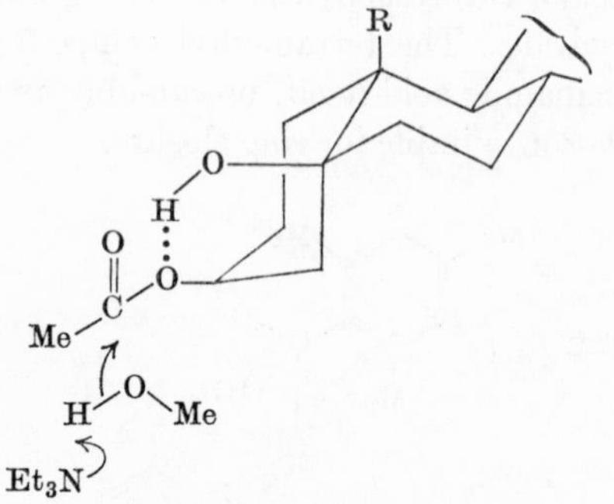

(9) R = Me
(10) R = CH₂OH
(11) R = COOMe

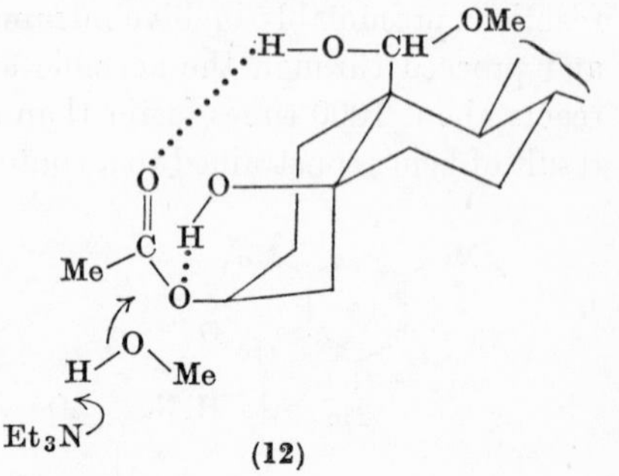

(12)

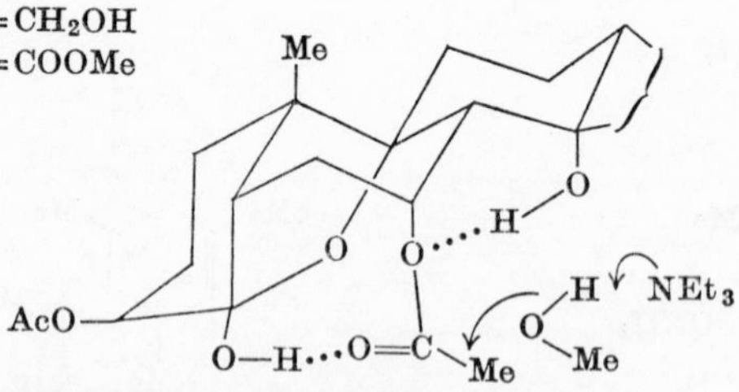

(13)

and 320 times faster than that of coprostanol acetate. It was suggested that the 5β-hydroxyl group provides intramolecular catalysis by hydrogen-bonding to the ether-oxygen of the ester group, as shown. The slightly greater

[18] G. Dahlgren and N. L. Simmerman, *J. Phys. Chem.*, **69**, 3626 (1965).
[19] R. M. Topping and D. E. Tutt, *Chem. Commun.*, **1966**, 698.
[20] S. M. Kupchan, S. P. Eriksen, and M. Friedman, *J. Am. Chem. Soc.*, **88**, 343 (1966); S. M. Kupchan, S. P. Eriksen, and Y.-T. S. Liang, *ibid.*, p. 347.

rates for strophanthidin 3-acetate and neogermitrine, which reacted 1200 and 4200 times faster than coprostanol acetate, was attributed to additional hydrogen-bonding to the carbonyl-oxygen atom by the hemiketal-hydroxyl groups, as shown in (12) and (13), respectively.

Unlike those of the above esters, the rate constants for the methanolyses of the 16-acetate groups of cevadine orthoacetate diacetate and cevadine diacetate show only a slight dependence on the concentration of triethylamine, but they are proportional to the concentration of these compounds with the ring-nitrogen unprotonated. The rates are several thousand times greater than that for dehydrocevadine orthoacetate diacetate which lacks the 20-hydroxyl group, and 25—27-fold greater than that for a compound with the tertiary amino-group converted into a formamido-group. A mechanism involving intramolecular general base–general acid-catalysis, as shown in (14), was proposed.[20]

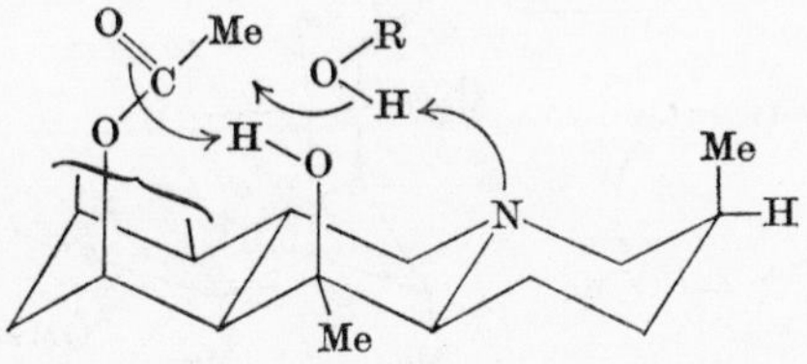

(14) 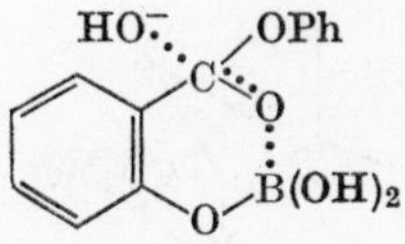   (15)

The hydrolyses of phenyl salicylate and catechol monobenzoate at moderately alkaline pH's occur 50 and 200—600 times faster than those of phenyl *o*-methoxybenzoate and *o*-methoxyphenyl benzoate, respectively.[21] This was interpreted as being the result of intramolecular general base-catalysis by ionized phenolic hydroxyl group in the reactions of the catechol and salicylate esters. The hydrolysis of phenyl salicylate shows specific catalysis by borate, which was attributed to stabilization of the transition state for the formation of the terahedral intermediate, by complex formation as shown in (15).

The methanolysis of catechol monobenzoate was also thought to involve intramolecular general base-catalysis.[22]

The major reaction of monoacyl *o*-phenylenediamines in alkaline solution is to give benzimidazoles.[23] The slow step was thought to be elimination of water from the intermediate 2-hydroxybenzimidazoline (16). The hydrolysis of di-*N*-acyl-*o*-phenylenediamines to the monoacyl derivatives was also investigated. There was no participation by one amide group in the hydrolysis of the other.[23]

[21] B. Capon and B. C. Ghosh, *J. Chem. Soc., B*, **1966**, 472.
[22] R. Biggins and E. Haslam, *J. Chem. Soc.*, **1965**, 6883.
[23] K. J. Morgan and A. M. Turner, *Tetrahedron*, **22**, 1175 (1966).

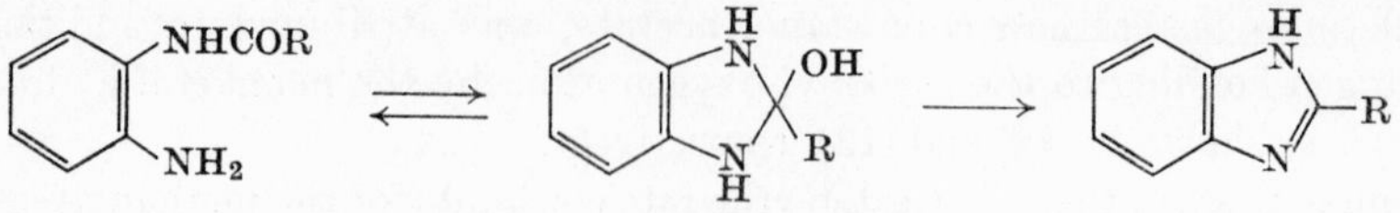

(16)

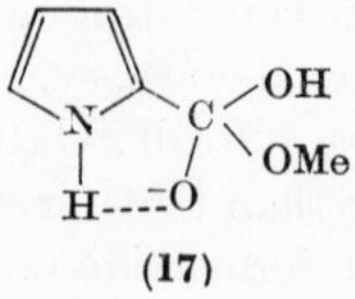

(17)

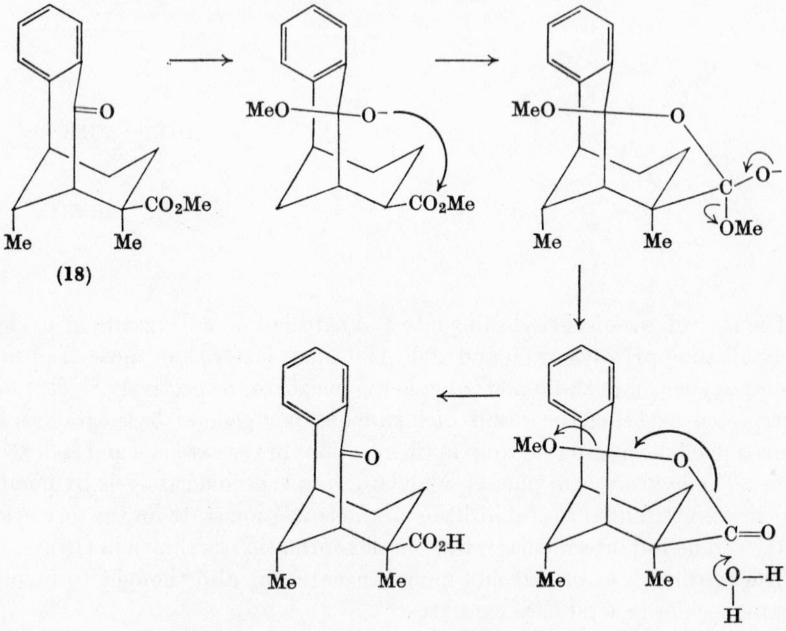

(18)

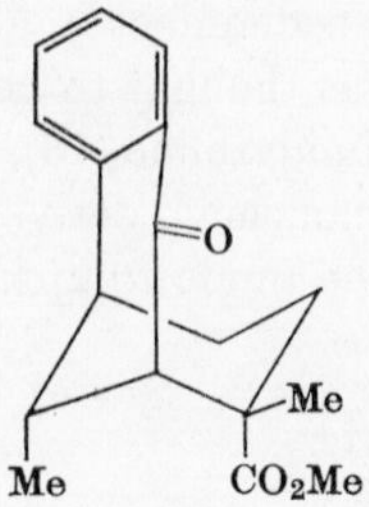

(19) 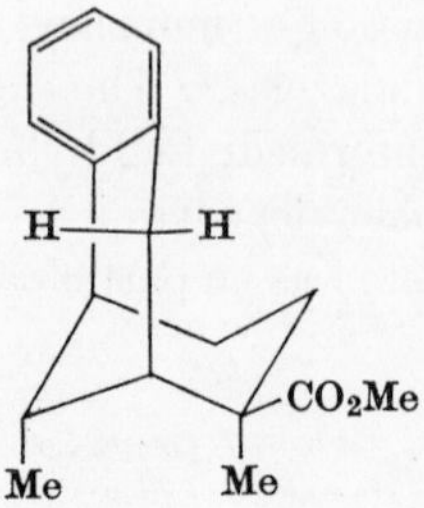   (20)

The 6—8-fold faster hydrolysis by alkali of methyl pyrrole-2-carboxylate than of the 3-carboxylate has been attributed to intramolecular hydrogen-bonding as shown in (17).[24]

Another example[25] has been reported of participation of a carbonyl group in ester hydrolysis via an initial adduct with a nucleophile.[26] The ester (18), on treatment with methanolic KOH followed by aqueous working-up, is rapidly cleaved under conditions where esters (19) and (20) are stable.

Rapid hydrolysis of 8-acetoxyquinoline has been attributed to intramolecular nucleophilic catalysis [reaction (10)],[27] but the rapid reaction of several 8-acyloxyquinolines with benzylamine was considered to result from

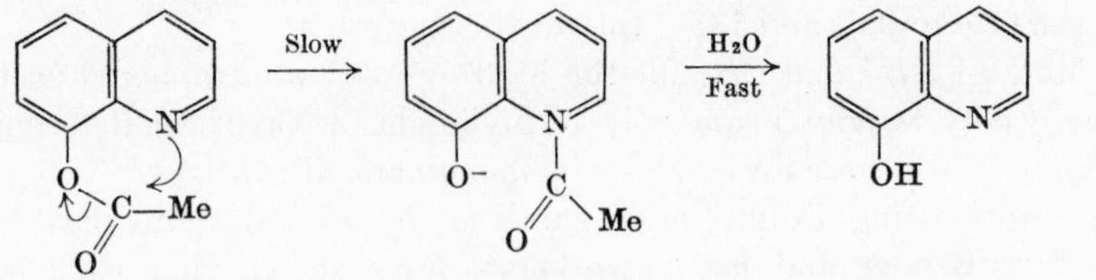

$$\text{(10)}$$

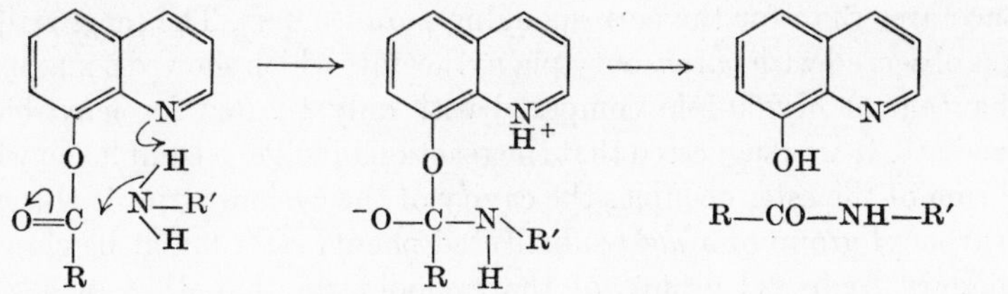

$$\text{(11)}$$

intramolecular general base-catalysis [reaction (11)].[28] The metal ion-catalysed hydrolysis of 8-acetoxyquinoline was also investigated.[27]

Other reactions involving neighbouring-group participation include hydrolyses of 2-diethylaminoethyl *p*-aminosalicylates,[29] conversion of *tert*-butyl *N,N*-dimethylcarbamoyl salicylate into methoxycarbonylsalicylic acid by methanolic hydrogen chloride,[30] hydrolysis of 3,5-dinitro-2-pyridylalanyl-glycine,[31a] alkaline hydrolysis of aliphatic ammonium esters,[31b] hydrolysis of

[24] M. A. Khan and K. J. Morgan, *Tetrahedron*, **21**, 2197 (1965).
[25] See *Organic Reaction Mechanisms*, **1965**, 264.
[26] U. R. Ghatak and J. Chakravarty, *Chem. Commun.*, **1966**, 184.
[27] R. H. Barca and H. Freiser, *J. Am. Chem. Soc.*, **88**, 3744 (1966).
[28] H.-D. Jakubke and A. Voigt, *Chem. Ber.*, **99**, 2419 (1966).
[29] G. Tsatsas, D. Kontonassios, and C. Sandris, *Tetrahedron Letters*, **1966**, 783.
[30] D. L. Goldhamer, A. Wilson, L. Weintraub, M. Onyskewycz, and J. Oren, *Tetrahedron Letters*, **1966**, 4031.
[31a] A. Signor, L. Biondi, and E. Bordignon, *J. Org. Chem.*, **31**, 1403 (1966).
[31b] G. Aksnes and P. Frøyen, *Acta Chem. Scand.*, **20**, 1451 (1966); see also, A. Agren, *Acta Pharm. Suecica*, **2**, 387 (1965).

citraconic amides,[31c] rearrangement of N-(N-tritylglycyl)benzanilide into the N-tritylanilide of N-benzoylglycine,[31d] and several acyl migrations.[32]

Striking specific "suppressor" and "antisuppressor" effects have been described in the hydrolysis of the nitrophenyl ester group of the p-nitrophenyl polyuridylic acid succinate catalysed by polyvinylimidazole.[33] At low concentration (3.3 × 10⁻⁵M in imidazole units), the latter is about 300 times more effective as catalyst than is imidazole, presumably owing to specific complexing between the oppositely charged polymer molecules. If, however, hexadecyltrimethylammonium bromide is added to a concentration of 1.3 × 10⁻⁵M, the rate is suppressed to 0.12 of that of a control, but further addition of sodium dodecyl sulphate, to a concentration of 1.2 × 10⁻⁵M or 2.3 × 10⁻⁵M, restores the rate to 0.65 and 1.0 of that of the control.

The values of $\varDelta H^{\ddagger}$ and $\varDelta S^{\ddagger}$ for the hydrolyses of p-nitrophenyl acetate catalysed by poly-4-, poly-5-, and poly-1-vinylimidazole have been determined and compared with those for catalysis by monomeric derivatives.[34]

Further interesting examples of catalysis by cyclodextrins has been reported.[35,36] Bender and his co-workers[35] have shown that cyclohexaamylose is a more efficient catalyst for the hydrolysis of *meta*-substituted phenyl acetates than for the corresponding *para*-isomers. The most striking result was observed with *m-tert*-butylphenyl acetate which showed a maximum rate enhancement of 260-fold compared with only 1.2-fold for *p-tert*-butylphenyl acetate. It was suggested that the reaction involves a complex in which the aryl ring of the ester occupies the cavity of the cyclodextrin. If this were so, the carbonyl group of a *meta*-substituted phenyl ester might be closer to the secondary hydroxyl groups of the cyclodextrin than that of a *para*-substituted ester and thus be better able to carry out a nucleophilic attack. This would lead to an acyl cyclohexa-amylose intermediate, and indeed one was shown to intervene in the hydrolysis of *m-tert*-butylphenyl benzoate, both spectroscopically and by its isolation.

An attempt to enhance the catalytic efficiency of cyclohepta-amylose for the hydrolysis of p-nitrophenyl acetate by introducing more effective catalytic groups than hydroxyl was not very successful. The various imidazole deriva-

[31e] T. V. Sheremeteva and V. A. Gusinskaya, *Izv. Akad. Nauk SSSR, Ser. Khim.*, **1966**, 695; *Chem. Abs.*, **65**, 8714 (1966).

[31d] C. Zioudrou and J. S. Fruton, *Biochemistry*, **5**, 2468 (1966).

[32] G. Adam and K. Schreiber, *Chem. Ber.*, **99**, 3173 (1966); P. E. Verkade, *Rec. Trav. Chim.*, **85**, 426 (1966); P. J. Garegg, *Arkiv Kemi*, **23**, 255 (1965); N. E. Alexandrou and D. N. Nicolaides, *Tetrahedron Letters*, **1966**, 2497.

[33] R. L. Letsinger and T. E. Wagner, *J. Am. Chem. Soc.*, **88**, 2062 (1966).

[34] C. G. Overberger, T. St. Pierre, C. Yaroslavsky, and S. Yaroslavsky, *J. Am. Chem. Soc.*, **88**, 1184 (1966).

[35] M. L. Bender, R. L. Van Etten, G. A. Clowes, and J. F. Sebastian, *J. Am. Chem. Soc.*, **88**, 2318 (1966); M. L. Bender, R. L. Van Etten, and G. A. Clowes, *ibid.*, p. 2319.

[36] Cf. *Organic Reaction Mechanisms*, **1965**, 282.

tives studied were only slightly more effective than would be expected, in the absence of any special binding effect, from the imidazole they contained.[37]

Addition of 3,5-dinitrobenzoate ion to solutions of 1-(3-indolylacryloyl)-imidazole, *p*-nitrophenyl 3-indolylacrylate, and *p*-nitrophenyl 3-indolylacetate results in formation of charge-transfer complexes which are less than 30% as reactive toward hydroxide ion and *n*-butylamine as the uncomplexed compounds.[38] It was thought unlikely that steric or electrostatic effects would be important since presumably the 3,5-dinitrobenzoate ion is complexed with the indole ring which in the indolylacrylic acid derivatives is remote from the reaction site. Possibly the 3,5-dinitrobenzoate ion stabilizes the initial substrates more than the transition state, i.e., the initial substrates are better donors than the transition states, which would certainly not be expected, or the charged carboxylate group modifies the water structure near the complex so that the transition state is solvated less readily.

The hydrolysis of 4-nitrophthalimide is enhanced in the presence of anthracene.[39] In the absence of this donor the rate constant can be expressed as $k'_A = k_A[^-OH] + k_{AS}$ and in its presence as $k'_{AD} = k_{A+D}[^-OH] + k_{A+DS}$. The rate enhancing effect is found mainly in the water-catalysed reaction with $k_{AS} = 4 \times 10^{-5}$ sec^{-1} and $k_{A+DS} = 9 \times 10^{-5}$ sec^{-1}.

A review of reactions proceeding through charge-transfer complexes has been published.[40]

Negatively charged nucleophiles are relatively more reactive towards *p*-nitrophenyl chloroacetate and dichloroacetate than towards *p*-nitrophenyl acetate, possibly as a result of "electrostatic stabilization of the transition state resulting from ion–dipole or dipole–dipole interactions."[41]

L-Seryl-γ-aminobutyryl-L-histidyl-γ-aminobutyryl-L-aspartic acid is about seven times as effective a catalyst as imidazole for the hydrolysis of *p*-nitrophenyl acetate. It also shows a small stereoselectivity in the hydrolysis of the enantiomers of *N*-methoxycarbonylphenylalanine *p*-nitrophenyl ester, the L-ester reacting about 20% faster than the D-ester.[42]

The rate of hydrolysis of allyl acetate is faster when catalysed by a sulphonic acid resin partially exchanged with Ag$^+$ than by the unexchanged resin, owing possibly to complexing of Ag$^+$ with the olefin.[43]

The interesting observation has been made that nitriles are converted into the corresponding amides on treatment with manganese dioxide in methylene

[37] F. Cramer and G. Mackensen, *Angew. Chem. Internat. Ed. Engl.*, **5**, 601 (1966).
[38] F. M. Menger and M. L. Bender, *J. Am. Chem. Soc.*, **88**, 131 (1966).
[39] A. Bruylants and J. B. Nagy, *Bull. Soc. Chim. Belg.*, **75**, 246 (1966).
[40] E. M. Kosower, *Progr. Phys. Org. Chem.*, **3**, 81 (1965).
[41] K. Koehler, R. Skora, and E. H. Cordes, *J. Am. Chem. Soc.*, **88**, 3577 (1966).
[42] J. C. Sheehan, G. B. Bennett, and J. A. Schneider, *J. Am. Chem. Soc.*, **88**, 3455 (1966).
[43] S. Affrossman and J. P. Murray, *J. Chem. Soc., B*, **1966**, 1015.

352 Organic Reaction Mechanisms 1966*Organic Reaction Mechanisms 1966*

chloride.[44] The reaction presumably occurs at the surface of the MnO_2 and involves adsorbed water.

Specific catalytic effects of polymeric sulphonic acids in ester hydrolysis have been observed.[45]

The mechanism of chymotrypsin action has been reviewed.[1]

Further structural studies of chymotrypsinogen A and trypsinogen have been reported.[46—47]

Commercial preparations of trypsin[48] and chymotrypsin[49] frequently contain impurities that may affect the kinetics of the reactions they catalyse.

In chymotrypsin A and B, trypsin, and elastase, two histidine residues are brought close together by a disulphide bridge and it has been suggested that both are implicated in the mechanism of action of these enzymes.[50]

There have been several discussions of the structural[51] and stereochemical specificity[52] of chymotrypsin.

The serine residue (195) at the active site of chymotrypsin has been converted into a dehydroalanine residue by converting it into the toluene-*p*-sulphonate and carrying out an elimination reaction with alkali. The resulting anhydrochymotrypsin was enzymically inactive but had essentially the same ability to bind substrates and inhibitors.[53]

Polgar and Bender[54] have transformed the hydroxyl group of the active

[44] M. J. Cooke, E. J. Forbes, and G. M. Khan, *Chem. Commun.*, **1966**, 121; see also, K. Watanabe and K. Sakai, *Bull. Chem. Soc. Japan*, **39**, 8 (1966).

[45] S. Yoshikawa and O.-K. Kim, *Bull. Chem. Soc. Japan*, **39**, 1515, 1729 (1966); I. Sakurada, Y. Sakaguchi, T. Ono, and T. Ueda, *Kobunshi Kagaku*, **22**, 696, 701, 706, 711 (1965); I. Sakurada, T. Ono, Y. Sakaguchi, and J. Nishino, *ibid.*, p. 804; I. Sakurada, T. Ono, and Y. Sakaguchi, *ibid.*, p. 808; *Chem. Abs.*, **64**, 19344, 19345 (1966).

[46] J. R. Brown and B. S. Hartley, *Biochem. J.*, **101**, 214 (1966); B. S. Hartley and D. L. Kauffman, *ibid.*, p. 229.

[47] I. Kluh, L. Morávek, J. M. Junge, B. Meloun, and F. Šorm, *Coll. Czech. Chem. Commun.*, **31**, 152 (1966); B. Meloun, V. Kostka, J. Vaneček, I. Kluh, and F. Šorm, *ibid.*, p. 321; V. Dlouhá, D. Pospíšilová, B. Meloun, and F. Šorm, *ibid.*, p. 346; F. Franěk p. 1142; Z. Prusik, B. Keil, and F. Šorm, *ibid.*, p. 2565; O. Mikeš, V. Holeyšouský, V. Tomášek, and F. Šorm, *Biochem. Biophys. Res. Commun.*, **24**, 346 (1966); O. Mikeš, V. Tomášek, V. Holeyšouský, and F. Šorm, *Biochem. Biophys. Acta*, **117**, 281 (1966).

[48] P. O. Ganrot, *Acta Chem. Scand.*, **20**, 175 (1966).

[49] A. Yapel, M. Han, R. Lumry, A. Rosenberg, and D. F. Shiao, *J. Am. Chem. Soc.*, **88**, 2573 (1966).

[50] L. B. Smillie and B. S. Hartley, *Biochem. J.*, **101**, 232 (1966).

[51] J. R. Knowles, *J. Theoret. Biol.*, **9**, 213 (1965); C. H. Johnson and J. R. Knowles, *Biochem. J.*, **101**, 56 (1966); D. W. Ingles and J. R. Knowles, *ibid.*, **99**, 275 (1966); D. W. Ingles, J. R. Knowles, and J. A. Tomlinson, *Biochem. Biophys. Res. Commun.*, **23**, 619 (1966).

[52] M. S. Silver, *J. Am. Chem. Soc.*, **88**, 4247 (1966); S. G. Cohen, L. H. Klee, and S. Y. Weinstein, *ibid.*, p. 5302; S. G. Cohen, Z. Neuwirth, and S. Y. Weinstein, *ibid.*, p. 5306; S. G. Cohen, R. M. Schultz, and S. Y. Weinstein, *ibid.*, p. 5315.

[53] H. Weiner, W. N. White, D. G. Hoare, and D. E. Koshland, *J. Am. Chem. Soc.*, **88**, 3851 (1966).

[54] L. Polgar and M. L. Bender, *J. Am. Chem. Soc.*, **88**, 3153 (1966).

serine of subtilisin into a thiol group. The modified enzyme, thiolsubtilisin, is active and was shown to catalyse the hydrolysis of *N-trans*-cinnamoyl-imidazole by means of an *S*-cinnamoyl enzyme.

There have been many other investigations of the mechanism of action of chymotrypsin,[55] trypsin,[56] carboxy-peptidase A,[57] papain,[58] pepsin,[59] acetylcholinesterase,[60] elastase,[61] and carbonic anhydrase.[62]

[55] A. Himoe and G. P. Hess, *Biochem. Biophys. Res. Commun.*, **23**, 234 (1966); L. Berliner and H. M. McConnell, *Proc. Natl. Acad. Sci. U.S.*, **55**, 708 (1966); J. Schafer, P. Baronosky, R. Laursen, F. Finn, and F. W. Westheimer, *J. Biol. Chem.*, **241**, 421 (1966); D. R. Ponzi and G. E. Hein, *Biochem. Biophys. Res. Commun.*, **25**, 60 (1966); C. L. Hamilton, C. Niemann, and G. S. Hammond, *Proc. Natl. Acad. Sci. U.S.*, **55**, 664 (1966); Y. Shalitan and J. R. Brown, *Biochem. Biophys. Res. Commun.*, **24**, 817 (1966); T. Yamamoto and N. Izumiya, *Arch. Biochem. Biophys.*, **116**, 459 (1966); G. L. Neil, C. Niemann, and G. E. Hein, *Nature*, **210**, 903 (1966); L. Faller and J. M. Sturtevant, *J. Biol. Chem.*, **241**, 4825 (1966); R. A. Wallace, R. L. Peterson, C. Niemann, and G. E. Hein, *Biochem. Biophys. Res. Commun.*, **23**, 246 (1966); K. G. Brandt and G. P. Hess, *ibid.*, **22**, 447 (1966); R. A. Wallace, R. L. Peterson, C. Niemann, and G. A. Hein, *ibid.*, **23**, 246 (1966); S. C. Glauser and H. Wagner, *ibid.*, **21**, 494 (1965); M. M. Botvinik, I. P. Kuranova, and L. L. Ivanov, *Khim. Prirodn. Soedin.*, *Akad. Nauk. Uz. SSR*, **2**, 134 (1966); *Chem. Abs.*, **65**, 10655 (1966); T. F. Spande, N. M. Green, and B. Witkop, *Biochemistry*, **5**, 1926 (1966); J. C. Warren and S. G. Cheatum, *ibid.*, p. 1702; J. Kallos and K. Avatis, *ibid.*, p. 1979; D. A. Deranleau and H. Neurath, *ibid.*, p. 1413; P. S. Safare, G. Kegeles, and S. J. Kwon-Rhee, *ibid.*, p. 1389; C. J. Martin and G. M. Bhatnagar, *ibid.*, p. 1230; H. F. Bundy and C. L. Moore, *ibid.*, p. 808; B. F. Erlanger, A. G. Cooper, and W. Cohen, *ibid.*, p. 190; R. Wildnauer and W. J. Canady, *ibid.*, p. 2885; D. W. Wooley, *J. Am. Chem. Soc.*, **88**, 2309 (1966); K. Brocklehurst and K. Williamson, *Chem. Commun.*, **1966**, 462.

[56] H. L. Trenholm, W. E. Spomer, and J. F. Wootton, *J. Am. Chem. Soc.*, **88**, 4281 (1966); G. Johannin and J. Yon, *Biochem. Biophys. Res. Commun.*, **25**, 320 (1966); P. H. Petra, W. Cohen, and E. N. Shaw, *ibid.*, **21**, 612 (1965); S. Maroux, M. Rovery, and P. Desnuelle, *Biochim. Biophys. Acta*, **122**, 147 (1966).

[57] H. I. Lehrer, H. Van Vunakis, and G. D. Fasman, *J. Biol. Chem.*, **240**, 4585 (1965); J. R. Whitaker, *Biochem. Biophys. Res. Commun.*, **22**, 6 (1966); E. T. Kaiser, S. Awazu, and F. W. Carson, *ibid.*, **21**, 444 (1965); F. W. Carson and E. T. Kaiser, *J. Am. Chem. Soc.*, **88**, 1212 (1966); J. E. Coleman, P. Pulido, and B. L. Vallee, *Biochemistry*, **5**, 2019 (1966); W. O. McClure and H. Neurath, *ibid.*, p. 1425; R. Piras and B. L. Vallee, *ibid.*, p. 849; L. I. Slobin and F. H. Carpenter, *ibid.*, p. 499; J. R. Whitaker, F. Menger, and M. L. Bender, *ibid.*, p. 386; T. H. Plummer and W. B. Lawson, *J. Biol. Chem.*, **241**, 1648 (1966).

[58] J. F. Kirsch and M. Ingelström, *Biochemistry*, **5**, 783 (1966); A. N. Glazer, *J. Biol. Chem.*, **241**, 3811 (1966); M. Ebata, J. Tsunoda, and K. T. Yasunobu, *Biochem. Biophys. Res. Commun.*, **22**, 455 (1966); K. P. Carty and D. M. Kirschanbaum, *Biochem. Biophys. Acta*, **110**, 399 (1965).

[59] B. F. Erlanger, S. M. Vratsanos, N. Wasserman, and A. G. Copper, *Biochem. Biophys. Res. Commun.*, **23**, 243 (1966); E. Zeffren and E. T. Kaiser, *J. Am. Chem. Soc.*, **88**, 3129 (1966); G. E. Clement, and S. L. Snyder, *ibid.*, p. 5338; K. Inouye, I. M. Voynick, G. R. Delpierre, and J. S. Fruton, *Biochemistry*, **5**, 2473 (1966); N. I. Mal'tsev, L. M. Ginodman, and V. N. Orekhovich, *Dokl. Akad. Nauk SSSR*, **165**, 1192 (1965); *Chem. Abs.*, **64**, 9814.

[60] R. M. Krupka, *Biochemistry*, **5**, 1983, 1988 (1966); K. P. Jacobsohn and M. D. Azevedo, *Bull. Soc. Chim. Biol.*, **48**, 323 (1966); A. P. Brestkin, L. A. Ivanova, and V. V. Svechnikova, *Biokhimiya*, **31**, 416 (1966); *Chem. Abs.*, **65**, 2562; K. B. Shaw, *Can. J. Chem.*, **43**, 3265 (1965); K. W. Lo and E. T. Kaiser, *Chem. Commun.*, **1966**, 834.

[61] V. Ling and R. A. Anwar, *Biochem. Biophys. Res. Commun.*, **24**, 593 (1966).

[62] Y. Pocker and J. T. Stone, *J. Am. Chem. Soc.*, **87**, 5497 (1965); J. E. Coleman, *Biochemistry*, **4**, 2644 (1965).

3-Hydroxymethyl- and 3-methyl-3-phenylazetidine react, respectively, 120 and 180 times faster with phenyl acetate than predicted from the Brønsted plot for the reactions of other amines. This enhanced nucleophilicity was attributed to C–N–C bond-angle constraint.[63]

Large solvent isotope effects, attributable to differences in the solvating properties of MeOH and MeOD, have been found in the reaction of methoxide ion with p-nitrophenyl acetate ($k^{MeOD}/k^{MeOH} = 2.6$ at $-78.2°$) and phenyl benzoate ($k^{MeOD}/k^{MeOH} = 1.9$ at $25°$).[64]

The rates of acetylation of a large number of alkyl-substituted cyclohexanols with acetic anhydride in pyridine have been measured.[65] There were significant variations in rate within the conformationally homogeneous axial and equatorial series. Thus *cis,cis*-3,5-dimethylcyclohexanol reacted significantly faster than *trans*-4-*tert*-butylcyclohexanol. It was concluded that the kinetic method for establishing the position of conformational equilibria of

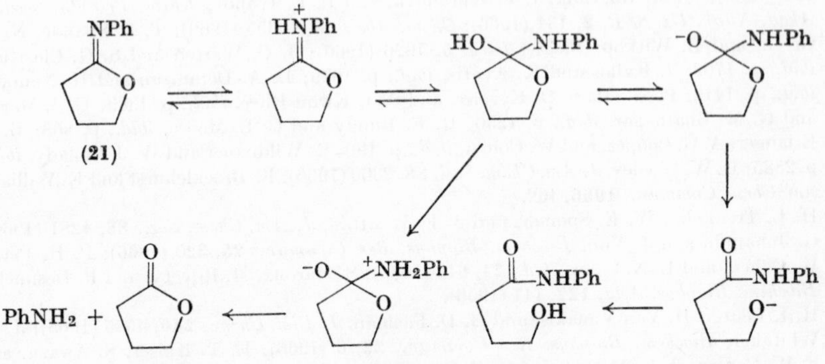

(21)

PhNH₂ +

Scheme 1a

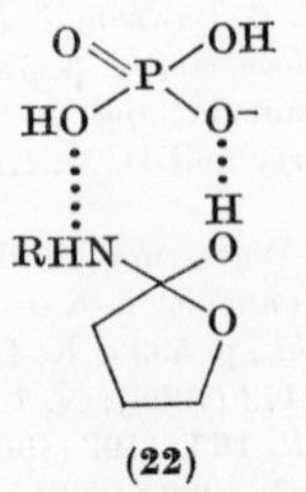

(22)

63 L. R. Fedor, T. C. Bruice, K. L. Kirk, and J. Meinwald, *J. Am. Chem. Soc.*, **88**, 108 (1966).
64 F. M. Menger, *J. Am. Chem. Soc.*, **88**, 5356 (1966).
65 E. L. Eliel and F. J. Biros, *J. Am. Chem. Soc.*, **88**, 3334 (1966).

cyclohexane systems should be viewed with reserve and used only when other methods are not readily available.

The pH-rate profile for the hydrolysis of iminolactone (**21**) is bell-shaped.[66] In the pH range 4—7 attack by water on the protonated iminolactone to yield a tetrahedral intermediate is the rate-limiting step, but at low pH's this changes to decomposition of the intermediate. Above pH 8, the rate is independent of pH and the reaction is one of hydroxide ions with protonated iminolactone. In the pH range 6—8 there is a transition in the products from aniline and butyrolactone (below pH 6) to γ-hydroxybutyranilide (above pH 8); the former are not formed from the latter. The mechanism of Scheme 1a was suggested, with the un-ionized tetrahedral intermediate decomposing to aniline and butyrolactone and the ionized form decomposing to γ-hydroxybutyranilide. The reason suggested for this was the slowness of expulsion of the amine anion from the ionized form. At pH's 7—8, phosphate, arsenate, acetate, and hydrogen carbonate, but not imidazole and tris, have a specific effect on diverting the products to aniline and lactone without affecting the overall rate of reaction.[67] It was suggested that these ions facilitated the decomposition of the tetrahedral intermediate in this way via cyclic transition states such as (**22**).

The pH–rate profile for the hydrolysis of N-phenylphthalisoimide (**23a**) to phthalanilic acid has been determined.[68] There is a slow water reaction

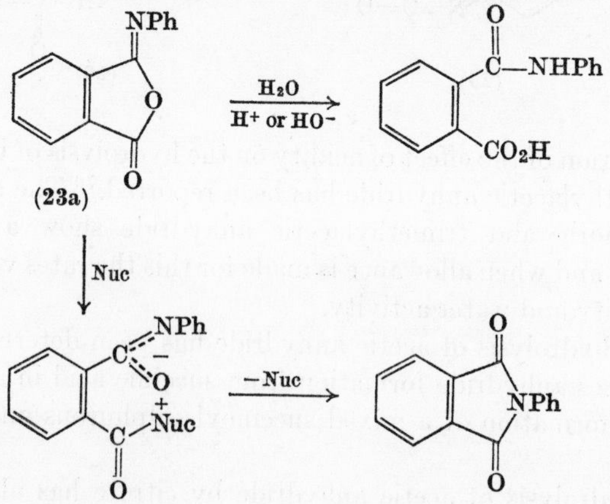

as well as both H_3O^+ and HO^- catalysis. The addition of nucleophiles to the system increases the rate of disappearance of (**23a**) but diverts the product to phthalimide, presumably as shown in the above equation.

[66] G. L. Schmir and B. A. Cunningham, *J. Am. Chem. Soc.*, **87**, 5692 (1965).
[67] B. A. Cunningham and G. L. Schmir, *J. Am. Chem. Soc.*, **88**, 551 (1966).
[68] M. L. Ernst and G. L. Schmir, *J. Am. Chem. Soc.*, **88**, 5001 (1966).

Bunnett and Naff[69] have suggested that the reaction of isatoic acid (**23b**) with amines, to yield anthranilamide (**24**), proceeds with nucleophilic attack at $C_{(4)}$, but that the concurrent reaction to yield ureido-acids (**26**) involves an intermediate isocyanate (**25**). This proposal is consistent with the kinetic behaviour in aqueous solutions, also with the observations that the proportion of ureido-acid decreases with increasing steric requirements of the amine and that these are not formed at all from N-methylisatoic acid.

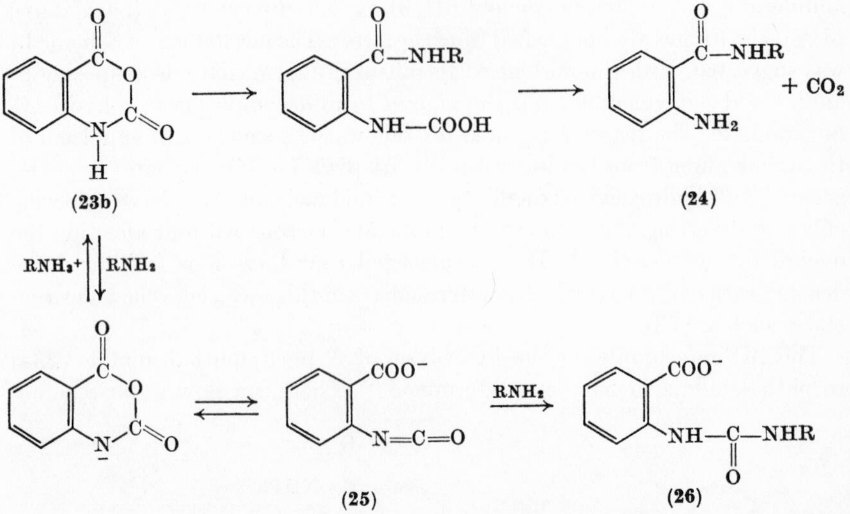

A detailed investigation of the effect of acidity on the hydrolysis of benzoic, camphoric, and trimethylacetic anhydride has been reported.[70] The activity coefficients of camphoric and trimethylacetic anhydride show a strong dependence on acidity and when allowance is made for this the rates vary in a regular way with acidity and water activity.

The free energy of hydrolysis of acetic anhydride has been determined.[71]

Sulphite ion catalyses anhydride formation from succinic acid in aqueous solution, possibly by formation of a mixed succinoyl sulphurous anhydride which then cyclizes.[72]

Catalysis of the hydrolysis of acetic anhydride by citrate has also been investigated.[73]

In contrast to diacetyl sulphide which is hydrolysed spontaneously in water

[69] J. F. Bunnett and M. B. Naff, *J. Am. Chem. Soc.*, **88**, 4001 (1966).
[70] C. A. Bunton and J. H. Fendler, *J. Org. Chem.*, **31**, 3764 (1966).
[71] W. P. Jencks, F. Barley, R. Barnett, and M. Gilchrist, *J. Am. Chem. Soc.*, **88**. 4464 (1966).
[72] T. Higuchi, J. D. McRae, and A. C. Shah, *J. Am. Chem. Soc.*, **88**, 4015 (1966).
[73] A. J. Repta, R. J. Robinson, and T. Higuchi, *J. Pharm. Sci.*, **55**, 1200 (1966).

more slowly than acetic anhydride, dibenzoyl sulphide is hydrolysed three times more rapidly than benzoic anhydride.[74]

The base-catalysed addition of alcohols to diphenylketene, methyl phenyl ketene, and 1-naphthylphenylketene in toluene has been investigated.[75] The reaction of butan-1-ol with diphenylketene gave a Brønsted plot, but one with the points for the sterically hindered bases triethylamine, dicyclohexylethylamine, and dimethylaniline falling below the line.

The reaction of diphenylketene with aniline in benzene to form diphenylacetanilide shows terms which are first- and second-order in aniline:

$$\text{Rate} = k_1[\text{Ketene}][\text{Aniline}] + k_2[\text{Ketene}][\text{Aniline}]^2$$

k_1 is much less sensitive to substituent effects than is k_2. Isotope effects in k_1 and k_2 for N-deuteriated amines are small, but with p-toluidine there is the indication that it is larger with k_2: $k_1^H/k_1^D = 1.0$, $k_2^H/k_2^D = 1.2$. Possibly the k_1 term corresponds to a direct attack on ketene by monomeric amine and k_2 to nucleophilic attack by a dimeric species.[76]

Reactions of carboxylic acid derivatives are discussed in a paper on linear free-energy relationships for reactions in moderately concentrated mineral acids.[77]

The use of salt effects as a mechanistic criterion in acid-catalysed reactions has been discussed.[78]

There have also been important investigations of the mechanism of biotin-catalysis[79] and of carbodi-imide-promoted reactions.[80]

Reactions of acid chlorides which have been investigated include: alcoholyses of aromatic thioacid chlorides,[81] pivaloyl chloride,[82] p-nitrobenzoyl chloride,[83] and ethyl chloroformate;[84] and reaction of benzoyl chloride with aniline,[85] and of isopropyl chloroformate with silver nitrate.[86a] The hydrolysis of acetyl fluoride has also been investigated.[86b]

Other reactions investigated include: hydrolysis of N-acylimidazoles,[87] and

[74] J. Hipkin and D. P. N. Satchell, *J. Chem. Soc.*, B, **1966**, 345.
[75] H. Pracejus and J. Leska, *Z. Naturforsch.*, b, **21**, 30 (1966).
[76] J. M. Briody and D. P. N. Satchell, *Tetrahedron*, **22**, 2649 (1966).
[77] J. F. Bunnett and F. P. Olsen, *Can. J. Chem.*, **44**, 1899, 1917 (1966).
[78] P. T. McTigue and A. R. Watkins, *Australian J. Chem.*, **18**, 1943 (1965).
[79] M. Caplow, *J. Am. Chem. Soc.*, **87**, 5774 (1965).
[80] D. F. DeTar and R. Silverstein, *J. Am. Chem. Soc.*, **88**, 1013 (1966); D. F. DeTar and R. Silverstein, *ibid.*, p. 1020; D. F. DeTar, R. Silverstein, and F. F. Rogers, *ibid.*, p. 1024.
[81] S. Scheithauer and R. Mayer, *Chem. Ber.*, **98**, 838 (1965).
[82] A. Kivinen, *Suomen Kemistilehti*, B, **38**, 209 (1965).
[83] R. F. Hudson, G. W. Loveday, S. Fliszar, and G. Salvadori, *J. Chem. Soc.*, B, **1966**, 769.
[84] A. Kivinen and A. Viitala, *Suomen Kemistilehti*, A, **39**, 111.
[85] N. K. Vorob'ev, L. V. Kuritsyn, and O. K. Varenkova, *Izv. Vysshikh. Uchebn. Zavedenii, Khim. i. Khim. Tekhnol.*, **9**, 53 (1966); *Chem. Abs.*, **65**, 5345 (1966).
[86a] D. N. Kevill and G. H. Johnson, *Chem. Commun.*, **1966**, 235.
[86b] C. A. Bunton and J. H. Fendler, *J. Org. Chem.*, **31**, 2307 (1966).
[87] J. A. Fee, and T. H. Fife, *J. Org. Chem.*, **31**, 2343 (1966); *J. Phys. Chem.*, **70**, 3258 (1966).

piperazine-2,5-dione,[88] benzanilides,[89] α- and ε-peptides of lysine,[90] isopropyl-phenyl carbamate,[91] aliphatic amides,[92] ε-caprolactam,[93] nitriles,[94] esters of *p*-aminobenzoic acids,[95] ethyl 4,4-dimethylpentanoate,[96] benzoates and cinnamates,[97] 1-*O*-acetyl-tetra-*O*-methyl-D-glucopyranoses,[98] 3-*O*-aminoacyl-glucoses,[99] benzohydroxamic acid,[100] ethyl trichloro-, dichloro-, and nitro-acetate,[101] barbituric acids,[102] ethyl acetate in mixed solvents,[103] diethyl dicarbonate,[104] and of the lactone ring of 6-alkylhydrocoumarins;[105] alkaline hydrolysis of ethyl benzoates,[106] alkyl acetates and propionates,[107] aryl acetates,[108] ethyl nitrobenzoates,[109] ethyl 3-phenylpropionates ($\rho = +0.63$),[110] furan- and thiophen-dicarboxylic esters,[111] amino-acid esters,[112] peptides,[113] methyl 1-[114] and 2-naphthoates,[115] methyl acrylates,[116] diesters of dicar-

[88] B. D. Sykes, E. B. Robertson, H. B. Dunford, and D. Konasewich, *Biochemistry*, **5**, 697 (1966).
[89] V. F. Mandyuk and N. P. Lushina, *Ukr. Khim. Zh.*, **32**, 607 (1966); *Chem. Abs.*, **65**, 15175 (1966).
[90] J. D. Padayatty, and H. Van Kley, *J. Org. Chem.*, **31**, 1934 (1966).
[91] M. Briquet and P. Dondeyne, *Agriculture (Louvain)*, **13**, 529 (1965); *Chem. Abs.*, **65**, 8701.
[92] P. D. Bolton, *Australian J. Chem.*, **19**, 1013 (1966).
[93] S. J. Farber and J. A. Brieux, *Chem. Ind. (London)*, **1966**, 599.
[94] N. C. Deno, R. W. Gaugler, and M. J. Wisotsky, *J. Org. Chem.*, **31**, 1967 (1966).
[95] I. F. Mueller and P. Speiser, *Pharm. Acta Helv.*, **40**, 620, 671 (1965); A. Agren and L. Nilsson, *Acta Pharm., Suecica*, **2**, 201 (1965); *Chem. Abs.*, **63**, 17820 (1965).
[96] W. Drenth, *Rec. Trav. Chim.*, **85**, 455 (1966).
[97] S. V. Anantakrishnan and P. S. Radhakrishnamurti, *Indian J. Chem.*, **3**, 336 (1965).
[98] M. Van Dyke, S. G. Sunderwirth, and G. Johnson, *J. Org. Chem.*, **30**, 4349 (1965).
[99] N. Muramatsu, *Bull. Chem. Soc. Japan*, **39**, 1273 (1966).
[100] D. C. Berndt, and R. L. Fuller, *J. Org. Chem.*, **31**, 3312 (1966).
[101] I. Talvik and V. Palm, *Reaktsionnaya Sposobnost Organ. Soedin, Tartusk. Gos. Univ.*, **2**, 110 (1965); *Chem. Abs.*, **63**, 17821 (1965).
[102] S. O. Eriksson and A. Holmgren, *Acta Pharm. Suecica*, **2**, 293 (1965); S. O. Eriksson, *ibid.*, p. 305.
[103] D. D. Singh and K. Rai, *Res. Bull. Panjab Univ.*, **16**, 159 (1965); *Chem. Abs.*, **64**, 11038 (1966).
[104] A. Kivinen, *Suomen Kemistilehti, B*, **38**, 106, 143, 159, 205, 207 (1965).
[105] B. M. Sheiman, A. N. Kost, and L. Y. Denisova, *J. Gen., Chem. USSR*, **35**, 873 (1965).
[106] M. Hojo, M. Utaka, and Z. Yoshida, *Tetrahedron Letters*, **1966**, 19, 25; H. Hojo, M. Utaka, Z. Yoshida, *Yuki. Gosei. Kagaku Kyokai. Shi.*, **23**, 1034, 1040, 1105 (1965); *Chem. Abs.*, **64**, 4916 (1966).
[107] R. W. A. Jones and J. D. R. Thomas, *J. Chem. Soc., B*, **1966**, 661.
[108] J. J. Ryan and A. A. Humffray, *J. Chem. Soc., B*, **1966**, 842.
[109] Y. Iskander, R. Tewfik, and S. Wasif, *J. Chem. Soc., B*, **1966**, 424.
[110] R. Fuchs and J. A. Caputo, *J. Org. Chem.*, **31**, 1524 (1966).
[111] S. Oae, N. Furukawa, T. Watanabe, Y. Otsuji, and M. Hamada, *Bull. Chem. Soc. Japan*, **38**, 1247 (1965).
[112] R. W. Hay, L. J. Porter, and P. J. Morris, *Australian J. Chem.*, **19**, 1197 (1966).
[113] I. G. Orlov, Y. V. Moiseev, M. I. Vinnik, and U. I. Khurgin, *Reaktsionnaya Sposobnost Organ. Soedin. Tartusk. Gos. Univ.*, **2**, 180 (1965); I. G. Orlov, Y. V. Moiseev, and M. I. Vinnik, *ibid.*, pp. 192, 211, 218; *Chem. Abs.*, **56**, 12280 (1966).
[114] E. F. J. Duynstee and E. Grunwald, *Tetrahedron*, **21**, 2401 (1965).
[115] P. R. Wells and W. Adcock, *Australian J. Chem.*, **19**, 221 (1966).
[116] K. Bowden, *Can. J. Chem.*, **44**, 661 (1966).

boxylic acids,[117] methyl pyridinecarboxylates,[118] esters of amino-alcohols,[119] ethylene, propylene, and vinylene carbonates,[120] N-phenyl-α-methylsuccinimides,[121] and poly-(3-acetamidostyrene);[122] displacement reactions of 2-acetyl-3,4-dimethylthiazolium iodide;[123] reaction of butyrolactone with alcohols;[124a] formation of peracids;[124b] acid-catalysed formation of peracetic acid from acetic anhydride and hydrogen peroxide;[125] esterification of acrylic acids[126] and heterocyclic dicarboxylic acids with diphenyldiazomethane;[127] reaction of N-ethylmaleimide with cysteine;[128] polymerization of N-carboxy-anhydrides;[129] base-catalysed ring-opening of 1-(N,N-dimethylcarbamoyl)pyridinium chloride;[130] reactions of trihalogenoacetates with primary and secondary amines;[131] decomposition of α-amino-thiol esters;[132] reaction of N,N'-carbonyldiimidazole with acids;[133] reactions of isocyanates and isothiocyanates;[134] oxygen-exchange between phenylacetic acid and water;[135] reaction of acetic and benzoic anhydride with aromatic amines;[136] and esterification of phthalic acid.[137]

[117] R. Gelin, S. Gelin, and C. Boutin, *Compt. Rend.*, Ser. *C*, **262**, 1084 (1966).
[118] A. Feinstein and P. H. Gore, *Acta Pharm. Suecica*, **2**, 267 (1965).
[119] E. A. Guseva and B. A. Porai-Koshits, *Reaktsionnaya Sposobnost Organ. Soedin. Tartusk. Gos. Univ.*, **2**, 19 (1965); *Chem. Abs.*, **65**, 8696 (1966).
[120] A. H. Saadi and W. H. Lee, *J. Chem. Soc.*, *B*, **1966**, 1, 5.
[121] A. K. Herd, L. Eberson, and T. Higuchi, *J. Pharm. Sci.*, **55**, 162 (1966).
[122] C. L. Arcus and R. H. Still, *J. Chem. Soc.*, *B*, **1966**, 401.
[123] T. C. Bruice and N. G. Kundu, *J. Am. Chem. Soc.*, **88**, 4097 (1966).
[124a] H. C. Brown and K. A. Keblys, *J. Org. Chem.*, **31**, 485 (1966).
[124b] T. Suzuki, *Nippon Kagaku Zasshi*, **86**, 1318 (1966); T. Suzuki and S. Suzuki, *ibid.*, **87**, 476 (1966); T. Suzuki, K. Mitsui, and S. Suzuki, *ibid.*, p. 479; *Chem. Abs.*, **65**, 15190—15191 (1966).
[125] Y. Sawaki and Y. Ogata, *Bull. Chem. Soc. Japan*, **38**, 2103 (1965).
[126] K. Bowden, *Can. J. Chem.*, **43**, 3354 (1965).
[127] K. Bowden and D. C. Parkin, *Can. J. Chem.*, **44**, 1493 (1966).
[128] G. Gorin, P. A. Martic, and G. Doughty, *Arch. Biochem. Biophys.*, **115**, 593 (1966).
[129] M. Goodman and J. Hutchinson, *J. Am. Chem. Soc.*, **88**, 3627 (1966); N. H. Grant, D. E. Grant, and H. E. Alburn, *ibid.*, p. 4071; E. Peggion, M. Terbojevich, A. Cosani, and C. Colombini, *ibid.*, p. 3630.
[130] S. L. Johnson and K. A. Rumon, *Tetrahedron Letters*, **1966**, 1721.
[131] R. H. Yocum and M. M. Joullie, *J. Org. Chem.*, **31**, 3823 (1966); see also I. Talvik, *Reaktsionnaya Sposobnost. Organ. Soedin. Tartusk. Gos. Univ.*, **2**, 229 (1965); *Chem. Abs.*, **65**, 8699 (1966).
[132] S. Searles, and S. Nukina, *J. Am. Chem. Soc.*, **87**, 5656 (1965).
[133] H. A. Staab and G. Maleck, *Chem. Ber.*, **99**, 2955 (1966).
[134] J. J. Monagle and J. V. Mengenhauser, *J. Org. Chem.*, **31**, 2321 (1966); P. Kristián and L. Drobnica, *Coll. Czech. Chem. Commun.*, **31**, 1333 (1966); R. E. Buckles, and L. A. McGrew, *J. Am. Chem. Soc.*, **88**, 3582 (1966); A. J. Leusink, H. A. Budding, and J. G. Noltes, *Rec. Trav. Chim.*, **85**, 151 (1966); S. G. Entelis and O. V. Nesterov, *Kinetika i Kataliz*, **7**, 464 (1966); *Chem. Abs.*, **65**, 10462 (1966).
[135] F. Monacelli, *Ric. Sci. Rend.*, *Sez*, *A.*, **8**, 49 (1965).
[136] L. M. Litvinenko and N. M. Oleinik, *Ukr. Khim. Zh.*, **32**, 174 (1966); *Chem. Abs.*, **64**, 15690 (1966).
[137] E. N. Gur'yanova, P. I. Saukov, A. I. Kutepova, R. A. Soboleva, and N. I. Grishko, *Zh. Organ. Khim.*, **2**, 493 (1966); *Chem. Abs.*, **65**, 7008 (1966).

There have also been several investigations of metal-ion catalysis[138] and of decarboxylation.[139]

Non-carboxylic Acids

Most of the work this year has again been on derivatives of phosphoric acids and their alkyl esters, the mechanisms of whose reactions have been the subject of an extensive review.[1]

Hydrolyses of cyclic phosphate esters and related compounds, which frequently proceed at enhanced rates, continue to provoke interest. Sometimes cyclic as well as acyclic products are formed. Thus, although the rapid hydrolysis of methyl pinacol phosphate (27) in 0.1M-sodium hydroxide in

$$
\begin{array}{ccc}
\text{(26a)} & \text{(27)} & \text{(28)}
\end{array}
$$

50% aqueous 1,2-dimethoxyethane yields O-pinacol phosphate monoanion (26a), in the absence of base it yields pinacolphosphoric acid (28).[140] Similarly 30% of the product from the acid-hydrolysis of methyl ethylene phosphate

[138] A. Agren, G. Ekenved, S. O. Nilsson, and E. Svensjo, *Acta Pharm. Suecica*, **2**, 421 (1965); J. Nyilasi, M. Bihari-Varga, and P. Orsós, *Acta Chim. Acad. Sci. Hung.*, **47**, 291 (1966); R. S. Bruenner and A. E. Oberth, *J. Org. Chem.*, **31**, 887 (1966); M. D. Alexander and D. H. Bush, *J. Am. Chem. Soc.*, **88**, 1130 (1966); D. H. Huchital and H. Taube, *ibid.*, **87**, 5371 (1965); H. Brintzinger, *Z. Naturwiss. Med. Grundlagenforsch.*, **2**, 188 (1965); C. G. Regardh, *Acta Pharm. Suecica*, **3**, 101 (1966); E. Bamann and H. Muenstermann, *Arch. Pharm.*, **298**, 750; *Chem. Abs.*, **64**, 6741 (1966).

[139] R. A. Laursen and F. H. Westheimer, *J. Am. Chem. Soc.*, **88**, 3426 (1966); B. Zerner, S. M. Coutts, F. Lederer, H. H. Waters, and F. H. Westheimer, *Biochemistry*, **5**, 813 (1966); S. Warren, B. Zerner, and F. H. Westheimer, *ibid.*, p. 817; F. Lederer, S. M. Coutts, R. A. Laursen, and F. H. Westheimer, *ibid.*, p. 823; P. P. Lee and F. H. Westheimer, *ibid.*, p. 834; L. W. Clark, *J. Phys. Chem.*, **70**, 627, 1597, 2523 (1966); K. R. Brower, B. Gay, and T. L. Konkol, *J. Am. Chem. Soc.*, **88**, 1681 (1966); G. Lapidus, D. Barton, and P. E. Yankwich, *J. Phys. Chem.*, **70**, 3135 (1966); W. E. Buddenbaum, W. G. Koch, and P. E. Yankwich, *ibid.*, p. 673; C. Rüchardt and O. Krätz, *Tetrahedron Letters*, **1966**, 5915; B. D. Bigley and J. C. Thurman, *ibid.*, **1965**, 4687; *J. Chem. Soc.*, *B*, **1966**, 1076; J. Tsuji and K. Ohno, *Tetrahedron Letters*, **1966**, 4713, 5224; L. W. Clarke, *J. Phys. Chem.*, **70**, 1597 (1966); G. Lapidus, D. Barton, and P. Yankwich, *ibid.*, p. 1575; A. Wood, *Trans. Faraday Soc.*, **62**, 1231 (1966); J. P. Ferris and N. C. Miller, *J. Am. Chem. Soc.*, **88**, 3522 (1966); J. Tsuji and K. Ohno, *ibid.*, p. 3452; E. F. J. Duynstee and E. A. H. Mevis, *Rec. Trav. Chim.*, **85**, 373 (1966); A. C. Andrews and E. W. Grundemeier, *J. Inorg. Nucl. Chem.*, **28**, 455 (1966); P. I. Abell and R. Tien, *J. Org. Chem.*, **30**, 4212 (1965); A. Padwa and R. Hartman, *Tetrahedron Letters*, **1966**, 2277; J. Bus, H. Steinberg, and T. J. de Boer, *ibid.*, p. 1979; G. E. Dunn, P. Leggate, and I. E. Scheffler, *Can. J. Chem.*, **43**, 3080 (1965); N. R. Fetter, *ibid.*, **44**, 1463 (1966).

[140] M. G. Newton, J. R. Cox, and J. A. Bertrand, *J. Am. Chem. Soc.*, **88**, 1503 (1966).

(**29**) is formed without ring-cleavage.[141a] Hydrolysis of the methyl ester of the phosphonic acid (**32**), on the other hand, proceeds with more than 99.8% ring-cleavage. The following explanation was offered.[141a] It was first assumed

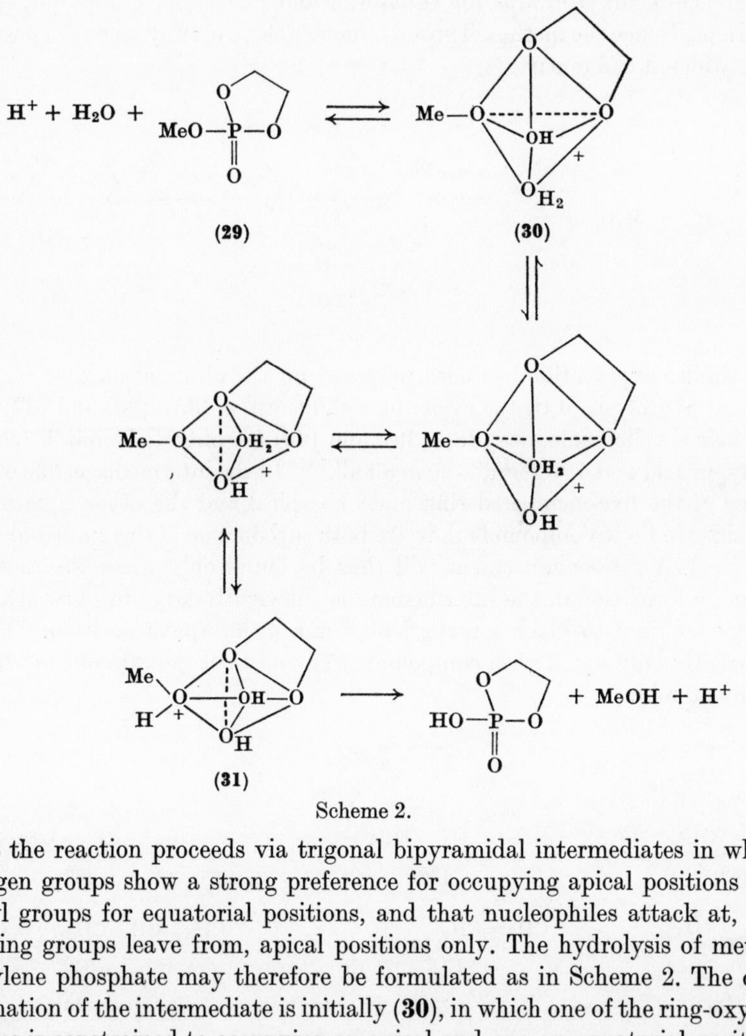

$$H^+ + H_2O +$$

(**29**) (**30**)

(**31**) $+ MeOH + H^+$

Scheme 2.

that the reaction proceeds via trigonal bipyramidal intermediates in which oxygen groups show a strong preference for occupying apical positions and alkyl groups for equatorial positions, and that nucleophiles attack at, and leaving groups leave from, apical positions only. The hydrolysis of methyl ethylene phosphate may therefore be formulated as in Scheme 2. The conformation of the intermediate is initially (**30**), in which one of the ring-oxygen atoms is constrained to occupying an apical and one an equatorial position, the methoxyl group being equatorial. This may be transformed by proton-transfers and pseudorotation into conformation (**31**) in which the ring-oxygen atoms have exchanged positions and the methoxyl group is apical and suitable for departure. With the phosphonate ester (**32**), however, conversion of the

---

[141a] E. A. Dennis, and F. H. Westheimer, *J. Am. Chem. Soc.*, **88**, 3432 (1966).

12*

initial conformation of the intermediate (**33**), with the methylene group equatorial and the ring-oxygen apical, into conformation (**34**) with the positions reversed will be unfavourable owing to the above-mentioned preference of alkyl groups for equatorial and of oxygen groups for apical positions. Hence the methoxyl group is never able to occupy an apical position from which it can depart.

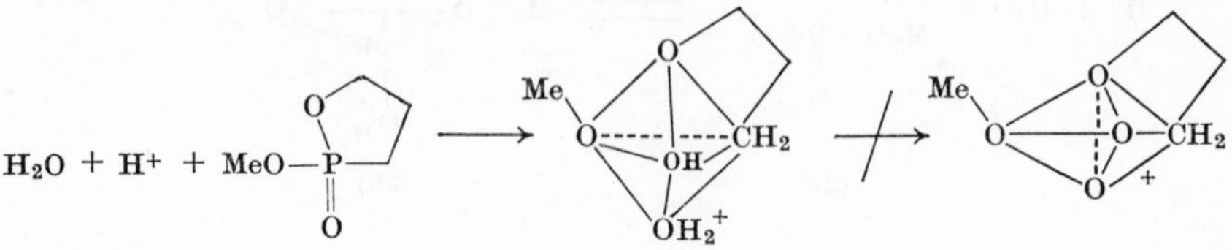

$$H_2O + H^+ + MeO-P$$

(**32**)   (**33**)   (**34**)

A similar explanation has been proposed for the observation that ratio of rates of hydrolysis of (i) the cyclic phosphinic esters (**35**), (**36**) and (**37**) and (ii) their acyclic analogues (**38**), (**39**), and (**40**) are only 1, 1, and 3, respectively, in acid and 4, 1/7, and ~60 in alkali.[141b] In the intermediate, one of the atoms of the five-membered ring must be apical and the other equatorial; and since in these compounds they are both carbon, one of them must always be apical. A rate-enhancement will thus be found only when the relief of strain on formation of the intermediate is sufficiently large to outweigh the energy required to place a methylene group in an apical position. This is apparently only found with compound (**37**), and then the rate-enhancement is only 60-fold.

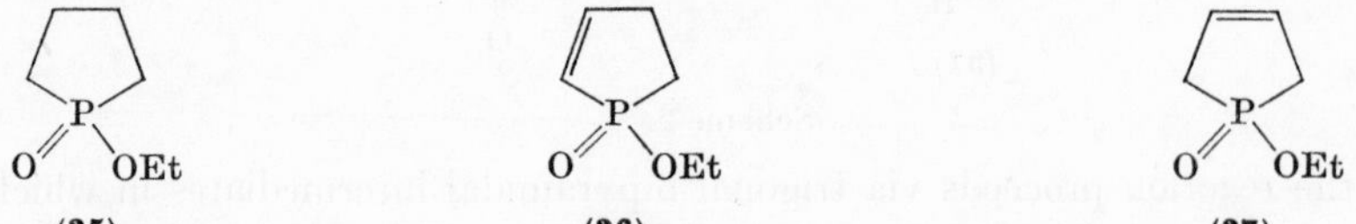

(**35**)   (**36**)   (**37**)

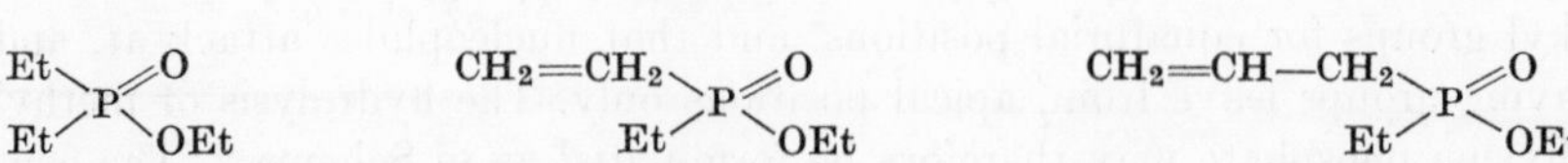

(**38**)   (**39**)   (**40**)

To complement last year's report[142a] of the rapid hydrolysis of a cyclic sulphate ester, namely, catechol sulphate, this year a cyclic sulphonate ester, namely, the sultone from 2-hydroxytoluene-α-sulphonic acid, has been

[141b] E. A. Dennis and F. H. Westheimer, *J. Am. Chem. Soc.*, **88**, 3431 (1966).
[142a] See *Organic Reaction Mechanisms*, **1965**, 281.

shown[142b] to undergo hydrolysis 7×10^5 times faster than phenyl toluene-α-sulphonate.

Intramolecular nucleophilic displacement reactions occur readily with phosphate esters having vicinal hydroxyl and amino-groups.[143] Aromatic amines readily displace the more strongly basic aliphatic amines from phosphoramidic monoesters, yet no intramolecular displacement of the aliphatic by the aromatic amino-group is found to occur with compounds (41) and (42). This was taken as evidence that there is a linear arrangement of entering and leaving amino groups in the transition state as shown in (43).[143]

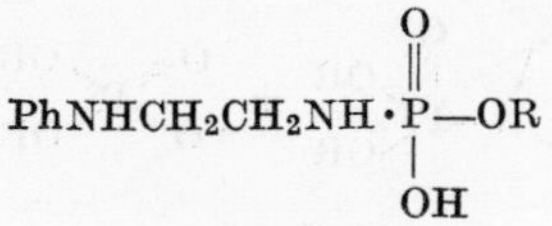

$$
\begin{array}{ccc}
\text{PhNHCH}_2\text{CH}_2\text{NH}\cdot\overset{\displaystyle O}{\underset{\displaystyle OH}{\overset{\|}{P}}}\text{—OR} & & \\
R = \text{Ph or Me} & & \\
(41) & (42) & (43)
\end{array}
$$

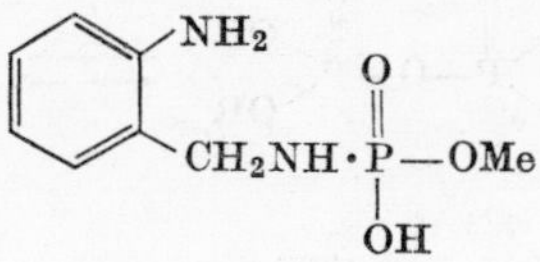

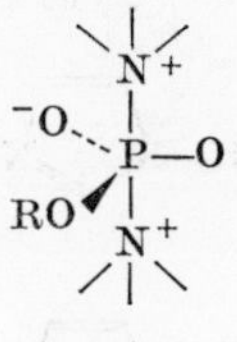

Evidence for the intervention of a "metaphosphate-like" intermediate in the base-catalysed hydrolysis of methyl p-nitrophenyl N-cyclohexylphosphoramidothioate (44) has been provided by Gerrard and Hamer.[144] The optically active form of this ester, on reaction with sodium hydroxide in aqueous dioxan, yields racemic methyl hydrogen phosphoramidothioate (46) with phosphorus–oxygen fission. The intervention of a planar intermediate is therefore indicated and this was written by the authors as (45). The analogous morpholino-ester (47) ($[\phi]_b + 19°$), lacking the abstractable hydrogen, yields an optically active product ($[\phi]_b - 9°$) and so must react by a different mechanism, presumably an S_N2 displacement. The rate is, however, only 100 times slower than that for (44), so that a proton-abstraction mechanism

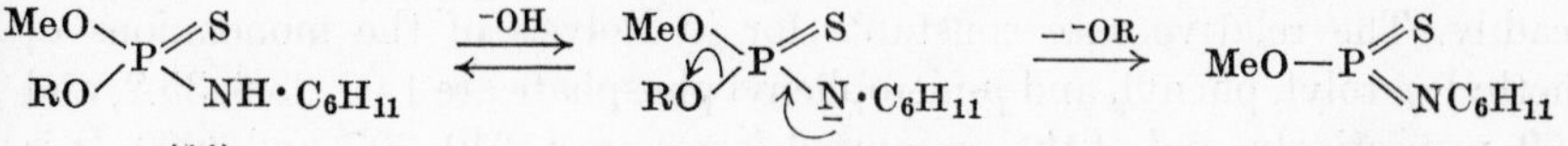

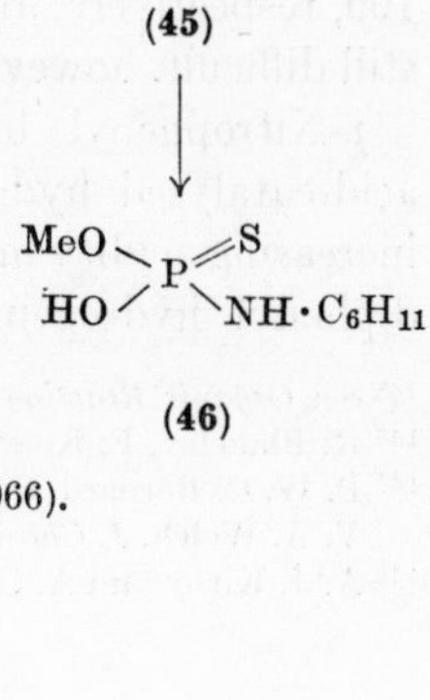

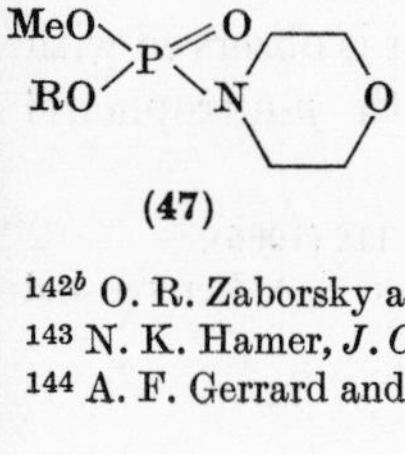

[142b] O. R. Zaborsky and E. T. Kaiser, *J. Am. Chem. Soc.*, **88**, 3084 (1966).
[143] N. K. Hamer, *J. Chem. Soc.*, C, **1966**, 404.
[144] A. F. Gerrard and N. K. Hamer, *Chem. Commun.*, **1966**, 475.

is much less favoured for these p-nitrophenyl esters than for the halides previously studied.[145]

The imidazole-catalysed solvolysis of tetrabenzyl pyrophosphate in propan-1-ol proceeds with nucleophilic attack on phosphorus, with the N-(dibenzylphosphoryl)imidate as an intermediate.[146] The solvolysis of the latter was shown to proceed with general acid-catalysis by imidazolinium ion which was considered, in fact, to be the kinetically equivalent general base–specific acid catalysis. The overall mechanism is, therefore, as shown in Scheme 3. These and earlier results show then that imidazole attacks tetrabenzyl pyrophosphate on phosphorus, but that pyridine attacks it on carbon.

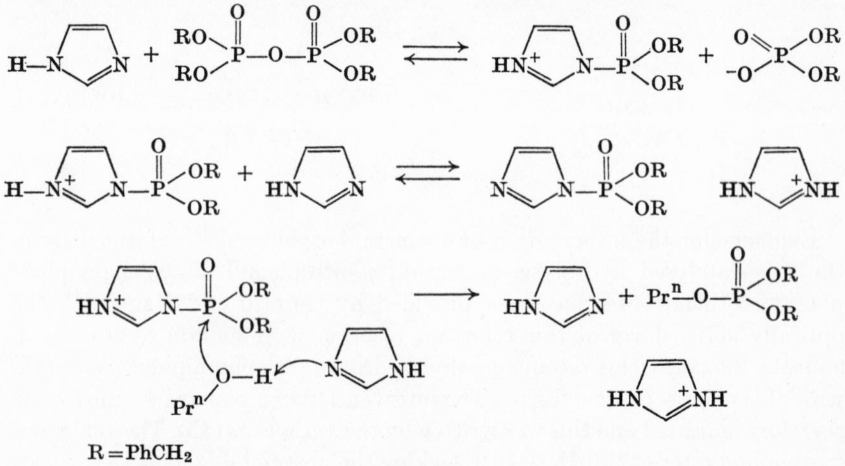

R = PhCH₂

Scheme 3

The pH–rate profiles for the hydrolyses of phenyl, p-tolyl, and p-nitrophenyl,[147] but not 2,4-dinitrophenyl,[148] phosphate are bell-shaped, indicating that, as with alkyl phosphates, hydrolysis of the monoanions occurs especially readily. The relative rate constants for hydrolysis of the monoanions of methyl, p-tolyl, phenyl, and p-nitrophenyl phosphate are 1.00, 28.6, 35.2, and 199, respectively, and of the un-ionized forms are 1, 240, 305, and 3000. It is still difficult, however, to assign definite mechanisms.

p-Nitrophenyl, but not phenyl or p-tolyl, phosphate also undergoes an acid-catalysed hydrolysis and the rate passes through a maximum with increasing acidity in 4M-perchloric acid.[147] Similar behaviour is observed with diphenyl hydrogen and triphenyl phosphate[147] and with p-nitrophenyl

145 See *Organic Reaction Mechanisms*, **1965**, 281.
146 R. Blakeley, F. Kerst, and F. H. Westheimer, *J. Am. Chem. Soc.*, **88**, 112 (1966).
147 P. W. C. Barnard, C. A. Bunton, D. Kellerman, M. M. Mhala, B. Silver, C. A. Vernon, and
   V. A. Welch, *J. Chem. Soc.*, B, **1966**, 227.
148 A. J. Kirby and A. G. Varvoglis, *J. Am. Chem. Soc.*, **88**, 1823 (1966).

diphenylphosphinate.[149] These maxima are, however, the result of a salt effect since maxima are not observed when the reactions are carried out at constant ionic strength. It was thought that this behaviour might be characteristic of the acid-catalysed hydrolysis of phosphate and phosphinate esters proceeding with phosphorus–oxygen bond fission. This is not so, however, since hydrolysis of neopentyl phosphate shows no maximum with increasing acidity, even when ionic strength is not maintained constant.[150]

Hydrolysis of the nucleotide analogues 3-phenylpropyl di- and tri-phosphates over the pH range 0.3—10 and of the enzymic and metal-ion-catalysed reactions have been investigated.[151]

Participation by the carbonyl group was postulated to occur in the hydrolysis of *p*-nitrophenyl phenacyl methylphosphonate, which is 9000 times faster than that of *p*-nitrophenyl methylphosphonate.[152] Possible mechanisms were discussed.[153]

Two investigations of the hydrolysis of D-glucose 6-phosphate have been reported.[154,155] Hydrolysis of the neutral molecule and of the monoanion involve complete P–O bond fission and that of the dianion mainly C–O bond fission.[154] Application of the Hammett–Zucker and the Bunnett hypotheses suggest that a water molecule participates in the rate-determining step of the reaction in acid solution. Under these conditions the phosphate undergoes rapid oxygen-exchange (~2.5 times faster than hydrolysis in $6M$-$HClO_4$ at $100°$) which was thought to involve formation of a 4,6-cyclic phosphate, as shown in equation (12). Contrary to what is normally found for monoalkyl phosphates, the rate constant for hydrolysis of the dianion was reported to be

$$\text{(12)}$$

[149] P. Haake and G. Hurst, *J. Am. Chem. Soc.*, **88**, 2544 (1966).
[150] C. A. Bunton, D. Kellerman, K. G. Oldham, and C. A. Vernon, *J. Chem. Soc.*, *B*, **1966**, 292.
[151] D. L. Miller and F. H. Westheimer, *J. Am. Chem. Soc.*, **88**, 1507, 1511, 1514 (1966).
[152] C. N. Lieske, E. G. Miller, J. J. Zeger, and G. M. Steinberg, *J. Am. Chem. Soc.*, **88**, 188 (1966).
[153] See also, *Organic Reaction Mechanisms*, **1965**, 283.
[154] C. Degani and M. Halmann, *J. Am. Chem. Soc.*, **88**, 4075 (1966).
[155] C. A. Bunton and H. Chaimovich, *J. Am. Chem. Soc.*, **88**, 4082 (1966).

about five times that for hydrolysis of the monoanion. It was suggested that the dianion reacts in the normally unfavourable alternative conformation, the 1-hydroxyl group providing intramolecular general acid-catalysis as symbolized by (48).[155] The rate of disappearance of glucose 6-phosphate was, however, reported to be more than twice the rate of formation of inorganic phosphate under these strongly alkaline conditions,[154] so more complex mechanisms seem probably necessary.

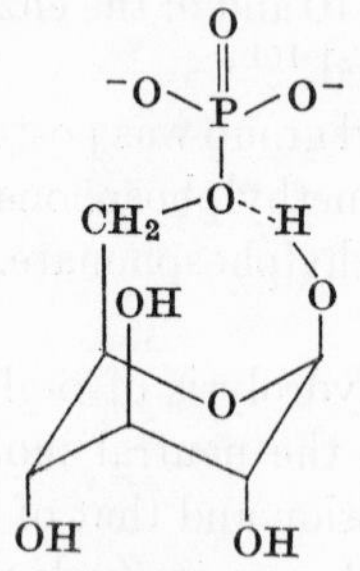

(48)

Hydrolysis of glycerol 1- and 2-phosphate has been investigated. In acid solution it is preceded by rapid interconversion of the isomers, but above pH 2 the rate of this is negligible compared with that of hydrolysis.[156]

The following reactions have also been investigated: formation of nucleoside 3',5'-cyclic phosphates from nucleoside 3'- and 5'-monophosphate *p*-nitrophenyl esters and base;[157] ring opening of the trimetaphosphate ion by phenoxide ions;[158] reactions of phosphonates with amines,[159] and of *N,N'*-diphenylethylenediamidophosphoric acid with formic acid;[160] alcoholysis of amides of tervalent phosphorus[161] and polyphosphoric acid;[162] and hydrolysis of fluorophosphorus compounds,[163] dialkylphosphinic chlorides,[164] alkoxy-

[156] L. Kugel and M. Halmann, *J. Am. Chem. Soc.*, **88**, 3566 (1966).
[157] R. K. Borden and M. Smith, *J. Org. Chem.*, **31**, 3247 (1966).
[158] W. Feldmann, *Chem. Ber.*, **99**, 3251 (1966).
[159] N. N. Mel'nikov, B. A. Khaskin, and L. T. Elepina, *Biol. Aktiun. Sodein. Akad. Nauk SSSR*, **1965**, 248; *Chem. Abs.*, **64**, 3304 (1966).
[160] C. Kutzbach and L. Jaenicke, *Ann. Chem.*, **692**, 26 (1966).
[161] E. E. Nifantev, N. L. Ivanova, and N. K. Bliznyuk, *Zh. Obshch. Khim.*, **36**, 765 (1966); *Chem. Abs.*, **65**, 8698 (1966).
[162] F. B. Clarke and J. W. Lyons, *J. Am. Chem. Soc.*, **88**, 4401 (1966); J. van Steveninck, *Biochemistry*, **5**, 1998 (1966).
[163] B. Uhlik and K. Weber, *Arhiv Hig. Rada Toksikol.*, **16**, 329 (1965); *Chem. Abs.*, **65**, 2082 (1966); J. W. Grochowski, E. Bukowski, and E. Lisowski, *Biul. Wojskowej Akad. Tech.*, **14**, 93 (1965); *Chem. Abs.*, **65**, 3685 (1966); J. W. Grochowski and J. Korecki, *Biul. Wojskowej Akad. Tech.*, **14**, 177 (1965); *Chem. Abs.*, **65**, 3685 (1966).
[164] A. A. Neimysheva and I. L. Knunyants, *Zh. Obshch. Khim.*, **36**, 1090 (1966); *Chem. Abs.*, **65**, 12068 (1966).

diethylphosphine oxides,[165] phosphonates,[166] phosphorylcholine,[167] dialkyl phosphites,[168] and pyrophosphite.[169]

There have been extensive investigations of the mechanism of action of ribonuclease[170] and alkaline phosphatase.[171]

Triethylamine-catalysed hydrolyses of phenylmethanesulphonyl chloride, methanesulphonyl chloride, ethanesulphonyl chloride, and 2-phenylethane-sulphonyl chloride in dioxan–deuterium oxide, and their alcoholyses in O-deuteriated alcohols all proceed with the incorporation of one, and only one, α-deuterium per molecule.[172] The reactions, therefore, proceed through sulphene intermediates:

$$RCH_2SO_2Cl \rightarrow RCH{=}SO_2 \rightarrow RCHD{-}SO_3H$$

Hydrolysis of o-phenylene sulphite is retarded by acids because the rate-decrease from a negative salt effect is greater than the rate-enhancement by acid catalysis. However, fluoride ion is a very effective nucleophilic catalyst.[173]

Other reactions investigated include: disproportionation of sulphinic acids;[174] reactions of toluene-p-sulphonyl chloride with benzylamines,[175] and of p-nitrobenzenesulphonyl bromide with aromatic amines;[176] solvolysis of

[165] L. Larsson and G. Wallerberg, *Acta Chem. Scand.*, **20**, 1247 (1966).
[166] L. Ginjaar and S. Blasse-Vel, *Rec. Trav. Chim.*, **85**, 694 (1966).
[167] J. Attias, *Chimia (Aarau)*, **20**, 17 (1966).
[168] G. Aksnes and O. Grahl-Neilsen, *Acta Chem. Scand.*, **19**, 2373 (1965).
[169] R. E. Mesmer and R. L. Carroll, *J. Am. Chem. Soc.*, **88**, 1381 (1966).
[170] G. G. Hammes and H. A. Scheraga, *Biochemistry*, **5**, 3690 (1966); J. P. Riehm and H. A. Scheraga, *ibid.*, pp. 93, 99; R. W. Woody, M. E. Friedman, and H. A. Scheraga, *ibid.*, p. 2034; L.-K. Li, J. P. Riehm, and H. A. Scheraga, *ibid.*, p. 2043; R. E. Cathou, G. G. Hammes, and P. R. Schimmel, *ibid.*, **4**, 2687 (1965); J. H. Bradbury and H. A. Scheraga, *J. Am. Chem. Soc.*, **88**, 4240 (1966); G. C. Kresheck, and H. A. Scheraga, *ibid.*, p. 4588; A. Deavin, A. P. Mathias, and B. R. Rabin, *Biochem. J.*, **101**, 14c (1966); *Nature*, **211**, 252 (1966); R. L. Heinrikson, *J. Biol. Chem.*, **241**, 1393 (1966); A. Williams, *Chem. Commun.*, **1966**, 590; K. Hofmann, N. J. Smithers, and F. M. Finn, *J. Am. Chem. Soc.*, **88**, 4107 (1966); K. Hofmann, F. M. Finn, M. Limetti, J. Montibelle, and G. Zanetti, *ibid.*, p. 3633; J. E. Shields and H. Renner, *ibid.*, p. 2304; E. Scoffone, F. Marchiori, R. Rocchi, G. Vidali, A. Tamburro, A. Scatturin, and A. Marzotto, *Tetrahedron Letters*, **1966**, 943; N. S. T. Lui and L. Cunningham, *Biochemistry*, **5**, 144 (1966); J. R. Clark and L. Cunningham, *ibid.*, **4**, 2637 (1965); F. C. Hartman and F. Wold, *J. Am. Chem. Soc.*, **88**, 3890 (1966); J. P. Hummel and H. Witzel, *J. Biol. Chem.*, **241**, 1023 (1966); J. S. Roth and D. Hurley, *Biochem. J.*, **101**, 112 (1966); R. T. Simpson and B. L. Vallee, *Biochemistry*, **5**, 2531 (1966); E. N. Ramsden and K. J. Laidler, *Can. J. Chem.*, **44**, 2597 (1966).
[171] A. Williams, *Chem. Commun.*, **1966**, 676; S. G. Agus, R. P. Cox, and H. J. Griffin, *Biochem. Biophys. Acta*, **118**, 363 (1966).
[172] J. F. King and T. Durst, *J. Am. Chem. Soc.*, **87**, 5684 (1965); W. E. Truce and R. W. Campbell, *ibid.*, **88**, 3599 (1966); see also, T. J. Wallace, *Quart. Rev. (London)*, **20**, 67 (1966).
[173] C. A. Bunton and G. Schwerin, *J. Org. Chem.*, **31**, 842 (1966).
[174] J. L. Kice, G. Guaraldi, and C. G. Venier, *J. Org. Chem.*, **31**, 3561 (1966).
[175] A. Fischer, R. S. H. Hickford, G. R. Scott, and J. Vaughan, *J. Chem. Soc.*, B, **1966**, 466.
[176] L. M. Litvinenko, V. A. Savelova, and V. E. Kochkalda, *Reaktsionnaya Sposobnost Organ. Soedin., Tartusk. Gos. Univ.*, **2**, 101 (1965); *Chem. Abs.*, **65**, 7035 (1966).

arylsulphinylsulphones;[177] and hydrolysis of N-arenesulphonylimidazoles,[178] N-substituted sulphonamides,[179] phenyl toluene-p-sulphonates,[180] alkyl and aryl hydrogen sulphates,[181] S-alkyl and S-aryl thiosulphates (Bunte salts),[182] and trimethylene sulphites.[183]

Nitrosation and diazotization have also been investigated.[184]

[177] J. L. Kice, and G. Guaraldi, *J. Org. Chem.*, **31**, 3568 (1966); *J. Am. Chem. Soc.*, **88**, 5236 (1966).

[178] H. A. Staab and K. Wendel, *Ann. Chem.*, **694**, 91 (1966).

[179] K. F. Funk and W. Oelssner, *Pharmazie*, **21**, 470 (1966).

[180] V. Maremae and J. Asenbush, *Reaktsionnaya Sposobnost Organ. Soedin.*, *Tartusk. Gos. Univ.*, **2**, 83 (1965) [*Chem. Abs.*, **64**, 545 (1966)]; V. Maramae and V. Palm, *ibid.*, p. 209 (1965) [*Chem. Abs.*, **65**, 3684 (1966)].

[181] B. D. Batts, *J. Chem. Soc.*, B, **1966**, 547, 551; J. L. Kice and J. M. Anderson, *J. Am. Chem. Soc.*, **88**, 5242 (1966).

[182] J. L. Kice, J. M. Anderson, and N. E. Pawlowski, *J. Am. Chem. Soc.*, **88**, 5245 (1966).

[183] H. F. van Woerden, *Tetrahedron Letters*, **1966**, 2407; G. Wood, and M. Miskow, *ibid.*, p. 4433.

[184] S. Ghosal and B. Mukherjee, *Indian J. Chem.*, **4**, 30 (1966); R. M. Yasyunas and S. I. Burmistrov, *Ukr. Khim. Zh.*, **32**, 50 (1966); *Chem. Abs.*, **64**, 19349 (1966); A. Aboul-Seoud, *Bull. Soc. Chim. Belg.*, **75**, 249 (1966); *Chem. Abs.*, **65**, 13498; V. Sterba, Z. Sagner, and M. Matrka, *Chem. Listy*, **59**, 1361 (1965); *Chem. Abs.*, **64**, 6429 (1966); E. Kalatzis and J. H. Ridd, *J. Chem. Soc.*, B, **1966**, 529; E. C. R. de Fabrizio, E. Kalatzis, and J. H. Ridd, *ibid.*, p. 533.

CHAPTER 13

Photochemistry

Organic photochemistry is a rapidly expanding subject, and whilst many of the mechanisms outlined on the following pages must be considered conjectural much work in this field is now being directed towards fuller mechanistic understanding of photochemical processes. Flash-photolysis techniques are being widely used, and development of the phosphorescence excitation method[1] for the direct observation of singlet triplet absorption spectra holds promise. It has, for example, been possible to distinguish lowest $n\pi^*$ from $\pi\pi^*$ triplet states by an external heavy-atom effect on these spectra. The results for a series of carbonyl compounds correlate well with reactivities anticipated for the different triplet states.[2]

Three books of general interest have appeared,[3a—c] as well as a further volume of "Advances in Photochemistry"[3d] and an extensive review of photochemical processes involving cycloelectronic redistribution in unsaturated systems.[4]

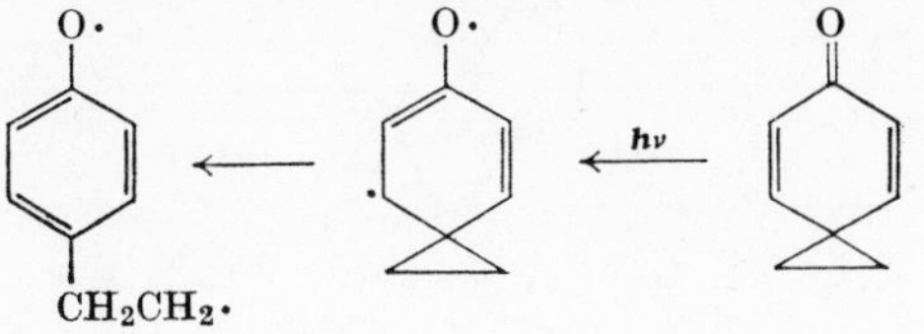

(3)   (1)

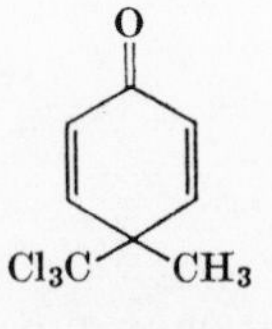

(2) 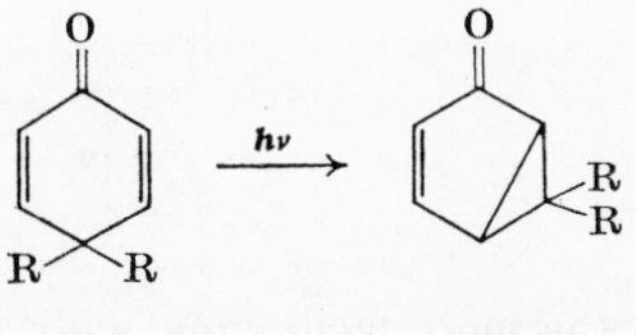   (4)   (5)

[1] W. Rothman, A. Case, and D. R. Kearns, *J. Chem. Phys.*, **43**, 1067 (1965); R. F. Borkman and D. R. Kearns, *Chem. Commun.*, **1966**, 446.

[2] D. R. Kearns and W. A. Case, *J. Am. Chem. Soc.*, **88**, 5087 (1966).

[3] (a) N. J. Turro, "Molecular Photochemistry", W. A. Benjamin, New York, N.Y. 1965; (b) J. G. Calvert and J. N. Pitts, "Photochemistry", John Wiley and Sons, New York, N.Y., 1966; (c) R. O. Kan, "Organic Photochemistry", McGraw-Hill, New York, N.Y., 1966; (d) "Advances in Photochemistry", Vol. IV, Interscience Publishers, New York, London, Sydney, 1966.

[4] R. N. Warrener and J. B. Bremner, *Rev. Pure Appl. Chem.*, **16**, 117 (1966).

The photochemistry of cyclohexenones and cyclohexadienones continues to attract attention. Schuster and his colleagues[5] have elaborated their evidence for homolytic decomposition of the excited states of dienones (1) and (2). The former compound gives products derivable by interaction of the diradical (3) and solvent; the latter gives products arising from ·CCl₃ radicals.

Zimmerman and his co-workers have designated rearrangements of the type (4) → (5) as "type A". These rearrangements are also observed to occur in conjugated cyclohexenones, but quantum yields are smaller by a factor of 200. Quenching experiments confirm the involvement of a triplet state (possibly $\pi\pi^*$) in the conversion of (6) into (7);[6] the relative inefficiency is attributable to the alkyl migration, unprecedented in ground-state radical reactions. A different pathway is open to the dienone,[7] though the analogous mechanism

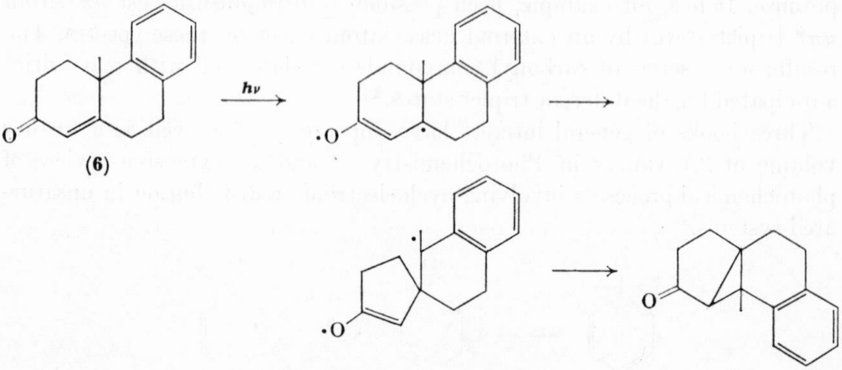

would involve the more facile vinyl radical migration, a process which *has* been observed in ground-state reactions.[8] The planar diradical intermediate (8) is clearly not involved in the above enone rearrangement, as Chapman and

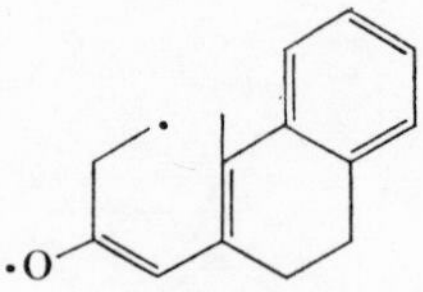

[5] D. I. Schuster and C. J. Polowczyk, *J. Am. Chem. Soc.*, **88**, 1722 (1966); D. I. Schuster and D. J. Patel, *ibid.*, p. 1825.

[6] H. E. Zimmerman, R. G. Lewis, J. J. McCullough, A. Padwa, S. Staley, and M. Semmelhack, *J. Am. Chem. Soc.*, **88**, 159, 1965 (1966).

[7] H. E. Zimmerman and J. S. Swenton, *J. Am. Chem. Soc.*, **89**, 906 (1967).

[8] See *Organic Reaction Mechanisms*, **1965**, 119, 187.

his co-workers have resolved the ketone (6) (by a novel procedure) and shown the transformation to lead to optically active (7) of high optical purity.[9]

It is at first sight surprising that migration of the aryl group does not occur in the rearrangement of compound (6), but closer inspection shows that the aryl-bridged intermediate in such a rearrangement would experience excessive strain in the B ring. However, aryl migration *is* observed in the rearrangement of Pummerer's ketone (9) [→ (10)][10] (in alcoholic solvents, a major side

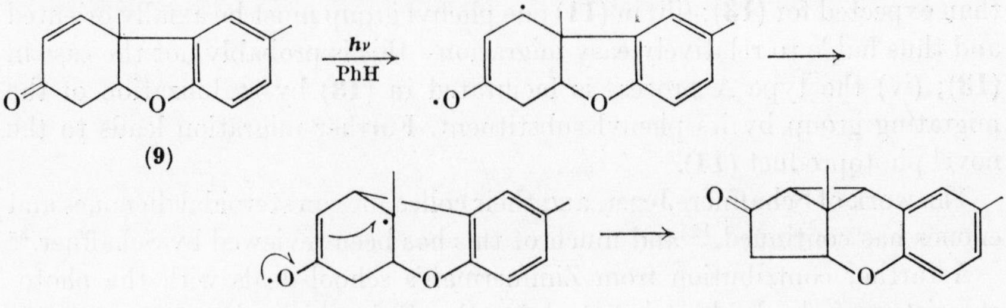

(9)

(10)

reaction is the addition of solvent to the double bond). Aryl migrations [e.g., (11) → (12)] are also known where no bridging is present to inhibit such a

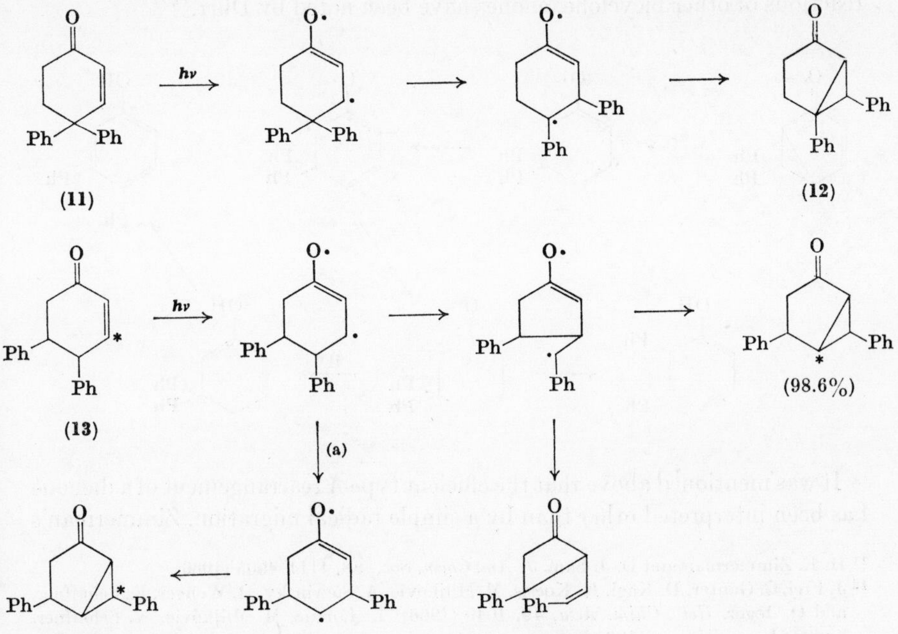

(11)

(12)

(13)

(a)

(98.6%)

(1.4%)

(14)

[9] O. L. Chapman, J. B. Sieja, and W. J. Welstead, *J. Am. Chem. Soc.*, **88**, 161 (1966).
[10] T. Matsuura and K. Ogura, *J. Am. Chem. Soc.*, **88**, 2602 (1966).

process. Zimmerman and Sam[11] have now extended their study of these systems to the enone (13) and have shown by isotopic labelling that the type A product is almost exclusively formed by a similar process to that giving (7). No more than 1.4% of the product can arise from phenyl migration. The factors favouring the type A process for (13) are considered to be: (i) in (13) [but not (11)] migration of phenyl [path (a)] leaves a non-stabilized radical; (ii) in (11) separation of geminal diphenyl groups gives greater relief of strain than expected for (13); (iii) in (11) one phenyl group must be axially oriented and thus liable to relatively easy migration—this is probably not the case in (13); (iv) the type A process is facilitated in (13) by stabilization of the migrating group by its phenyl substituent. Further migration leads to the novel photoproduct (14).

The work of Schaffner, Jeger, and their colleagues on steroidal dienones and enones has continued,[12] and much of this has been reviewed by Schaffner.[3d]

A further contribution from Zimmerman's school deals with the photo-chemistry of the bridged ketone [(5); R = Ph], which gives 2,3- and 3,4-diphenylphenol in proportions depending on pH. The variation results from protonation of the proposed zwitterionic intermediate at low pH. Molecular-orbital calculations are consistent with the observed results.[13a] Photochemical reactions of other bicyclohexenones have been noted by Dürr.[13b]

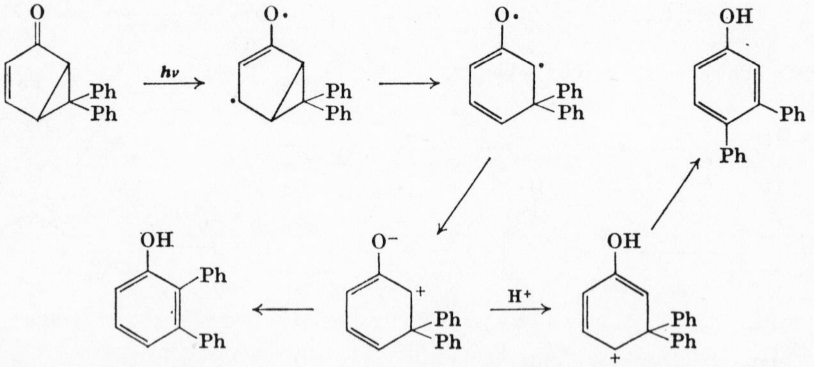

It was mentioned above that the efficient type A rearrangement of a dienone has been interpreted other than by a simple radical migration. Zimmerman's

[11] H. E. Zimmerman and D. J. Sam, *J. Am. Chem. Soc.*, **88**, 4114, 4905 (1966).
[12] J. Frei, C. Ganter, D. Kägi, K. Kocsis, M. Miljković, A. Siewinsky, R. Wenger, K. Schaffner, and O. Jeger, *Helv. Chim. Acta*, **49**, 1049 (1966); L. Lorenc, M. Miljkovic, K. Schaffner, and O. Jeger, *ibid.*, p. 1183.
[13a] H. E. Zimmerman, R. Keese, J. Nasielski, and J. S. Swenton, *J. Am. Chem. Soc.*, **88**, 4895 (1966).
[13b] H. Dürr, *Tetrahedron Letters*, **1966**, 5829.

group has approached the supposed zwitterionic intermediate (15) via a ground-state (Favorskii) reaction. A high yield of the rearranged compound [(5); R = Ph] was isolated, and this is held to support the intermediacy of (15) in the photochemical process.[14]

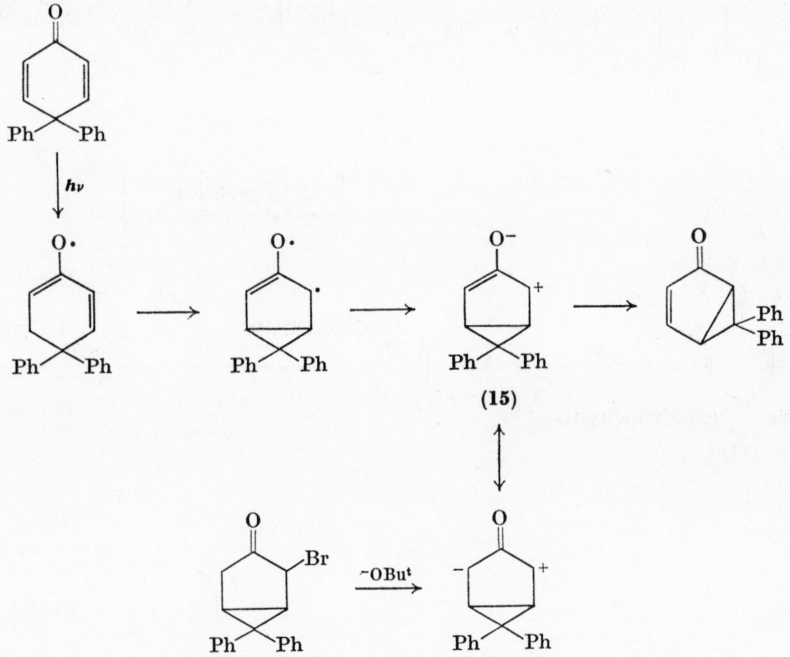

The keto-acid (16) rearranges to hydroazulene derivatives in a process controlled by intramolecular protonation in the excited state.[15] In his work with crowded dienones Miller has observed the transformation (17) → (18), in which a key step is the unusual nucleophilic attack of bromide on a *C*-methyl group.[16] What appears to be the first example of transformation of a linearly conjugated cyclohexadienone to a bicyclohexenone has been revealed.[17]

Many photochemical reactions of simple aliphatic and aromatic ketones and aldehydes have received attention. Photoreduction of benzophenone in propan-2-ol is well known. In new work, other hydrogen donors have been investigated.[18] For reaction in propan-2-ol, extrapolation to infinite dilution suggests that the only product would then be a charge-transfer complex

[14] H. E. Zimmerman, D. Döpp, and P. S. Huyffer, *J. Am. Chem. Soc.*, 1966, **88**, 5352 (1966).
[15] D. Caine, J. F. DeBardeleben, and J. B. Dawson, *Tetrahedron Letters*, **1966**, 3627.
[16] B. Miller, *Chem. Commun.*, **1966**, 327.
[17] H. Hart, P. M. Collins, and A. J. Waring, *J. Am. Chem. Soc.*, 1966, **88**, 1005 (1966).
[18] R. S. Davidson, *Chem. Commun.*, **1966**, 575; M. J. Cziesla, K. F. Mueller, and O. Jones, *Tetrahedron Letters*, **1966**, 813.

between $Me_2\overset{\cdot}{C}OH$ and $Ph_2\overset{\cdot}{C}OH$;[19] at finite concentration this constitutes a by-product with λ_{max} 325 mμ. Further work has appeared from Cohen's

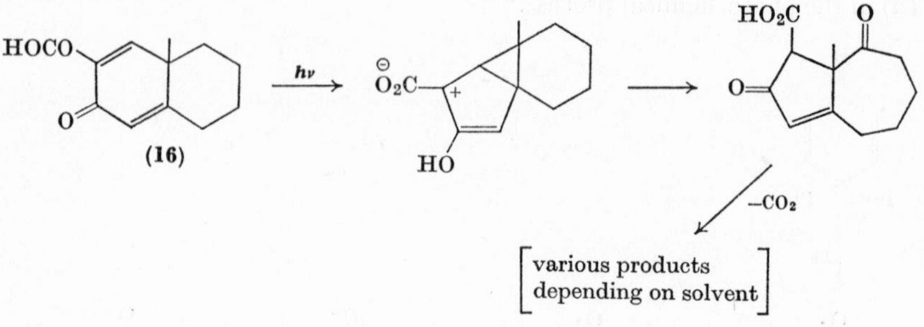

(16)

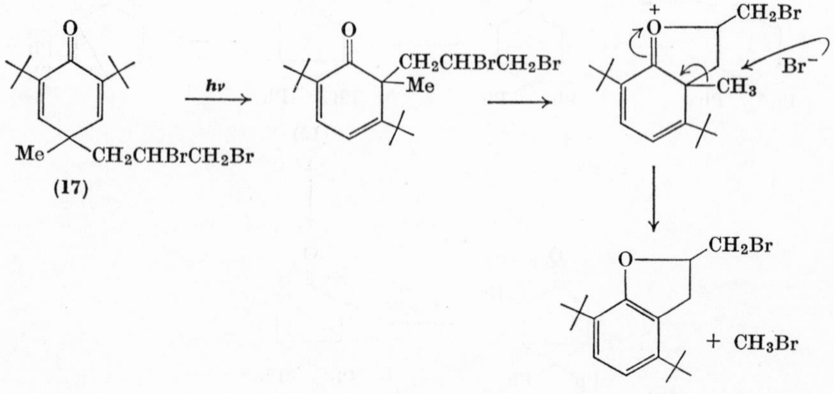

(17)

$$\begin{bmatrix} \text{various products} \\ \text{depending on solvent} \end{bmatrix}$$

$-CO_2$

$+ CH_3Br$

(18)

group,[20] and includes the direct observation of $Ph_2\overset{\cdot}{C}OH$ radicals in flash-photolysis experiments; diphenyl disulphide slows the reaction by scavenging the ketyl, and not by triplet quenching. With high radiation intensity (but no additive), the quantum yield is also reduced, owing, according to Yang and Murov,[21] to radical quenching of the benzophenone triplets.

Photoreduction of aroyl cyanides,[22] benzophenone imines,[23] and pyruvic acid has been observed.[24] Surprisingly, the photoreduction of pyruvic acid is slower in *tert*-butyl alcohol than in propan-2-ol by a factor of only 20.

[19] H. L. J. Bäckstrom, K. L. Appelgren, and R. J. V. Niklasson, *Acta Chem. Scand.*, **19**, 1555 (1965).

[20] W. V. Sherman and S. G. Cohen, *J. Phys. Chem.*, **70**, 178 (1966); S. G. Cohen and S. Aktipis, *J. Am. Chem. Soc.*, **88**, 3587 (1966).

[21] N. C. Yang and S. Murov, *J. Am. Chem. Soc.*, **88**, 2852 (1966).

[22] V. F. Raaen, *J. Org. Chem.*, **31**, 3310 (1966).

[23] M. Fischer, *Tetrahedron Letters*, **1966**, 5273.

[24] D. S. Kendall and P. A. Leermakers, *J. Am. Chem. Soc.*, **88**, 2766 (1966).

Triplet ketones with γ-hydrogen may react by intramolecular hydrogen transfer, leading to cyclobutanol or to Norrish "type II" fragmentation. γ-Deuterium-transfer in deuterated hexan-2-ones is a slower process, but the deuteriated triplet is longer-lived, and overall gives higher yields of the above products.[25] Wagner and Hammond have detailed their work[26] on these reactions with various ketones and discussed factors affecting the relative importance of the hydrogen transfer in singlet and triplet† excited states of aliphatic ketones. In alkyl aryl ketones, only the triplet reacts, and when the lowest triplet is $\pi\pi^*$ there is no reaction.[26, 27] In the gas phase, only the triplet state of purely aliphatic carbonyl compounds has been reported to participate.[28]

1,5-Hydrogen-transfer in compounds (**19**),[28] (**20**),[29] and (**21**)[30] has been examined. In the last case, the fragmentation process would yield allene, but this was not detected. In (**22**), which has no hydrogen on the γ-carbon, deuterium- and ^{14}C-labelling experiments accord with migration of a benzoyl group, possibly as indicated.[31]

New studies of the fundamental processes following irradiation of acetone[32a]

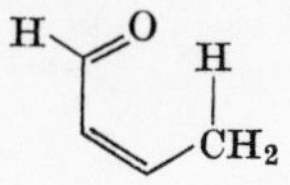

(19) 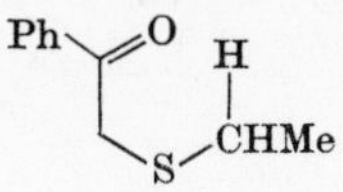   (20) 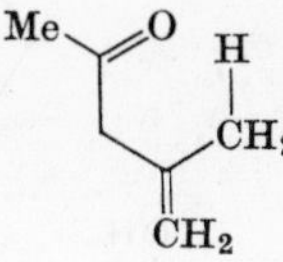   (21)

(22)

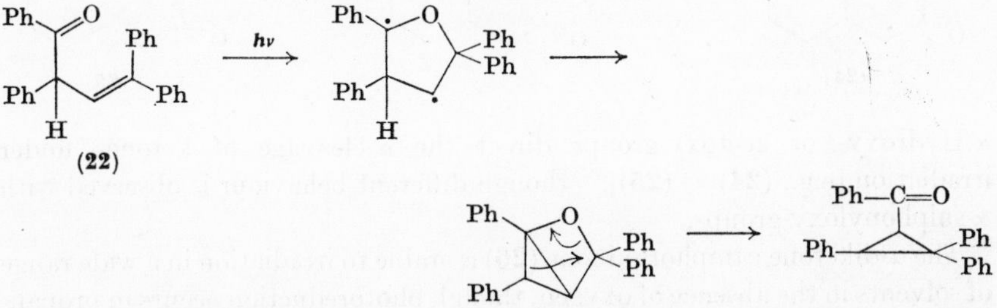

† It is emphasized that the reactivities of the excited $n\pi^*$ singlet and triplet states should be similar; which one is observed to react depends principally on its life-time in the reaction system.

25 D. R. Coulson and N. C. Yang, *J. Am. Chem. Soc.*, **88**, 4511 (1966).

26 P. J. Wagner and G. S. Hammond, *J. Am. Chem. Soc.*, **88**, 1245 (1966); *Organic Reaction Mechanisms*, **1965**, 290.

27 E. J. Baum, J. K. S. Wan, and J. N. Pitts, *J. Am. Chem. Soc.*, **88**, 2652 (1966).

28 R. B. Cundall and A. S. Davies, *Trans. Faraday Soc.*, **62**, 2444 (1966).

29 H. Hogeveen and P. J. Smit, *Rec. Trav. Chim.*, **85**, 489 (1966).

30 N. C. Yang and D.-M. Thap, *Tetrahedron Letters*, **1966**, 3671.

31 L. P. Tenney, D. W. Boykin, and R. E. Lutz, *J. Am. Chem. Soc.*, **88**, 1835 (1966).

32a R. B. Cundall, *Proc. Roy. Soc., A*, **290**, 563 (1966).

and acetaldehyde[32b] have been reported. The factors facilitating photodecarbonylation of complex cyclic ketones have been examined. These include β,γ-unsaturation, and α-alkylation, features expected to stabilize the intermediate biradical.[33] Gas-phase photodecarbonylation of *trans*-2,3-dimethylcyclopentanone gives both *cis*- and *trans*-1,2-dimethylcyclobutane,[34] which also is consistent with a biradical mechanism. Decarbonylation of steroidal 19-aldehydes has been examined.[35, 36] The unsaturated compound (23) reacts by an intramolecular mechanism.[35] The absence of isotope "crossing", observed when two different unsaturated aldehydes, one labelled and the other not, were decarbonylated together, is consistent with a cage or concerted mechanism.[37a] However, the caged-radical mechanism was considered unlikely in view of the failure to observe any incorporation of protium when the decarbonylation was effected in the presence of 2-molar unlabelled thiol.[37a]

O
‖
D—C

$\xrightarrow[-CO]{h\nu}$

(23)

OH   OH   HO

HO...   HO.

O   O   O

$\xrightarrow{h\nu}$ $\longrightarrow$

(24)   (25)

α-Hydroxy- or acetoxy-groups direct the α-cleavage of ketones under irradiation [e.g., (24) → (25)],[37] though different behaviour is observed with α-sulphonyloxy-groups.

The α-diketone camphorquinone (26) is stable to irradiation in a wide range of solvents in the absence of oxygen, though photoreduction occurs in propan-2-ol[38] (to give a mixture of acyloins) and in xylenes[39] [to give the derivatives

[32b] R. B. Cundall and A. S. Davies, *Trans. Faraday Soc.*, **62**, 2793 (1966).
[33] J. E. Starr and R. H. Eastman, *J. Org. Chem.*, **31**, 1393 (1966).
[34] H. M. Frey, *Chem. Ind. (London)*, **1966**, 947.
[35] J. Hill, J. Iriarte, K. Schaffner, and O. Jeger, *Helv. Chim. Acta*, **49**, 292 (1966); K. Schaffner, *Chimia*, **19**, 575 (1965).
[36] M. E. Wolff and S.-Y. Cheng, *Tetrahedron Letters*, **1966**, 2507.
[37a] M. Alchtar, *Tetrahedron Letters*, **1965**, 4727.
[37b] G. Hüppi, F. G. Eggart, S. Iwasaki, H. Wehrli, K. Schaffner, and O. Jeger, *Helv. Chim. Acta*, **49**, 1986 (1966).
[38] J. Meinwald and H. O. Klingele, *J. Am. Chem. Soc.*, **88**, 2071 (1966).
[39] M. B. Rubin and R. G. LaBarge, *J. Org. Chem.*, **31**, 3283 (1966).

(27) and **(28)**]. Oxygen modifies the course of the reaction, and a variety of products is observed, including camphoric anhydride and isomeric lactones **(29)** and **(30)**.[38] Diketone **(31)** gives analogous products in the presence of air, but decarbonylates in oxygen-free conditions.[40]

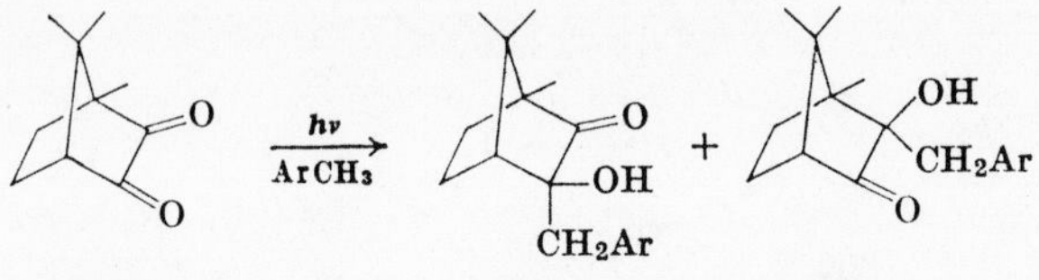

There are conflicting conclusions[41,42] concerning the structure of one photodimer from benzocyclobutenedione; however, in both reports a similar mechanism is advocated (see overleaf) and this is supported by trapping experiments.[42]

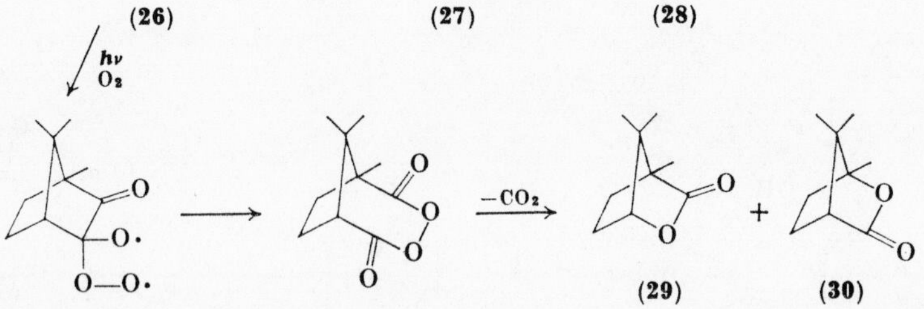

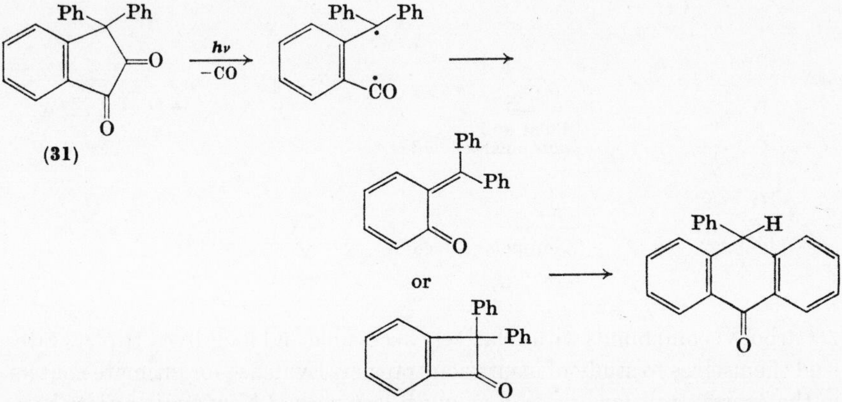

Further studies of the photochemistry of 1,3-diketones and cyclobutane-diones have appeared,[43] and Hammond and his co-workers have made a

[40] J. Rigaudy and N. Paillous, *Tetrahedron Letters*, **1966**, 4825.
[41] R. F. C. Brown and R. K. Solly, *Tetrahedron Letters*, **1966**, 169.
[42] H. A. Staab and J. Ipaktschi, *Tetrahedron Letters*, **1966**, 583.
[43] See *Organic Reaction Mechanisms*, **1965**, 290; I. Haller and R. Srinivasan, *Can. J. Chem.*, **43**, 3165 (1965); J. Rigaudy and P. Derible, *Bull. Soc. Chim. France*, **1965**, 3047, 3055.

detailed study of the related tetramethyloxetanone (32).[44] This fragments from its singlet excited state by two different pathways according to solvent polarity, and with an overall quantum yield of unity. The difference is *not* due to protonation by the polar solvents.

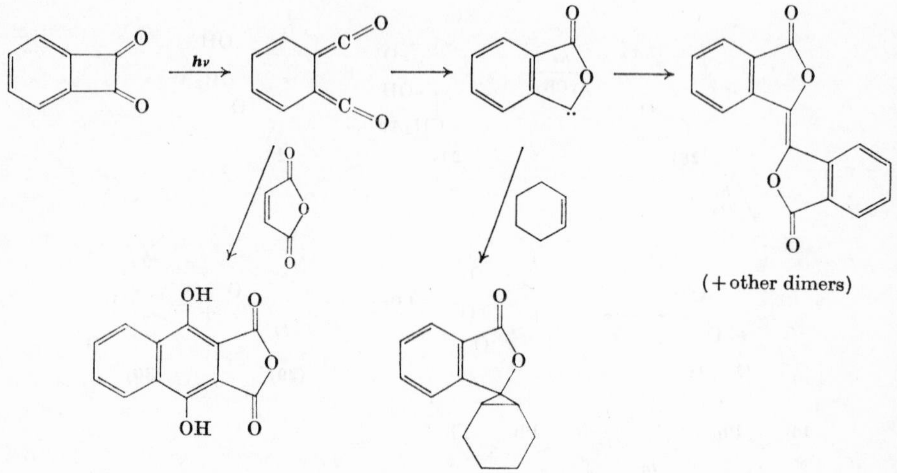

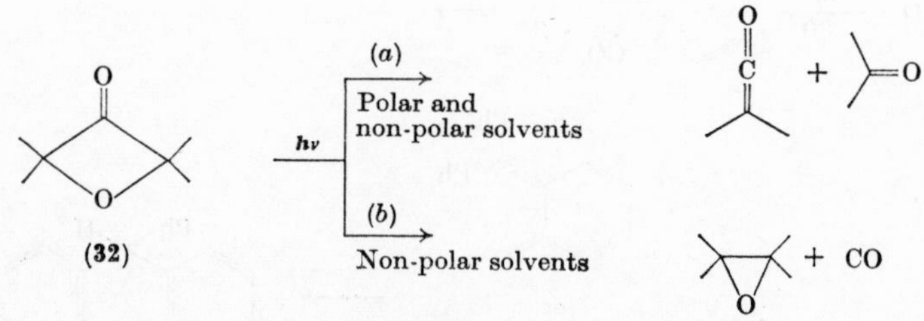

(+other dimers)

(a)
Polar and non-polar solvents

(b)
Non-polar solvents

+ CO

(32)

Carbonyl compounds with relatively accessible and long-lived triplet states lend themselves to study of excitation transfer. Evidence for intimate contact in the energy-transfer process was given last year.[45] Now steric effects have been detected by using *ortho*-substituted benzophenones.[46] Quenching by metal chelates also shows dependence on bulky substituents, though in such cases quenching may not involve transfer of triplet energy.[47] In the gas phase, quenching of triplet acetone and biacetyl has been studied with a series of olefins.[48a] In instances where the process is endothermic the rate of quenching depends on the endothermicity. Exothermic quenching is much faster, with

[44] P. J. Wagner, C. A. Stout, S. Searles, and G. S. Hammond, *J. Am. Chem. Soc.*, **88**, 1242 (1966).
[45] See *Organic Reaction Mechanisms*, **1965**, 296.
[46] W. G. Herkstroeter, L. B. Jones, and G. S. Hammond, *J. Am. Chem. Soc.*, **88**, 4777 (1966).
[47] A. J. Fry, R. S. H. Liu, and G. S. Hammond, *J. Am. Chem. Soc.*, **88**, 4781 (1966).
[48a] R. E. Rebbert and P. Ausloos, *J. Am. Chem. Soc.*, **87**, 5569 (1965).

no obvious correlation between rate and excess energy. The quenching of acetone triplets by *cis*-pent-2-ene has also been studied.[48b]

In flash-photolysis experiments on the photosensitized isomerization of *cis*- and *trans*-stilbene and of the α-methylstilbenes, the rate of quenching of the sensitizers was followed by observing the decay of their triplet–triplet absorption, and was compared with their triplet energy.[48c] Except in the case of *trans*-stilbene, energy-transfer can apparently proceed efficiently in a non-vertical fashion, leading to a twisted excited state of lower energy than the planar (Frank–Condon) excited state. In the case of *trans*-stilbene, energy transfer was inefficient from all sensitizers having triplet energy lower than that of the spectroscopic stilbene triplet. It was concluded that in this case, where steric repulsions are unimportant, the planar and the non-planar excited states must be of comparable energy.

In a further study of stilbene isomerization, in this case sensitized by phenanthraquinone,[48d] a complex is considered to be formed between triplet quinone and either stilbene isomer. This complex may collapse to adduct, or dissociate, again leaving the stilbene in a non-spectroscopic excited state. The latter may lead to either the *cis*- or the *trans*-ground state. In a related field of study there is evidence that the dianions of stilbene and its derivatives adopt a twisted conformation.[48e]

It has been concluded by Saltiel and his co-workers[48f] that, contrary to the usually accepted view, direct photoisomerization of stilbene does not involve the triplet state.

Photochemical transformations of simple aromatic compounds have continued to attract attention. Adducts of benzene with maleimide and

(33)

(34)

N-substituted maleimides are analogous to those formed from maleic anhydride,[49] though there is no evidence for charge-transfer phenomena in the

[48b] R. F. Borkman and D. R. Kearns, *J. Am. Chem. Soc.*, **88**, 3467 (1966).
[48c] W. G. Herkstroeter and G. S. Hammond, *J. Am. Chem. Soc.*, **88**, 4769 (1966).
[48d] J. J. Bohning and K. Weiss, *J. Am. Chem. Soc.*, **88**, 2893 (1966).
[48e] J. F. Garst, J. G. Pacifici, and E. R. Zabolotny, *J. Am. Chem. Soc.*, **88**, 3872 (1966).
[48f] J. Saltiel, E. D. Megarity, and K. G. Kneipp, *J. Am. Chem. Soc.*, **88**, 2336 (1966).
[49] D. Bryce-Smith and M. A. Hems, *Tetrahedron Letters*, **1966**, 1895; J. S. Bradshaw, *ibid.*, p. 2039.

reaction. With olefins[50] and hydroxy-compounds[51,52] 1,3-adducts [(**33**) and (**34**)] apparently arising from the benzvalene form of benzene (or an excited state of benzene possessing similar geometry) have been isolated. Benzvalene itself is thought[53] to be a product of gas-phase irradiation of benzene at 185 mμ. Collisional quenching by added nitrogen is extremely rapid, perhaps explaining the failure to observe this product in solution photochemistry. Ring-opening processes occur when benzene is irradiated in a rigid glass at 77°K.[54] Linear hexatrienes are formed, together with solvent-produced radicals which have been detected by electron spin resonance. Radical reactions of benzene irradiated in liquid ether/HCl have also been observed.[52]

Irradiation of liquid hexafluorobenzene in the absence of solvent causes no chemical change.[55] However, in the gas-phase the Dewar form is produced.[56] Haller extrapolates this result to the xylenes, where 1,2-shifts occur in the vapour phase, but both 1,2- and 1,3-shifts are evident in solution. If it is assumed that xylenes may also produce Dewar forms in the vapour phase, these cannot isomerize [e.g., (**35**) → (**36**)] or 1,3-shifts would be anticipated.

(**35**)   (**36**)

This is presumably also true for solutions, for which Haller therefore argues that the 1,3-shifts must involve Ladenburg intermediates.

The photochemistry of some substituted 1,2-dihydrophthalic anhydrides and related compounds has been investigated.[57] Particularly interesting is the fragmentation of (**37**), leading to both 1,2,3,4- and 1,2,3,5-tetraphenyl-benzene[57c] (at 25°; the rearranged product was not observed at −10°[57b]). Detection of the rearranged isomer was considered to constitute evidence for a benzvalene–benzvalene isomerization by one of the pathways indicated.

[50] K. E. Wilzbach and L. Kaplan, *J. Am. Chem. Soc.*, **88**, 2066 (1966); D. Bryce-Smith, A. Gilbert, and B. H. Orger, *Chem. Commun.*, **1966**, 512.
[51] L. Kaplan, J. S. Ritscher, and K. E. Wilzbach, *J. Am. Chem. Soc.*, **88**, 2881 (1966).
[52] E. Farenhorst and A. F. Bickel, *Tetrahedron Letters*, **1966**, 5911.
[53] J. K. Foote, M. H. Mallon, and J. N. Pitts, *J. Am. Chem. Soc.*, **88**, 3698 (1966).
[54] E. Migirdicyan, *J. Chim. Phys.*, **63**, 520, 535, 543 (1966); B. Brocklehurst, W. A. Gibbons, F. T. Long, G. Porter, and M. I. Savadatti, *Trans. Faraday Soc.*, **62**, 1743 (1966).
[55] D. Bryce-Smith, B. E. Connett, A. Gilbert, E. Kendrick, *Chem. Ind. (London)*, **1966**, 855.
[56] G. Camaggi, F. Gozzo, and G. Cevidalli, *Chem. Commun.*, **1966**, 313; I. Haller, *J. Am. Chem. Soc.*, **88**, 2070 (1966).
[57] (a) H. Prinzbach, R. Kitzing, E. Druckrey, and H. Achenbach, *Tetrahedron Letters*, **1966**, 4265; (b) R. N. Warrener and J. B. Bremmer, *Angew. Chem. Internat. Ed. Engl.*, **5**, 311 (1966); (c) R. N. Warrener and J. B. Bremmer, *Tetrahedron Letters*, **1966**, 5691.

Neither of the initially formed benzvalenes can open to the rearranged product. A similar mechanism has been advanced[58] to accommodate the formation of *meta-* and *para-* as well as *ortho*-terphenyls in a reaction involving the carbene

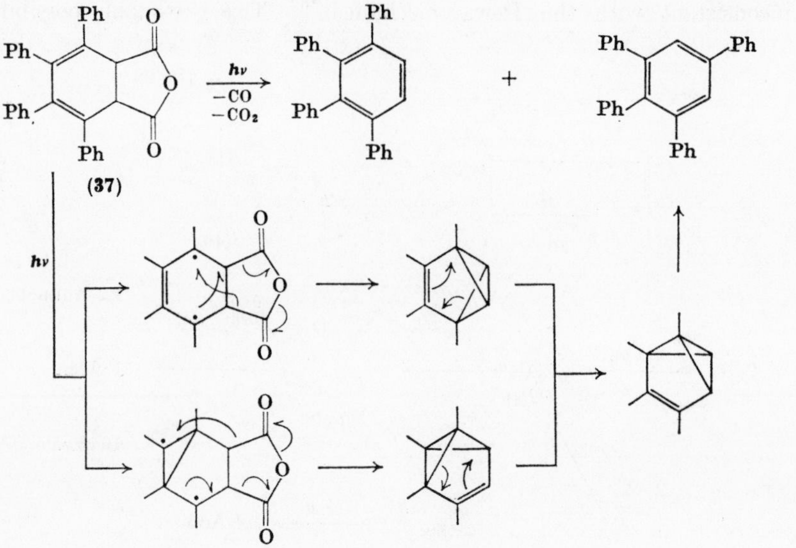

(37)

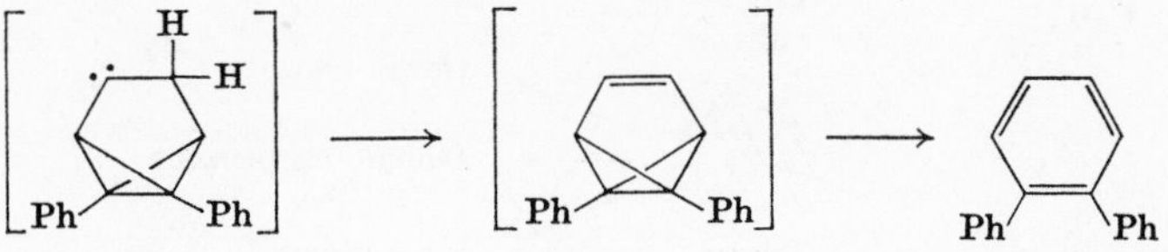

(+*m*- and *p*-isomers)

intermediate **(38)**. If these arguments are correct, then the benzvalene mechanism permits 1,3-shifts of substituents as well as the 1,2-shifts normally ascribed to it (as in the xylene isomerizations already mentioned). Evidently there is scope here for further investigation.

Dienes have been observed to undergo 1,2- and 1,4-addition to benzenes[59] [e.g., with isoprene → **(39)** and **(40)**] and also to participate in a non-product forming quenching of excited singlet aromatic molecules.[60]

The known photochemical reactions of benzene (and its derivatives) have

[58] S. Masamune, F. Fukumoto, Y. Yasunari, and D. Darwish, *Tetrahedron Letters*, **1966**, 193.
[59] G. Koltzenburg and K. Kraft, *Tetrahedron Letters*, **1966**, 389.
[60] L. M. Stephenson, D. G. Whitten, G. F. Vesley, and G. S. Hammond, *J. Am. Chem. Soc.*, **88**, 3665 (1966).

been analysed in terms of the symmetry of its lowest excited singlet and triplet states, as shown in Scheme 1.[61]

Further work has also been conducted on the mechanisms of isomerization of five-membered heterocycles. Double-labelling techniques[62] give results inconsistent with the Dewar mechanism.[63] Two reasonable possibilities

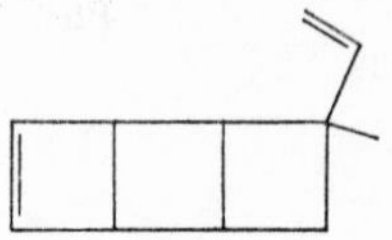

(39) 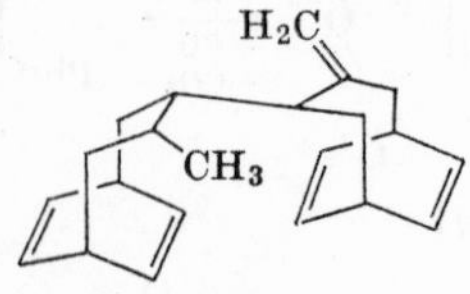   (40)

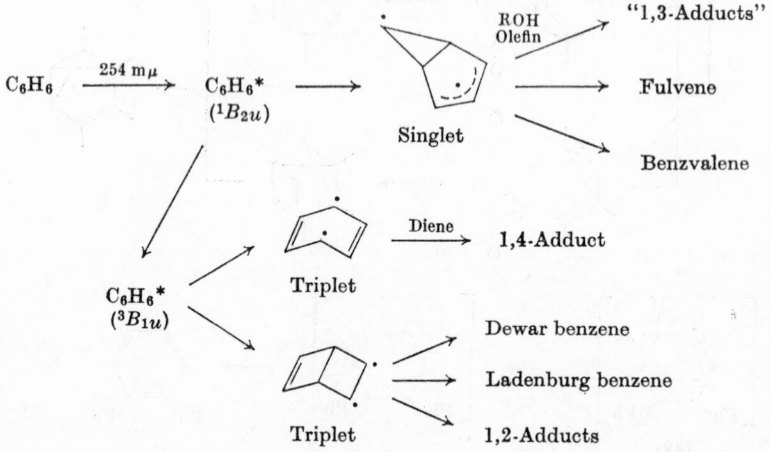

Scheme 1

remain: the intervention of an intermediate such as (41), or a ring-opened structure (42). Ring-opened isomers [e.g., (43)] have been isolated in the photoisomerization of isoxazoles to oxazoles[64] and are possibly also involved in the photochemical rearrangement of *N*-phenylsydnone (44).[65] Incorporation of external (^{14}C-labelled) carbon dioxide accords with the mechanism proposed for the latter reaction. It has been suggested that similar ring-opened structures merit consideration in the benzene isomerizations.[62b]

[61] D. Bryce-Smith and H. C. Longuet-Higgins, *Chem. Commun.*, **1966**, 593.

[62] (a) H. Wynberg and H. van Driel, *Chem. Commun.*, **1966**, 203; (b) H. Wynberg, R. M. Kellogg, H. van Driel, and G. E. Beekhuis, *J. Am. Chem. Soc.*, **88**, 5047 (1966).

[63] See *Organic Reaction Mechanisms*, **1965**, 291.

[64] E. F. Ullman and B. Singh, *J. Am. Chem. Soc.*, **88**, 1844 (1966); D. W. Kurtz and H. Schehter, *Chem. Commun.*, **1966**, 689.

[65] C. H. Krauch, J. Kuhls, and H.-J. Piek, *Tetrahedron Letters*, **1966**, 4043.

Photo-induced valency tautomerization in other systems,[66] and photo-enolization,[46, 67] have also received attention.

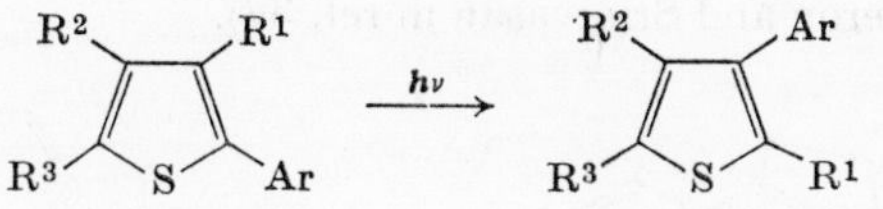

$$R^2 \quad R^1 \qquad \xrightarrow{h\nu} \qquad R^2 \quad Ar$$

(thiophene rearrangement with substituents R^2, R^1, Ar, R^3, S)

(41)   (42)

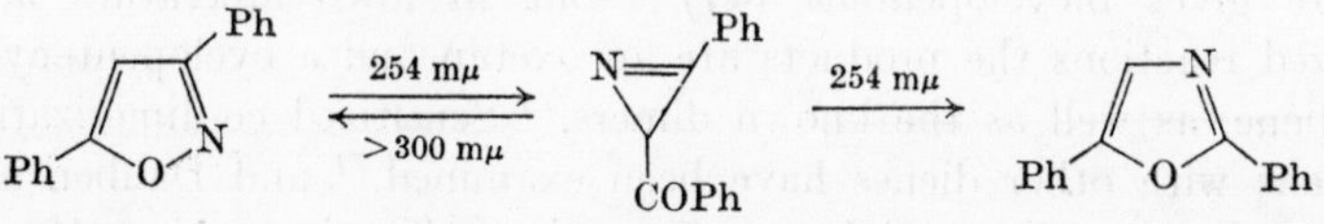

$$\xrightarrow[>300 \text{ m}\mu]{254 \text{ m}\mu}$$ $$\xrightarrow{254 \text{ m}\mu}$$

(isoxazole — azirine — oxazole interconversions)

(43)

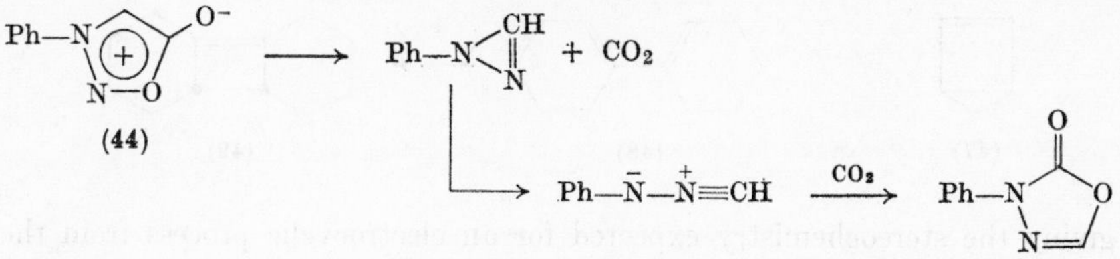

$$Ph-N \cdots \xrightarrow{\quad} Ph-N \overset{CH}{\underset{N}{\|}} + CO_2$$

(44)

$$\longrightarrow Ph-\bar{N}-\overset{+}{N}\equiv CH \xrightarrow{CO_2} Ph-N \overset{O}{\underset{N}{\diamond}}O$$

A fruitless search has been made for products arising from transannular bonding in the excited states of [2.2]paracyclophane,[68a] though products with transannular bonds have been isolated from photosensitized oxidation of [2.2]paracyclonaphthane (45) and of the unsymmetrical paracyclophane (46). However, in each case the first step is addition of singlet oxygen across one aromatic unit, followed by transannular bonding in a ground-state process.[68b]

[66] E. F. Ullman and W. A. Henderson, *J. Am. Chem. Soc.*, **88**, 4942 (1966).

[67] K. R. Huffman, M. Loy, and E. F. Ullman, *J. Am. Chem. Soc.*, **87**, 5417 (1965); **88**, 601 (1966); W. A. Henderson and E. F. Ullman, *ibid.*, **87**, 5424 (1965); A. L. Bluhm and J. Weinstein, *ibid.*, p. 5511; J. Weinstein, A. L. Bluhm, and J. A. Sousa, *J. Org. Chem.*, **31**, 1983 (1966); J. D. Margerum and R. G. Brault, *J. Am. Chem. Soc.*, **88**, 4733, 1966; M. A. J. Wilks and M. R. Willis, *Nature (London)*, **212**, 500 (1966); N. Kanamuru and S. Nagakura, *Bull. Chem. Soc. Japan*, **39**, 1355 (1966).

[68a] R. C. Helgeson and D. J. Cram, *J. Am. Chem. Soc.*, **88**, 509 (1966).

[68b] H. H. Wasserman, A. R. Doumaux, and R. E. Davis, *J. Am. Chem. Soc.*, **88**, 4517 (1966) H. H. Wasserman and P. M. Keehn, *ibid.*, p. 4522.

Many electrocyclic processes, both inter- and intra-molecular, may be induced photochemically, and reviews dealing with intramolecular cyclization in both conjugated[69] and non-conjugated[70] dienes have appeared (see also, chapters by Mousseron and Srinivasan in ref. 3d).

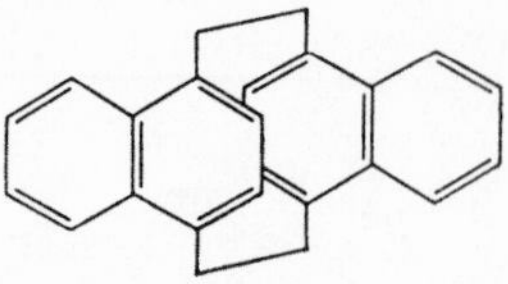

(45) 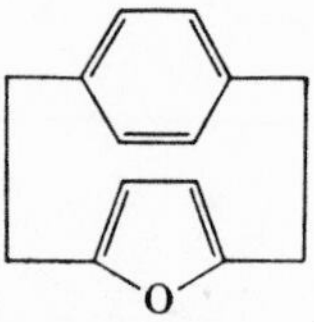   (46)

A novel product from cyclohexa-1,3-diene is 3-vinylcyclobutene, presumably arising via the ring-opened hexatriene.[71] Cyclopentadiene at low temperature gives bicyclopentene (47),[72] but in low-temperature acetone-sensitized reactions the products are an oxetan and a cyclopentenylcyclopentadiene, as well as the known dimers.[73] Sensitized co-dimerizations of butadiene with other dienes have been examined,[74] and Dauben and his colleagues have studied cyclobutene formation.[75] The conversion (48) → (49) proceeds under direct irradiation or photosensitizing conditions, in each case

(47)    (48)   →   (49)

giving the stereochemistry expected for an electrocyclic process from the excited singlet state. As the first spectroscopic excited cyclobutene singlet is of higher energy than that of the diene, it was suggested that partial bonding occurs with the anticipated stereochemistry, and then leads to cyclobutene in a non-spectroscopic excited state. With 2,3-dimethylbutadiene there is no comparable reaction under benzophenone sensitization, though the sensitizer triplets are effectively quenched. With excess of diene, the diphenylbutadiene (50) is formed, possibly as indicated.

The novel $(6 + 6)\pi$-type cycloaddition is observed when tropone is ir-

[69] J. P. M. Houbiers, *Chem. Weekblad*, **62**, 61 (1966).

[70] W. L. Dilling, *Chem. Rev.*, **66**, 373 (1966).

[71] J. Meinwald and P. H. Mazzocchi, *J. Am. Chem. Soc.*, **88**, 2850 (1966).

[72] J. I. Brauman, L. E. Ellis, and E. E. van Tamelen, *J. Am. Chem. Soc.*, **88**, 846 (1966).

[73] E. H. Gold and D. Ginsburg, *Angew. Chem. Internat. Ed. Engl.*, **5**, 246 (1966).

[74] G. Sartori, V. Turba, A. Valvassori, and M. Riva, *Tetrahedron Letters*, **1966**, 211, 4777.

[75] W. G. Dauben, R. L. Gargill, R. M. Coates, and J. Saltiel, *J. Am. Chem. Soc.*, **88**, 2742 (1966);
    J. Saltiel, R. M. Coates, and W. G. Dauben, *ibid.*, p. 2745.

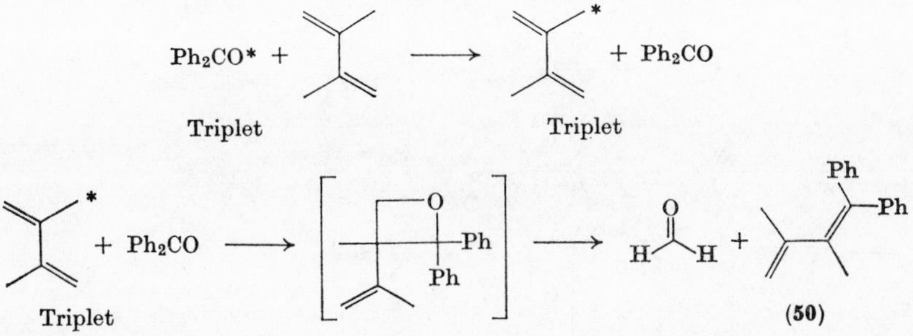

$$\text{Ph}_2\text{CO*} + \quad \longrightarrow \quad + \text{Ph}_2\text{CO}$$

Triplet   Triplet

Triplet   + Ph$_2$CO $\longrightarrow$ $\longrightarrow$ (50)

radiated in 2N-sulphuric acid[76] [giving (51)], though different dimers are formed in acetonitrile. Intramolecular cyclizations of oxepin and azepines,[77] and of cyclonona-1,3-diene,[78] have been reported, and a free-radical mechanism[79] for the conversion of cyclo-octa-1,5-diene into the tricyclo-octane (52) has been discredited.[80] Photodecyclization has afforded routes to [16]annulene[81] and tetravinylethylene.[82]

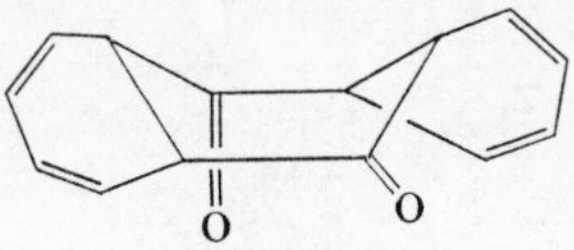

(51) 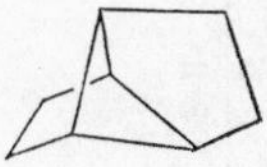   (52)

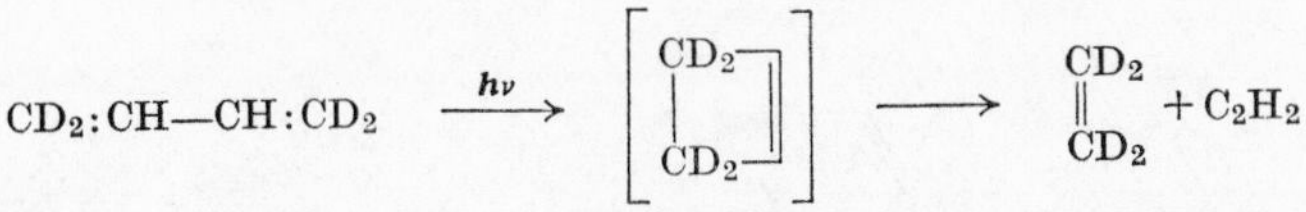

$$\text{CD}_2\text{:CH-CH:CD}_2 \quad \xrightarrow{h\nu} \quad \begin{bmatrix} \text{CD}_2 \\ | \\ \text{CD}_2 \end{bmatrix} \quad \longrightarrow \quad \begin{matrix} \text{CD}_2 \\ \| \\ \text{CD}_2 \end{matrix} + \text{C}_2\text{H}_2$$

1,1,4,4-Tetradeuteriobutadiene gives some tetradeuterioethylene on vapour-phase photolysis, which is consistent with the sequence shown. However, large quantities of di- and tri-deuterioethylene are also produced.[83]

Reactions of substituted 1,2-dihydrophthalic anhydrides have already been mentioned. The related unsubstituted *trans*-diester (53) gives the all-*trans*-triene (54) on irradiation,[84] and irradiation of (54) (R = Me) in the crystalline

76 T. Mukai, T. Tezuka, and Y. Akasaki, *J. Am. Chem. Soc.*, 88, 5025 (1966); A. S. Kende, *ibid.*, p. 5026.
77 L. A. Paquette and J. H. Barrett, *J. Am. Chem. Soc.*, 88, 1718 (1966).
78 K. M. Shumate and G. J. Fonken, *J. Am. Chem. Soc.*, 88, 1073 (1966).
79 J. E. Baldwin and R. H. Greeley, *J. Am. Chem. Soc.*, 87, 4515 (1965).
80 I. Haller and R. Srinivasan, *J. Am. Chem. Soc.*, 88, 5084 (1966).
81 G. Schröder and J. F. M. Oth, *Tetrahedron Letters*, 1966, 4083.
82 L. Skattebøl, J. L. Charlton, and P. de Mayo, *Tetrahedron Letters*, 1966, 2257.
83 I. Haller and R. Srinivasan, *J. Am. Chem. Soc.*, 88, 3694 (1966).
84 P. Courtot and J. M. Robert, *Bull. Soc. Chim. France*, 1965, 3362.

13

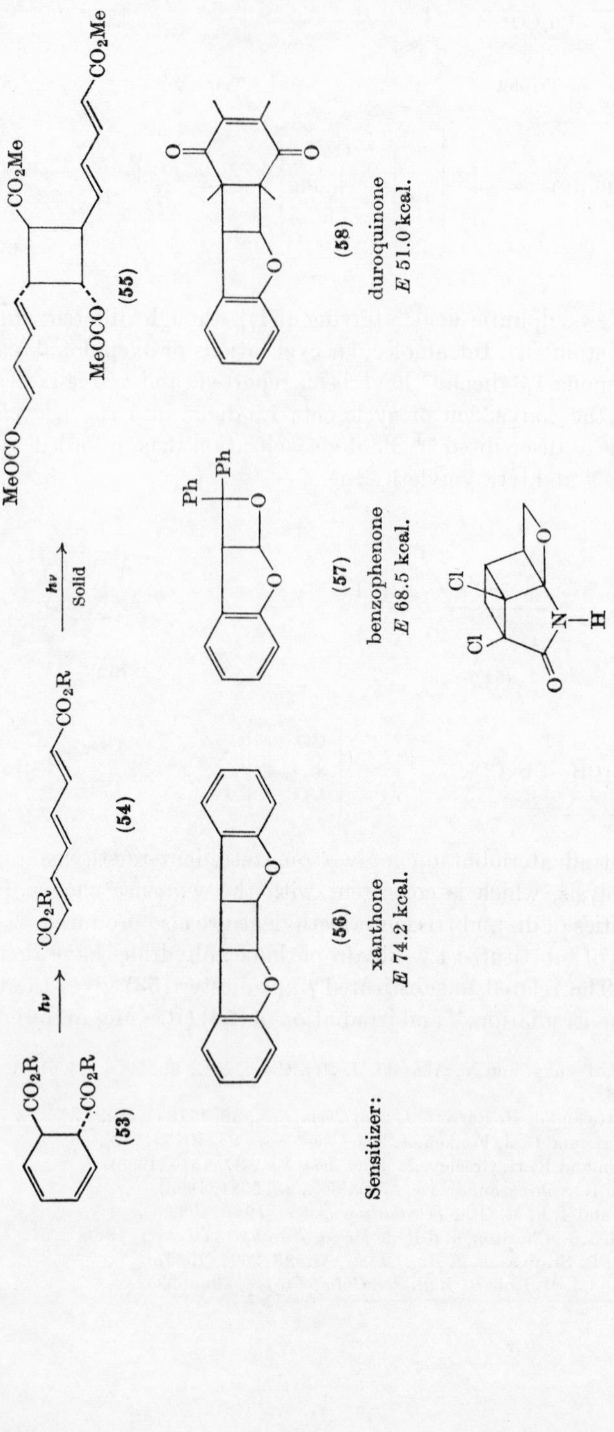
CO2R
CO2R
(53)
hν
CO2R
CO2R
(54)
hν
Solid
MeOCO
CO2Me
MeOCO
CO2Me
(55)
Sensitizer:
(56)
xanthone
E 74.2 kcal.
Ph
Ph
(57)
benzophenone
E 68.5 kcal.
(58)
duroquinone
E 51.0 kcal.
Cl
Cl
N
H
O
(59)

state gives a good yield of the cyclobutane (**55**) retaining the all-*trans*-stereo-chemistry.[85]

Formation of oxetans by addition of carbonyl compounds to furan was observed,[86] but benzofuran gave a dimer (**56**), an oxetan (**57**), or a cyclobutane derivative (**58**), apparently depending on the triplet energy of the sensitizer.[87]

Numerous studies of four-membered ring formation (dimer, adduct with olefin, etc.) have been reported.[88] Dichloromaleic anhydride and dichloro-maleimide give vinylcyclobutane derivatives on irradiation with butadiene; the imide also gives the tetracyclic product (**59**).[89] The photosensitized reactions of maleic anhydride and dimethylmaleic anhydride with conjugated dienes give 1,4-adducts of *exo*-configuration, contrasting with the *endo*-products of the thermal reaction and with 1,2-adducts from the direct photo-chemical reaction.[90] The stereochemistry of the cyclobutane formed from the sensitized reaction of maleic anhydride with 1-chlorocyclohexene shows a marked solvent-dependence.[91a] Triplet dimethyl maleate adds to cyclohexene in a photosensitized reaction, but in the absence of sensitizer, at least a portion of the cyclobutanes produced comes from addition of singlet excited maleate.[91b]

Intramolecular reactions include the photosensitized conversion of the triene (**60**) into (**62**). Isolation of identical isomer mixtures from [(**60**); R = Me, R' = H; or R = H, R' = Me] is consistent with a relatively long-lived biradical intermediate (**61**).[92] Compound (**64**) has been isolated on irradiation of the quadricyclene adduct (**63**).[93]

Photosensitized reactions of cyclobutene,[94] cyclopentene,[95] and cyclo-hexene[96] have been reported. Oxetan formation is observed from cyclohexene, and inferred in cyclobutene [equation (1)], but only products from radical

[85] M. Lahar and G. M. J. Schmidt, *Tetrahedron Letters*, **1966**, 2957.

[86] K. Shima and H. Sakurai, *Bull. Chem. Soc. Japan*, **39**, 1806 (1966).

[87] C. H. Krauch, W. Metzner, and G. O. Schenck, *Chem. Ber.*, **99**, 1723 (1966); C. H. Krauch and S. Farid, *Tetrahedron Letters*, **1966**, 4783.

[88] N. Sugiyama, K. Yamada, Y. Watari, and T. Koyama, *Nippon Kagaku Zasshi*, **87**, 737 (1966); *Chem. Abs.*, **65**, 15188 (1966); G. Kolzenburg, P. G. Fuss, and J. Leitich, *Tetrahedron Letters*, **1966**, 3409; J. W. Hanifin and E. Cohen, *ibid.*, pp. 1419, 5421; M. Hara, Y. Odaira, and S. Tsutsumi, *Tetrahedron*, **22**, 95 (1966); C. H. Krauch, S. Farid, and G. O. Schenck, *Chem. Ber.*, **99**, 625 (1966); D. Bryce-Smith, G. J. Bullen, N. H. Clark, B. E. Connett, and A. Gilbert, *J. Chem. Soc., C*, **1966**, 167; P. E. Eaton, and W. S. Hurt, *J. Am. Chem. Soc.*, **88**, 5038 (1966).

[89] H.-D. Scharf, and F. Korte, *Tetrahedron Letters*, **1966**, 2033; *Chem. Ber.*, **99**, 1299 (1966).

[90] G. O. Schenck, J. Kuhls, and C. H. Krauch, *Ann. Chem.*, **693**, 20 (1966).

[91a] R. Steinmetz, W. Hartmann, and G. O. Schenck, *Chem. Ber.*, **98**, 3854 (1965).

[91b] A. Cox, P. de Mayo, and R. W. Yip, *J. Am. Chem. Soc.*, **88**, 1043 (1966).

[92] R. S. H. Liu, *Tetrahedron Letters*, **1966**, 2159.

[93] C. F. Huebner, E. Donoghue, L. Dorfman, E. Wenkert, W. E. Streth, and S. W. Donely, *Chem. Commun.*, **1966**, 419.

[94] R. Srinivasan and K. A. Hill, *J. Am. Chem. Soc.*, **88**, 3765 (1966).

[95] K. S. Sidhu, O. P. Strausz, and H. E. Gunning, *Can. J. Chem.*, **44**, 531 (1966).

[96] J. S. Bradshaw, *J. Org. Chem.*, **31**, 237 (1966).

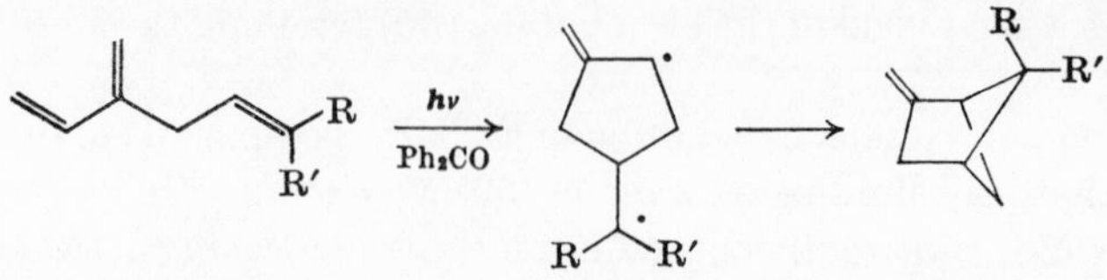

(60)   (61)   (62)

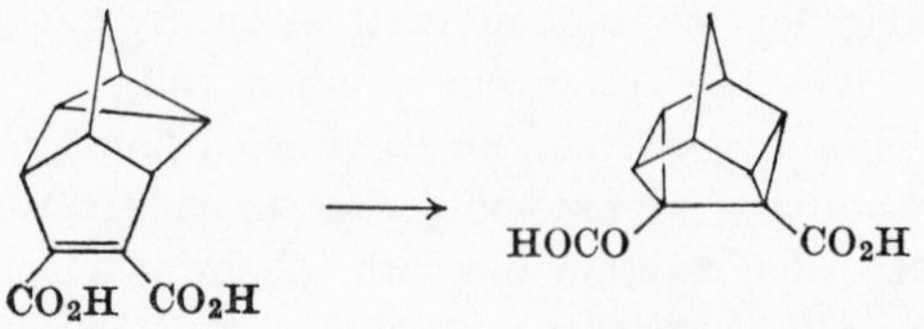

(63)   (64)

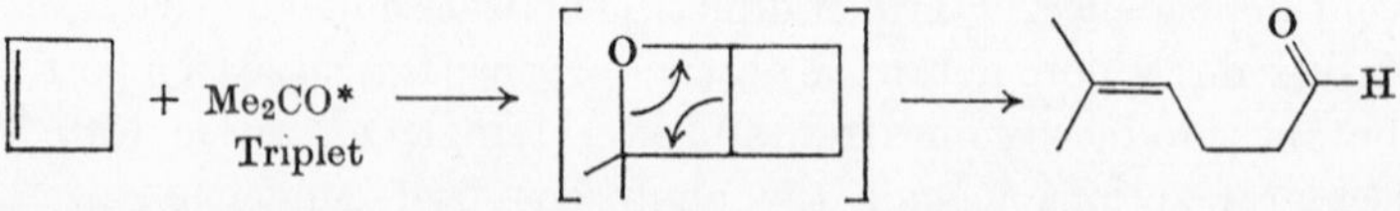

$$\square + \text{Me}_2\text{CO}^* \longrightarrow \left[\begin{array}{c} \text{O} \\ \end{array} \right] \longrightarrow \begin{array}{c} \text{O} \\ \text{H} \end{array} \qquad (1)$$
Triplet

reactions are observed for cyclopentene. Oxetans and 1,5- and 1,6-dioxa-spiro[3,3]heptanes are obtained from irradiation of tetramethylallene in acetone.[97] The cuprous halide-promoted photodimerization of norbornene[98] has been interpreted in terms of a transient 3:1 olefin–cuprous halide complex.[99]

Stilbene molecules are too far apart in the crystal for photodimerization, and failure to observe dimerization of the *cis*-isomer in the liquid has been

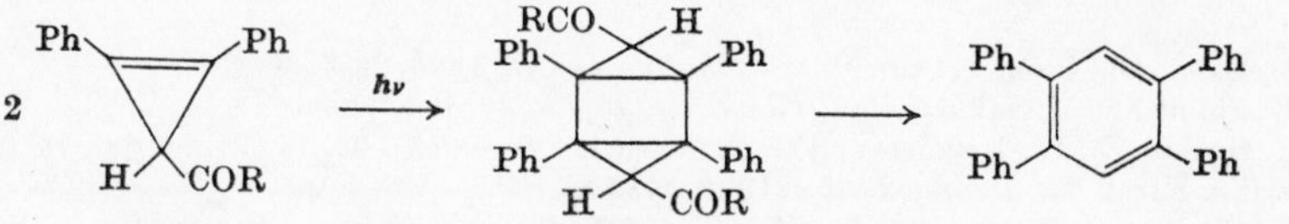

(65)   (66)

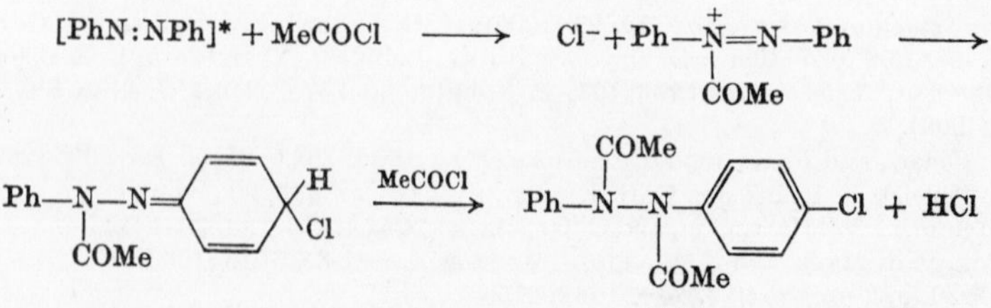

$$[\text{PhN:NPh}]^* + \text{MeCOCl} \longrightarrow \text{Cl}^- + \text{Ph}-\overset{+}{\text{N}}=\text{N}-\text{Ph} \longrightarrow$$
                                                          |
                                                        COMe

·(67)

[97] D. R. Arnold and A. H. Glick, *Chem. Commun.*, **1966**, 813.
[98] See *Organic Reaction Mechanisms*, **1965**, 299.
[99] D. J. Trecker, R. S. Foote, J. P. Henry, and J. E. McKeon, *J. Am. Chem. Soc.*, **88**, 3021 (1966).

attributed to the very short life of the excited singlet.[100] The acylcyclopropene [(**65**); R = Ph] gives 1,2,4,5-tetraphenylbenzene on irradiation in tetrahydrofuran. When R = Me, the intermediate (**66**) could be isolated.[101]

Cyclizations of stilbenes and related compounds to phenanthrenes continue to appear, particularly in the heterocyclic field.[102] A "photo-induced nucleophilic substitution" occurs when azobenzene is irradiated in acetyl chloride, the observed product being (**67**).[103] Benzocinnoline formation may, however, be promoted by some Lewis acids such as $FeCl_3$, in addition to the normally required strong proton acid conditions.[103]

Whereas irradiation of azoxybenzene leads to o-hydroxyazobenzene, in the benzophenone-sensitized reaction deoxygenation to azobenzene is observed.[104a] The products of irradiation of 2,2'-dimethylazoxybenzene include 2-hydroxy-2',4-dimethylazobenzene.[104b]

The measurement of modest concentrations (ca. 20%) of the red polyene (**69**) during irradiation of cis-dimesitylethylene (**68**),[105] was omitted from last year's report.

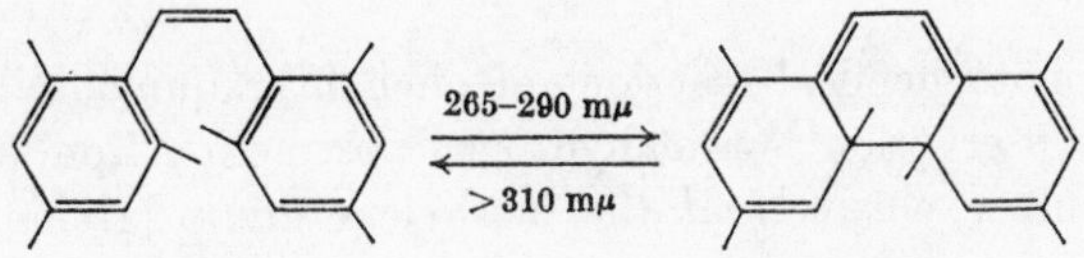

(**68**)   265–290 mμ ⟶ >310 mμ (**69**)

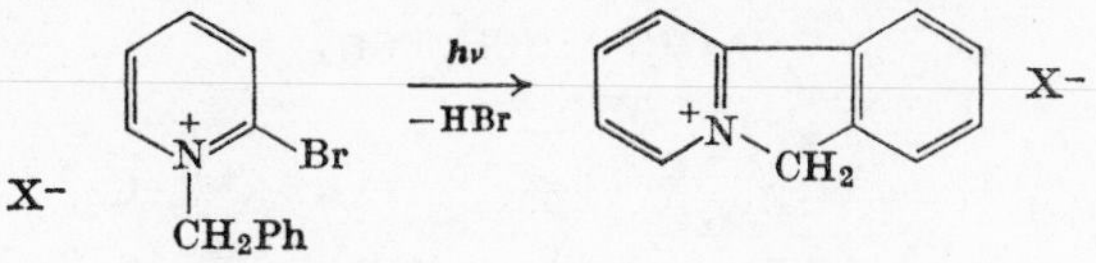

(**70**)   (**71**)

The interesting cyclization (**70**) → (**71**) has been disclosed.[106] No reaction occurs with the N-methyl or N-nitrobenzyl compound, or with o-bromodiphenylmethane.

Competing with phenanthrene formation in the cyclization of the carbamate

[100] H. Stegemeyer, *Chimia (Aarau)*, **19**, 536 (1965).
[101] N. Obata and I. Moritani, *Tetrahedron Letters*, **1966**, 1503.
[102] P. Bortolus, G. Cauzo, and G. Galiazzo, *Tetrahedron Letters*, **1966**, 239, 3717; C. P. Joshua and G. E. Lewis, *ibid.*, p. 4533; G. M. Badger, R. J. Drewer, and G. E. Lewis, *Australian J. Chem.*, **19**, 643 (1966); H.-H. Perkampus and G. Kassebeer, *Ann. Chem.*, **696**, 1 (1966).
[103] G. E. Lewis and R. J. Mayfield, *Tetrahedron Letters*, **1966**, 269; *Australian J. Chem.*, **19**, 1445 (1966).
[104a] R. Tanikaga, K. Maruyama, R. Goto, and A. Kaji, *Tetrahedron Letters*, **1966**, 5925.
[104b] G. E. Lewis and J. A. Reiss, *Australian J. Chem.*, **19**, 1887 (1966).
[105] K. A. Muszcat, D. Gegiou, and E. Fischer, *Chem. Commun.*, **1965**, 447.
[106] A. Fozard and C. K. Bradsher, *Tetrahedron Letters*, **1966**, 3341.

(72) is the acylation leading to (73). This reaction seems to have some generality and has also been observed with carbonates (→ lactones).[107]

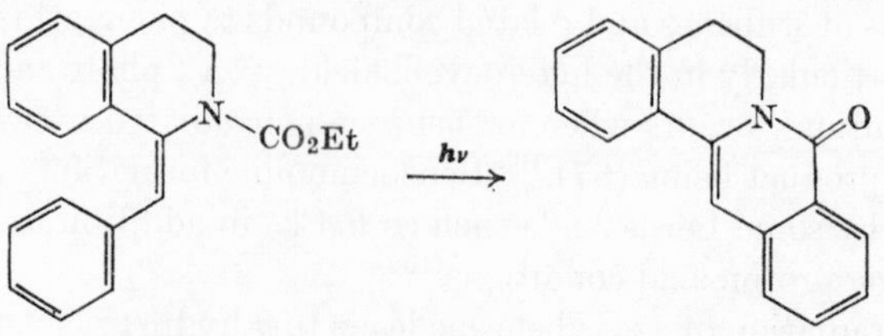

(72)   (73)

Acylation by the photochemical analogue of the Fries reaction has been extended to migration of arylsulphonyl groups,[108a] and a similar O-alkyl → C-alkyl migration has been reported,[108b] and effects of steric and electronic factors in the photo-Fries reaction have been investigated.[108c] Other papers emphasize alternative reaction paths observed on irradiation of phenolic or enolic esters.[109]

Reports of photochemical reactions of phenanthraquinone[110,111] include the surprising observation[111] that hydrogen abstraction from ethyl acetate as solvent occurs exclusively at the methylene group [giving (74)]. In a

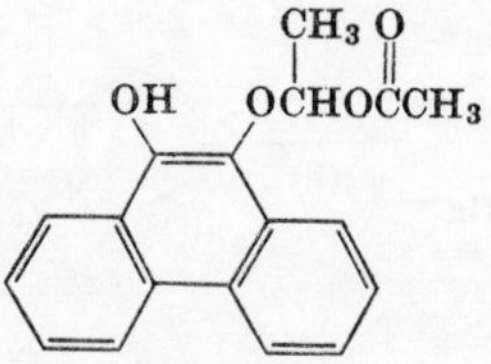

(74)

detailed study[112] of the photochemical reaction between benzoquinone and acetaldehyde, it has been shown that acylation occurs by attack of acetyl radicals on the ground-state quinone. Some of the results were replicated using di-*tert*-butyl peroxide as a radical initiator, and extensive scavenging studies were carried out. Comparable results were obtained with chloranil

[107] N. C. Yang, A. Shani, and G. R. Lenz, *J. Am. Chem. Soc.*, **88**, 5369 (1966).
[108a] J. L. Stratenus and E. Havinga, *Rec. Trav. Chim.*, **85**, 434 (1966).
[108b] J. Hill, *Chem. Commun.*, **1966**, 260.
[108c] G. M. Coppinger and E. R. Bell, *J. Phys. Chem.*, **70**, 3479 (1966).
[109] S. T. Reid and G. Subramanian, *Chem. Commun.*, **1966**, 245; R. A. Finnegan and D. Knutson, *ibid.*, p. 172; M. Gorodetsky and Y. Mazur, *Tetrahedron*, **22**, 3607 (1966).
[110] C. H. Krauch, S. Farid, and D. Hess, *Chem. Ber.*, **99**, 1881 (1966).
[111] M. B. Rubin and R. A. Reith, *Chem. Commun.*, **1966**, 431.
[112] J. M. Bruce and E. Cutts, *J. Chem. Soc.*, C, **1966**, 449.

and acetaldehyde.[113] Several examples of intramolecular photocyclization in substituted quinones have been reported,[114] including the rearrangement (75) → (76).[115]

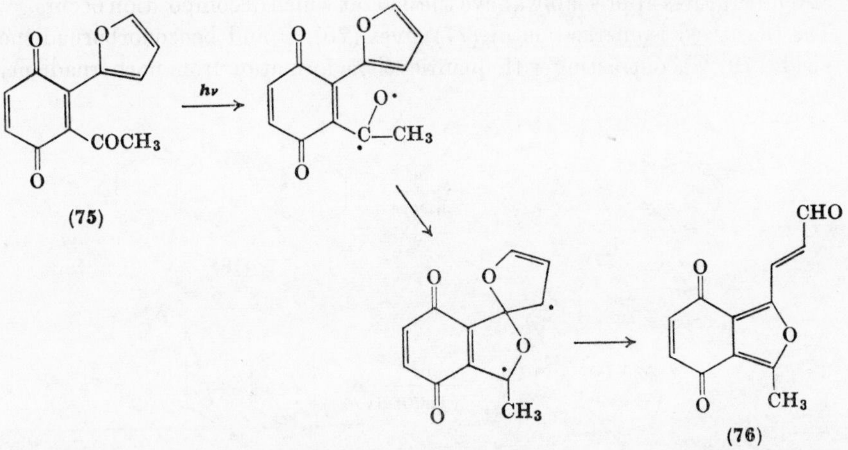

(75)

(76)

The photochemistry of heterocyclic N-oxides has attracted attention, and a variety of rearrangements has been disclosed. Many probably involve oxazirane intermediates, and these have been isolated from 2-cyanoquinoline N-oxide and 1-cyanoisoquinoline N-oxide.[116] Pyridine N-oxide gives pyrrole-2-carboxaldehyde[117] [equation (2)], but quinoline N-oxide gives 1-formyl-indole.[118] These and other[119] results have been obtained in a variety of solvents, and it is clear that a full understanding of the mechanisms involved will require an adequate interpretation of the solvent dependence—with particular regard to hydrogen-bonding[120]—in these systems.

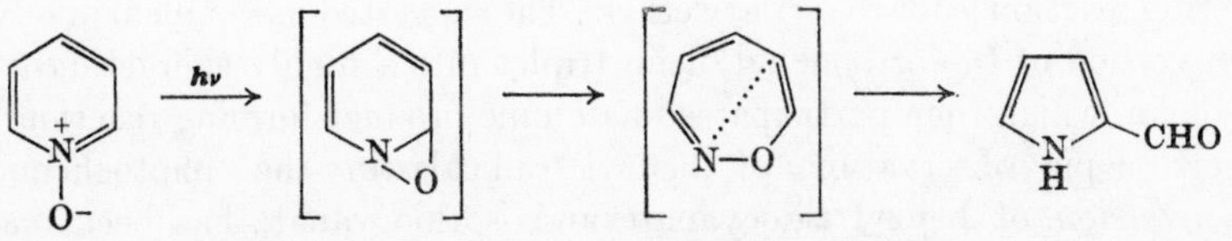

(2)

113 J. M. Bruce and J. N. Ellis, *J. Chem. Soc.*, *C*, **1966**, 1624.
114 C. M. Orlando, H. Mark, A. K. Bose, and M. S. Manhas, *Tetrahedron Letters*, **1966**, 3003; *Chem. Commun.*, **1966**, 714; J. M. Bruce and P. Knowles, *J. Chem. Soc.*, *C*, **1966**, 1627.
115 G. Weisgerber and C. H. Eugster, *Helv. Chim. Acta*, **49**, 1806 (1966).
116 C. Kaneko, S. Yamada, and M. Ishikawa, *Tetrahedron Letters*, **1966**, 2145.
117 J. Streith and C. Sigwalt, *Tetrahedron Letters*, **1966**, 1347.
118 J. Streith, H. K. Darrah, and M. Weil, *Tetrahedron Letters*, **1966**, 5555.
119 E. C. Taylor and G. G. Spence, *Chem. Commun.*, **1966**, 767; H. Mantsch and V. Zanker, *Tetrahedron Letters*, **1966**, 4211; C. Kaneko, S. Yamada, I. Yokoe, N. Hota, and Y. Ubukata, *ibid.*, p. 4729; H. Mantsch and V. Zanker, *ibid.*, p. 4211.
120 O. Buchardt, J. Becher, C. Lohse and J. Møller, *Acta Chem. Scand.*, **20**, 262 (1966); M. Ishikawa, S. Yamada, and C. Kaneko, *Chem. Pharm. Bull.* (*Tokyo*), **13**, 747 (1965).

Miscellaneous photochemically induced isomerizations include the racemization of tertiary arsines, from which, by use of sensitizers of different triplet energy, it was concluded that the isomers would retain optical stability at temperatures appreciably above the 330° at which decomposition occurs.[121] The sensitized isomerization of (77) gives (78),[122] and benzonorbornadiene yields (79),[123] contrasting with quadricyclene formation from norbornadiene.

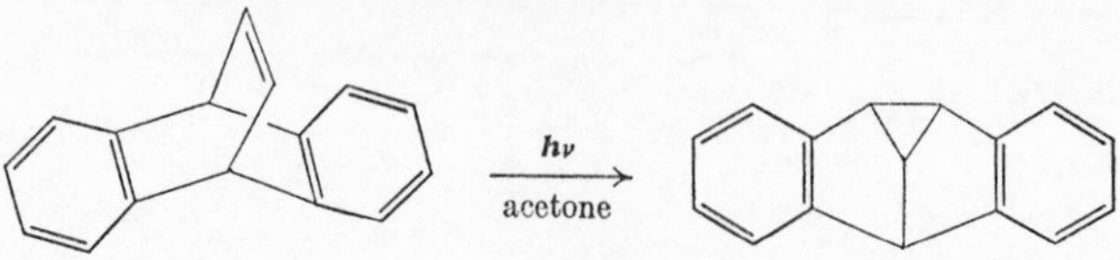

$$\xrightarrow[\text{acetone}]{h\nu}$$

(77)   (78)

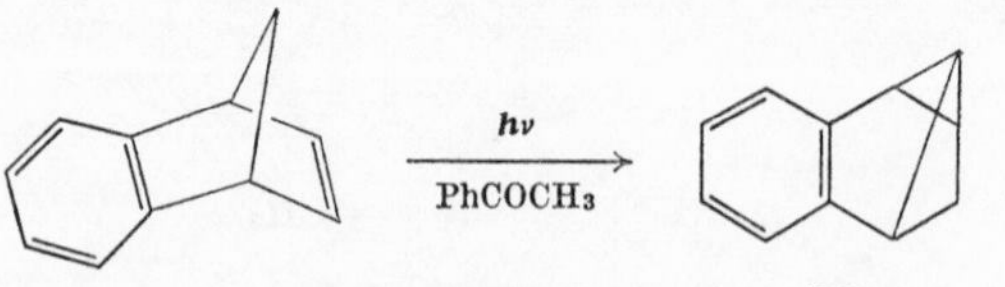

$$\xrightarrow[\text{PhCOCH}_3]{h\nu}$$

(79)

MeO
 CH₃   CH₂

$$\xleftarrow[\substack{\text{PhH} \\ \text{MeOH}}]{h\nu} \qquad \xrightarrow[\text{PhH}]{h\nu}$$

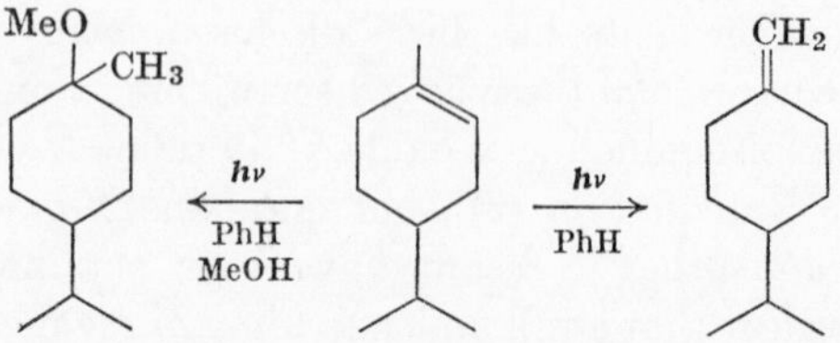

Benzene or toluene photosensitizes the isomerization of 1-alkylcyclohexenes to compounds with an exocyclic double bond. In the presence of alcohols a competing reaction leads to tertiary ethers. The suggested mechanism involves the conversion of the orthogonal olefin triplet into a highly energetic *trans*-cyclo-olefin, which then participates in an ionic product-forming reaction.[124]

Spectroscopic observation of benzyl radicals in the photochemical interconversion of benzyl thiocyanate and isothiocyanate has been made at liquid-nitrogen temperatures.[125]

The photoreduction of nitrobenzene by tetrahydrofuran involves the nitrobenzene triplet;[126] the same is true in propan-2-ol,[127] where the quantum

[121] L. Horner and W. Hofer, *Tetrahedron Letters*, **1966**, 3323.
[122] E. Ciganek, *J. Am. Chem. Soc.*, **88**, 2882 (1966).
[123] J. R. Edman, *J. Am. Chem. Soc.*, **88**, 3454 (1966).
[124] P. J. Kropp, *J. Am. Chem. Soc.*, **88**, 4091 (1966); J. A. Marshall and R. D. Carroll, *J. Am. Chem. Soc.*, **88**, 4092 (1966).
[125] U. Mazzucato, G. Beggiato, and G. Favaro, *Tetrahedron Letters*, **1966**, 5455.
[126] J. K. Brown and W. G. Williams, *Chem. Commun.*, **1966**, 495.
[127] R. Hurley and A. C. Testa, *J. Am. Chem. Soc.*, **88**, 4330, 1966.

yield is lower than for reduction of benzophenone. This may be due to relatively inefficient intersystem crossing to the nitrobenzene triplet, or to relatively rapid decay of this species to the ground state. Intramolecular reductions of aromatic nitro-compounds[128,129] include the demethylation sequence [equation (3)] which may constitute a model for enzymic N-dealkyla-

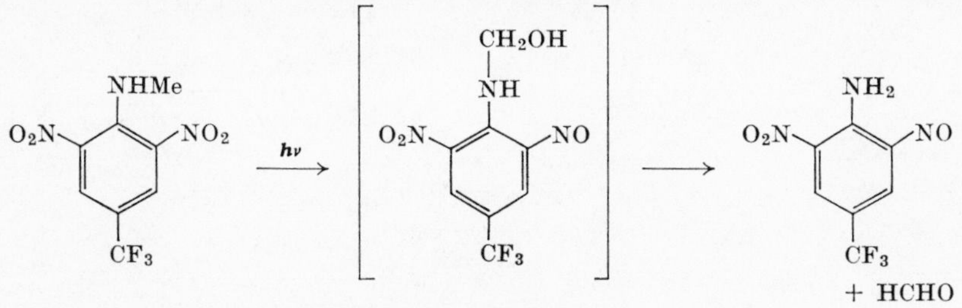

(3)

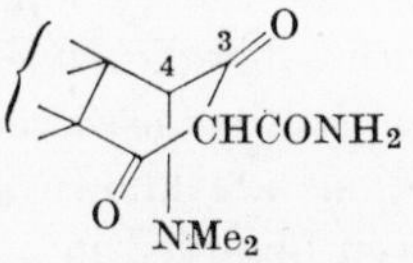

(80)

tion.[129] The de Mayo–Reid mechanism[130] apparently cannot operate here, as the methyl group is separated from the aromatic ring.

Homolytic cleavage is considered responsible for the photodeamination of tetracyclines. Orbital overlap of the C–N bond with the π-electron at C-3 is considered important [structure (80)], because the C-4 epimers do not react.[131]

o-Nitrobenzaldehyde, on irradiation in methanol, gives methyl o-nitrobenzoate, radical intermediates being identified by electron spin resonance.[132]

Among reactions of three-membered ring compounds, the photochemistry of episulphides has been elaborated,[133] and a new reaction pathway has been found for excited-state phenyloxirans,[134] [e.g., (81) → (82)]. The alternative reaction shown, as well as carbene formation, is already recognized. The photochemistry of an epoxypyrone[135] and of a cyclopentadienone oxide[136] has also been studied.

128 J. A. Barltrop, P. J. Plant, and P. Schofield, *Chem. Commun.*, **1966**, 822.
129 R. E. McMahon, *Tetrahedron Letters*, **1966**, 2307.
130 P. de Mayo and S. T. Reid, *Quart. Rev. (London)*, **15**, 393 (1961).
131 J. J. Hlavka and P. Bitha, *Tetrahedron Letters*, **1966**, 3843.
132 H. Mauser and H. Heitzer, *Z. Naturforsch., b*, **21**, 109 (1966).
133 A. Padwa, D. Crumrine, and A. Shubber, *J. Am. Chem. Soc.*, **88**, 3064 (1966); *Organic Reaction Mechanisms*, **1965**, 296.
134 H. Kristinsson, R. A. Mateer, and G. W. Griffin, *Chem. Commun.*, **1966**, 415.
135 A. Padwa and R. Hartman, *J. Am. Chem. Soc.*, **88**, 3759 (1966).
136 A. Padwa and R. Hartman, *J. Am. Chem. Soc.*, **88**, 1518 (1966).

13*

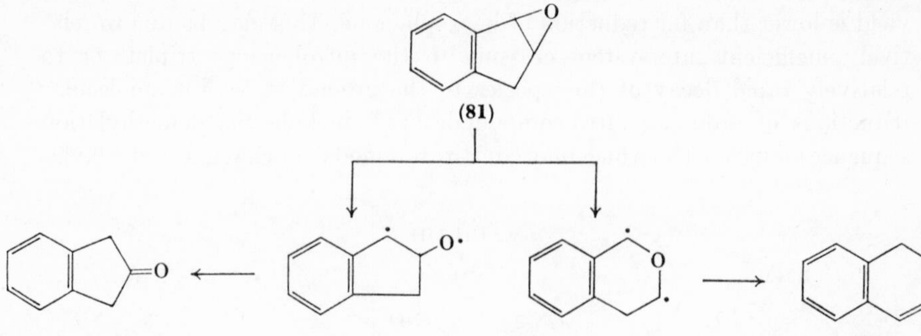

(81)

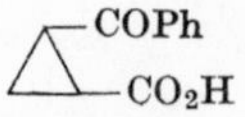

(83)

Both asymmetric centres of the cyclopropane (83) are racemized on irradiation, consistently with a biradical mechanism;[137] furthermore, there is no deuterium exchange in hydroxylic solvents.

Although methyl migrations are known in $n\pi^*$ excited state processes, they have only recently been observed in a $\pi\pi^*$ reaction [equation (4)],[138] where the excited state is considered to have less ionic character. The second

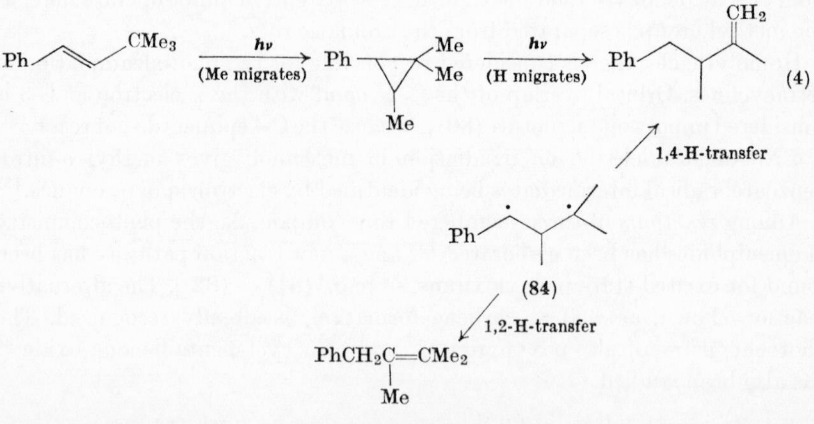

step in equation (4) involves 1,4-hydrogen transfer in the intermediate diradical (84). This has been further examined[139] and a competing 1,2-transfer observed in favourable cases. These cyclopropane rearrangements are not quenched by piperylene, suggesting singlet intermediates.

[137] W. G. Brown and J. F. Neumer, *Tetrahedron*, **22**, 473 (1966).
[138] H. Kristinsson and G. W. Griffin, *J. Am. Chem. Soc.*, **88**, 378 (1966).
[139] H. Kristinsson and G. W. Griffin, *Tetrahedron Letters*, **1966**, 3259.

Irradiation of (85) leads to a product interpreted as arising via a cyclopropylcarbinyl cation;[140] corresponding ground-state radical rearrangements

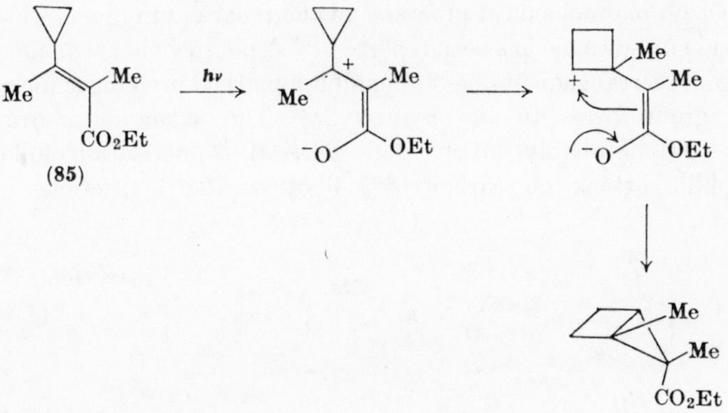

to cyclobutanes are unknown.

Fragmentation reactions may accompany photolysis of nitrites[141] (Barton reaction) or N-chloroamines[142, 143] (Hoffmann–Loeffler reaction), and further work on N-nitroso-compounds has also been reported.[143, 144]

Irradiation of organic compounds in the vacuum-ultraviolet region[145, 146] causes much fragmentation. The reactions of the but-2-enes contrast with their photosensitized isomerization at 254 mμ.[147]

Miscellaneous gas-phase reactions studied include the photochemistry of ethylene oxide[148] and of 1,3-dioxolan,[149] the trimerization of acetylene with dideuterioacetylene,[150] the decomposition of diacetylene,[151] and the photosensitized scrambling of deuterium in *cis*-dideuterioethylene.[152]

A charge-transfer complex is involved in the photochemical addition of tetrahydrofuran to maleic anhydride.[153]

Photochemical extrusion of carbon from the methylenedioxy-group of

[140] M. J. Jorgenson, *J. Am. Chem. Soc.*, **88**, 3463 (1966).
[141] H. Suginome, M. Murakami, and T. Masamune, *Chem. Commun.*, **1966**, 343.
[142] E. Leete and A. R. Hargens, *Tetrahedron Letters*, **1966**, 4901.
[143] G. Adam and K. Schreiber, *Tetrahedron*, **22**, 3581, 3591 (1966).
[144] Y. L. Chow, *Tetrahedron Letters*, **1965**, 2473.
[145] N. C. Yang, D. P. C. Tang, D.-M. Thap, and J. S. Sallo, *J. Am. Chem. Soc.*, **88**, 2851 (1966)
[146] Y. Hatano and S. Shida, *Bull. Chem. Soc. Japan*, **39**, 456 (1966); P. Borrell and F. C. James, *Trans. Faraday Soc.*, **62**, 2452 (1966); I. Unger and G. P. Semeluk, *Can. J. Chem.*, **44**, 1427 (1966).
[147] M. Tanaka, M. Kato, and S. Sato, *Bull. Chem. Soc. Japan*, **39**, 1423.
[148] B. C. Roquitte, *J. Phys. Chem.*, **70**, 2699 (1966).
[149] B. C. Roquitte, *J. Phys. Chem.*, **70**, 2863 (1966).
[150] M. Tsukuda and S. Shida, *J. Chem. Phys.*, **44**, 3133 (1966).
[151] G. J. Pontrelli, *J. Chem. Phys.*, **43**, 2571 (1965)
[152] T. Terao, S. Hirokami, S. Sato, and R. J. Cvetanović, *Can. J. Chem.*, **44**, 2173 (1966),
[153] A. Ledwith and M. Sambhi, *J. Chem. Soc., B*, **1966**, 670.

piperonal has been observed.[154] The results of a detailed study of the photo-chemistry of phenylketene acetals have been interpreted in terms of initial homolysis to form an alkoxy-radical and a vinyl radical.[155] Further work on the effect on photochemical processes of the polar environment obtained by adsorption on silica gel has been reported.[156] A photochemical analogue of the Beckmann rearrangement does not exhibit a marked preference for migration of the group *trans* to the hydroxyl.[157] The azlactone rearrangement [(86) → (87)] probably involves geometrical isomerization followed by nucleophilic attack on carbonyl.[158] Photosensitized reactions of benzil

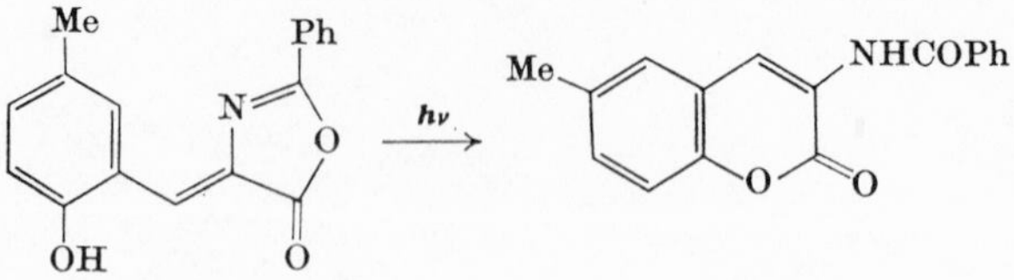

(86)   (87)

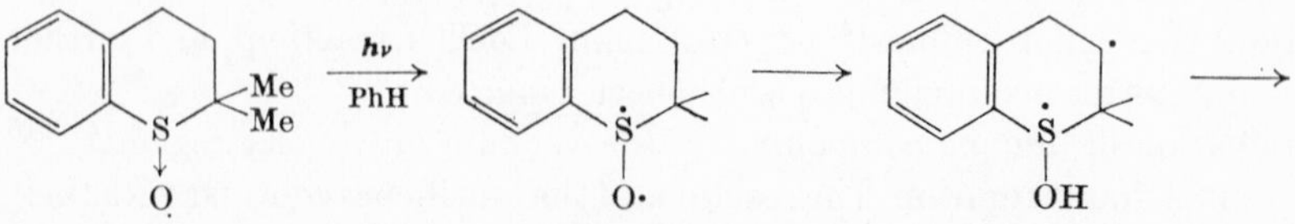

(88)

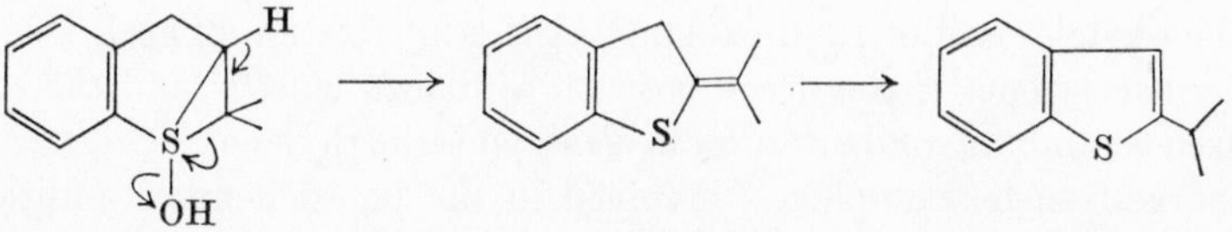

(5)

monoanil lead to products arising from benzoyl and PhṄCOPh radicals.[159] The novel sulphoxide rearrangement [equation (5)] presumably involves a singlet intermediate [represented as (88)], as sensitized reactions yield different products.[160] The sultam (89) on irradiation gives a pyrrole, arising by nucleophilic attack of nitrogen on the carbon of a sulphene intermediate.[161] The normal mode of attack, on sulphur, regenerates starting material. An

154 L. Fishbein, W. L. Zielinski, R. O. Thomas, and H. L. Falk, *Nature*, **212**, 180 (1966).
155 J. E. Baldwin and L. E. Walker, *J. Am. Chem. Soc.*, **88**, 3769, 4191 (1966).
156 L. D. Weis, B. W. Bowen, and P. A. Leermakers, *J. Am. Chem. Soc.*, **88**, 3176 (1966);
    P. A. Leermakers, H. T. Thomas, L. D. Weis, and F. C. James, *ibid.*, p. 5075.
157 R. T. Taylor, M. Douek, and G. Just, *Tetrahedron Letters*, **1966**. 4143.
158 R. Walter, T. C. Purcell, and H. Zimmer, *J. Heterocyclic Chem.*, **3**, 235 (1966).
159 R. O. Kan and R. L. Furey, *Tetrahedron Letters*, **1966**, 2573.
160 R. A. Archer and B. S. Kitchell, *J. Am. Chem. Soc.*, **88**, 3462 (1966).
161 T. Durst and J. F. King, *Can. J. Chem.*, **44**, 1869 (1966).

external nucleophile competes with nitrogen, and gives normal products arising from attack on sulphur at the expense of the pyrrole.

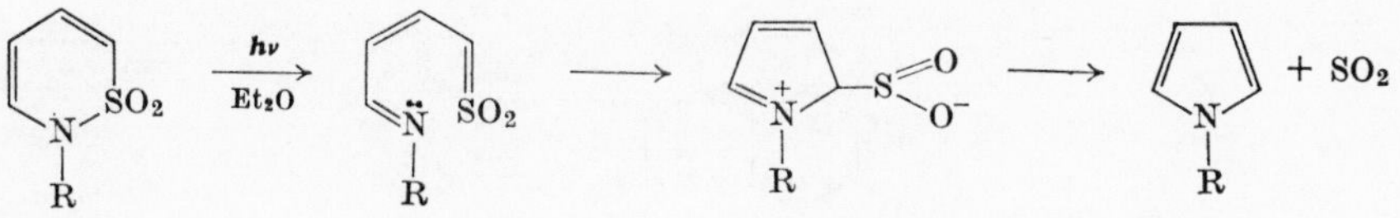

(89)

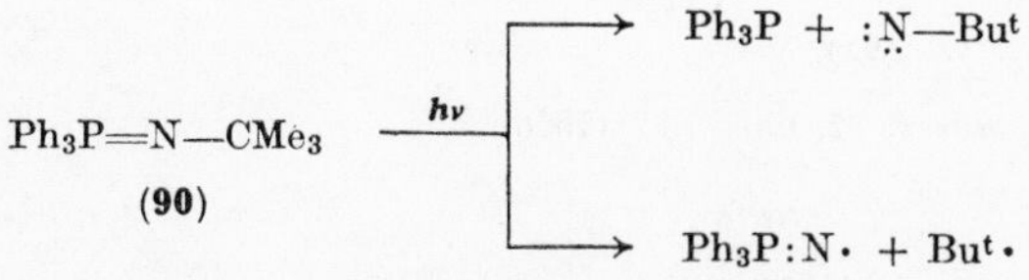

Photolysis of the phosphine imine **(90)** gives products arising from the two primary processes shown.[162]

In a hydrocarbon matrix at $77°$K a solution of tetramethyl-p-phenylene-diamine and pyrene undergoes photoionization to the cation and anion, respectively, in spite of the fact that the dilution is such that the solute molecules are on average 80 Å apart.[163]

Photochemical reactions of uracil,[164] bromouracil,[165] tryptophan,[166] and thymidine[167] have received attention, and the photolysis of the Co–Me bond in methylcobalamin has been studied.[168] Oligonucleotides with a pseudo-uridylic acid residue give 5-formyluracil on irradiation.[169]

The photoaddition of ethanol to acridine is not affected by eosin,[170] and the photoreduction of eosin itself has been examined.[171]

Photochemical oxidation of alkanes, alkenes, and aromatics,[172] and of ethylene glycol and its methyl ethers in the presence of ferric salts,[173] have received attention, as well as photo-oxygenation of steroidal 3,5,7-trienes.[174]

Acetal formation is observed on irradiation of certain steroidal 3,5-dien-3-ol

[162] H. Zimmer and M. Jayawant, *Tetrahedron Letters*, **1966**, 5061,
[163] H. Tsubormura, N. Yamamoto, and Y. Nakato, *Bull. Chem. Soc. Japan*, **39**, 1092 (1966).
[164] A. Wacker, A. Kornhauser, and L. Traeger, *Z. Naturforsch.*, b, **20**, 1043 (1965).
[165] H. Ishihara and S. Y. Wang, *Nature*, **210**, 1222 (1966).
[166] O. Yonemitsu, P. Cerutti, and B. Witkop, *J. Am. Chem. Soc.*, **88**, 3941 (1966).
[167] G. Ballé, P. Cerutti, and B. Witkop, *J. Am. Chem. Soc.*, **88**, 3946 (1966).
[168] H. P. C. Hogenkamp, *Biochemistry*, **5**, 417 (1966).
[169] M. Tomasz and R. W. Chambers, *Biochemistry*, **5**, 773 (1966).
[170] A. Kira, S. Kato, and M. Koizumi, *Bull. Chem. Soc. Japan*, **39**, 1221 (1966); A. Kira, Y. Ikeda, and M. Koizumi, *ibid.*, p. 1673.
[171] T. Ohno, S. Kato, and M. Koizumi, *Bull. Chem. Soc. Japan.*, **39**, 232 (1966).
[172] J. C. W. Chien, *J. Phys. Chem.*, **69**, 4317 (1965).
[173] H. Inoue, K. Tamaki, N. Komakine, and E. Imoto, *Bull. Chem. Soc. Japan*, **39**, 1577 (1966).
[174] P. Bladon and T. Sleigh, *J. Chem. Soc.*, **1965**, 6991.

ethers in menthanol.[175] Compound (91) ketalizes in methanol when irradiated
at its 228 mμ absorption band, but undergoes photoisomerization of the
semicarbazone with light of 313 mμ.

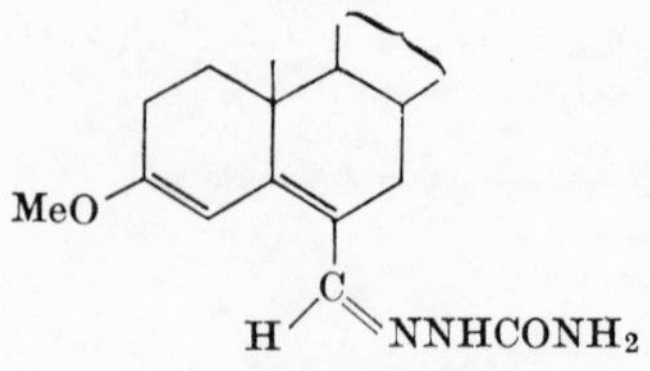

(91)

[175] G. Just and C. Pace-Asciak, *Tetrahedron*, **22**, 1063, 1069 (1966).

CHAPTER 14

Oxidations[1] and Reductions

Ozonolysis

Following the work reported last year[2] Murray, Youssefyeh, and Story,[3] and Greenwood,[4] have now obtained evidence that the Criegee fragmentation–recombination mechanism cannot be the sole mechanism for the ozonolysis of olefins. Contrary to the Criegee mechanism it is found that not only do *cis*- and *trans*-olefins sometimes yield different proportions of *cis*- and *trans*-ozonides, but that the ratios of the *cis:trans* crossed ozonides also differ. Thus *cis*-4-methylpent-2-ene yields a *cis:trans* ratio of 49:51 for both of the crossed

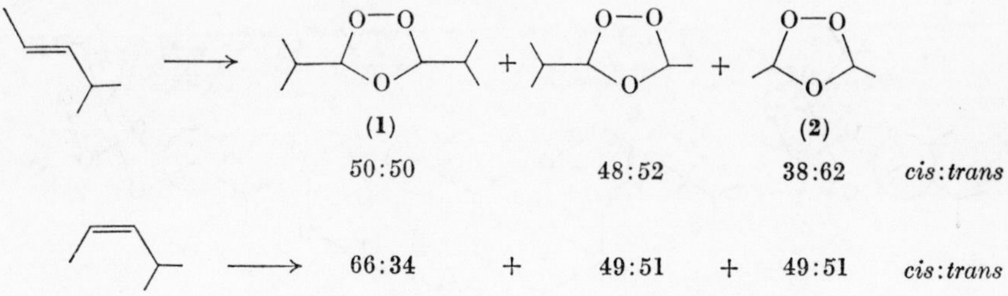

	(1)	(2)	
	50:50	48:52	38:62	*cis:trans*
	66:34	49:51	49:51	*cis:trans*

ozonides (1) and (2), whereas *trans*-4-methylpent-2-ene yields ratios of 48:52 and 38:62. Also when the ozonolysis is carried out in the presence of acetaldehyde the *cis:trans* ratio of isopropyl methyl ozonide is 47:53 from the *trans*- and 40:60 from the *cis*-olefin. It was proposed[5] that a *trans*-olefin and ozone first form a π-complex (3), which collapses to molozonide (4), but that this does not (all) fragment to a zwitterion (5) and carbonyl compound, as in the Criegee mechanism, but rather to a zwitterion (6) which is intercepted by aldehyde to yield intermediates (7)—(10). Two of these can collapse to *cis*-ozonide (12) and two to *trans*-ozonide (11) and it was claimed that there would be little steric preference for any one of them so that the proportions of *cis:trans*-ozonides would be similar, as was found.

With *cis*-olefins which do not carry bulky substituents a similar rearrange-

---

[1] Cf. K. B. Wiberg, "Oxidation in Organic Chemistry," Part A, Academic Press, New York, N.Y., 1966.
[2] See *Organic Reaction Mechanisms*, **1965**, 301.
[3] R. W. Murray, R. D. Youssefyeh, and P. R. Story, *J. Am. Chem. Soc.*, **88**, 3143 (1966).
[4] F. L. Greenwood, *J. Am. Chem. Soc.*, **88**, 3146 (1966).
[5] P. R. Story, R. W. Murray, and R. D. Youssefyeh, *J. Am. Chem. Soc.*, **88**, 3144 (1966).

ment of the initial π-complex to molozonide (**13**), which undergoes fragmentation, was proposed. It was thought here, though, that one of the intermediates

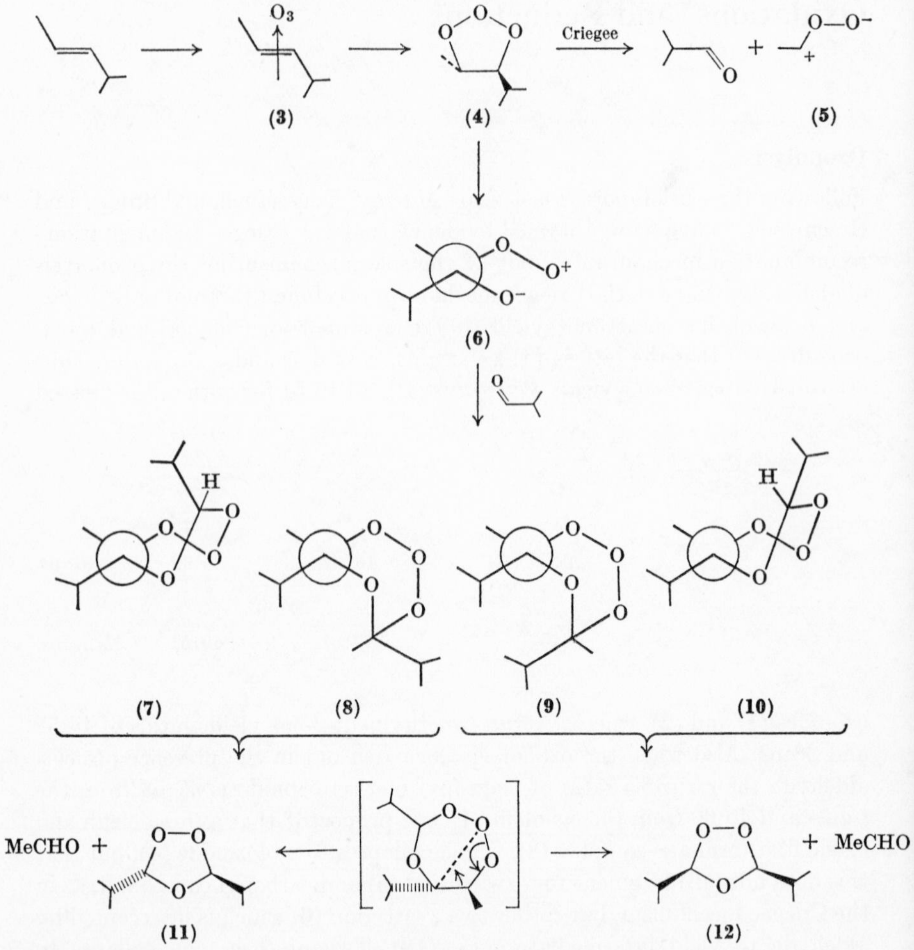

(**15**) which results from capture of the fragmentation product (**14**) by aldehyde would be favoured sterically and that this would lead to a predominance of *cis*-ozonide.

Striking differences in the proportions of *cis*- and *trans*-ozonides resulting from *cis*- and *trans*-olefins with bulky groups are sometimes observed. Thus *cis*-di-*tert*-butylethylene yields 70% of *cis*-ozonide and its *trans*-isomer yields 100% of *trans*-ozonide.[6] It was suggested that the π-complex from the

6 G. Schröder, *Chem. Ber.*, **95**, 733 (1962).

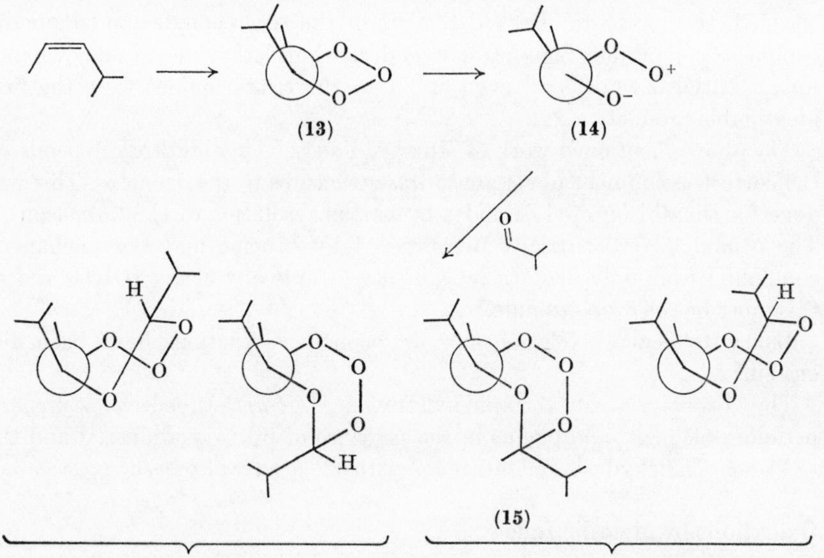

(13)   (14)

(15)

(11) + MeCHO   (12) + MeCHO

cis-olefin here rearranges to a σ-complex (16) rather than to a molozonide which would bring the bulky groups close together. The σ-complex could then possibly rearrange in a concerted manner to yield *cis*-ozonide.

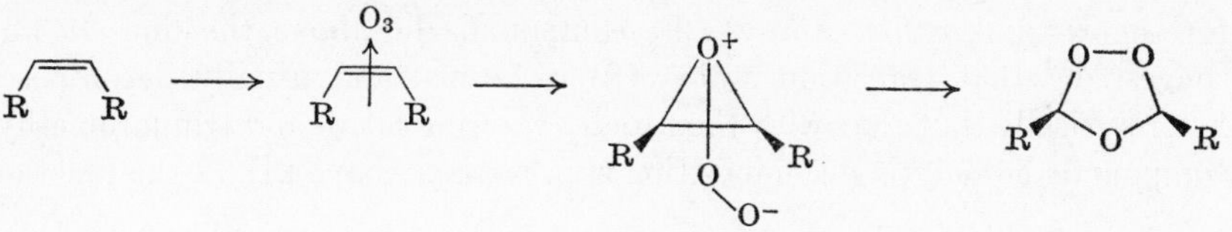

(16)

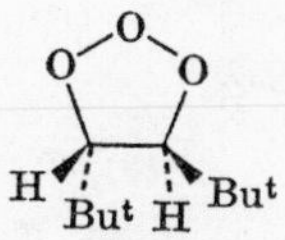

(17)

Evidence for the initial ozonide from *trans*-di-*tert*-butylethylene having a symmetrical structure, presumably (17), has been obtained by Bailey, Thompson, and Shoulders[7] who showed that at −110° in CFCl₃ the NMR spectrum consisted of two singlets, one for the *tert*-butyl protons and one for the methine protons in the expected ratio of 9:1. When the solution was

[7] P. S. Bailey, J. A. Thompson, and B. A. Shoulders, *J. Am. Chem. Soc.*, 88, 4098 (1966).

warmed, the spectrum changed to that of the true ozonides and their decomposition products. Significantly *cis*-di-*tert*-butylethylene gave no evidence for an initial ozonide, and even at $-110°$ the true ozonides were the first identifiable products.

The above-mentioned work of Murray, Youssefyeh, and Story depends on the correct assignment of *cis*- and *trans*-structures to the ozonides. This was done for the di-isopropyl ozonides by partial resolution of the *trans*-isomer. The ozonides were partially decomposed by brucine and the unchanged compound from only one of the isomers was optically active (ORD) and so this must be the *trans*-ozonide.[8]

Linear free-energy relationships for ozonolysis reactions have been discussed.[9]

The ozonolysis of tetraphenylethylene,[10] *trans*-stilbene,[11] styrene,[12] perfluoro-olefins,[13] and olefins in the presence of primary amines,[14] and the reactions of aldehydes[15] and nitrones[16] with ozone have also been investigated.

Oxidations by Metallic Ions

The oxidation of benzylamine by alkaline permanganate to benzaldehyde, benzoic acid, and benzamide is first-order in un-ionized amine and first-order in permanganate in the pH range 6—12. The entropy of activation is -22.5 e.u. and the isotope effect for the oxidation of α,α-dideuteriobenzylamine is $k_H/k_D = 7.0$. The rates of most *meta*- and *para*-substituted benzylamines are correlated by the σ^+ constants to give a ρ constant of -0.28, but the points for the *m*- and *p*-NO$_2$ and *m*-CF$_3$ compounds lie above the line. It was suggested[17] that transition state (18) is formed and usually decomposes heterolytically, but that with the rapidly reacting nitro- and trifluoromethyl compounds homolytic decomposition supervenes. Above pH 12 the reaction

$$\text{Ar}-\overset{\overset{\displaystyle \text{NH}_2}{|}}{\underset{\underset{\displaystyle \text{H}}{|}}{\text{C}}}\text{-{-}H{-}{-}OMnO}_3{}^-$$

(18)

[8] R. W. Murray, R. D. Youssefyeh, and P. R. Story, *J. Am. Chem. Soc.*, **88**, 3655 (1966).

[9] T. Ledaal, *Tetrahedron Letters*, **1966**, 2425; T. Ledaal, *Tetrahedron Letters*, **1966**, 3861.

[10] S. Fliszár, D. Gravel, and E. Cavalieri, *Can. J. Chem.*, **44**, 67 (1966).

[11] S. Fliszár, D. Gravel, and E. Cavalieri, *Can. J. Chem.*, **44**, 1013 (1966).

[12] S. Fliszár, *Can. J. Chem.*, **44**, 2351 (1966).

[13] J. Heicklen, *J. Phys. Chem.*, **70**, 477 (1966).

[14] M. Schulz, A. Rieche, and D. Becker, *Chem. Ber.*, **99**, 3233.

[15] R. E. Erickson, D. Bakalik, C. Richards, M. Scanlon, and G. Huddleston, *J. Org. Chem.*, **31**, 461 (1966).

[16] R. E. Erickson and T. M. Myszkiewicz, *J. Org. Chem.*, **30**, 4326 (1965).

[17] M.-M. Wei and R. Stewart, *J. Am. Chem. Soc.*, **88**, 1974 (1966).

is first-order in hydroxide ion, and possibly here the mechanism is termolecular with the hydroxide attacking one of the nitrogen-bound hydrogen atoms simultaneously with the permanganate attacking the benzyl-hydrogen atoms.

The oxidation of cyclohexanone with thallic ion in aqueous perchloric acid yields mainly cyclopentanecarboxylic acid and a little 2-hydroxycyclo-hexanone; the acid was shown not to result from the hydroxy-ketone. Mechanisms (1) and (2) were considered and to distinguish between them the

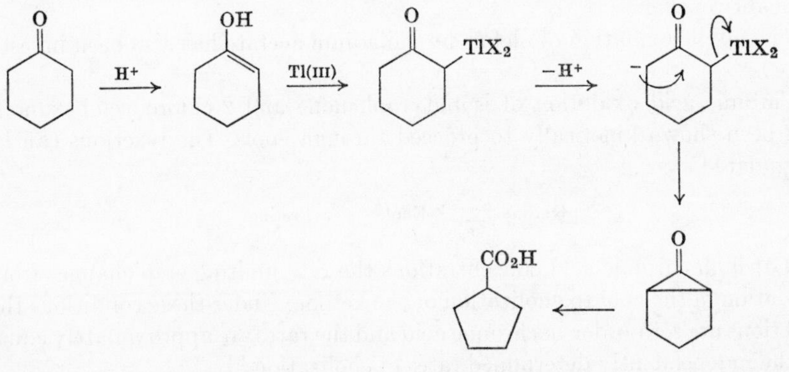

(1)

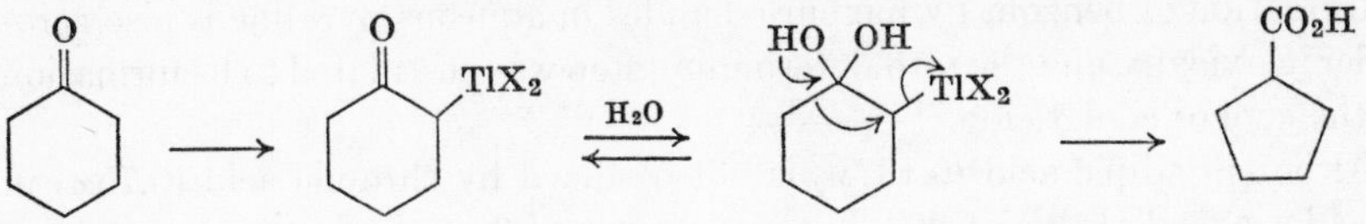

(2)

oxidation of 2,2,6,6-tetradeuteriocyclohexanone was investigated.[18] The reaction mixture was extracted with pentane and reduced with lithium aluminium hydride, whereupon the cyclohexanol from unchanged cyclo-hexanone was found to contain 4% of tetra-, 19% of tri-, 33% of di, and 45% of mono-deuterium compound, and the cyclopentylmethyl alcohol from cyclopentanecarboxylic acid contained 60% of tri-, 25% of di-, and 15% of mono-deuterio-product. Clearly the cyclohexanone undergoes deuterium-exchange at a rate similar to that of its oxidation, but the large amount of deuterium retained in the product supports mechanism (2).

Following the work reported last year[19] on the oxidation of olefins by thallic ion in aqueous solution, this year the reaction in aqueous acetic acid has been studied.[20] The most important reactive species is $Tl(OAc)_2{}^+$ which is only about 18 times less effective than Tl^{3+}; it was presumed that the reactivity of the latter was strongly reduced by solvation.

[18] K. B. Wiberg and W. Koch, *Tetrahedron Letters*, **1966**, 1779.
[19] See *Organic Reaction Mechanisms*, **1965**, 302.
[20] P. M. Henry, *J. Am. Chem. Soc.*, **88**, 1597 (1966).

The oxidation of olefins to carbonyl compounds by palladium(II) has also been investigated. The rate expression is

$$-\frac{d[\text{Olefin}]}{dt} = k' K_1 \frac{[\text{PdCl}_4^-][\text{Olefin}]}{[\text{Cl}^-]^2[\text{H}^+]}$$

where K_1 is the equilibrium constant for the formation of a palladium(II)–olefin π-complex. The value of k' is less for the butenes and propene, indicating that the transition state can have little carbonium ion character and is probably cyclic.[21]

The allylic oxidation of olefins by palladium acetate has also been investigated.[22]

Chromic acid oxidation of isobutyrophenone and 2-chlorocyclohexanone has been shown kinetically to proceed through enols. The reactions can be formulated as:

$$\text{Ketone} \underset{k_K}{\overset{k_E}{\rightleftarrows}} \text{Enol} \xrightarrow[k]{\text{CrO}_3} \text{Product}$$

and at high chromic acid concentrations the rate-limiting step changes from oxidation of the enol to enolization of the ketone. Under these conditions the reactions are zero-order in chromic acid and the rates are approximately equal to the independently determined rates of enolization.[23]

Oxidation of benzoin by mercuric halides in aqueous pyridine is also zero-order in oxidant, and the rate-determining step was postulated to be formation of the enol or enolate ion.[24]

Although adipic acid (0.137M) is not oxidized by chromic acid (0.75M) in perchloric acid (1.0M) at 50°, in the presence of 3-methylbutan-2-one about 6% oxidation to succinic and glutaric acid does occur. This presumably results from an induced oxidation by chromium(V) and it was concluded that, although 3-methylbutan-2-one is oxidized about 15,000 times faster than adipic acid by chromium(VI), the rates are approximately equal with chromium(V).[25]

Bunton and his colleagues[26, 27] have extended their work on periodate oxidation of glycols. The oxidation of pinacol in acid solutions (pH 0—6) is kinetically second-order and the rate shows a maximum at pH 1. The observed kinetics are consistent with the scheme:

Pinacol + Periodate → Monoester → Cyclic ester → Products

[21] P. M. Henry, *J. Am. Chem. Soc.*, **88**, 1595 (1966); R. Jira, J. Sedlmeier, and J. Smidt, *Ann. Chem.*, **693**, 99 (1966).
[22] W. Kitching, Z. Rappoport, S. Winstein, and W. G. Young, *J. Am. Chem. Soc.*, **88**, 2054 (1966).
[23] J. Roček and A. Riehl, *J. Am. Chem. Soc.*, **88**, 4749 (1966).
[24] S. Patai and I. Shenfeld, *J. Chem. Soc.*, B, **1966**, 366.
[25] J. Roček and A. Riehl, *Tetrahedron Letters*, **1966**, 1437.
[26] G. J. Buist, C. A. Bunton, and J. Lomas, *J. Chem. Soc.*, B, **1966**, 1094.
[27] G. J. Buist, C. A. Bunton, and J. Lomas, *J. Chem. Soc.*, B, **1966**, 1099.

At pH's below 2 formation of the monoester is slow but above 2 it is rapid and reversible.[26] The reaction shows general base-catalysis at pH > 6. This was considered to be associated with ring closure of the mono- to the cyclic ester which was considered to be slow and partly rate-determining. In support of this interpretation no general base-catalysis was observed in the oxidation of ethanediol where the cyclic ester is thought to be formed rapidly. The oxidation of pinacol also shows a rate maximum at pH 9, possibly because the rate-determining step changes to reaction of pinacol and periodate mono-anion whose concentration decreases with increasing pH.[27]

Kinetic studies on the periodate oxidation of amino-sugars have been reported.[28]

A π-complex mechanism has been proposed for the oxidation of propene by mercuric salts in aqueous acid.[29]

The oxidation of cyclohexanols,[30] cyclopentanol,[31] secondary alcohols,[32] pinacols,[33] diastereoisomeric 1,2-diols,[34] hydroquinone,[35] and organoboranes by chromic acid,[36] the Etard reaction,[37] and the oxidation of alcohols with *tert*-butyl chromate[38] have been studied. The oxidation of toluenes,[39] the methyl esters of oxalic acid,[40] malic acid,[41] alcohols,[42] and benzyl alcohol[43] have also been studied. Other oxidations investigated include that of ethylene by selenium dioxide,[44] of propan-2-ol by cobaltic acetylacetonate,[45] of 1-naphthylamine by molybdenum(VI) and bromate ions,[46] of ethylenediamine-tetra-acetic acid by ferricyanide,[47] of methanol and ethanol by ferricyanide

28 C. B. Barlow, R. D. Guthrie, and A. M. Prior, *Chem. Commun.*, **1965**, 268.
29 J.-C. Strini and J. Metzger, *Bull. Soc. Chim. France*, **1966**, 3150.
30 E. L. Eliel, S. H. Schroeter, T. J. Brett, F. J. Biros, and J.-C. Richer, *J. Am. Chem. Soc.*, **88**, 3327 (1966).
31 B. Fuchs and R. G. Haber, *Tetrahedron Letters*, **1966**, 1323.
32 N. Venkatasubramanian, *Current. Sci. (India)*, **35**, 171 (1966); *Chem. Abs.*, **64**, 19339 (1966).
33 H. Kwart, *Bol. Inst. Quim. Univ. Nacl. Auton. Mex.*, **17**, 243 (1965); *Chem. Abs.*, **65**, 8691 (1966).
34 N. D. Heindel, E. S. Hanrahan, and R. J. Sinkovitz, *J. Org. Chem.*, **31**, 2019 (1966).
35 J. C. Sullivan and J. E. French, *J. Am. Chem. Soc.*, **87**, 5380 (1965).
36 P. T. Lansbury and E. J. Nienhouse, *Chem. Commun.*, **1966**, 273.
37 I. Necsoiu, V. Przemetchi, A. Ghenciulescu, C. N. Rentea, and C. D. Nenitzescu, *Tetrahedron*, **22**, 3037 (1966); C. N. Rentea, I. Necsoiu, M. Rentea, A. Ghenciulescu, and C. D. Nenitzescu, *Tetrahedron*, **22**, 3501 (1966); H. L. Duffin and R. B. Tucker, *Chem. Ind. (London)*, **1966**, 1262.
38 T. Suga and T. Matsuura, *Bull. Chem. Soc. Japan*, **39**, 326 (1966).
39 W. S. Trahanovsky and L. B. Young, *J. Org. Chem.*, **31**, 2033 (1966).
40 C. Andrade and H. Taube, *Inorg. Chem.*, **5**, 495 (1966).
41 K. K. Sengupta, *J. Indian Chem. Soc.*, **42**, 725 (1965).
42 B. Sethuram and S. S. Muhammad, *Acta Chem. Acad. Sci. Hung.*, **46**, 115, 125 (1965).
43 M. Rangaswamy and M. Santappa, *Current Sci. (India)* **35**, 332 (1966).
44 D. H. Olson, *Tetrahedron Letters*, **1966**, 2053.
45 V. M. Solyanikov and E. T. Denisov, *Neftekhimiya*, **6**, 97 (1966); *Chem. Abs.*, **64**, 19354 (1966).
46 K. B. Yatsimivskii and A. P. Filippov, *Kinetika i Kataliz*, **6**, 674 (1965).
47 D. G. Lambert and M. M. Jones, *J. Am. Chem. Soc.*, **88**, 4615 (1966).

with osmium tetroxide catalyst,[48] of aldopentoses by ferricyanide,[49] of toluene by cobaltic perchlorate in the absence and presence of aliphatic acids,[50] and of toluene,[51] aromatic amines, and phenols[52a] and glycollic acid[52b] by vanadium(v), and the autoxidation of vanadium(iv)–picolinic acid complexes.[53]

Other Oxidations

Oxidation of 4-nitrobenzyl alcohol with dimethyl [^{18}O]sulphoxide and dicyclohexylcarbodi-imide (Moffatt reaction) yielded unlabelled *p*-nitro-benzaldehyde but labelled dicyclohexylurea. Similar oxidation of 1,1-dideuteriobutan-1-ol yielded 1-deuteriobutyraldehyde and monodeuterio-dimethyl sulphide, and that of unlabelled butanol with hexadeuteriodimethyl sulphoxide yielded a pentadeuterio-sulphide. The mechanism of Scheme 1

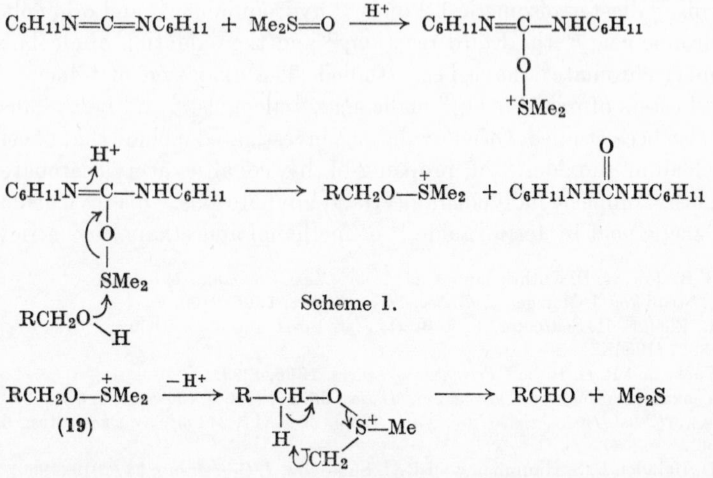

$$C_6H_{11}N{=}C{=}NC_6H_{11} + Me_2S{=}O \xrightarrow{\ H^+\ } C_6H_{11}N{=}C{-}NHC_6H_{11}$$

$$\underset{^+SMe_2}{\overset{O}{\underset{|}{\overset{|}{}}}}$$

$$\overset{H^+}{\overset{\nearrow}{C_6H_{11}N{=}C{-}NHC_6H_{11}}} \longrightarrow RCH_2O{-}\overset{+}{S}Me_2 + C_6H_{11}NH\overset{O}{\overset{\|}{C}}NHC_6H_{11}$$

$$\underset{\underset{RCH_2O}{\overset{\nwarrow}{}}{\overset{\nearrow}{H}}}{\overset{O}{\underset{|}{\overset{|}{}}}}$$
$$SMe_2$$

Scheme 1.

$$RCH_2O{-}\overset{+}{S}Me_2 \xrightarrow{\ -H^+\ } R{-}CH{-}O \longrightarrow RCHO + Me_2S$$
$$(19)$$

was therefore proposed.[54] This has been criticized by Torssell[55] who prepared the alkoxysulphonium intermediate [(19); R = Pr^i] from isobutyl alcohol as its tetraphenylborate. When this was subjected to the oxidation conditions the yield of aldehyde was lower than that obtained from isobutyl alcohol.

[48] B. Khrishna and H. S. Singh, *Z. Physik. Chem. (Leipzig)*, **231**, 399 (1966).
[49] R. K. Srivastava, N. Nath, and M. P. Singh, *Bull. Chem. Soc. Japan*, **39**, 833 (1966).
[50] T. A. Cooper, A. A. Clifford, D. J. Mills, and W. A. Waters, *J. Chem. Soc.*, B, **1966**, 793.
[51] P. S. R. Murti and S. C. Pati, *Chem. Ind. (London)*, **1966**, 1722.
[52a] P. R. Bonchev and K. B. Yatsimirskii, *Zh. Fiz. Khim.*, **39**, 1995 (1965).
[52b] G. V. Bakove and R. Shankev, *Can. J. Chem.*, **44**, 1717 (1966).
[53] T. Kaden, *Helv. Chim. Acta*, **49**, 1915 (1966).
[54] A. H. Fenselau and J. G. Moffatt, *J. Am. Chem. Soc.*, **88**, 1762 (1966); K. E. Pfitzner and J. G. Moffatt, *ibid.*, **87**, 5661, 5670 (1965).
[55] K. Torssell, *Tetrahedron Letters*, **1966**, 4445.

Mechanism (3) was therefore proposed. In this the strongly basic anion of dicyclohexylurea, generated on fission of the sulphur–oxygen bond, abstracts a proton from the *S*-methyl group.

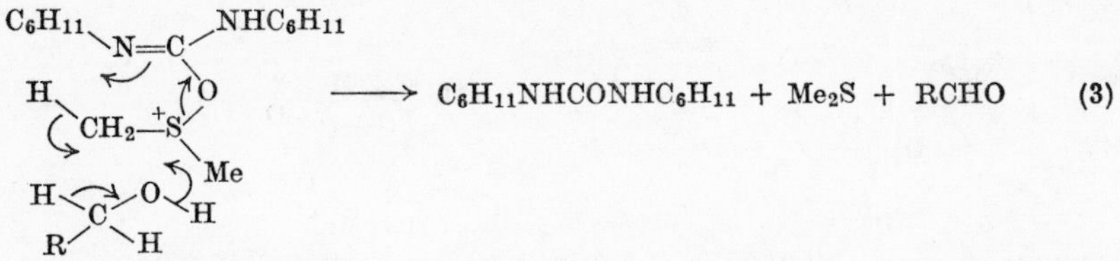

$$\longrightarrow C_6H_{11}NHCONHC_6H_{11} + Me_2S + RCHO \qquad (3)$$

Oxidation of propionaldehyde with bromine in aqueous solution is first-order in each reactant and it catalysed by acetate ion; tribromide ions are inactive.[56] Oxidation of butane-2,3-diol by bromine[57] and of lysine by sodium hypochlorite[58] has been studied. The first example of a tetrazene synthesis which gives both *cis*- and *trans*-forms has been reported. Oxidation of 3-amino-2-oxazolidinone (**20**) with aqueous bromine gave the *trans*-tetrazene (**21**), whilst mercuric oxide in dioxan or tetrahydrofuran gave the *cis*-isomer (**22**) [which could be photoisomerized to (**21**) in the solid state]. Formation of the less stable *cis*-isomer was attributed to steric control by the polymeric mercuric oxide, oxidation and coupling occurring between molecules chelated to the surface mercury atoms.[59]

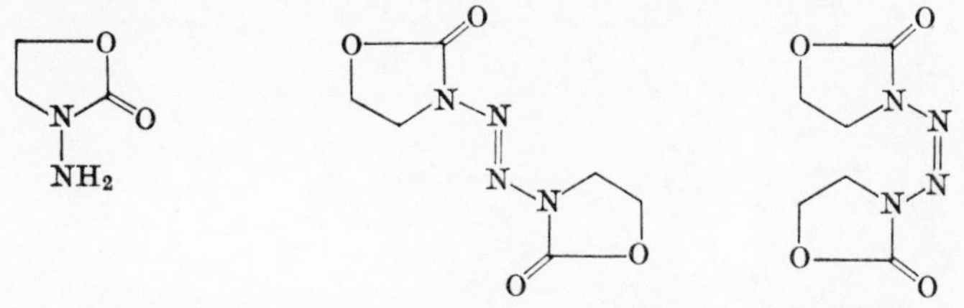

(**20**)　　　　　(**21**)　　　　　(**22**)

Amino-acids are oxidized to keto-acids by molecular oxygen in the presence of pyridoxal and manganese ions:

$$RCHNH_2CO_2H + O_2 + H_2O \rightarrow RCOCO_2H + NH_3 + H_2O_2$$

salicaldehyde and pyridine cannot replace pyridoxal but pyridoxamine can. The reaction is inhibited by ethylenediaminetetra-acetic acid but is unaffected

[56] J. Konecny, *Helv. Chim. Acta*, **48**, 1817 (1965).
[57] N. Venkatasubramanian and A. Sabesan, *Indian J. Chem.*, **4**, 327 (1966).
[58] B. Franck and D. Randau, *Angew. Chem. Internat. Ed. Engl.*, **5**, 131 (1966).
[59] P. S. Forgione, G. S. Sprague, and H. J. Troffkin, *J. Am. Chem. Soc.*, **88**, 1079 (1966).

by light or radical inhibitors. Simple amines react slowly, if at all, and glycine reacts 5—6 times faster than α,α-dideuterioglycine. The mechanism of Scheme 2 was proposed and it was suggested that the mechanism of the enzymic oxidation of amines proceeded similarly.[60]

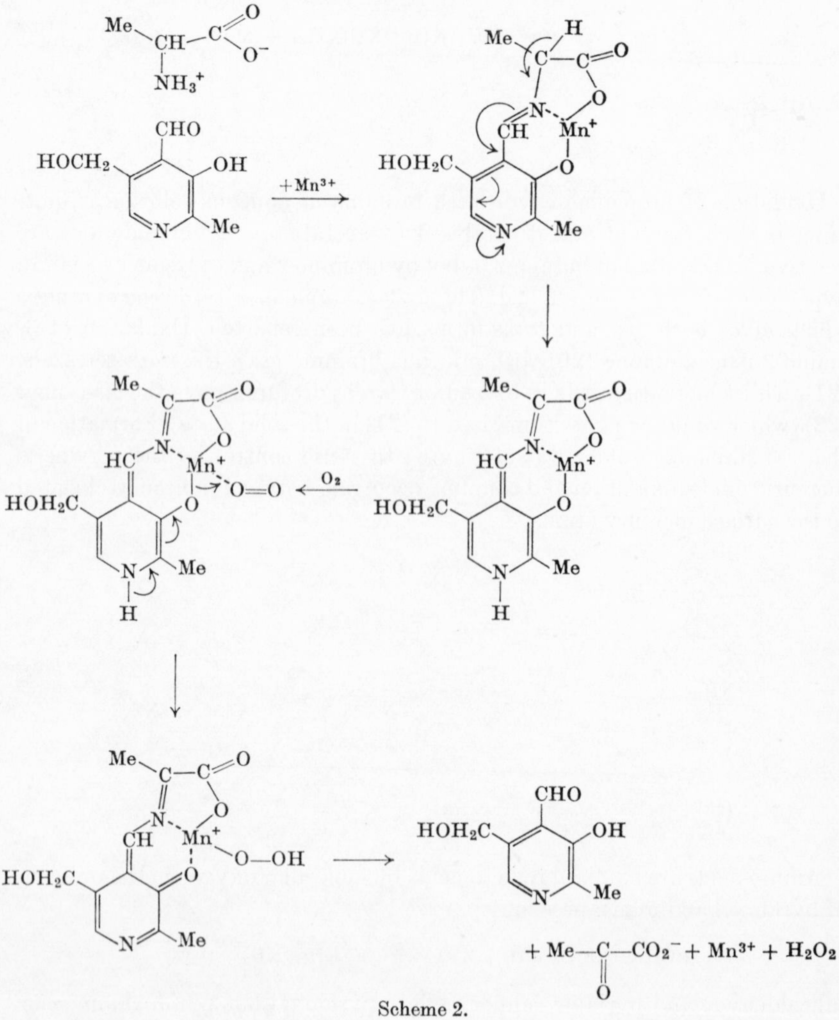

Scheme 2.

The generation of "singlet oxygen", $O=O$, by heterolytic decomposition of peroxides, and its chemical reactions have been described. Structurally

[60] G. A. Hamilton and A. Revesz, *J. Am. Chem. Soc.*, **88**, 2069 (1966).

analogous to ethylene, it is an active dienophile, adding to dienes in the absence of irradiation or catalysts.[61] Excited singlet molecular oxygen has been proposed as the reactive species in the photo-oxidation of organic compounds which form transannular peroxides.[62]

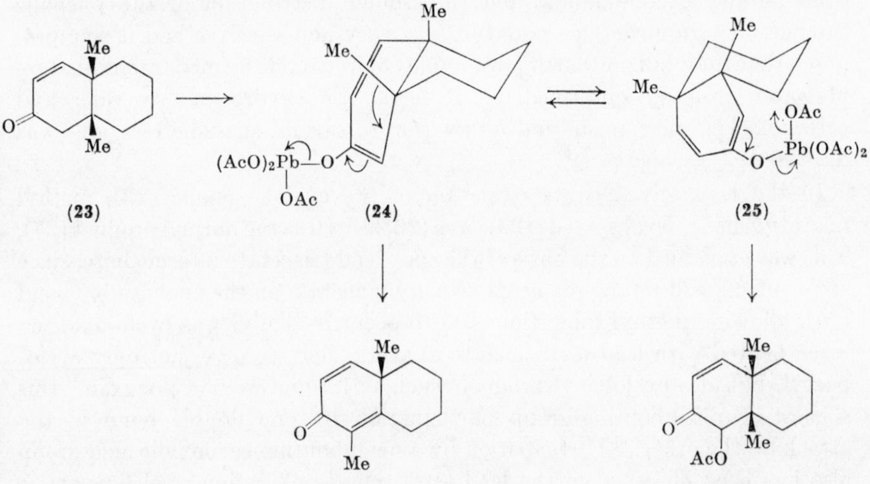

(23)   (24)   (25)

(26)   (27)

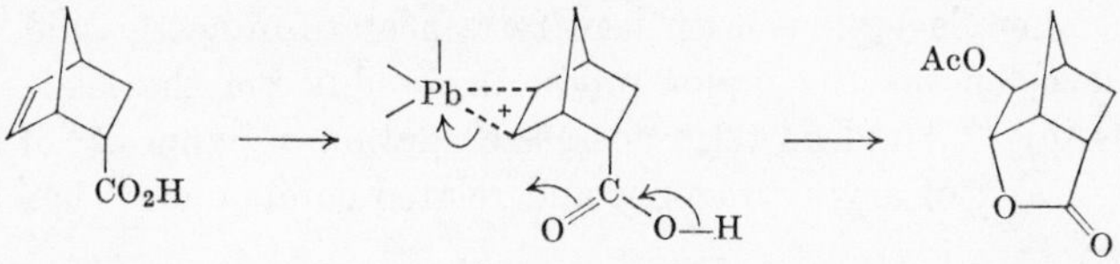

(28)   (29)   (30)

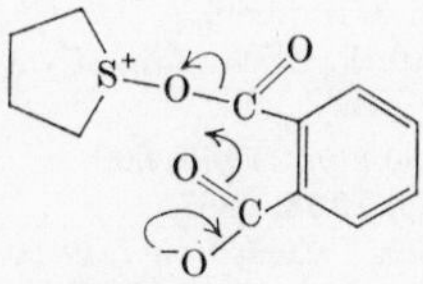

(31)

[61] E. McKeown and W. A. Waters, *J. Chem. Soc.*, *B*, **1966**, 1040.
[62] T. Wilson, *J. Am. Chem. Soc.*, **88**, 2898 (1966).

A detailed investigation of the scope and kinetics of the hydroxylation of anisole by aqueous hydrogen peroxide in the presence of catalytic amounts of ferric ions and catechol gave results which were inconsistent with any radical-chain mechanism. It was suggested that the hydroxylating agent is a complex of ferric ion, catechol, and hydrogen peroxide.[63] The reaction was extended to other aromatic compounds, and the isomer distribution of the phenolic products determined. The oxidation was very non-selective and it was proposed that the oxidizing agent is a complex of iron oxide formed by elimination of water from an intermediate of ferric ion, hydrogen peroxide, and catechol. The mechanism and its relation to several enzymic reactions was discussed;[64] see also p. 192.

In the lead tetra-acetate oxidation of the cyclohexenone (23), methyl migration has been observed; (23) gave (26) as well as the normal product (27). This was explained on the basis of the enol–lead triacetate intermediate, since steric effects will retard the usual attack by acetate on the enol double bond (25), allowing methyl migration (24) to occur.[65] Biallyl was cyclo-oxidized when heated with lead tetra-acetate in acetic acid, to give, not only cyclopentyl, but also cyclohexyl products such as 1,4-diacetoxycyclohexane, this suggesting neighbouring-group participation by one double bond in the attack on the other.[66] Participation by a neighbouring carboxylic acid group also has been observed in the lead tetra-acetate oxidation of olefinic acids. For example, acid (28) gave lactone (30); initial electrophilic addition of lead tetra-acetate to the double bond, followed by nucleophilic attack by the acid group (29), was preferred to the alternative, reverse sequence.[67]

Oxidation of phenylacetylene with lead tetra-acetate in acetic acid gave methylphenylacetylene as the major product, possibly via the lead ester, $Ph-C{\equiv}C-Pb(OAc)_3$.[68] The lead tetra-acetate oxidation of oximes,[69] of rigid glycol systems,[70] and of arylhydrazones and related compounds[71] has been described.

Oxidation of the following by peroxydisulphate ions has been investigated: methanol and ethanol,[72] ethanol and dioxan,[73] alcohols, aldehydes, and

[63] G. A. Hamilton, J. P. Friedman, and P. M. Campbell, *J. Am. Chem. Soc.*, **88**, 5266 (1966).
[64] G. A. Hamilton, J. W. Hanifin, and J. P. Friedman, *J. Am. Chem. Soc.*, **88**, 5269 (1966).
[65] J. A. Marshall and G. L. Bundy, *Chem. Commun.*, **1966**, 500.
[66] I. Tabushi and R. Oda, *Tetrahedron Letters*, **1966**, 2487.
[67] R. M. Moriarty, H. G. Walsh, and H. Gopal, *Tetrahedron Letters*, **1966**, 4363, 4369.
[68] S. Moon and W. J. Campbell, *Chem. Commun.*, **1966**, 470.
[69] G. Just and K. Dahl, *Tetrahedron Letters*, **1966**, 2441.
[70] H. Mohrle, *Arch. Pharm.*, **299**, 225 (1966).
[71] W. A. F. Gladstone, M. J. Harrison, and R. O. C. Norman, *J. Chem. Soc.*, *C.*, **1966**, 1781; W. A. F. Gladstone and R. O. C. Norman, *ibid.*, pp. 1527, 1531, 1536.
[72] J. O. Edwards, A. R. Gallopo, and J. E. McIsaac, *J. Am. Chem. Soc.*, **88**, 3891 (1966).
[73] D. D. Mishra and S. Ghosh, *Proc. Natl. Inst. Sci. India*, Pt. A, **31**, 119 (1965).

ketones,[74] carboxylic acids,[75] lactic acid,[76] and primary[77] and secondary[78] aliphatic amines.

The mechanisms of various anodic oxidations have been investigated.[79]

The oxidation of phenols, especially highly hindered ones, and phenol oxidative coupling has received further attention,[80] as has the oxidation of sulphides. Sulphides react very slowly with iodine in the absence of nucleophiles, but tetrahydrothiophen was oxidized very rapidly to the sulphoxide by iodine in a phthalate buffer. Spectral evidence for the formation of phthalic anhydride was obtained and a mechanism with (31) as the key step was proposed.[81] Oxidations of sulphides, sulphoxides, and dibenzothiophen have been reported.[82] The oxidative decarboxylation[83] of [^{18}O]benzoic acid in an air–steam mixture yields phenol labelled with ^{18}O. A free-radical mechanism has been considered[84] and demonstrated[85] for the autoxidation of organoboranes. Reactions by molecular oxygen that have been studied include: oxidation of methanol catalysed by copper–phenanthroline complexes;[86] silver-catalysed oxidation of alkoxide anions;[87] oxidation of aldehydes and ketones catalysed by copper–pyridine;[88] ferric ion-catalysed oxidation of cysteine;[89] oxidation of sorbic acid;[90] radiation-induced reaction of ethane

---

[74] L. R. Subbaraman and M. Santappa, *Z. Physik. Chem. (Frankfurt)*, **48**, 163, 172 (1966).

[75] R. H. Thomson and A. G. Wylie, *J. Chem. Soc., C*, **1966**, 321.

[76] N. Venkatasubranamian and A. Sabesan, *Tetrahedron Letters*, **1966**, 4919.

[77] R. G. R. Bacon and D. Stewart, *J. Chem. Soc., C*, **1966**, 1384.

[78] R. G. R. Bacon, W. J. W. Hanna, and D. Stewart, *J. Chem. Soc., C*, **1966**, 1388.

[79] C. A. Chambers and J. Q. Chambers, *J. Am. Chem. Soc.*, **88**, 2922 (1966); S. D. Ross, M. Finkelstein, and R. C. Petersen, *ibid.*, p. 4657; *J. Org. Chem.*, **31**, 128 (1966); L. Eberson and K. Nyberg, *Tetrahedron Letters*, **1966**, 2389; M. Oyama and M. Ohno, *ibid.*, p. 5201.

[80] E. C. Horswill and K. U. Ingold, *Can. J. Chem.*, **44**, 263, 269 (1966); E. C. Horswill, J. A. Howard, and K. U. Ingold, *ibid.*, p. 985; H. Musso and D. Maassen, *Ann. Chem.*, **689**, 93 (1965); H. Musso, U. von Gizycki, H. Krämer, and H. Döpp, *Chem. Ber.*, **98**, 3952 (1965); D. A. Bolon, *J. Am. Chem. Soc.*, **88**, 3148 (1966); E. McNelis, *J. Org. Chem.*, **31**, 1255 (1966); V. P. Bhatia and K. B. L. Mathur, *Tetrahedron Letters*, **1966**, 4057; R. G. R. Bacon and A. R. Izzat, *J. Chem. Soc., C*, **1966**, 791; A. H. Jackson and J. A. Martin, *ibid.*, p. 2061; A. Rieker, N. Zeller, K. Schurr, and E. Müller, *Ann. Chem.*, **697**, 1 (1966).

[81] T. Higuchi and K.-H. Gensch, *J. Am. Chem. Soc.*, **88**, 3874 (1966).

[82] E. N. Karaulova, T. A. Bardina, G. D. Gal'pern, and T. S. Bobruiskaya, *Neftekhimaya*, **6**, 480 (1966); *Chem. Abs.*, **65**, 10452 (1966); T. J. Wallace, *J. Org. Chem.*, **31**, 3071, 4017 (1966); D. Carnimeo and R. Curci, *Boll. Sci. Fac. Chim. Ind. Bologna*, **23**, 293 (1965); *Chem. Abs.*, **64**, 17401 (1966); T. J. Wallace and H. A. Weiss, *Chem. Ind. (London)*, **1966**, 1558; R. Curci and G. Modena, *Tetrahedron*, **22**, 1227 (1966); R. Curci, A. Giovine, and G. Modena, *ibid.*, p. 1235; B. N. Heimlick and T. J. Wallace, *ibid.*, p. 3571.

[83] S. Oae, T. Watanabe, and N. Furukawa, *Bull. Chem. Soc. Japan*, **39**, 1329 (1966).

[84] E. C. J. Coffee and A. G. Davies, *J. Chem. Soc., C*, **1966**, 1493.

[85] A. G. Davies and B. P. Roberts, *Chem. Commun.*, **1966**, 298.

[86] W. Brackman and C. J. Gaasbeek, *Rec. Trav. Chim.*, **85**, 242 (1966).

[87] J. Kubias, *Coll. Czech. Chem. Commun.*, **31**, 1666 (1966).

[88] W. Brackman, C. J. Gaasbeek, and P. J. Smit, *Rec. Trav. Chim.*, **85**, 437 (1966); W. Brackman and H. C. Volger, *ibid.*, p. 446.

[89] J. E. Taylor, J. F. Yan, and J. Wang, *J. Am. Chem. Soc.*, **88**, 1663 (1966).

[90] L. Pekkarinen and P. Rissanen, *Suomen Kemistilehti, B*, **39**, 50 (1966).

and oxygen;[91] reaction of styrene and oxygen catalysed by cobalt stearate or acetylacetonate;[92] and photo-oxidation of polystyrene in solution.[93]

There have been many more autoxidation reactions studied, including those of hydrocarbons,[94] benzene,[95] α-methylstyrene,[96] ethylbenzene,[97] styrene,[98] isopropyl compounds,[99] cumene and tetralin,[100] tetralin,[101] alkylidenecyclohexanes,[102] N-alkylamides,[103] N,N-dialkylanilines,[104] oxazoles,[105] and N-benzoyl-leucomethylene blue,[106] as well as photosensitized autoxidations.[107]

Reductions

Some new kinetic measurements on the reduction of benzene with lithium and ethanol in liquid ammonia [equation (4)] show that the rate law is fourth-order in reactants, not third as previously supposed, and that the rate is markedly dependent on the concentration of lithium ethoxide, one of the products:

$$C_6H_6 + 2Li + 2EtOH \rightarrow 2EtOLi + C_6H_8 \qquad (4)$$

When the concentration of lithium ethoxide was initially sufficient for saturation, the rate was proportional to $[C_6H_6][EtOH][Li]^2$. The rate law and the effect of lithium ethoxide are consistent with reversible addition of the first electron followed by the first proton, then reversible addition of the second electron to give a π-complex; this rearranges in the rate-determining step to the cyclohexadienyl anion which is rapidly protonated to dihydrobenzene (Scheme 3).[108] Reductive opening, with lithium in liquid ammonia, of the cyclopropane ring of conjugated cyclopropyl ketones which are part of

[91] M. Ahmad and P. G. Clay, *J. Chem. Soc., B,* **1966**, 845.

[92] L. N. Denisova, E. T. Denisov, and T. G. Degtyareva, *Izv. Akad. Nauk SSSR, Ser. Khim.,* **1966**, 1095; *Chem. Abs.,* **65**, 10453 (1966).

[93] J. B. Lawrence and N. A. Weir, *Chem. Commun.,* **1966**, 257.

[94] J. A. Howard and K. U. Ingold, *Can. J. Chem.,* **44**, 1113, 1119 (1966).

[95] H. Hotta and N. Suzuki, *Nippon Kagaku Zasshi,* **86**, 651 (1965); *Chem. Abs.,* **64**, 4895 (1966).

[96] E. Niki and Y. Kamiya, *Bull. Chem. Soc. Japan,* **39**, 1095 (1966).

[97] F. W. K. Altes and P. J. van den Berg, *Rec. Trav. Chim.,* **85**, 538 (1966).

[98] I. T. Brownlie and K. U. Ingold, *Can. J. Chem.,* **44**, 861 (1966).

[99] K. Itoh, S. Sakai, and Y. Ishii, *Tetrahedron,* **22**, 509 (1966).

[100] T. Ikawa, M. Muto, and T. Shinatani, *Bull. Japan Petrol Inst.,* **7**, 41; *Chem. Abs.,* **63**, 17816 (1965).

[101] Y. Kamiya, *Tetrahedron,* **22**, 2029 (1966).

[102] H. Miki, M. Sato, Y. Murata, and Y. Fushizaki, *Kogyo Kagaku Zasshi,* **68**, 1698 (1965); *Chem. Abs.,* **64**, 4895 (1966).

[103] M. V. Lock and B. F. Sagar, *J. Chem. Soc., B,* **1966**, 690.

[104] L. Horner and K. H. Knapp, *Makromol. Chem.,* **93**, 69 (1966).

[105] H. H. Wasserman and M. B. Floyd, *Tetrahedron, Suppl.* No. 7, 441 (1966).

[106] W. J. Gensler, J. R. Jones, R. Rein, J. J. Bruno, and D. M. Bryan, *J. Org. Chem.,* **31**, 2324 (1966).

[107] H. H. Wasserman, A. R. Doumaux, and R. E. Davis, *J. Am. Chem. Soc.,* **88**, 4517 (1966); H. H. Wasserman and P. M. Keehn, *ibid.,* p. 4522.

[108] O. J. Jacobus and J. F. Eastham, *J. Am. Chem. Soc.,* **87**, 5799 (1965).

$$C_6H_6 + e^- \rightleftharpoons \cdot C_6H_6^-$$

$$\cdot C_6H_6^- + EtOH \rightleftharpoons H \cdot C_6H_6 + EtO^-$$

$$H \cdot C_6H_6 + e^- \rightleftharpoons H : C_6H_6^-$$

$$H : C_6H_6^- \xrightarrow{Slow} C_6H_7^-$$

$$C_6H_7^- + EtOH \xrightarrow{Fast} C_6H_8 + EtO^-$$

Scheme 3.

bicyclo[3.1.0]hexane and bicyclo[4.1.0]heptane systems is highly stereo-specific, cleaving the bond with maximum overlap with the π-orbital of the carbonyl group.[109] The double bond of α,β-olefinic ketones is reduced by lithium and propylamine; with N-deuteriated propylamine deuterium is introduced specifically β to the carbonyl group.[110] The nature of the anion radical formed in the Birch reduction of anisole has been studied by ESR spectroscopy.[111]

The rate of Wolff–Kishner reduction of benzophenone hydrazone in butyl carbitol–dimethyl sulphoxide (DMSO) mixtures increases and then decreases with increasing DMSO concentration. This result seems to demonstrate for the first time the importance of a proton-donor; a more or less concerted making of the C–H bond and breaking of the N–H bond in the hydrazone anion was proposed as rate-determining step. This is shown in equation (5) where BH is a protic solvent molecule (butyl carbitol) and S is an acceptor solvent. Since DMSO is probably a better proton-acceptor than the alcohol it will accelerate the reaction until BH becomes significantly depleted.[112]

The complexing of chromous ions with ligands such as ethylenediamine (en), and even more so with ethanolamine, greatly enhances its ability to

$$BH + \overset{\overset{\displaystyle R}{|}}{\underset{\underset{\displaystyle R}{|}}{C}} \overset{\delta-}{=\!=\!=} N \overset{\delta-}{=\!=\!=} N - H + S \longrightarrow B^- + H - \overset{\overset{\displaystyle R}{|}}{\underset{\underset{\displaystyle R}{|}}{C}} - N = N^- + {}^+SH \qquad (5)$$

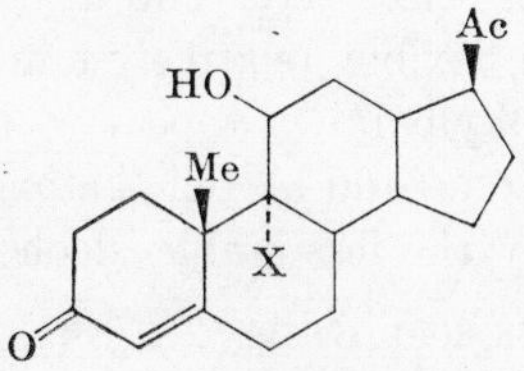

(32)

$$R - Br \xrightarrow{Cr(OAc)_2} R \cdot \xrightarrow{BuSH} RH + \tfrac{1}{2} BuSSBu \qquad (6)$$

[109] W. G. Dauben and E. J. Deviny, *J. Org. Chem.*, **31**, 3794 (1966).
[110] M. Fetizon and J. Gore, *Tetrahedron Letters*, **1966**, 471.
[111] J. K. Brown, D. R. Burnham, and N. A. J. Rogers, *Tetrahedron Letters*, **1966**, 2621.
[112] H. H. Szmant and M. N. Román, *J. Am. Chem. Soc.*, **88**, 4034 (1966).

reduce alkyl halides to alkanes. The reactivity of halides towards $Cr(en)^{2+}$ is tertiary > secondary > primary > and iodides > bromides > chlorides. The chromium(II)–ethanolamine complex reduces primary chlorides at room temperature. Differences in the rate of disappearance of alkyl halide and rate of appearance of alkane suggested the intervention of alkylchromium species and these have been detected spectroscopically.[113] That a radical mechanism is valid for the reduction of tertiary bromides, e.g., progesterone bromohydrin [(32); X = Br] to hydroxyprogesterone [(32); X = H], by chromous ion has been proved by studying the role of various hydrogen-atom donors; in the reaction of chromous acetate and butane-1-thiol the latter is converted quantitatively into disulphide [equation (6)].[114] Chromous sulphate in dimethylformamide at room temperature reduces olefins containing on the double bond electron-withdrawing groups that are also capable of co-ordinating with the metal ion. The stoichiometry, stereochemistry, and kinetics are consistent with a mechanism in which chromium(II) attacks an olefin–Cr(II) complex, to yield product.[115] The rates of reduction by chromous ion of a wide range of carboxylatopenta-aminecobalt(III) complexes have been measured and discussed in terms of electron-transfer through the organic ligands.[116]

The composition of mixtures of lithium aluminium hydride and aluminium chloride ("mixed hydride" reducing agents) in ether has been investigated. The reduction of aluminium chloride to aluminium hydride occurs stepwise through the hydridoaluminium halides. The actual reducing species from $LiAlH_4:3AlCl_3$ and from $3LiAlH_4:AlCl_3$ are $AlHCl_2$ and AlH_3, respectively.[117] Certain of the mechanistic proposals were, however, not borne out by the stereochemistry of the reduction of 1-phenylcyclopentene oxide by mixed hydride.[118] Lithium hydridotrimethoxyaluminate resembles lithium aluminium hydride in reducing power much more closely than does tri-*tert*-butoxy-aluminium hydride,[119] but the trimethoxy-compound is more stereoselective than either in the reduction of ketones.[120] From bicyclic ketones the tri-methoxy-reagent gave the less stable alcohol selectively. The direction of reduction is controlled by product stability in flexible, relatively unhindered ketones and otherwise by steric factors. Dialkylboranes appear to be very consistent in reducing α-substituted cyclic ketones and bicyclic ketones from the less hindered side, to give predominantly the less stable alcohol.[121] A

113 J. K. Kochi and P. E. Mocadlo, *J. Am. Chem. Soc.*, **88**, 4094 (1966).
114 D. H. R. Barton, N. K. Basu, R. H. Hesse, F. S. Morehouse, and M. M. Pechet, *J. Am. Chem. Soc.*, **88**, 3016 (1966).
115 C. E. Castro, R. D. Stephens, and S. Mojé, *J. Am. Chem. Soc.*, **88**, 4964 (1966).
116 E. S. Gould, *J. Am. Chem. Soc.*, **88**, 2983 (1966).
117 E. C. Ashby and J. Prather, *J. Am. Chem. Soc.*, **88**, 729 (1966).
118 P. T. Lansbury and V. A. Pattison, *Tetrahedron Letters*, **1966**, 3073.
119 H. C. Brown and P. M. Weissman, *J. Am. Chem. Soc.*, **87**, 5614 (1965).
120 H. C. Brown and H. R. Deck, *J. Am. Chem. Soc.*, **87**, 5620 (1965).
121 M. W. Rathke, N. Inoue, K. R. Varma, and H. C. Brown, *J. Am. Chem. Soc.*, **88**, 2870 (1966).

modified hydroboration–amination procedure for the stereospecific synthesis of alicyclic and bicyclic amines has been described.[122] A note has appeared on how to predict the products of hydride reduction of α,β-unsaturated ketones by considering steric factors in the possible transition states.[123] Reduction of the piperidones (33) with sodium borohydride gave mixture of the epimeric alcohols (34) and (35) in proportions which depended markedly on the solvent. This was rationalized by considering the electrostatic effect of the neighbouring ester-carbonyl dipoles; the directive effect was most pronounced in non-polar solvents, to give (34), whilst in polar solvents the normal products (35) were formed.[124] The asymmetric reduction of ketones to secondary alcohols by complexes of lithium aluminium hydride with glucose derivatives,[125] and the stereochemistry of the reduction of iminium salts with lithium aluminium hydride[126] have been described. Other reductions of ketones are discussed on pp. 335–337.

(33)   (34)   (35)

$R = Me, Et; R' = 2\text{-pyridyl}; R'' = H, alkyl$

In an effort to distinguish between attack on carbon or on halogen in reduction of alkyl halides, the polarographic and zinc reduction of optically active 1-bromo-2,2-diphenylcyclopropanecarboxylic acid, its methyl ester, and 1-bromo-1-methyl-2,2-diphenylcyclopropane have been studied. The two methods of reductions had identical stereospecificity. The acid and its ester gave products of partially inverted configuration, whilst the anion and the C-methyl compound gave products with partial retention of configuration. The results were interpreted by a mechanism involving initial attack by the electrode on bromine, to give an electrode complex with the same configuration as the reactant; the overall stereochemistry is determined by a stereoselective reaction of the free or shielded carbanion with solvent or proton.[127] The effects of methyl substituents on the polarographic reduction potentials of dibenzofuran and biphenyl accord with the predictions of LCAO–MO theory, but for dibenzothiophen agreement is not obtained if the $3d$-orbitals of sulphur

[122] H. C. Brown and V. Varma, *J. Am. Chem. Soc.*, **88**, 2871 (1966).

[123] E. Toromanoff, *Bull. Soc. Chim. France*, **1966**, 1445.

[124] R. Haller, *Tetrahedron Letters*, **1965**, 4347.

[125] S. R. Landor, B. J. Miller, and A. R. Tatchell, *J. Chem. Soc., C*, **1966**, 1822.

[126] D. Cabaret, G. Chauvière, and Z. Welvart, *Tetrahedron Letters*, **1966**, 4109.

[127] R. Annino, R. E. Erickson, J. Michalovic, and B. McKay, *J. Am. Chem. Soc.*, **88**, 4424 (1966).

are included in the conjugated system.[128] The polarographic reduction of
N-alkyl-N-nitrosoureas[129] and of thiocarboxylic acid derivatives and their
analogues[130] have been reported.

A detailed investigation of the steric course of the reduction of cyclo-
hexanones with nicotinamide–adenine dinucleotide and horse-liver alcohol
dehydrogenase has been reported.[131] α-Deuterio-benzaldehyde and -butyr-
aldehyde were reduced by actively fermenting yeast to the corresponding
optically active 1-deuterio-alcohols, as previously demonstrated for 1-
deuteriotrimethylacetaldehyde; thus the stereospecific binding of the aldehyde group by the enzyme system responsible for reduction appears to be
insensitive to the rest of the molecule.[132]

Mechanisms have been proposed to explain the stereospecificity of catalytic
hydrogenolysis of benzyl compounds which usually gives retention or inversion
of configuration.[133]

Other mechanistic reduction studies reported have been on: formation of
intermediates from hydroxyanthraquinonesulphonic acids;[134] characteriza-
tion of an intermediate in the dithionite reduction of a diphosphopyridine
nucleotide model as a 1,4-addition product,[135] and an intermediate in the
reduction of quinoline analogues of model compounds for a coenzyme;[136]
reduction of aromatic nitro-compounds with sodium monosulphide,[137] of
cis- and *trans*-3-(benzylsulphinyl)crotonic acid with acidic iodide solution,[138]
of p-nitrophenol with titanium(III) chloride in hydrochloric acid,[139] of
3-methylenenorbornanone,[140] of norbornanone,[141] and of dimethyl sulphoxide
with iodide ions in aqueous perchloric acid;[142] an ESR study of nitroamine
anion radicals formed by reduction of aromatic polynitro-compounds;[143] and
photoreduction of α,β-unsaturated ketones.[144]

[128] R. Gerdil and E. A. C. Lucken, *J. Am. Chem. Soc.*, **88**, 733 (1966).
[129] E. R. Garrett and A. G. Cusimano, *J. Pharm. Sci.*, **55**, 702 (1966).
[130] R. Mayer, S. Scheithauer, and D. Kunz, *Chem. Ber.*, **99**, 1393 (1966).
[131] J. M. H. Graves, A. Clark, and H. J. Ringold, *Biochemistry*, **4**, 2655 (1965).
[132] V. E. Althouse, D. M. Feigl, W. A. Sanderson, and H. S. Mosher, *J. Am. Chem. Soc.*, **88**, 3595 (1966).
[133] A. M. Khan, F. J. McQuillin, and I. Jardine, *Tetrahedron Letters*, **1966**, 2649.
[134] A. D. Broadbent and H. Zollinger, *Helv. Chim. Acta*, **49**, 1729 (1966).
[135] W. S. Caughey and K. A. Schellenberg, *J. Org. Chem.*, **31**, 1978 (1966); J.-F. Biellmann and H. Callot, *Tetrahedron Letters*, **1966**, 3991.
[136] J. F. Munshi and M. M. Joullié, *Chem. Commun.*, **1965**, 607.
[137] S. Hashimoto and J. Sunamoto, *Bull. Chem. Soc. Japan*, **39**, 1207 (1966).
[138] S. Allenmark, *Acta Chem. Scand.*, **19**, 2075 (1966).
[139] R. Mueller and K. Schwabe, *Coll. Czech. Chem. Commun.*, **30**, 4016 (1965).
[140] H. Krieger, K. Manninen, and J. Paasivirta, *Suomen Kemistilehti, B*, **39**, 8 (1966).
[141] P. J. Malkoanen and J. Korvola, *Suomen Kemistilehti, A*, **39**, 118 (1966); E. Heinanen and P. Hirsjarvi, *ibid., B*, **39**, 77.
[142] G. Modena, G. Scorrano, D. Landini, and F. Montanari, *Tetrahedron Letters*, **1966**, 3309.
[143] R. D. Allendoerfer and P. H. Rieger, *J. Am. Chem. Soc.*, **88**, 3711 (1966).
[144] R. L. Cargill, J. R. Damewood, and M. M. Cooper, *J. Am. Chem. Soc.*, **88**, 1330 (1966).

Hydrogenations

There have been a number of interesting reports on homogeneous catalytic hydrogenation[145] this year, and this and related topics have been discussed by Halpern.[146] The homogeneous hydrogenation of maleic and fumaric acid to succinic acid in aqueous solution with ruthenium(II) chloride as catalyst has been fully investigated. A Ru(II)–olefin complex appears to be formed and to react homogeneously with hydrogen, the rate law being $k[H_2][Ru^{II}(\text{Olefin})]$. Tracer studies with D_2 and D_2O show that the hydrogen atoms added to the double bond originate from the solvent rather than from the hydrogen gas, and that the addition is stereospecifically *cis*. Ru(II) complexes of non-activated olefins are not reduced by hydrogen, but do catalyse the exchange of D_2 with H_2O. A mechanism to accommodate these facts was proposed.[147] The kinetics of the formation of a 1:1 π-complex between ethylene and Ru(II) in aqueous hydrochloric acid over a range of temperatures and concentration of all the reactants suggest that complex formation proceeds through a stepwise S_N1 mechanism in which the initial step is dissociation of a chloro-ruthenate(II) complex.[148] Rhodium(III) chloride in dimethylacetamide is an effective homogeneous catalyst for the hydrogenation of maleic acid to succinic acid.[149] Aspects of homogeneous hydrogenation of olefins generally,[150] and of steroids,[151] with tris(triphenylphosphine)chlororhodium as catalyst, including the stereospecific *cis*-addition of deuterium,[152] have been discussed. A close correspondence between heterogeneous hydrogenation and homogeneous hydrogenation catalysed by soluble transition-metal hydrides has been noted.[153] Lithium aluminium hydride is a homogeneous catalyst for the selective hydrogenation of pent-2-yne (*trans*) and conjugated dienes to mono-olefins; deuterium tracer experiments with penta-1,3-diene showed that the metal hydride and the gaseous hydrogen each contributed one hydrogen to the diene.[154]

The mechanisms of hydrogenation of unsaturated hydrocarbons have been reviewed with particular attention given to stereochemical aspects.[155] In the metal-catalysed hydrogenation of olefins a phenyl substituent at the double bond increases the extent of pure 1,2-*cis*-addition relative to other processes such as exchange, racemization, double-bond migration, and geometrical

---

[145] For a review see J.-C. Lauer, *Ann. Chim. (Paris)*, **1965**, 301.

[146] J. Halpern, *Chem. Eng. News*, 1966, Oct. 31st, 68.

[147] J. Halpern, J. F. Harrod, and B. R. James, *J. Am. Chem. Soc.*, **88**, 5150 (1966).

[148] J. Halpern and B. R. James, *Can. J. Chem.*, **44**, 495 (1966).

[149] B. R. James and G. L. Rempel, *Can. J. Chem.*, **44**, 233 (1966).

[150] A. J. Birch and K. A. M. Walker, *J. Chem. Soc.*, *C*, **1966**, 1894.

[151] C. Djerassi, and J. Gutzwiller, *J. Am. Chem. Soc.*, **88**, 4537 (1966).

[152] A. J. Birch and K. A. M. Walker, *Tetrahedron Letters*, **1966**, 4939.

[153] I. Jardine and F. J. McQuillin, *Tetrahedron Letters*, **1966**, 4871.

[154] S. Siegel, *Adv. Catalysis*, **16**, 124 (1966).

[155] L. A. Slaugh, *Tetrahedron*, **22**, 1741 (1966).

isomerization; this was shown by the deuterium distribution in the products of addition of deuterium over 5% palladium–carbon. The proportion of 1,2-*cis*-addition increased whenever hydrogen, methyl, or methoxycarbonyl was replaced by phenyl ("phenyl effect"). This was considered to result from a change of mechanism caused by effective adsorption of the phenyl derivatives on to the metallic surface through an aromatic π-complex.[156]

Jardine and McQuillin[157] have shown that, at least for a series of cyclic olefins, adsorption is a reflexion of molecular geometry, whilst the rate of hydrogenation follows the same order as the heats of hydrogenation. Thus cyclo-octene is more strongly adsorbed than cyclohexene but more slowly hydrogenated, probably because of transannular interactions in cyclo-octane; norbornadiene is least strongly adsorbed but most rapidly hydrogenated. Chemisorption of olefins compared closely with their transition-metal-ion π-complex formation. For a series of alkyl-substituted pentenes the hydrogenation rates parallel the equilibrium constants for complexing with silver nitrate. If the chemisorbed olefin, S, is regarded as a π-complex, S_π, the hydrogenation process may be written:

$$S_{soln.} \rightleftarrows S_\pi \rightleftarrows SH_\sigma \rightarrow SH_{2ads.} \rightarrow SH_{2soln.}$$

where SH_σ is a σ-bonded half-hydrogenated state. The rate of hydrogenation may depend on the rate of hydrogen-transfer, although steric interference with the adsorption equilibrium is generally more important, and for highly adsorbed substrates hydrogen supply may become limiting. Examples of each case are reported.[157]

The stereochemistry of the hydrogenation products from methylenecyclohexanes over platinum oxide is a function of the hydrogen pressure. Different product-controlling reactions are considered to operate: the formation of a 1,2-diadsorbed alkane at high pressures and the formation of a "half-hydrogenated state" at low pressures of hydrogen.[158] It was suggested that the slow step in the hydrogenation of ethylene over palladium hydride or deuteride is addition of adsorbed hydrogen atoms to adsorbed ethylene or ethyl radicals.[159] The stereochemistry of the hydrogenation of some steroidal ketones in the presence and absence of acids has been clarified.[160] The chemisorbed state of propene on platinum,[161] the hydrogenation of ethylene catalysed by ethylene-platinum dichloride dimer,[162] the stereospecific hydrogen-exchange accom-

[156] G. V. Smith and J. A. Roth, *J. Am. Chem. Soc.*, **88**, 3879 (1966).
[157] I. Jardine and F. J. McQuillin, *J. Chem. Soc.*, *C*, **1966**, 458.
[158] S. Siegel, M. Dunkel, G. V. Smith, W. Halpern, and J. Cozort, *J. Org. Chem.*, **31**, 2802 (1966).
[159] R. J. Rennard and R. J. Kokes, *J. Phys. Chem.*, **70**, 2543 (1966).
[160] S. Nishimura, M. Shimahara, and M. Shiota, *J. Org. Chem.*, **31**, 2394 (1966); J. T. Edward and J.-M. Ferland, *Can. J. Chem.*, **44**, 1311 (1966).
[161] Y. Hironaka, K. Hirota, and E. Hirota, *Tetrahedron Letters*, **1966**, 2437.
[162] K. E. Hayes, *Nature*, **210**, 412 (1966).

panying catalytic hydrogenation of methyl 3,3-dimethylacrylate,[163] the mechanism of isotopic exchange between deuterium and cycloalkanes on palladium,[164] the hydrogenation of pinenes and carenes,[165] and the reaction of ethylene and propene with deuterium over alumina-supported palladium and rhodium[166] have also been investigated.

[163] F. Battig, P. Jordan, J. Seibl, and B. Serdarevic, Exchange Reactions, Proc. Symp. Upton, N.Y., 1965, 269; *Chem. Abs.*, **65**, 12076.

[164] K. Schrage and R. L. Burwell, *J. Am. Chem. Soc.*, **88**, 4555 (1966).

[165] W. Cocker, P. V. R. Shannon, and P. A. Staniland, *J. Chem. Soc.*, *C*, **1966**, 41.

[166] G. C. Bond, J. J. Philipson, P. B. Wells, and J. M. Winterbottom, *Trans. Faraday Soc.*, **62**, 443 (1966).

Author Index 1966

15*

Cumulative Subject Index 1965 and 1966

P. 1: Formula (**3**) should have a methyl group at position 1.

P. 14, line 5: *For* potential diagram *read* potential energy diagram

P. 41, line 2: *For endo*bicyclo[3.3.1]nonan-1-yl acetate *read endo*-bicyclo[3.3.1]nonan-2-yl acetate

P. 42: The first block is incorrect. It should be:

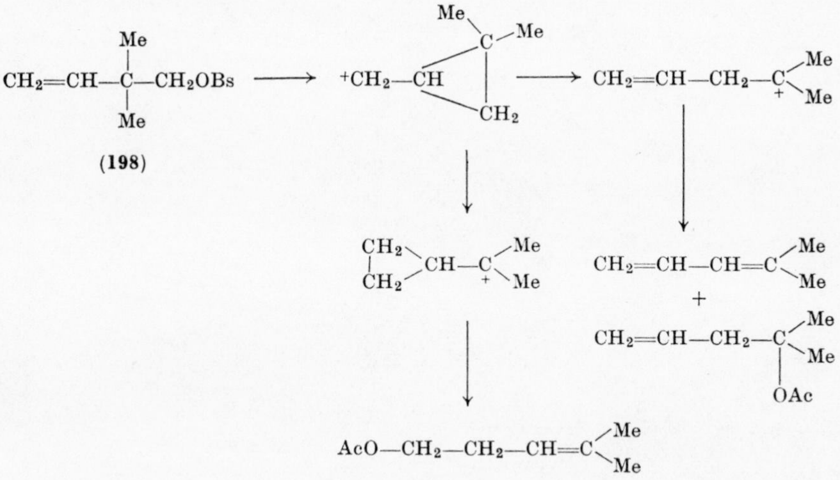

$$CH_2=CH-\underset{\underset{Me}{|}}{\overset{\overset{Me}{|}}{C}}-CH_2OBs \longrightarrow {}^+CH_2-CH\underset{CH_2}{\overset{\overset{Me}{\diagdown}\underset{\diagup Me}{C}}{|}} \longrightarrow CH_2=CH-CH_2-\underset{+}{C}\overset{Me}{\underset{Me}{\diagdown}}$$

(**198**)

$$\underset{CH_2}{\overset{CH_2}{\diagdown}}CH-\underset{+}{C}\overset{Me}{\underset{Me}{\diagdown}}$$

$$CH_2=CH-CH=C\overset{Me}{\underset{Me}{\diagdown}}$$
+
$$CH_2=CH-CH_2-\underset{OAc}{C}\overset{Me}{\underset{Me}{\diagdown}}$$

$$AcO-CH_2-CH_2-CH=C\overset{Me}{\underset{Me}{\diagdown}}$$

P. 50, equation (1): *For* $HOOCC_6H_4NO_1$ *read* $HOOCC_6H_4NO_2$

P. 70: The sulphur atom at the front of formula (**64**) should be doubly bonded to an $=NTs$ group.

P. 95, 5 lines from bottom: *For* rate *read* range

P. 163, line 15: *For* Freidel–Crafts *read* Friedel–Crafts

P. 234, line 8: *For* than *read* rather than

P. 278, line 12: *Delete* the

P. 280, lines 13 and 16: *For* phosphonate *read* phostonate